An Introduction to
Animal Husbandry in the Tropics

TROPICAL AGRICULTURE SERIES

The Tropical Agriculture Series, of which this volume forms part, is published under the editorship of D. Rhind, CMG, OBE, BSc, FLS, FIBiol.

ALREADY PUBLISHED

Tobacco *B. C. Akehurst*
Tropical Pasture and Fodder Plants *A. V. Bogdan*
Coconuts *R. Child*
Yams *D. G. Coursey*
Sorghum *H. Doggett*
Tea *T. Eden*
Rice *D. H. Grist*
Termites *W. V. Harris*
The Oil Palm *C. W. S. Hartley*
Tropical Farming Economics *M. R. Haswell*
Sisal *G. W. Lock*
Cattle Production in the Tropics Volume I
W. J. A. Payne
Cotton *A. N. Prentice*
Bananas *N. W. Simmonds*
Tropical Pulses *J. Smartt*
Agriculture in the Tropics
C. C. Webster and P. N. Wilson
An Introduction to Animal Husbandry in the Tropics
G. Williamson and W. J. A. Payne
Cocoa *G. A. R. Wood*

An Introduction to
Animal Husbandry
in the Tropics

Third Edition

G. Williamson CBE, MRCVS, DVSM
W. J. A. Payne MA, Dip. Agric. Sci., PhD, FIBiol.

Longman
London and New York

Longman Group Limited
Longman House, Burnt Mill, Harlow,
Essex CM20 2JE, England
Associated Companies throughout the World

*Published in the United States of America
by Longman Inc., New York*

First published 1959
Second edition 1965
Third edition 1978
Reprinted 1980
Third impression 1984

Library of Congress Cataloging in Publication Data
Williamson, Grahame.
    An introduction to animal husbandry in the tropics.

    (Tropical agriculture series)
    Includes index.
    1. Stock and stock-breeding–Tropics. I. Payne,
William John Arthur, joint author. II. Title.
SF75.W5   1977   636'.00913   76-58000
ISBN 0-582-46813-2

Printed in Hong Kong by
Astros Printing Ltd

Preface to third edition

The original concept, when the first edition of this book was published in the late 1950s, was to summarize such knowledge of tropical domestic animals as was available at that time and which could be considered useful for students, livestock extension specialists, progressive livestock owners and administrators concerned with the development of livestock industries and the economy.

The difficulties of adequately dealing with such a wide subject in one volume were anticipated and discussed when the first edition was published. These difficulties have now multiplied as the frontiers of fundamental knowledge in animal science have steadily expanded and an ever increasing volume of experimental data in different aspects of tropical animal husbandry has been published. In addition, the total number of animal science students in tropical countries has increased very rapidly, livestock extension agencies have grown and multiplied, there are more technically educated tropical livestock owners and livestock development projects are numerous in tropical countries.

In view of all these circumstances it was decided that it was not only essential to expand and upgrade the information content of this third edition but that it was also necessary to rewrite almost all the original, and to add additional chapters. This edition is, therefore, in some respects a different type of book from its predecessors. It is also different in another manner. One of the authors (G. W.) has now died and the edition is the sole responsibility of the other author (W. J. A. P.).

The opportunity is taken by the author to express thanks to all collaborators for the revision of their original contributions or for new contributions, to the General Editor for his advice and to all others who have assisted in the publication of this edition.

Contents

Part I: Basic Principles

Chapter 1

The Effect of Climate

Tropical climates

The term 'tropical' is used geographically to designate the area between the Tropics of Cancer and Capricorn. However, climate in this region is not uniform and it is meaningless to talk of a typical tropical climate. It varies with unalterable factors such as latitude, altitude, distribution of land and water, soils and topography and variable factors such as ocean currents, winds, rainfall and vegetation. The interaction of all these factors results in specific micro-climates at specific localities. However, for all their diversity tropical climates exhibit certain common characteristics. Except in the very dry areas daily and seasonal temperature variability is relatively small, being least at the equator. Day length is also fairly constant throughout the area, so that differences in the total hours of sunshine and the total solar radiation depend primarily on the degree of cloud cover.

Climate is a combination of elements that include temperature, humidity, rainfall, air movement, radiative conditions, barometric pressure and ionization. Of these, temperature (Figs. 1.1 and 1.2) and rainfall (Fig. 1.3) are the most important. In practice, effective rainfall, that is the amount ultimately available to the vegetation, is a more important index than total rainfall.

Many attempts have been made to classify climates, the best-known classifications being those of Köeppen (1931) and Thornthwaite (1948). Holdridge (1967) has recently proposed a 'Life Zone Ecology' classification combining latitude, altitude, rainfall and mean temperatures that is particularly useful for agriculturists. A simple classification is that proposed by the United States Department of Agriculture (1941). In this system climate in the tropics is classified into the following categories: equatorial or super-humid, humid, sub-humid, semi-arid and arid. As shown below and in Fig. 1.4 and 1.5, it has been found that there is a close relationship between these climatic zones and the major vegetation climax types and soils, and a modified form of this simple classification is used here.

2

Climate	Vegetation	Soil
Equatorial or super-humid	Rain-forest	Podzols (grey-brown, red and yellow) and laterites
Humid	Forest	
Sub-humid	Grassland	Chernozems and degraded chernozems
Semi-arid	Steppe and thornbush	Chestnut and brown soils
Arid	Ephemeral and desert	Sierozems and desert soils

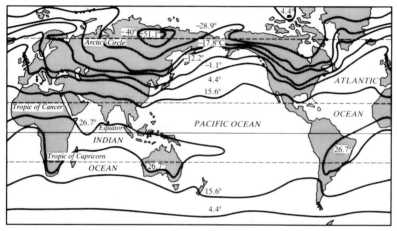

Fig. 1.1 January isotherms of the world in °C: slightly simplified.

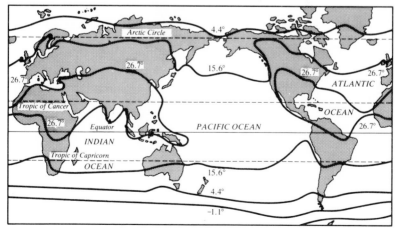

Fig. 1.2 July isotherms of the world in °C; slightly simplified.

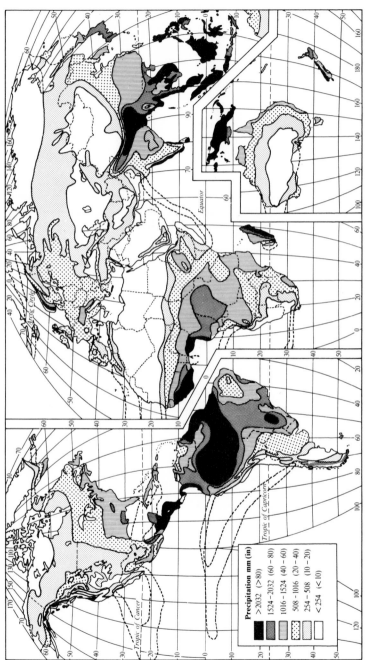

Fig. 1.3   Distribution of precipitation over the earth.

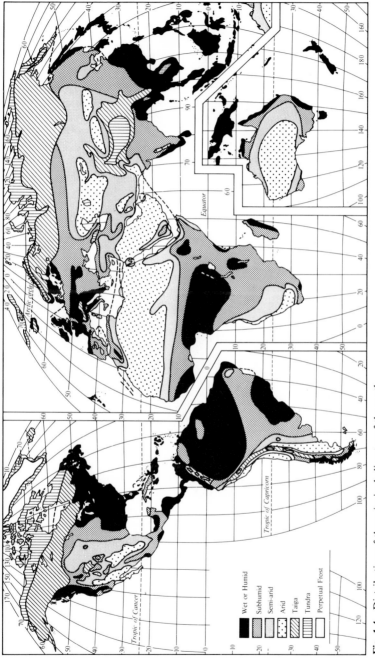

Fig. 1.4 Distribution of the principal climates of the earth.

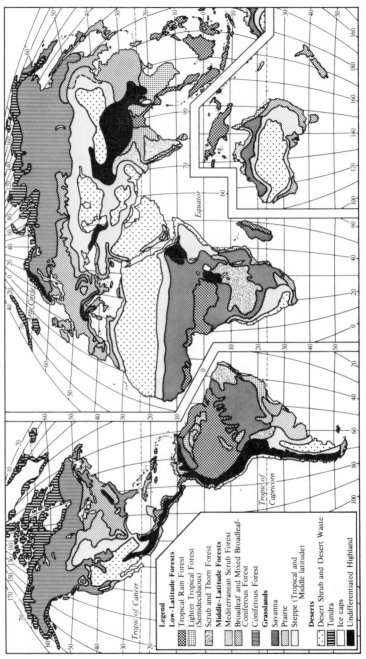

Fig. 1.5 World distribution of the principal plant associations.

Legend

Low-Latitude Forests
Tropical Rain Forest
Lighter Tropical Forest
(Semideciduous)
Scrub and Thorn Forest

Middle-Latitude Forests
Mediterranean Scrub Forest
Broadleaf and Mixed Broadleaf-
Coniferous Forest
Coniferous Forest

Grasslands
Savanna
Prairie
Steppe (Tropical and
Middle latitude)

Deserts
Desert Shrub and Desert Waste
Tundra
Ice caps
Undifferentiated Highland

The general extent of these major climatic divisions in the tropics is shown in Fig. 1.4. This map does not, of course, show local variations in climate within the larger climatic zones.

Equatorial or super-humid climate. This climatic zone is characterized by constant heat, rainfall and humidity. The mean annual temperature varies around 27°C (80°F) and total annual rainfall is usually within the range of 2,032 to 3,048 mm (80 to 120 in). Although in any 2- or 3-week period there is almost always an excess of precipitation over evaporation, it is not usual for rainfall to be evenly distributed throughout the year. In some areas, one season is slightly wetter, while in others there are two wetter seasons.

Equatorial climates are found 5° to 7° latitude north and south of the equator and specifically in the Congo basin and part of the Guinea coast of Africa, in the Indian sub-continent, the Malaysian peninsula, Indonesia, New Guinea, the southern Philippines and the Amazon basin. It is also found in isolated areas further from the equator, such as the west coast of Colombia and the east coast of Madagascar.

The typical vegetation of this climatic zone is tropical rain-forest, characterized by a multiplicity of evergreen tree species, some of them hardwood, covered with epiphytes and intertwined with lianes.

Climatic stress on domestic livestock is considerable in this region. In general, indigenous domestic breeds of livestock are not numerous, but the climate favours plant growth so that forage could be plentiful and available all the year around. Internal and external parasites are favoured by the climate and animal products rapidly deteriorate when stored.

The apparent 'high fertility' of tropical rain-forest soils is illusionary rather than real as they rapidly deteriorate once the forest has been cleared. Although the potential for animal production is high, a great deal of basic and applied research is needed before this region can become capable of supporting a dense and productive animal population.

Humid climate. This climatic zone is characterized by high though seasonal temperatures, humidity and rainfall. Temperature extremes are wider than in the equatorial region. There are usually three seasons: cool-dry, hot-dry and hot-wet. Climates of this type are found adjacent to the equatorial areas, north and south of the equator, in the monsoonal lands. Somewhat similar climates also occur on the windward side of volcanic oceanic tropical islands.

The natural vegetation of the zone is rain-forest, but plant growth is not quite so vigorous as in the equatorial zone, deciduous are mixed with evergreen species and there are fewer epiphytes and lianes. Climatic stress on domestic livestock is not quite so severe as in the equatorial areas, but forage supplies are more seasonal.

Sub-humid climate. In general the sub-humid areas are found north and south of the humid forest areas in the northern and southern hemispheres, respectively. They are characterized by a more seasonal climate than in the humid zone. There is usually a relatively short rainy season and a longer dry one, though in some regions there are two rainy seasons. Temperature variations are much wider, with hotter summers due to a high intensity of radiation combined with a longer day.

The natural vegetation of these areas is usually some form of 'savanna', an open grassland association interspersed with trees. Large areas of savanna are found north and south of the equator in Africa, particularly in the east of the continent. There are also large areas in the Indian peninsula, inland in Southeast Asia, in northern Australia, in Central and South America and on the leeward side of many oceanic tropical islands. There are many types of savanna with various combinations of high, medium and low trees and tall and short grasses. In the wetter areas savanna imperceptibly merges into dry-land forest, such as the *miombo* of Central Africa, while in the drier areas it merges into open short-grass steppes or desert scrub.

This is one of the regions where nomadic livestock husbandry has flourished in the past in Africa and Asia and where European settlers in the Americas and Australia established a ranching industry. It is also a region where, in the past, wild game flourished in vast numbers.

Generally, climatic stress on domestic livestock is less intense than in the more humid areas, but forage production is very seasonal and nutritional stress can be a major problem. This is also the region where epizootic animal diseases are rife, though some internal and external parasites of domestic livestock are easier to control in this region than in the more humid forest areas.

Semi-arid climate.   This climatic region is characterized by extremely seasonal conditions, with relatively low rainfall and very long dry seasons. Diurnal and seasonal temperature fluctuations are very wide, humidity is low for most of the year and there is a high intensity of solar radiation due to the dry atmosphere and clear skies. Although total rainfall may be within the range of 254 to 508 mm (10 to 20 in), it may be very intense when it falls and very irregular in incidence.

There are large semi-arid areas in Africa, north and south of the savanna regions, in western Asia and India, and in northern Australia and smaller areas in North, Central and South America. There are also some small lowlying oceanic tropical islands that possess a semi-arid climate.

This climatic region is more suited for livestock production than for any other form of agriculture, though productivity is severely curtailed by lack of feed and water, with consequent nutritional stress, as well as by climatic stress. Internal and external parasites can be controlled with relative ease, though control of epizootic disease is more difficult. Often semi-arid areas are more suitable for the management of sheep, goats and camels than they are for cattle, and in the driest areas wild game may be the most suitable and economic exploiters of the environment.

Arid climate.   There are few truly desert areas in the tropics as the great deserts of the world are found in the sub-tropics or even further from the equator. However, small areas of desert are located within the tropics in the southern Sahara, southwest Arabia and the Pacific coast of northern Chile. Tropical desert climates are characterized by temperature extremes of the order of 0° to 52°C (32° to 122°F) and by the fact that there is no seasonal rhythm in rainfall, which is insignificant in total amount.

Deserts may seasonally support very limited numbers of livestock, and in Africa and western Asia nomadic herdsmen may at certain times follow the rain showers across the deserts, feeding their herds and flocks on the ephemeral plants that spring up as soon as it rains. In parts of Arabia and the Sahara a unique and particularly valuable type of desert vegetation occurs irregularly only after a specific sequence of climatic phenomena. It is known in Arabic as *gizzu*.

This simplified account of tropical climates does not take into account one other major zone, the montane region. A very considerable area of land in the tropics is situated at an altitude varying between 305 and 1,524 m (1,000 and 5,000 ft) and an appreciable area lies above 1,524 m (5,000 ft). Altitude influences climate in at least four ways. Mean annual temperature decreases by 1·7°C (3°F) for every 305 m (1,000 ft) increase in altitude. This decrease is even higher on oceanic islands or where there are very steep mountains. Secondly, the higher the altitude the larger the diurnal though not the seasonal variation in ambient temperature. Thirdly, rainfall is usually greater at higher altitude and there are more cloudy days. Finally, the higher the altitude the lower the atmospheric pressure, the latter being halved at 5,486 m (18,000 ft). Three of these influences – namely a decrease in mean annual temperature, an increase in diurnal temperature variation and a higher rainfall – are likely to assist in the improvement of livestock productivity.

It is difficult to generalize, but in equatorial and humid tropical rainforest areas the species composition of the forest alters with increasing altitude and gradually merges into other vegetation complexes. In the drier tropical areas the open plains vegetation merges into cool, humid forest as the annual rainfall increases with increasing altitude. Above 3,965 m (13,000 ft) there is usually an alpine-type vegetation even on the equator.

To date little has been done to exploit these montane areas for livestock production, though they offer opportunity for the development of dairy industries based on temperate-type dairy cattle, temperate-type beef-breeding operations for the production of bulls that could provide semen for use in crossbreeding schemes at lower altitudes, large-scale hill sheep production, and in South America major increases in the production of meat and wool from the domesticated and wild llamoids such as the alpaca, the llama and the vicuña.

The effect of climate on livestock

Livestock production in all tropical countries is affected by the climate in two ways. First, by a direct influence on the animals utilized, and secondly by indirect effects on the animal's environment.

The direct effect of climate on the animal

Experimental evidence on the direct effect of climate on domestic livestock has been obtained from two sources: direct observations in the field and observations on livestock kept in controlled-temperature laboratories or psychrometric chambers. The disadvantage of direct observations is that it is difficult to set up adequately controlled field experiments, while the disadvantage of using a psychrometric chamber is that only a small number of the larger domestic livestock can be studied at any one time while it is known that there are profound differences between species (Findlay, 1954), breeds or types within a species (Worstell and Brody, 1953) and individuals within a breed (Payne and Hancock, 1957) in their ability to withstand the direct effects of climate.

All domestic livestock are homeotherms. That is, they attempt to maintain their body temperatures within a range most suitable for optimal biological activity. The normal range in mammals is 37° to 39°C (98·6° to 102·2°F), while in birds it is 40° to 44°C (104° to 111·2°F) though there are some exceptions. Typical deep-body temperatures of some domestic livestock are shown in Table 1.1.

Table 1.1 *Typical deep body temperatures of domestic livestock*

Type of livestock	Deep body temperature	
	(°C)	(°F)
Horses	37·2–38·2	(99·0–100·8)
Asses	36·0–38·0	(96·8–100·4)
Cattle	38·0–39.3	(100·4–102·8)
Camels	36·0–38·0	(96·8–100·4)
Sheep	38·3–39·9	(100·9–103·8)
Goats	38·7–40·7	(101·7–105·3)
Pigs	38·9–39·4	(102·0–103·0)
Fowl (chickens)	41·9	(107·4)
Ducks	42·1	(107·8)
Geese	41·3	(106·3)
Turkeys	41·2	(106·2)

In order to maintain their body temperature while subject to a wide range of environmental conditions, domestic livestock must preserve a thermal balance between their heat production or gain from the environment and their heat loss to the environment. This thermal balance can be expressed by the equation:

$$M - E \pm F \pm Cd \pm Cv \pm R = 0$$

where M is the metabolic heat production, E the heat loss from skin and respiratory passages by evaporation, F the heat lost or gained bringing ingested food and/or water to body temperature, Cd heat lost or gained by direct contacts between the body and surrounding surfaces, Cv heat lost or gained by convection due to contact between the air and skin and/or linings of the respiratory passages, and R heat lost or gained by radiation.

Metabolic heat production depends on:

1. Basal heat production for maintaining essential body processes such as deep body temperature, cardio-respiratory activities and muscle tone;
2. Digestive heat production that varies with the type of digestive system the animal possesses and on the quantity and quality of the food that it ingests;
3. Muscular heat production that varies according to how much the animal moves about grazing, etc., and
4. Increased metabolism due to productive processes such as growth, milk production and reproduction.

In general, the means by which domestic livestock can vary their heat production are limited in comparison with the methods by which they can dispose of heat. They can reduce productive processes and muscular heat production and to a more limited extent digestive heat production, but they cannot normally reduce basal heat production as minimal body processes must be maintained.

Of the methods of heat loss available to domestic livestock, evaporative loss is potentially the most important under normal circumstances. It depends on the ambient air temperature, the amount of available moisture, the area of evaporating surface, the absolute humidity of the air surrounding the animal and the degree of air movement. The factors in this situation influenced by the animal are some part of the available moisture and the area of the evaporating surface. The amount of available moisture normally depends upon the quantity of sweat and insensible perspiration produced by the animal, unless it is mechanically sprinkled with water. The area of the evaporating surface depends upon the surface area of the animal and the size of the lungs, as considerable evaporation is achieved by the mechanism of panting.

In the case of cattle, although all types possess sweat glands, those of the *Bos indicus* breeds usually have a higher total volume than those of

B. taurus breeds (Yeates, 1965). Even if all cattle possess sweat glands and some types sweat more freely than others, cattle in general are poor sweaters as compared with some other mammalian species, as are buffaloes, sheep, goats and pigs. Cattle and sheep to some extent make up for their lack of sweating by having relatively high respiration rates. Buffaloes possess few, if any, sweat glands.

Poultry possess no sweat glands, as birds could not possibly evolve sweating as a cooling mechanism and still fly. If they had to evaporate water from their skin the air between the feathers would have to be constantly renewed and this would cause turbulence and drag in flight. They accomplish some evaporative cooling by panting and the extensive air-sac system connected with their lungs may also have an important heat-regulatory function.

The heat gained or lost by the animal bringing the food and/or water ingested to body temperature can have a considerable effect on total heat production and loss. Any water consumed in excess of metabolic needs, at a temperature lower than body temperature, and then excreted at body temperature as urine or in the faeces, assists in reducing the heat load on the animal. Lowering the temperature of ingested water is known to have a more marked effect on the heat load than increasing the volume ingested. This effect has practical significance and workers in California, including Kelly *et al.* (1955), have shown that cooling drinking water can increase the liveweight gain of beef cattle managed at high ambient temperatures.

The ability of livestock to lose heat through conduction is very limited. Convection heat loss is of course increased when cool breezes blow on the animal, and increased air movement may also increase evaporative heat loss. Consequently, livestock accommodation in the tropics should always be built in such a way as to encourage maximal air movement on and around the animals.

Solar radiation may not only increase the heat load on the animal but also directly affect the skin, causing skin cancers and other photosensitive disorders. This means that the colour and thickness of the skin are of some importance as adaptive mechanisms. A pigmented skin is considered more desirable than an unpigmented skin everywhere in the tropics and the majority of tropical-type breeds possess pigmented skins, while many temperate-type breeds possess unpigmented skins. Individuals of the Hereford breed of cattle often suffer from an eye condition known as epithelioma because they possess unpigmented eyelids, and white-skinned breeds of pigs such as the Large White are particularly susceptible to sunburn.

The amount of solar radiation absorbed by the coat of the animal is partly determined by its colour. Approximately half the energy in the solar spectrum is in the visible and half in the invisible infra-red portion. The proportion of the visible portion that will be absorbed by an animal can be approximately estimated by the colour of the coat, as a white surface may absorb only 20 per cent while a black surface may absorb 100 per cent of the visible radiation. Energy from the invisible infra-red part of the solar spectrum is completely absorbed whatever the colour of the coat. Colour is not the only factor that affects the influence of solar radiation on the heat load of the animal – length, density and condition of the hair may also have some effect. Smooth-coated animals with short hair appear to be more heat tolerant, so that Bonsma (1949) suggested that the degree of 'felting' of samples of cattle hair could be used as a measure of heat tolerance. Yeates (1965) has reviewed the available experimental data and these indicate that a short, light-coloured coat with a smooth and glossy texture is best for minimizing the adverse effects of solar radiation on growth and other productive processes. Posture also has some effect on minimizing the heat load due to solar radiation, as animals that are standing do not receive as much solar radiation per unit body area as do those that are lying down.

There is one effect of length of daylight that influences the ability of some temperate-type cattle to adapt themselves to a tropical climate. It is considered that the length of daylight in the tropics is insufficiently variable to efficiently operate the photoperiodic mechanism that is known partly to control the seasonal hair-growth cycle of temperate-type cattle (Yeates, 1954). Under these circumstances some individuals of temperate breeds of cattle are unable to shed their woolly, winter-grown coat and consequently suffer from a heavy heat load when subjected to high ambient temperatures. Individuals of this type never thrive in the tropics and should be culled.

1. Grazing behaviour

The effect of climate on cattle is reflected in their grazing behaviour. Data from the experimental work on this subject have been summarized by Payne (1969).

The length of daytime grazing of cattle apparently varies according to the degree of climatic stress, the breed and type of cattle utilized and the quantity and quality of the pasture available. When high-grade *Bos taurus*-type cattle are grazed in a humid tropical climate the length of daylight grazing is radically curtailed and confined almost entirely to early morning and late afternoon periods (Plate 1.1), and the length of the night grazing period fluctuates according to the degree of climatic stress. Even crossbred *B. taurus* × *B. indicus* cattle graze for such a short period in the middle of the day that Wilson (1961) reported that yarding such cattle for a 4-hour period at this time, without access to feed, did not reduce total dry matter intake, and that if the cattle were not yarded they ceased grazing and made use of any natural shade available.

In many parts of the tropics, indigenous cattle are removed from the grazings and confined during the night. It is usually stated that this is done to protect them from predators, human and animal. However, the majority of observers suggest that whenever possible *Bos indicus* and

Plate 1.1   Crossbred cattle seeking shade under an oil palm in Brunei.

other indigenous cattle should be allowed to graze at night, particularly when the quantity and quality of the feed available is sub-optimal. If the quantity of feed available is limited total grazing time increases, as it does when the quality is poor, the animal then becoming more selective in grazing. Part of this extra grazing must take place at night if climatic stress is excessive during the middle of the day. Joblin (1960), working at Serere in Uganda, where seasonal fluctuations in the quantity and quality of feed are considerable, concluded that the availability of night grazing is critical for *B. indicus* cattle during periods of marginal forage shortage; while under the best conditions the daylight period is sufficiently long for the cattle to obtain their needs, under very dry conditions no amount of grazing time will allow for adequate intake. Restriction of night grazing led, in the Serere environment, to a significant decline of 30 per cent in liveweight gain. These experimental findings have since been verified by other workers.

No detailed observations have been made of the grazing behaviour of cattle managed under nomadic or semi-nomadic conditions in the semi-arid tropics. During the dry season the decreasing water content of the available forage increases the animal's demand for water at a time when surface water resources are dwindling, and the animal has to walk further and further to obtain adequate feed and water. Additional walking raises feed and water demand, as increased muscular activity requires additional feed and generates extra heat that has to be dissipated, further depleting the animal's water resources. At the same time, the nutrient content of the available feed decreases as the dry season advances, the decreasing supplies of free water may become highly mineralized, and ambient temperatures may rise with a consequent further increase in the animal's water requirements. All these factors combine to subject nomadic or partially nomadic livestock in the semi-arid tropics to very considerable physiological stress that may substantially reduce productivity.

2. Intake and utilization

(a) *Feed intake*

As would be expected from the effect of temperature on grazing behaviour the available climatic chamber data suggest that high ambient temperatures depress the feed intake of all cattle, but that the feed intake of *Bos taurus* is depressed at lower ambient temperatures than is that of *B. indicus* breeds. The effect of very high temperatures is very pronounced, food consumption and rumination practically ceasing in *B. taurus*-type cattle as ambient temperatures rise above 40°C (104°F).

Increasing humidity at ambient temperatures above 23·9°C (75°F) also depresses the feed intake of all cattle (Ragsdale *et al.*, 1953), while increasing radiation stress has the same effect on *Bos taurus* but not on *B. indicus*-type cattle (Brody *et al.*, 1954).

Field data should reflect more accurately than climatic chamber data the overall effect of the climatic environment on the feed intake of livestock. Unfortunately, the available data are limited. Hancock and Payne (1955) and Payne and Hancock (1957) compared the performance of sets of *Bos taurus* identical twins fed hay and concentrates, one twin of each set being raised in a tropical and the other in a temperate climate. They showed that hay intake was significantly lower in a tropical climate although overall total digestible nutrient (TDN) intake was approximately the same in both environments.

(b) *Water intake*

The direct effect of climate on the water intake of livestock is very complex, as water is required by the animal for at least two different purposes: first as an essential nutrient and component of the body, and secondly to assist the animal lose heat by conductive or evaporative cooling.

Although, in general, the water intake of livestock increases with increasing ambient temperature the relationship between water intake and ambient temperature is not simple. For example, in *Bos taurus*-type milking cows water intake increases with increasing ambient temperature up to 29·4°C (85°F), but above this temperature it declines. This decline has been attributed to a decline in feed intake and productivity and to a rise in body temperature (Winchester, 1964).

Ambient temperature has a differential effect on the water intake of different types of livestock and on different breeds within one type, and it appears that acclimatized animals require less water than unacclimatized when managed at high ambient temperatures.

Humidity also affects water intake, and at ambient temperatures above

23·9°C (75°F) increasing humidity decreases water consumption (Ragsdale *et al.*, 1953) and increases the frequency of drinking of cattle. According to Brody *et al.* (1954) the effect of increased radiation intensity on cattle is to increase water consumption. Presumably this is due to the animal utilizing an increasing quantity of water for evaporative cooling purposes when subject to radiation stress.

(c) *Efficiency of utilization*

The experimental evidence available suggests that under controlled conditions increasing ambient temperature decreases the efficiency of feed utilization, although under field conditions any differences may be insignificant.

(d) *Loss of nutrients by sweating and drooling*

Sweating is not of the same importance in all livestock, though it can be important in cattle. In the latter, sweating behaviour differs between breeds as ambient temperature rises, although generally the loss of nutrients and particularly minerals through sweating and drooling is not of practical significance.

3. Growth

If climatic stress depresses appetite, reducing feed intake and grazing time, then it is likely to affect productivity as measured by growth and milk production.

Although many generalized statements have been made with regard to the adverse effects of a tropical climate on growth there is remarkably little objective field experimental evidence available. In the Fiji–New Zealand twin experiment mentioned in a previous section the growth of the twins was studied from $7\frac{1}{2}$ months of age until the end of their first lactation (Hancock and Payne, 1955). The only appreciable differences in growth rates were when air temperatures in Fiji were at their highest: at calving the heifers reared in the temperate climate were only 9·6 per cent heavier than the heifers reared in the tropics, and by the end of the first lactation this difference was substantially reduced. The check in growth rate was reasonably uniform, in so far as all body measurements except belly girth were adversely affected. The belly girth of the twins reared in the tropics was greater and this was attributed to the fact that they had a much greater water intake. Management conditions were good in this experiment, and the results suggest that an oceanic tropical climate does not appreciably affect the growth rate of temperate-type cattle if management and feeding conditions are good.

There is very little experimental evidence on the effect of the different climatic factors on the growth rate of *Bos indicus*-type cattle. The birth weights of most *B. indicus* calves are low and they often grow rather slowly, but what part if any of this poor growth can be attributed to the direct effect of the climate is unknown.

Information on the effect of climate on the growth of sheep and goats is also scanty. Temperate-type sheep in the Australian tropics exposed to high ambient temperatures often have a low lambing percentage and give birth to small, weak lambs that have a high post-natal mortality. It is also reported from Australia that autumn-born lambs which have been carried through the hot summer are usually smaller at birth than spring-born lambs, but it is very difficult to disentangle the direct from the indirect effects of the climate. The young lamb or kid, like the young calf, is certainly less well adapted to high ambient temperatures than adult animals. The effect of climate on sheep is further discussed in Chapter 7 (Part II).

At birth the piglet does not appear to possess a very efficient temperature-regulating mechanism and is incapable of protecting itself against either excessive heat or cold. During the first 2 days of life the ambient air temperature for piglets should exceed 32·2°C (90°F) and be gradually lowered as they grow older. It is now normal practice in temperate countries to use infra-red lamps to warm the piglets immediately after birth, so that they do not get chilled. As in the tropics the mean annual temperature varies around 26·7°C (80°F) and in the daytime temperatures are often of the order of 32·2°C (90°F) or higher, the problem is not so acute, but it has been found that even in a tropical climate piglet mortality due to overlying may be reduced by the use of an additional heat source during the first few days of life. As the pig ages and grows the optimal air temperature for maximum liveweight gain and efficiency of food conversion falls and pigs weighing 31·8 to 65·3 kg (70 to 144 lb) are probably being reared under almost optimal environmental conditions. At higher liveweights normal tropical temperatures are too high for maximum productivity (Heitman and Hughes, 1949).

Chicks are more tolerant of high ambient temperatures than are adult birds, but when the air temperature is above 35°C (95°F) there is a danger of day-old chicks overheating in chick boxes when they are transported from the hatcheries. High ambient temperatures probably reduce the rate of growth of poultry though there are considerable differences in the reactions of different breeds (Hutchinson, 1954), light breeds withstanding heat better than heavy breeds.

4. Milk production

Experimental evidence on the effect of climate on milk, butterfat and solids-not-fat production has been reviewed by Findlay (1954). Most of the available experimental evidence indicates that milk, butterfat and solids-not-fat production are depressed by high ambient temperature, but as in growth studies it is difficult to disentangle the direct and indirect effects of climate. In the Fiji–New Zealand identical twin experiment, where it was possible to assess the effect of the climatic environment independent of management and feeding (Payne and Hancock, 1957), climate had a marked effect on milk and butterfat but not on solids-not-fat production. The average milk production of the twins in the temperate climate was 44 per cent higher than that of their co-twins in the tropics and their butterfat production was 56 per cent larger. There were, however, profound differences in the reaction of individual twins at the same centre to the climatic environment.

Experimental work with dairy cattle in psychrometric chambers has provided more detailed information as to the effect of individual climatic factors on milk and milk solids production.

The optimal temperature for milk production in temperate-type cattle breeds appears to be 10°C (50°F), while the critical temperature after which milk production steeply declines is 21° to 27°C (70° to 80°F) in Jersey and Holstein, 29° to 32°C (85° to 90°F) in Brown Swiss and higher in the case of tropical-type cattle. The butterfat content of the milk of temperate cows declines slowly until the ambient temperature reaches 29°C (85°F) and then rises. This is presumably due to the fact that above 29°C (85°F) the decline in milk production is more rapid than the decline in the percentage of butterfat in the milk.

High ambient temperatures also affect other constituents of the milk of temperate-type milking cattle. Cobble and Herman (1951) have shown that there is a rise in the chloride content and a fall in the lactose and total nitrogen content of milk when ambient temperatures rise above 27° to 32°C (80° to 90°F).

5. Reproduction

The major climatic factors affecting reproduction are ambient temperature, humidity and the length of daylight.

Branton (1970) has reviewed the experimental evidence with regard to the effect of climate on reproduction in cattle and he concluded that high environmental temperatures or sudden violent fluctuations in ambient temperature, such as occur in the sub-tropics, can directly affect the reproductive performance of cattle and that high humidities reinforce the effect of high temperatures. The known effects of climatic stress on the reproductive behaviour of cattle are depicted in Fig. 1.6. The practical implications of these effects will be discussed in detail in later chapters.

Salisbury and Van Demark (1961) have stated that day length appears to be the primary factor affecting the seasonal incidence of fertility, and that where day length varies considerably the highest fertility occurs in the spring with increasing hours of daylight. In the tropics the length of daylight varies very little and this small variation in daylight hours does not appear to have any pronounced effect on the reproductive behaviour of cattle.

High environmental temperatures appear to have a marked effect on the reproductive behaviour of sheep (Moule, 1970). In the ewe there is evidence from field observations that both embryonic death and foetal dwarfing occur in a hot environment, and from climate chamber work that continuous exposure to air temperatures that raise rectal tempera-

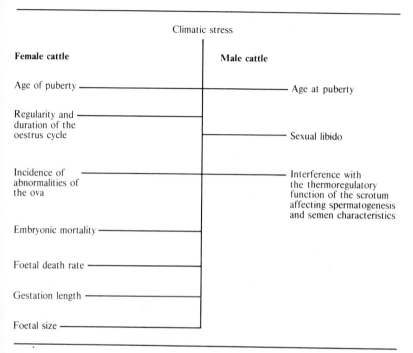

Climatic stress

Female cattle   **Male cattle**

Age of puberty ——————————————— Age at puberty

Regularity and
duration of the
oestrus cycle

           Sexual libido

Incidence of
abnormalities of
the ova   Interference with
the thermoregulatory
function of the scrotum
affecting spermatogenesis
and semen characteristics

Embryonic mortality

Foetal death rate

Gestation length

Foetal size

Fig. 1.6 Known effects of climatic stress on the reproductive behaviour of cattle.

tures by 1·1° to 1·7°C (2° to 3°F) will eventually kill all embryos. Dutt (1960) stated that air temperatures of 32·2°C (90°F) affect both ova and semen in the female tract of ewes, presumably by raising body temperature. In rams exposed to high air temperatures in the field, degenerative changes in survival characteristics are reported, though there appears to be considerable variation in the testicular temperature of individual Merino rams exposed to high ambient temperatures (Moule, 1970).

Male sheep (Moule, 1970) and goats imported into the tropics from the temperate zone appear to be less fecund or even sterile for up to a year after importation and this is presumed to be a photoperiodic effect.

High ambient temperatures also appear to affect embryo survival in sows and may have some effect on oestrus (Warnick *et al.*, 1965).

Egg production in poultry is highest when air temperatures are within the thermoneutral range (Osbaldiston and Sainsbury, 1963). Constant high ambient temperatures affect the rate of laying of eggs and the total number laid, and there is a diminution in egg weight and shell thickness (Wilson, 1949). Water deprivation enhances these inhibiting effects. The fertility and hatchability of eggs is also decreased by high ambient temperatures (Huston and Carmon, 1958). Variation in the intensity of light does not appear to affect egg production significantly.

The indirect effect of climate on the animal

The major indirect effect of climate on livestock is on the quantity and quality of the feed available for them. Experimental data on this subject have been reviewed by Payne (1969). Other indirect effects are on the incidence of disease and parasites and on the storage and handling of animal products.

1. Feed supply

The most important climatic factors that limit plant growth, and hence the quantity of the feed available, are ambient temperature, effective rainfall, length of daylight and the intensity of solar radiation. The quality of feed depends mainly on effective rainfall and on the intensity of solar radiation. The very real differences in climate that exist between the humid and the arid and semi-arid tropical regions thus present two broadly distinct livestock nutritional problems, although there are many exceptions and the distinctions become blurred in the intermediate climatic zones.

(a) *Equatorial and humid tropics*

In general, forage growth is continuous and very rapid though still seasonal, and under 'high' farming conditions very heavy annual yields may be obtained. There are numerous papers detailing yields of humid tropical forage plants and much information has been obtained during the last several decades on their composition and digestibility. Predictions of the productivity of humid tropical forage – in terms of milk production – have been reviewed by Hardison (1966).

(i) *Effect on feed and water intake.*   It is logical to expect that forage grown under conditions of abundant rainfall and high humidity should possess a high water content and most studies show that this is so. Whether this high water content of humid tropical forage inhibits ruminant animals from obtaining a sufficiently high dry matter intake is a controversial question, but the balance of evidence suggests that the high water content of, or the free water on, humid forage may affect the total quantity of feed consumed (Payne, 1969).

(ii) *Effect on the nutrient content of the forage.*   The experimental evidence is conflicting but, in general, it suggests that forage plants are more nutritious in the wet than in the dry season. Most, but not all, reports conclude that there is a positive correlation between rainfall and the crude protein (CP), silica-free ash and nitrogen-free-extract content of the forage, and an inverse relationship between the rainfall and the crude fibre (CF) content. It is possible that these conflicting reports may be due to an attempt to compare the behaviour of different forage species in what are really different climatic environments, and to the fact that although cutting intervals may be the same, the species may be at different stages of growth at different periods within the same season. Field observations suggest that, after the first 'flush' at the beginning of the rainy season, growth slows down owing to continuous cloudy weather, but that it may increase very rapidly during sunny intervals.

It has generally been assumed that the nutritive value of humid tropical forage is severely limited by its reported low CP content, but Hardison (1966) concluded that the digestible crude protein (DCP) content of the herbage for which data were available was considerably more variable throughout the year than the TDN content and that the latter was likely to limit milk production for more months of the year than the level of DCP.

The CF content of humid tropical forage is not only inversely related to the amount of rainfall but appears to be consistently higher than that of temperate forage at the same stage of growth. This is an additional disadvantage to animals that are already under heat stress and are finding difficulty in eating a sufficient bulk of 'watery' forage.

(b) *Semi-arid and arid tropics*

It is characteristic of semi-arid and arid regions that the total rainfall is low, varying widely in amount from year to year and strongly seasonal and/or erratic in incidence. Thus, it is usual for the rainy season flush of highly nutritious forage to be followed by a long dry period, when growth ceases completely and the forage dries up. If a drought intervenes, the dry season may not be followed by a normal rainy season, but by a few scattered showers and an even longer dry period. Under these circumstances ruminant livestock have to graze for the major part of the year on what is essentially standing hay, and in drought periods they may have to exist on this type of feed for very long periods, at a time when surface-water resources are diminishing. In the truly arid areas forage growth is ephemeral, occurring only after the infrequent rains.

Thus, the major problems of the nutrition of livestock in the semi-arid and arid tropics are the intensely seasonal nature of the forage resources and the possibility of low nutrient intake and water deprivation during the dry season.

(i) *Effect on feed intake.*

The dry matter (DM) content of forage in the arid and semi-arid tropics is high throughout most of the year and grazing animals have no difficulty in obtaining an adequate DM intake if ample supplies of forage are available. Thus, the crucial factor in the feeding of livestock in these areas is that of keeping the stocking rate within the 'carrying capacity' of the dry season grazings.

(ii) *Effect of water intake.*

All domestic livestock require access to some free water sometimes, but the needs of different types of livestock vary. Cattle require access to free water at all times, though the water demands of different types of cattle vary and *Bos indicus* apparently require less free water than *B. taurus* breeds when managed in the same environment. The water demands of sheep, goats and camels are not as high as those of cattle. When adequate free water is available the water intake of all cattle rises during the dry season but they can be acclimatized to a certain degree of water deprivation.

(iii) *Water deprivation.* This affects water and feed intake, metabolism and productivity.

Cattle restrict their DM intake when they are water-deprived, but *Bos indicus* breeds do not reduce their DM intake to the same extent as do *B. taurus* breeds (Payne, 1965). The higher the ambient temperature the more depressing the effect of the same level of water deprivation on DM intake. If at the same time cattle are managed in such a way as to restrict their grazing time – being normal managerial practice in many tropical countries (Smith, 1965) – this may decrease feed intake still further. While the animal is water-deprived, the nutritive content of available feed may decrease, as is normal in the semi-arid tropics with the advancing dry season, and this may lead to a further decrease in voluntary DM intake (Payne, 1965). The cumulative effect of all these factors may mean that the nutritive intake of cattle in this environment is very inadequate.

As rumen fluid provides the most suitable source of water to offset water losses during the initial stages of dehydration it could be expected that water deprivation would affect rumen function. It is thought that this happens, and there is experimental evidence that water deprivation in cattle increases the digestibility of the feed ingested and in particular the digestibility of the crude fibre component of the feed. Of course, this improvement in digestibility need not be the direct result of water deprivation but could be due to an indirect effect, such as reduced feed intake.

Subjective field observations suggest that some cattle thrive better than could be expected in the very severe nutritional stress environment experienced towards the end of the dry season in semi-arid tropical areas. One obvious reason for the better-than-expected performance is an animal's undoubted ability to select those parts of the forage plant that are usually of the highest nutritive value. However, towards the end of the dry season, there is often no leaf material left on the grazing or browse species and the animal is forced to ingest feed of extremely low nutritive value. It is therefore likely that there are other factors that assist the survival of cattle under extreme nutritional stress conditions. Livingston *et al.* (1962) investigated the metabolism of *Bos taurus* and *B. indicus* cattle under simulated nutritional stress conditions and found that they were able to reduce nitrogen output and particularly urea excretion in their urine to a low level. Payne (1965) has since reported that when the CP intake of *B. taurus* and *B. indicus* cattle was so low that they were in negative nitrogen balance, severe water deprivation improved their nitrogen balance. Rogerson (1963) investigated the effect of declining nutrient intake and water deprivation on energy metabolism in *B. taurus* and *B. indicus* and concluded that cattle on a low-protein roughage diet might also be better able to maintain themselves in positive energy balance if they were subjected to some form of water restriction.

Water-deprived sheep and camels also appear to behave in a similar manner and it has been suggested that when nitrogen intake is low, nitrogen output is reduced and nitrogen is recycled in the body (Schmidt-Nielsen *et al.*, 1958; Houpt, 1959), possibly via the salivary glands and/or other channels. Severe water deprivation reduces nitrogen output still further, thus enhancing the value of any recycling mechanism.

In many semi-arid areas the mineral content of the only free water available progressively rises as the dry season advances, and may become so concentrated as to be unsuitable for drinking purposes. This is yet another hazard for cattle living in these areas. Tolerance to highly mineralized water can be induced (Mulhearn, 1957), is a function of adaptation, and presumably happens in practice during the dry season in the semi-arid areas as the free water supplies contract.

The short-term effect of water deprivation on the liveweight of cattle can be very dramatic (Payne, 1965), but this may be mainly due to loss of body water. The long-term effects are not so well documented, but as water deprivation reduces feed intake it would be expected that it would also decrease liveweight gain. The experimental evidence available suggests that this is so. Payne (1965) reported that over a 2-year experimental period intermittently water-deprived *Bos indicus*-type identical twins weighed 14·9 per cent less than their normally watered co-twins, but that the difference in liveweight gain between the two groups occurred during the first 6 months of the experiment. In this experiment the effect of seasonal changes in the quantity and quality of the forage available was far more marked than the effect of water deprivation on liveweight gain.

(iv) *Effect on the nutrient content of the forage.*   Cattle in the arid and semi-arid regions have to exist for long periods on forage that is essentially mature standing hay of low nutrient value.

The low protein content, often only averaging between 2 and 4 per cent CP, and the even lower protein digestibility of this forage, is one of the major reasons for the poor performance of cattle in these regions. The reasons for this are that many of the indigenous forage plants are inherently not particularly nutritious, that the forage is usually mature when it is consumed, and that as the forage plants dry out leaf fall increases, leaving feed material with a high stem:leaf ratio.

The crude fibre content of the standing hay is high as the forage plants are mature and there is evidence that environmental conditions in the arid and semi-arid tropics favour the early onset of lignification. Livestock are therefore forced to digest highly lignified fibrous feeds, and as the digestion of fibre increases the heat output the heat load on the animal is increased at a time when it is already under considerable heat stress.

2. Parasites and disease

High ambient temperatures and humidities provide a favourable breeding environment for internal and external parasites, fungi and disease vectors. Internal parasites are not so important in the semi-arid tropics, but external parasites usually remain very important, though their importance diminishes in the very arid tropics. In so far as the type of vegetation in a region influences the incidence of insect vectors of disease, so climate has quite dramatic indirect effects on animal production. In those regions of tropical Africa where the rainfall is sufficiently high to support a dense growth of bush, and other factors are favourable, the high incidence of tsetse fly (*Glossina* spp.) makes some forms of livestock production difficult, if not impossible. Similarly, climatic conditions that favour *Stomoxys* spp. make it impossible in a country such as Mauritius to graze livestock outdoors at certain times of the year and compel livestock owners to build relatively expensive housing to protect their animals from the swarms of flies. In other countries, such as the Sudan, the seasonal incidence of biting flies greatly influences managerial methods.

3. Storage and handling of animal products

Any tropical climate, humid or arid, favours the rapid deterioration of stored animal products, thus increasing processing and handling costs. This indirectly affects animal production as increased processing, handling and storage charges, such as the provision of additional refrigerator capacity, may make increased production uneconomic in certain marginal areas that are otherwise suitable for the development of a livestock industry.

Acclimatization

Acclimatization is the name given to the complex of processes by which an animal adapts itself to the environment in which it has to live. If an animal is introduced into a new environment and the stresses on it are too great it will fail to acclimatize and will deteriorate. This often happens when temperate types of domestic livestock have been introduced into a tropical environment. Of course, climatic stress is only one of many stresses that the temperate type of animal has to withstand in a tropical environment, other major factors being nutritional and disease stress.

Acclimatization to heat stress may be temporary or permanent and depends either upon the animal increasing its heat loss, reducing its heat production, or increasing the tolerance of its tissues to more fluctuating and higher body temperatures.

Temperate-type domestic livestock are able to acclimatize more easily to considerable intermittent heat stress than to more moderate continuous heat stress. In the arid sub-tropical areas of the Americas and Australia, temperate-type beef breeds such as the Hereford are exposed to very considerable heat stress during the daytime in the summer months, yet this breed thrives in these areas presumably because heat stress is intermittent in effect – falling off at night during the summer months and non-existent during the day or night during the winter months. The same breeds do not thrive in the humid tropical areas of the Americas and Australia where heat stress during the daytime in the summer months is far less, but where there is some heat stress all through the year.

Permanent acclimatization to climatic stress may be due to changes in the behaviour of the animals or to changes in physiological reactions that may or may not be inherited. Natural or artificial selection for morphological characteristics that assist the animal to acclimatize may also take place.

Changes in the behaviour of domestic livestock are important in assisting acclimatization, and it should be the aim of good management of livestock in the tropics to facilitate these changes. Livestock become more sluggish in their movements in a tropical environment, thus reducing muscular heat production. Well-known examples of this are as follows: bulls are more tractable in the tropics than in the temperate zone, other factors being equal; poultry become more sluggish in their movements and when standing hold their wings slightly separated and if lying down adopt an extended position; temperate-type cattle in the tropics graze more at night and seek shade more often during the day than they do in the temperate zone; and all domestic livestock that are not specifically adapted to arid conditions drink and use more water in the tropics than they do in the temperate zone.

Physiological adaptation may be achieved by changes in hormonal activity. There is some evidence that when temperate-type stock are introduced into the tropics there is a reduction in their thyro-adrenal activity, with a consequent reduction in basal energy production and perhaps some effect on reproductive performance. Yousef and Johnson (1965) stated that part of this depression can be directly attributed to high ambient temperature.

Some knowledge of the factors concerned with acclimatization is very important if deliberate attempts are to be made to breed productive animals that are acclimatized to a tropical environment.

Animals may be selected for certain morphological characteristics that possibly assist acclimatization, such as a large skin area in relation to body size and short, light-coloured hair and a pigmented skin.

When the importation of a breed into a new environment is con-

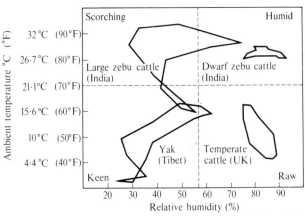

Fig. 1.7   Typical climographs for cattle in Europe and Asia (modified from Wright, 1954).

templated a method of evaluating the possibility of the breed acclimatizing easily has been described by Wright (1954). This consists of constructing climographs made by plotting the mean monthly air temperatures against the mean monthly relative humidities, using climate data collected in both environments. If, when the resulting points are joined, the position, shape and area of the two climographs are similar, then there is a reasonable possibility that the breed will readily acclimatize to its new climatic environment (Fig. 1.7).

References

Bonsma, J. C. (1949) Breeding cattle for increased adaptability to tropical and subtropical environments. *J. agric. Sci. (Camb.)*, **39**, 204–21.
Branton, C. (1970) 'Fertility', Chapter 7 in Payne, W. J. A. (ed.), *Cattle Production in the Tropics*, Vol. 1. Longman: London.
Brody, S., Ragsdale, A. C., Thompson, H. J. and Worstell, D. M. (1954) Environmental Physiology and Shelter Engineering with Special Reference to Domestic Animals. XXV. The effect of wind on milk production, feed and water consumption and body weight in dairy cattle. *Res. Bull. Mo. agric. Exp. Stn*, No. 545.
Cobble, J. W. and Herman, H. A. (1951) The influence of environmental temperatures on the composition of milk of the dairy cow. *Res. Bull. Mo. agric. Exp. Stn*, No. 485.
Dutt, R. H. (1960) Temperature and light as factors in reproduction amongst farm animals. Proc. 4th Biennial Symp. Anim. Reprod., *J. Dairy Sci.*, **43** (Suppl.), 123–44.
Findlay, J. D. (1954) The climatic physiology of farm animals. *Met. Monogr.*, **2**, 19–29.
Hancock, J. and Payne, W. (1955) The direct effect of tropical climate on the performance of European-type cattle. I. Growth. *Emp. J. exp. Agric.*, **23**, 55–74.
Hardison, W. A. (1966) Chemical Composition, Nutrient Content and Potential Milk-

producing Capacity of Fresh Tropical Herbage. *Dairy Train. Res. Inst. Univ. Philipp., Res. Bull.,* No. 1. DTRI: Los Baños, Philippines.

Heitman, H. Jr. and Hughes, E. H. (1949) The effects of air temperature and relative humidity on the physiological wellbeing of swine. *J. Anim. Sci.,* **8,** 171–81.

Holdridge, L. R. (1967) *Life Zone Ecology* (rev. edn). Tropical Science Centre: San José, Costa Rica.

Houpt, T. R. (1959) Utilisation of blood urea in ruminants. *Am. J. Physiol.,* **197,** 115–20.

Huston, T. M. and Carmon, J. L. (1958) Influence of high environmental temperature on fertility and hatchability of eggs of domestic fowl. *Physiol. Zool.,* **31,** 232–5.

Hutchinson, J. C. D. (1954) 'Heat Regulation in Birds', in Hammond, J. (ed.), *Progress in the Physiology of Farm Animals,* Vol. 1. Butterworths: London.

Joblin, A. D. H. (1960) The influence of night grazing on the growth rates of Zebu cattle in East Africa. *J. Brit. Grassland Soc.,* **15,** 212–15.

Kelly, C. F., Bond, T. E. and Ittner, N. R. (1955) Water cooling for livestock in hot climates. *Agric. Engng* (St Joseph, Mich.), **36,** 173–80.

Köeppen, W. (1931) *Grudriss der Klimakunde.* Borntraeger: Berlin.

Livingston, H. G., Payne, W. J. A. and Friend, M. T. (1962) Urea excretion in ruminants. *Nature (Lond.),* **194,** 1057–8.

Moule, G. R. (1970) Australian research into reproduction in the ram. *Anim. Breed. Abstr.,* **38,** 185–202.

Mulhearn, C. J. (1957) Assessing the suitability of water for livestock. *J. Dep. Agric. S. Austral.,* **61,** 49–58.

Osbaldiston, G. W. and Sainsbury, D. W. B. (1963) Control of the Environment in a Poultry House. I. Principles and practice. II. Broiler house experiments. III. Practical aspects of controlled environment poultry housing. *Vet. Rec.,* **75,** 159–70, 193–202, 223–9.

Payne, W. J. A. and Hancock, J. (1957) The direct effect of tropical climate on the performance of European-type cattle. II. Production. *Emp. J. exp. Agric.,* **25,** 321–38.

Payne, W. J. A. (1965) Specific problems of semi-arid environments. *Qualitas Pl. Mater. veg.,* **12,** 268–94.

Payne, W. J. A. (1969) 'Problems of the Nutrition of Ruminants in the Tropics', in Cuthbertson, Sir D. P. (ed.), *Nutrition of Animals of Agricultural Importance,* Part 2, *Int. Encyc. Food Nutrit.,* Vol. 17. Pergamon: Oxford.

Ragsdale, A. C., Thompson, H. J., Worstell, D. M. and Brody, S. (1953) Environmental Physiology and Shelter Engineering with Special Reference to Domestic Animals. XXI. The effect of humidity on milk production and composition, feed and water composition and body weight of cattle. *Res. Bull. Mo. agric. Exp. Stn,* No. 521.

Rogerson, A. (1963) Energy utilisation of poor quality roughage by water-deprived steers. *Nature (Lond.),* **197,** 1222.

Salisbury, G. W. and van Demark, N. L. (1961) *Physiology of Reproduction and AI of Cattle.* Freeman: San Francisco.

Schmidt-Nielsen, B., Osaki, H., Murdaugh, H. V., Jr. and O'Dell, R. (1958) Renal regulation of urea excretion in sheep. *Amer. J. Physiol.,* **194,** 221–8.

Smith, C. A. (1965) The grazing habits of African-owned, East African Zebu cattle in Zambia (Northern Rhodesia). *J. agric. Sci. (Camb.),* **64,** 295–8.

Thornthwaite, C. W. (1948) An approach towards a rational classification of climate. *Geog. Rev.,* **38,** 55–94.

USDA (1941) 'Climate and Man.' *USDA Yearbook of Agriculture.* United States Department of Agriculture: Washington.

Warnick, A. C., Wallace, H. D., Palmer, A. Z., Soza, E., Duerre, D. J. and Caldwell, V. E. (1965) Effect of temperature on early embryo survival in gilts. *J. Anim. Sci.,* **24,** 89–92.

Wilson, P. N. (1961) Observations on the grazing behaviour of crossbred Zebu Holstein cattle managed on Pangola pasture in Trinidad. *Turrialba,* **11,** 57–71.

Wilson, W. O. (1949) High environmental temperatures as affecting the reaction of laying hens to iodized casein. *Poult. Sci.,* **28,** 581–92.

Winchester, C. F. (1964) Symposium on growth. Environment and growth. *J. Anim. Sci.,* **23,** 254–64.

Worstell, D. M. and Brody, S. (1953) Environmental Physiology and Shelter Engineering with Special Reference to Domestic Animals. XX. Comparative physiological reactions of European and Indian cattle to changing temperatures. *Res. Bull. Mo. agric. Exp. Stn,* No. 515.

Wright, N. C. (1954) 'The Ecology of Domesticated Animals', in Hammond, J. (ed.), *Progress in the Physiology of Farm Animals,* Vol. 1. Butterworths: London.

Yeates, N. T. M. (1954) Environmental control of coat changes in cattle. *Nature (Lond.),* **174,** 609–10.

Yeates, N. T. M. (1965) *Modern Aspects of Animal Production.* Butterworths: London.

Yousef, M. K. and Johnson, H. D. (1965) Feed and temperature effects on thyroid activity in cattle. *J. Dairy Sci.,* **48,** 813.

Further Reading

Bligh, J. *Temperature Regulation in Mammals and Other Vertebrates.* North-Holland: Amsterdam, 1973.

Brody, S. *Bioenergetics and Growth.* Reinhold: New York, 1945.

Moloiy, G. M. O. (ed.) *Comparative Physiology of Desert Animals.* Academic Press: London, 1972.

Mount, L. E. *The Climatic Physiology of the Pig.* Edward Arnold: London, 1968.

Schmidt-Nielsen, K. S. *Desert Animals: Physiological Problems of Heat and Water.* Oxford Univ. Press: London, 1964.

Sturkie, P. D. *Avian Physiology* (2nd edn.). Comstock: Ithaca, New York, 1965.

Chapter 2

Maintenance of Health

by **E. P. Lindley**
c/o FAO, Rome, Italy
(including a sub-chapter on Parasitism by **R. P. Lee**)

Importance of animal health

Profitable animal production demands efficient husbandry of healthy animals; as disease remains a profit-limiting factor in most tropical territories. Even in countries where there is intensive veterinary control it may cause losses of between 15 and 20 per cent of total production. Details of some of the more important diseases prevalent in the tropics are given in Table 2.1.

Some major epizootics are now being brought under control. Since the first edition of this book was published in 1959, rinderpest has been eliminated from many countries in Africa; certainly with the efficient vaccines now available this disease should present no problem to animal-production projects. Contagious bovine pleuro-pneumonia has been almost eradicated from Australia, but it remains widespread and prevalent in Africa. There is, however, ample evidence to suggest that with the improved stable and standardized vaccines now available it, too, should not jeopardize cattle-raising schemes. There still remains, however, a long list of diseases ranging from the acute enzootics such as foot and mouth disease to chronic parasitic infestations that present serious hazards to profitable livestock production.

Of course, low production may also be the result of other factors than disease, such as the climate, a low plane of nutrition and poor management. Good husbandry will minimize losses from these causes. Additional feeding and continuous medication can also sometimes reduce the effects of disease and parasitism, but these are usually expensive methods of maintaining production.

Relations between livestock owners and authorities

In developing countries several levels of husbandry often exist side by side, varying from primitive methods based on a subsistence economy to those found on state farms and commercial undertakings that may be sophisticated and efficient. These diverse patterns of husbandry are

Table 2.1 *Basic information concerning some infectious diseases of domestic livestock prevalent in the tropics*

Disease	Transmission	Incubation period	First symptoms	Animals affected	Preventive measures
African swine fever	Direct contact or through eating material contaminated with excretions	6 to 9 days	Sudden death, high fever, blotched skin, diarrhoea	Pigs	Sanitary segregation and destruction of affected animals
Anthrax	Water and food contaminated with blood and excretions or by wound infection	1 to 3 days or longer	Sudden death or very high fever	Mostly cattle. Buffaloes, sheep, goats, pigs and horses less frequently	Annual vaccination
Avian spirochaetosis	Infective ticks	2 to 7 days	Intense thirst, profuse diarrhoea	Poultry, ducks and turkeys, guinea-fowl and some wild birds	Tick elimination. Vaccination
Blackquarter	Water and food contaminated with blood and excretions or by wound infection	2 to 5 days	Gas gangrene, sudden death	Cattle and sheep	Annual vaccination
Contagious bovine abortion	Food, water, etc., contaminated by discharge and aborted foetus	7 days to several months	Abortions, full-term stillbirths, retained afterbirths	Cattle and buffaloes	Segregation and other sanitary measures. Vaccination before breeding
Contagious bovine pleuro-pneumonia	Direct contact	2 weeks to 4 months	Frequent painful subdued cough. Prolonged unthriftiness	Cattle	Annual vaccination, slaughter of affected animals

Disease	Transmission	Incubation	Symptoms	Animals affected	Control
East Coast fever	Infective ticks	1 to 4 weeks	High fever, unthriftiness, weakness	Cattle. Sometimes buffaloes in East Africa. Cattle indigenous to enzootic areas are immune	Tick control and elimination
Foot and mouth disease	Direct contact or with material contaminated with discharge from lesion	3 to 8 days	Salivation, vesicles on tongue and feet, lameness, fever	All domestic animals	Segregation and other sanitary measures. Vaccination
Fowl cholera	Direct contact or by eating or inhaling material contaminated with excretions	2 to 5 days	Sudden death or discharge from eyes and nose, inability to stand	Poultry, ducks and geese. Occasionally turkeys, guinea-fowl and some wild birds	Sanitary segregation
Fowl plague	Direct contact or by eating or inhaling material contamined with excretions	3 to 5 days	Sudden death or discharge from eyes and nose, inability to stand	Poultry, ducks and geese. Occasionally turkeys, guinea-fowl and some wild birds	Sanitary segregation. Vaccination
Fowl pox	Direct contact	3 to 15 days	Rough, brown wartlike sores about the head, sore mouth and eyes	Poultry, turkeys. Sometimes guinea-fowl, ducks and geese	Vaccination
Fowl typhoid	Ingestion of contaminated material	4 to 5 days	Diarrhoea, dejection	Poultry, ducks and geese. Occasionally turkeys, guinea-fowl and some wild birds	Sanitary segregation. Vaccination

Table 2.1 – *continued*

Disease	Transmission	Incubation period	First symptoms	Animals affected	Preventive measures
Heartwater	Infective ticks	9 to 28 days	Fever, nervous signs, convulsions	Sheep, goats and cattle	Tick control and elimination
Newcastle disease	Direct contact or by eating or inhaling material contaminated with excretions	3 to 5 days	Sudden death. Stringy discharge from beak, shaking of head and stretching of neck, prostration, diarrhoea	Poultry. Occasionally turkeys, guinea-fowl and some wild birds	Vaccination
Piroplasmosis (babesiosis)	Infective ticks	1 to 4 weeks	Fever, red urine, progressive weakness	All domestic animals	Tick control and elimination
Pleuro-pneumonia of goats	Direct contact	2 to 6 days	Fever, nasal discharge, lethargy	Goats	Sanitary segregation. Vaccination
Rinderpest	Direct contact or with material contaminated with discharge from lesions	3 to 15 days	High fever, bloodstained diarrhoea, mouth lesions	Cattle, buffaloes. Sometimes sheep and goats	Vaccination
Sheep pox	Inhalation and through broken skin of material contaminated with discharge	2 to 7 days	High fever, discharge from eyes and nose, skin lesions	Sheep	Vaccination
Trypanosomiasis (surra, nagana, etc.)	Tsetse and other infective flies	Few days to some weeks	Intermittent fever, unthriftiness	All domestic animals	Chemoprophylaxis and fly eradication

naturally associated with different attitudes to animal health and sickness and are influenced not only by economic but also by social and educational factors. Treatment and nursing of animals is a matter of cost, as well as of experience and training, so that any policy of disease control must be related to the economic level of the animal industry. A good example is bovine contagious abortion or brucellosis, control measures for which depend not only on the incidence of the disease and the degree of infection in the herd and surrounding local herds but also upon the monetary value of individual animals and social factors. On a government ranch or farm drastic culling or segregation of infected animals can be undertaken; for most commercial undertakings a vaccination scheme may be suitable; but in herds kept at subsistence level even the necessary continued vaccination coverage may not be possible so that the villager has to tolerate the disease in his herd.

On economic grounds it is always advisable to consider the timely and prudent culling of chronically sick animals rather than embark on a long period of cure. Whatever action is taken will depend, among other things, upon the nature of the disease and the attendant risk of extension to other stock. The fundamental approach should be the maintenance of health and the avoidance of disease, and owners should do everything in their power, using all available sources of information and expertise, to keep their animals healthy.

The stockman cannot expect to be an expert in veterinary science nor is it necessary that he should be. However, all governments expect him to be able to recognize the symptoms of certain diseases that are notifiable to the authorities. In most countries diseases such as rabies, glanders, rinderpest, fowl plague, anthrax, contagious bovine pleuropneumonia and swine fever are notifiable. The FAO/WHO/OIE *Animal Health Yearbook* contains details of the distribution of these diseases and the local government veterinary or agricultural officer has ready information and probably a copy of the relevant laws.

Government services are available to help owners maintain animal health because it is in the national interest to preserve the livestock wealth of the country. State animal health services are also organized to combat certain contagious diseases including those which are notifiable. This they achieve by applying regulations to control the internal movement and importation of animals, the cleansing of vehicles, isolation of premises, compulsory vaccination, etc. Usually there is also a government animal health and production advisory or extension service. Stockowners are strongly advised to acquaint themselves with the local representatives of these bodies and to use their services and advice as far as is practicable. For the treatment of individual animals, with which state services do not usually concern themselves, and for advice on general animal health matters, owners may consult a private veterinarian. Although there are as yet few private veterinarians outside the cities in most developing countries, there may be government veterinary clinics. As it is always through the owner's initiative that remedial action must be taken when an animal is sick he should not delay in seeking technical help.

An animal which is well fed and watered and in good condition will resist disease better than one that is undernourished or suffering from a mineral deficiency, climatic stress or parasitic infestation. Thus, in discussing the determinants of disease the underlying predisposing causes, especially those associated with the environment, cannot be ignored. Good management can do much to remove or reduce the effects of adverse environmental factors.

Diseases

Classification

Animal diseases may be conveniently classified according to their causative agent as follows:

1. microbiological (bacteria, viruses, protozoa and rickettsia);
2. parasitic (external and internal);
3. metabolic disorders (including nutritional deficiencies);
4. fungal;
5. poisoning (plants, snakes, and chemicals);
6. neoplasms;
7. physical injuries.

Diseases may also be referred to by the particular disability they cause or the part of the body principally affected, without reference to the causative agent, for instance pleuro-pneumonia and enteritis. On the other hand some micro-organisms are so specific in their effect that this may be included in the name, as for example infectious bovine rhinotracheitis and chronic respiratory disease. However, many infectious agents may affect more than one organ or have a generalized effect on the whole animal.

A disease is said to be contagious if transmitted by contact between sick and healthy animals, and infectious if spread from the sick to the healthy without direct contact. In the classification above, the infectious and contagious diseases are included in the first two groups.

The bacteria are a large group of unicellular micro-organisms of diverse shapes 0·5 to 5 μm in size and hence visible under the light microscope. Given favourable conditions they can multiply very rapidly, producing populations of millions within a few hours. Some of them may form resistant spores capable of survival under adverse conditions. Disease is caused when certain pathogenic bacteria invade the tissues, multiply and produce toxins. Examples are *Brucella abortus*, the agent of contagious bovine abortion, and *Clostridium tetani*, the cause of tetanus in man and animals. Most of the pathogenic bacteria are susceptible to one or other of the antibiotics.

Viruses form another large and very important group of disease determinants. Smaller than bacteria and generally comprising a nucleic acid core in a protein shell, they cannot be seen using ordinary techniques with the light microscope and are designated 'filter-passing' to differentiate them from bacteria. Viruses require living cells in which to multiply. Their morphology and mode of action have been much studied in recent years using electron microscopy. They are not susceptible to most available antibiotics and there is extensive research to find more efficient antiviral agents. Pathogenic viruses, such as those of rinderpest and foot and mouth disease, invade host cells, destroying them, and in this way, as many millions of cells may be involved, they produce cell dysfunction, tissue damage and hence disease. Arbor viruses that cause diseases, for example blue tongue and equine encephalomyelitis, are spread by arthropods such as mosquitoes – a complicating factor in their control.

Protozoa are unicellular micro-organisms belonging to the animal kingdom. They cause some of the most important, widespread and serious diseases in tropical countries. Some, for example the coccidia, are transmitted directly, but others, like the protozoal blood parasites such as trypanosomes, babesia and anaplasms, are spread by arthropod vectors such as ticks and insects, and the control of these vectors presents additional problems. A further complication with protozoal infections is that in some cases animals support a certain level of infection as long as they are under good conditions and well nourished, but as soon as they are stressed, they become clinically ill, for example coccidiosis in adult birds and trypanosomiasis in the West African humpless breeds of cattle.

There are other families of unicellular micro-organisms which are important pathogens and which cannot strictly be included in the aforementioned groups. Examples are the rickettsias which may cause Q-fever and heartwater and are spread directly by mites and ticks, and also the mycoplasmas which can cause contagious pleuro-pneumonia in goats and cattle as well as contagious agalactia in goats and sheep.

External and internal parasitic diseases are so important to the stockowner and their control is so dependent upon his competence and efficiency that they are discussed later in a separate section.

Metabolic diseases arise from dysfunction within the animal's body. Examples in tropical areas are bloat and hypomagnesemia. Milk fever and acetonaemia are not so common where milk production is less intensive. Nutritional and deficiency diseases, leading to abnormalities, arise from mineral imbalance or a faulty diet, and in particular may occur in rapidly growing animals. Examples are piglet anaemia and curled toe paralysis of poultry. At the end of the dry season in the tropics grazing animals are subject to a low plane of nutrition and/or nutritional imbalance and all species – but especially cattle – are particularly liable to secondary infection from parasitic and protozoal disease at this time.

Most fungi are saprophytic and beneficial, as for example the yeasts in fermenting processes, but some are pathogenic and cause external mycotic diseases such as ringworm or internal mycoses such as asper-gillosis in poultry or epizootic lymphangitis in horses. In general, mycotic diseases are very contagious and less host-specific than most pathogens; though some are found as saprophytes in and on the animal's body and only produce disease as a result of an increase in the susceptibility of the animal brought about by stress, for example streptothricosis caused by *Dermatophyllus congolensis*.

Animals do not normally eat poisonous plants, but starving cattle or sheep or any grazing animal recently introduced to a new area may do so, and owners should endeavour to remedy underlying mismanagement as it is usually impossible to remove all the offending plants. A stockman who can recognize the poisonous plants of his locality and the symptoms of their poisoning is very valuable indeed, as he is able to make an early differential diagnosis and take necessary remedial action before losses become serious.

Although the bites of most poisonous snakes are not usually fatal for cattle they often cause large oedematous swellings on forelimbs or brisket. If an animal is bitten in the region of the head, the subsequent swelling may interfere with breathing and lead to death. Prompt use of anti-snake venom is justified if the life of the animal is endangered, while pasture improvement naturally reduces the snake population.

Most domestic animals are slaughtered at a relatively young age and tumours or neoplasms are seldom a cause of loss of production. If the converse is the case the owner should seek expert advice.

If 'accidents' due to staff thoughtlessness or negligence account for regular losses – 'Monday-morning' diseases – the management should make a thorough investigation to ascertain the underlying causes of these mishaps.

Transmission

Healthy intact skin forms a natural obstacle to invading pathogens. These gain access to the body when cuts, scratches, continued heavy rain, chemicals or malnutrition reduce the effectiveness of the skin as a defensive barrier. Biting flies and ticks also breach normal skin, transmitting blood parasites, streptothricosis, etc.

Airborne micro-organisms enter with inspired air. Many are arrested on the mucosal surfaces of the nasal passages, larynx and trachea, but some, depending on the droplet size, may reach the inner membranes of the lung. Even at this stage infection is not inevitable for it depends on the dose, the susceptibility of the animal and the virulence of the organism.

The digestive tract is a continuous tube from mouth to anus and its contents are not, technically speaking, inside the tissues of the body. It provides a series of very special environments each endowed with its own specialized flora and/or sometimes fauna. In healthy animals these micro-organisms are commensals, often necessary, as in the ruminant animal, for proper functioning of the digestive system. Under certain circumstances these commensals may themselves set up disease, but usually the disease-causing organisms in the digestive tract are other specific pathogenic micro-organisms, perhaps closely related, introduced with the feed and water consumed by the animal.

Pathogens capable of causing generalized disease, such as vibriosis and brucellosis, may gain access via the genital tract during copulation. A similar transmission risk exists if artificial insemination is not carried out with strict sterile precautions.

Recent studies on nocturnal moths which suck lachrymal secretions in cattle have revealed another mode of disease transmission, although so far only infectious bovine kerato-conjunctivitis has been associated with these vectors.

For a clear understanding of the objectives and limitation of sanitary control measures such as isolation of sick animals, quarantine and disinfection one must appreciate the ways in which diseases are transmitted. In cases of direct transmission, physical separation of infected from healthy animals will prevent further spread, although most bacteria and viruses can also be transmitted by other means, for instance by soil, manure, sacks, food, boots of workers, water, etc., or by vectors like biting insects or ticks.

Quite apart from the innate resistance of stock there is the important factor of infective dose. Very few maladies can be initiated by one single micro-organism. Usually a certain minimal number of microbes, sometimes in repeated doses, is necessary. Thus, in spite of the seemingly alarming possibilities of extension, if practical sanitary precautions are formulated and consistently carried out, then the spread of infection can be arrested.

Included in Table 2.1 is the host range of some infections. In recent years it has become more and more evident that many wild animals and birds act as carriers of some of the infective agents which cause disease in domestic stock. In these cases a more rigid control of the environment is necessary to limit transmission. For this reason intensive methods of production based on control of the whole environment have been very successful. Modern pig and poultry units are not only completely isolated but their managers regulate the temperature, humidity and flow of air in the housing, in addition to the food and water supplies.

Inflammation, characterized by congestion, pain, swelling and the affected parts feeling hot to the touch, is the body response to injury or irritants – chemical, physical or biological. The physical result of the structural changes produced in the tissues by an inflammation or neoplasm is called a lesion. Examples of gross lesions include abscesses, ulcers, blisters, swollen lymph glands and corneal opacities. Lesions may not always be visible to the naked eye, even on post-mortem examination, for some diseases are the result of cellular damage or dysfunction due to biological change within cells. The study of the basic biochemical determinants of disease is not yet far advanced for it involves very complex chemistry and intricate experimentation.

Once organisms have invaded the body they multiply and produce specific toxins, with the rate of multiplication depending upon the virulence of the microbe and effectiveness of the defence mechanisms of the host.

The incubation period is the interval between the introduction of the infective agent and the first clinical signs in the host. Although the incubation period varies within certain limits it is specific for each disease (Table 2.1). During the incubation period the organism proliferates in the tissues, but eventually some abnormality becomes apparent such as liquid faeces, lachrymation, discharges, pus, etc., and animals present signs of discomfort such as coughing, straining or merely looking dejected.

Immunity

The defence mechanisms of the body and their reactions to invading micro-organisms make up one aspect of the study of immunology. Briefly, pathogenic bacteria, viruses, etc., and their toxic products consist of antigens which stimulate the immune system of the host which in turn produces antibodies capable of reacting with, or neutralizing, the antigens. The battle is fought on many fronts, but the specific humoral antibodies of the blood and the white blood cells are very important participants. The speed of their production and their specific effectiveness decide the fate of the animal, which may succumb in hours, may be ailing for only a few days or not at all, or may continue to suffer from chronic disease for years.

An animal's condition affects its response to infection. If it is weakened by inadequate feeding, bad accommodation, overwork or concurrent disease its resistance is low. On the other hand the robust vitality associated with proper management, good feeding and absence of stress minimizes the effects of the infection, for the body's natural defences are quickly brought into action, antibodies are elaborated and immunity acquired.

It is this ability of the body to react to the inoculation of foreign antigens which is the basis of the protection offered by vaccines and certain other biological products. These biologicals take three forms:

1. *Live vaccines* – the infective agent is so attenuated that after inoculation as vaccine it invades the tissues only to an extent sufficient for the stimulation of an active immunity – that is, to produce antibodies but not sufficient to set up the natural disease.
2. *Inactivated vaccines and toxoids* – the dead infective agent or its modified toxins are also used to evoke an active immunity.

3. *The specific antibodies themselves either as serum or in a more purified form* – these protective sera are obtained from donor animals, usually horses, which have been hyperimmunized using concentrated doses of the specific antigens made from the disease agents or their toxic products, and which have been altered to make them safe for inoculation.

Using the first two products, animals can be vaccinated prophylactically at the convenience of the owner while they are in good health and not exposed to the disease. Following active immunization, 2 to 4 weeks elapse before satisfactory antibody blood levels develop, but such immunity, whether from vaccination or infection, is long-lasting being effective for months, even years and sometimes for life. Vaccination of animals already infected is generally useless and may lead to exacerbation of the existing malady.

Specific immune serum and gammaglobulins, that is the purified antibody fraction of the immune serum, may be injected for passive immunization. Such passive immunity is only temporary, lasting days rather than weeks. It is conferred immediately on inoculation and can thus be used to aid the immune response of a sick animal. These products are especially useful in young animals in which the immune system has not fully developed, for example calves with coli-enteritis (calf scours).

Although in the pig some immunoglobulin may pass the placenta to the foetus, new-born stock usually receive the maternal antibodies in the colostrum. These antibodies are absorbed for about 36 hours after birth, and the young are thus enabled to survive the first few weeks of life before their own immune system has developed sufficiently to combat infection. It is for this reason that the newly born should be fed the colostrum.

Biological products designed to give protection against nearly all the bacterial and viral diseases are generally available, but vary in effectiveness owing to different inherent properties of the organisms and methods of preparation. Thus, it is possible to employ either a live or an inactivated vaccine depending on the circumstances, as for example against Newcastle disease or brucellosis. Commercial houses compete to produce more effective, better standardized, safer and cheaper vaccines, and the wide choice and differing claims made for the products may present a bewildering complex to the stockowner. For technical as well as economic reasons he should consult a veterinary adviser when planning his programme of prophylactic vaccinations. The instructions issued by the manufacturers regarding the storage and use of their vaccines should be followed carefully if the best results are to be obtained.

As yet, satisfactory vaccines have not been produced for the protozoal diseases, although procedures analogous to vaccination – such as the deliberate infection of calves – are successful with, for example, babesiosis. Generally, chemical medication has been satisfactory as in the cases of the phenanthridium compounds for the treatment of trypanosomiasis and the 'nitro' drugs for coccidiosis in poultry. Antibiotics have been shown to be useful in treating anaplasmosis.

Prophylactic vaccination should be considered as an additional safeguard rather than as an excuse for neglecting ordinary sanitary precautions. Vaccination cover is rarely 100 per cent and young animals may be susceptible so that strict measures should always be taken to reduce the chance, the intensity and the spread of infection. These measures are based on avoiding contact with infected animals, their discharges, faeces and objects in their immediate neighbourhood which may be contaminated.

Indigenous livestock which have been already exposed to certain diseases possess antibodies, therefore their immune system responds more quickly than that of imported animals with no such disease experience. An infection unimportant to the former may be fatal to the latter on first exposure. Thus newly imported animals are often exposed to considerable risk in their new environment, requiring good management, special vaccinations and treatments to acclimatize. This is particularly true in the humid tropics where even to move stock only a few hundred miles from their place of origin may entail risk of loss from disease.

Prevention and control

The ideal, for maintenance of health, is to keep animals in small herds or flocks, segregated on non-contaminated ground, in clean accommodation, watered and fed apart from other stock and kept free of external and internal parasites. However, such counsel of perfection can seldom be entirely followed.

Even though newly acquired animals may look fit and come from reputed disease-free areas, it is a mistake to introduce them without adequate quarantine precautions. Animals returning from markets or agricultural shows which have been exposed to the risk of infection must also be quarantined before being allowed back in the herd. Although quarantining is often inconvenient to management and staff, the temptation to dispense with it must be totally resisted. The duration of time spent in quarantine should be the maximum incubation period of the disease involved. Routine day-to-day management should be organized to reduce the risk of introducing disease and to control any outbreak which occurs with the least possible inconvenience and expenditure.

On account of increasing labour and construction costs livestock units tend to become more intensive and the herds and flocks larger and more crowded, but unless standards of hygiene are correspondingly high losses from disease may jeopardize such enterprises. Sanitary-control measures must be taken into consideration and incorporated into these projects from the beginning; neglecting to do so is to invite trouble at a later date.

Disease is a departure from the normal and time spent in observing healthy stock is never wasted. The first essential is to recognize all aspects of the sound animal – healthy eyes, skin, membranes, excretions, discharges, conformation, etc. Normal animals follow regular patterns of behaviour in their eating, resting, defaecating, etc., and they show definite response to outside stimuli and their sounds, odours and movements – or lack of them – are significant.

One of the duties of the stockowner is to be able to detect abnormality in his animals as a first sign of disease and to keep in mind the possibility of its infectious nature. It is of the utmost importance that infectious diseases should be detected early and, if in doubt, he should seek the help of his veterinarian.

First signs of disease may be obscure and often it is only when there is a radical change in behaviour or a drop in production that suspicions are aroused. Fortunately, most bouts of 'indisposition' are temporary and after a few days the animal is back to normal, but any deviation from the usual state of health must be taken as a warning. A disease which may be catastrophic in its final effects cannot, in the early stages, be differentiated from a minor or temporary malady; therefore it is prudent to take immediate precautions, keeping all sick animals under observation and, wherever possible, isolating them.

A consequence of some infections is that animals show a rise in body temperature. This is usually accompanied by other disturbances such as inappetence and shivering which indicate the presence of fever. As the febrile reaction may occur in the sick animal before other more specific signs are evident it can be used to differentiate some infected animals, which can then be isolated. On account of diurnal fluctuations in body temperatures measurements of body temperature should be taken at the same time each day, preferably early in the morning.

Laboratory examination of material from the sick or dead animal may be necessary in order to make a diagnosis. Samples required by the diagnostic laboratory differ according to the examination requested and the disease. Today specialized transport media and other refined techniques are available to facilitate veterinary investigations in remote areas. It is, however, essential that the correct material reaches the laboratory in a condition fit for examination. This point cannot be overemphasized and for this reason it is better that samples be collected and dispatched by someone trained for the work, but if this is impossible, technical guidance should be obtained from the laboratory concerned.

The actual mechanics of the application of sanitary control must depend upon local circumstances and the disease suspected. The quicker the control measures are implemented the more successful they are likely to be. Micro-organisms do not sleep from 22.00 to 06.00 hours. The sick animal should be placed in an isolation paddock or stable kept exclusively for this purpose. In-contacts must be segregated from the herd and other herds and kept under close surveillance. If the disease is notifiable or if doubt exists, the authorities should be informed. Movement of stock, staff and equipment should be organized to minimize possible spread of infection. Necessary vaccination and treatments of the various groups of stock should be initiated, and as these measures may have to be continued for several weeks, division and segregation of the herd may perhaps require the employment of extra labour for feeding and herding until all risk of spread of infection has passed.

Under no circumstances should there be any attempt at concealment. This invariably leads to greater loss and if the disease does eventually prove to be notifiable this will make the owner culpable.

Disinfection involves the removal or destruction of infection and success demands a clear understanding of the methods and materials available and their conscientious application. Heat is a most efficient disinfecting agent and burning is an excellent way of destroying infection in bedding, litter, brushes, sacks, etc., although the blowlamp and flame gun, albeit very efficient, are particularly dangerous for use on wooden structures in dry climates because of the risk of fire. Some microorganisms are destroyed by currents of hot dry air, but it is better to cleanse thoroughly yards, fittings and materials and then expose them to strong sunlight. Small items such as scissors and clippers can be sterilized by boiling in water for 30 minutes.

Many chemical disinfectants are manufactured, but often one has to use what is available. In all cases the manufacturer's instructions should be followed and the product used at the correct concentration. It is also essential that the disinfectant be left in contact with the surface to be treated for a sufficient time, the longer the better. To obtain the best results, all traces of dung, litter, etc., should be removed from posts, floors and walls before applying the disinfectant. However, if anthrax is suspected, because of the danger to personnel, surfaces should be treated at once with strong disinfectant and the cleaning carried out later.

Certain products are recommended for particular purposes. For example, formaldehyde for fumigation, 10 per cent ammonium hydroxide for coccidiosis, 70 per cent ethyl alcohol for skin disinfection, caustic and washing soda for foot and mouth and other virus diseases, chlorine and iodine for water sterilization, quaternary ammonium compounds – because of their low toxicity – for wound and skin disinfection, and lysol, creosote or limewash for buildings and other large surfaces.

Infected carcases should be buried or burned. Burying involves digging a deep pit and covering the carcase with quicklime under at least 2·0 m (6·6 ft) of earth. Burning can be carried out in a Bostock pit or over a crossed slit trench, each trench being 2·0 m (6·6 ft) long by 0·5 m (1·6 ft) wide by 0·5 m (1·6 ft) deep, the soil being piled in the angles formed by the cross and the iron bars lying across the heaps supporting wood, carcase and more wood. Several bales of straw, about a ton of wood and 2·0 litres (0·4 gal) of kerosene are required to burn completely a 250 to 300 kg (551 to 661 lb) carcase.

In conclusion, profitable animal production demands good husbandry with a positive endeavour to maintain health. To achieve this the stockman should use all available sources of technical assistance. He should be vigilant for early signs of disease and inculcate similar awareness in his staff. Efficient organization of the day-to-day running of the farm with an enlightened approach to preventive medicine and an intelligent application of sanitary-control measures will do much to prevent disease and to limit losses.

Parasitism

R. P. Lee
Department of Clinical Veterinary
Sciences, Veterinary College of Ireland,
Ballsbridge, Dublin, Ireland

Diseases caused by metazoan and protozoan parasites constitute a major obstacle to the development of profitable livestock industries in the tropics. In some of the drier pastoral areas that are at present generally more suitable for livestock, generations of cattle and sheep owners learned that constant movement of stock to fresh pastures was attended with better health, provided the risk of exposure to other herds and flocks suffering infectious disease was avoided. Animals kept under such systems escaped the dangers of parasitism associated with their remaining indefinitely on pastures which they themselves had contaminated.

Now that better utilization of land, involving set stocking, has become necessary parasitic diseases have assumed greater importance and they will become even more important as carrying capacities improve and stocking rates increase.

The tropical environment is for various reasons eminently suitable for the development of parasitic diseases. In the first place, many of the parasites encountered in temperate regions are also found in the tropics, together with the numerous species that are peculiar to the warmer parts of the world. Practically all parasites require to undergo a period of development outside the host before becoming infective for another host, and during this time in the outside world the rate of development and their chances of survival are influenced by climatic and other environmental factors. The rate of development of the extra-host stages tends to rise with increasing temperature, moisture is required for survival and extreme desiccation is usually lethal. In the wetter parts of the tropics extra-host stages are seldom exposed for long to the destructive effects of desiccation and temperatures are commonly optimal throughout the year. Under these conditions the survival rate of parasitic forms outside the host is high; they develop rapidly to the infective stage and large populations are established. Even where prolonged dry seasons alternate with very short wet seasons the extra-host stages of many endoparasites can take full advantage of the warm, wet conditions associated with the latter, while the adult stages which subsequently develop within the host are well protected and are safely carried over the ensuing dry season.

A second factor contributing to the importance of parasitism is the prevalence of malnutrition in the tropics. Animals with a high nutrient intake would, in many instances, have little difficulty in compensating for the harmful effects of parasitism such as blood loss, leakage of albumen or impaired digestive efficiency. On the other hand the combined effects of even light parasitic infestations and malnutrition may harm the animal, and a high incidence of parasitism may seriously reduce the production efficiency and even threaten the survival of individuals during seasonal periods of nutritional stress.

Some traditional husbandry systems commonly practised in the tropics are also conducive to parasitism. For instance, in many countries there is a tendency for the smaller ruminants, pigs and poultry to wander at large round villages where they scavenge for their food, mainly on fouled land. Under these conditions the infective stages of worms, intestinal protozoa and certain arthropods accumulate on the ground and stock are exposed to high infection pressures. Also, during drought periods, all types of livestock, unconfined as they usually are, concentrate in the vicinity of river beds and standing water where green herbage persists. Increased contamination occurs in such places and the moist environment favours the development and survival of infective material. Stock that concentrate in these areas are also exposed to specialized parasites which utilize water-snails and other aquatic invertebrates as intermediate hosts for completion of their life cycles. Furthermore, in many parts of the tropics cattle and sheep are herded or otherwise confined by night on permanent or semi-permanent sites. The surroundings become covered with a mixture of earth, organic matter and infected faeces that constitutes an ideal medium for the development of the infective stages of a wide variety of internal parasites. These are readily transferred to the adjacent herbage.

Diseases caused by worms

The common worm parasites are broadly classified into three groups: roundworms or nematodes, flukes or trematodes, and tapeworms or cestodes. Worms are ubiquitous in the tropics and one rarely examines an animal which does not harbour at least a few species. While worms occur in most parts of the body, including notably the respiratory, urinary, circulatory and the central nervous systems and the body cavities, the majority of species are found in their adult stages in the gastro-intestinal tract. All types of domestic animals have their own particular fauna of parasitic worms, and while there is a marked tendency to host specificity several economically important species are capable of infecting a variety of domestic animals.

Some worms which are essentially parasites of domestic animals are also capable of infecting man; others occur in man in the adult stages but use domestic animals as intermediate hosts. Therefore, worm parasites of domestic animals have public health as well as economic significance.

Roundworms or nematodes

Roundworms of the gastro-intestinal tract exceed in number and in economic importance those found in other organs. Those that generally cause major trouble to livestock in the tropics may be considered in two broad groups, namely the strongyle worms and the 'ascarids' or large roundworms.

The strongyle worms include such common species as *Haemonchus contortus*, a bright red worm with a twisted appearance which is from 10 to 30 mm (0·4 to 1·2 in) long, readily visible and occurs in the abomasum of ruminants; the voracious blood-sucking hookworms, *Bunostomum phlebotomum*, *B. trigonocephalum* and *Gaigeria pachyscelis*, which are found in the small intestine of ruminants and are easily seen by the naked eye; *Oesophagostomum* spp., distinctly white worms of about the same size as *H. contortus* occurring in the large intestine of ruminants and pigs where they produce nodules in the bowel wall; the somewhat bigger red worms such as *Strongylus* spp. of the large intestine of members of the Equidae, and various genera of less easily seen slender, threadlike worms, too numerous to name in an introductory work, which occur in the stomach and intestine of ruminants, pigs and poultry.

The 'ascarids' include *Ascaris suum*, *Neoascaris vitulorum*, *Parascaris equorum* and *Ascaridia* spp., of pigs, calves, horses and poultry, respectively. The sexually mature stages all occur in the small intestine of their host and are easily recognized by their large size, as they measure from about 6 cm (2·4 in) long in poultry to between 15 and 50 cm (5·9 and 19·7 in) in the other hosts.

The life cycles of all these worms have certain features in common. The sexually mature females, living in the digestive system of their hosts, lay enormous numbers of eggs which reach the exterior in the faeces where they develop further.

In the case of the strongyle worms development generally takes place in the faecal mass to the infective stage, which is a free larva capable of considerable activity. This assists it in moving from the faeces to herbage where it is more likely to be ingested. Oxygen, warmth and moisture are necessary for its development, but desiccation is soon lethal to both the pre-infective and infective stages so that the faecal mass, which retains moisture longer than the surrounding herbage, tends to serve as a reservoir of infection during short periods of drought. The eggs of ascarid worms develop in other media such as soil as well as in faeces, but the infective larvae remain within the eggshell which affords them considerable protection. In moist conditions the infective eggs remain viable for months or even years and are capable of resisting quite powerful chemical disinfectants, but they are susceptible to desiccation and drying is probably one of the most effective, practical means of killing these eggs.

Ingestion of infective larvae or infective eggs by the host is the most common mechanism of infection, though hookworms and a few other species are capable of penetrating the intact skin. In the case of hookworms and *Neoascaris vitulorum* (the large roundworm of the calf) the foetus or the neonate may become infected with immature, migratory stages which pass from the tissue of the dam across the placenta or into the colostrum. This is an example of the important link that exists in the transmission of worm populations from one generation of a host to the next. Another important example is the post-parturient rise in egg output of lactating animals which is briefly discussed in a later paragraph.

After entering the host some species of both strongyle and ascarid worms migrate extensively in the body before returning to the gastro-intestinal tract where they grow to maturity, copulate and begin to lay eggs; others do not migrate further than the mucous membrane lining the stomach and intestines.

Nematode parasites of the digestive tract produce their harmful effects in a variety of ways. Those that migrate extensively, notably *Ascaris suum* and *Parascaris equorum*, cause traumatic and inflammatory damage to the liver and lungs. *Haemonchus contortus*, hookworms and other blood-letting species produce anaemia which in suddenly acquired, heavy infestation may result in a fairly early death of the host. In lighter infestations the haemopoietic reserves of the body may be unable to compensate indefinitely for the more gradual loss of blood, especially where an inadequate intake of nutrients does not allow the blood-forming tissues to express their full potential, and a progressive anaemia develops. In other instances inflammatory reactions of the gastro-intestinal mucous membranes result in impaired digestive efficiency of the stomach and small intestine and in leakage of albumen into the lumen of the gut. Malnourished animals show clinical evidence of these harmful effects earlier and more noticeably than well-fed individuals.

In view of the variety of pathogenic effects it is not surprising that symptoms of parasitism vary considerably, depending on the type of worms predominating. In general, however, most cases show a progressive loss of condition, with or without diarrhoea, and productive efficiency is impaired. As the disease progresses weight is lost, the body is depleted of fat, and bony structures become prominent, the tissues may become oedematous and swellings may then appear on the dependent parts of the body. In ruminants these swellings are particularly apparent under the jaw and along the brisket. Finally, the animal becomes emaciated and so weak that it is unable to rise. In sub-clinical cases a vague unthriftiness is often all that is observed. The prevalence as well as the severity of worm disease is much higher in young than in older stock. In ascarid infestations trouble is more likely to be encountered before weaning, while the post-weaning period is generally a more critical time where strongyle worms are involved.

Diseases caused by the nematode parasites result from exposure of susceptible animals to the intake of infective eggs or larvae at an excessive rate, so that harmful effects are produced before the host succeeds in mounting an effective resistance to its parasites. Control measures should therefore be directed towards limiting the number of infective eggs and larvae on the ground to a level likely to result in susceptible animals developing an effective acquired resistance through continuous exposure to low infection pressures. At the same time the animals should be adequately fed so that they are given every opportunity to mount an immune response and to tolerate the harmful effects of any worms they happen to acquire. Another, more ambitious, approach is to attempt to maintain herds and flocks completely free of worms. This latter approach is now almost technically feasible in specially favourable circumstances where modern anthelmintics can be used intensively in conjunction with appropriate husbandry techniques; but it is seldom economically feasible. The first approach has more general application and a combination of the following measures may be used where this approach is favoured.

Herds and flocks should be maintained on an adequate plane of nutrition throughout the year, special attention being given to breeding stock towards the end of the gestation period and during lactation and to their progeny at and immediately after weaning. Where it is feasible to do so, overcrowding of stock, particularly young stock, should be avoided because dense stocking increases the contamination rate and consequently the infection pressure to which animals are exposed. Heavy stocking could be practised with less risk during prolonged periods of drought where extreme desiccation can be relied upon to destroy the pre-infective and infective stages on the ground, but it is unlikely that adequate feed would be available at such times. However, in these circumstances excessive localized contamination may occur in permanently damp patches such as in the vicinity of standing water. If possible, stock should be denied access to these places and the surrounds of watering points should be kept as dry as possible.

In general, sheep and goats are relatively resistant to the nematodes of cattle. The reverse is also true. Horses are even more resistant to the nematodes of ruminants. Therefore, if a given area is grazed by mixed stock, such as cattle and sheep, the contamination rate will be less than if it were grazed by only one of these species and the risk of disease will tend to be reduced. This is essentially an avoidance of overstocking with susceptible stock.

Adult animals of a given species are much more resistant to their nematodes than are younger animals, though lactating females may pass greatly increased numbers of eggs and are then a most important source of infection for their progeny. Therefore, non-lactating breeding stock and other adult animals should be used to graze pastures known to be highly infective for young stock.

Rotation of pastures was frequently recommended in the past as a method of worm control. Theoretically, animals can be reared free of strongyle worms if they are moved to worm-free ground within the minimum period liable to elapse between passage of eggs in the faeces and the development of infective larvae. Unfortunately, at the high temperatures encountered in the tropics this period may be as short as 3 days so it would be necessary to move stock at short intervals. It is often difficult to apply this principle because vacated pastures would have to be rested for very long periods, especially during the wet season, before larval mortality rendered the grazed areas as safe as they were originally. During these extended periods the new growth of grass must be used. Thus, while pasture rotation may well result in better nutrition by improved management of the sward it is unlikely to result in a decreased intake of infective material.

Anthelmintics may be used prophylactically to prevent potentially dangerous numbers of worm eggs reaching the ground, thereby reducing the infection pressure to which susceptible hosts are subsequently exposed.

Most modern anthelmintics have a broad spectrum of activity. That is to say, they are highly effective against the adult stages of a wide variety of nematodes found in the gastro-intestinal tract of domestic animals and they are fairly effective against the youngest, immature stages of many – though not all – of these parasites. Thus, a single treatment may remove practically all the adult nematodes and a high proportion of their immature stages from the gastro-intestinal tract, and some weeks may elapse, even where animals are kept on infective ground, before burdens of adult worms return to pre-treatment levels.

These properties of modern anthelmintics have improved the effectiveness of prophylactic anthelmintic medication, but a knowledge of the epidemiology of the worm diseases prevalent in an area is required for full benefits to be derived from their use. Such knowledge indicates when treatments should be given; it shows which categories of stock should be treated at a particular time and it enables appropriate husbandry techniques to be applied in order to supplement the effect of anthelmintic treatments on the worm populations. It is difficult to generalize on such matters because the epidemiology of worm disease varies from area to area depending on differences in climate, husbandry practices and other considerations, and systems of prophylactic medication for particular localities, and indeed for individual farms, can be devised only on expert veterinary advice based on local knowlege. Nevertheless, a few broad recommendations can be made.

In areas where the dry season is prolonged and severe, pastures are often free of infection long before the beginning of the rains. In such areas worm infection is carried over from one wet season to the next by infected carrier animals, therefore anthelmintic treatment of all potential carriers some weeks before the onset of the rains may delay the build-up of infection on the ground to dangerous levels after the return of wet weather provides suitable conditions for the development and survival of parasites outside the host. Unfortunately, such treatments cannot be relied upon to clear animals of their entire worm burdens hence some contamination of the pasture will occur after the return of wet weather; young susceptible stock will become lightly infected and they in turn will greatly increase the rate of contamination. It is therefore necessary to treat stock at appropriate intervals during the wet season, but it is impossible to make any generalizations as to how often such treatments should be given without a knowledge of the epidemiology of worm diseases in the area.

The beneficial effects of such anthelmintic treatments are more lasting where treated groups can be moved immediately after medication to worm-free ground or to the cleanest pasture available. A final anthelmintic treatment administered after the end of the rains when pastures are judged to be free of infection enables treated stock to be carried through the dry season with minimal worm burdens.

In areas where the wet season is prolonged, prophylactic anthelmintic medication may require so many treatments that the cost becomes prohibitive. Under these conditions very low stocking rates may be the only means of avoiding serious outbreaks of disease.

Finally, in considering the prophylactic use of anthelmintics, the special role which the dam plays after parturition in contaminating pasture should be appreciated. The number of worm eggs passed by adult females increases greatly at about the time of parturition to reach a peak some weeks later, and there is now evidence to show that this increase in the egg output of lactating animals is brought about by changes in the hormonal rhythm of the host. In many epidemiological situations the rise in worm-egg output occurs at a time when climatic conditions are becoming favourable for the development of the extra-host stages of the worms and, being linked to the post-parturient period, it coincides with the presence of relatively large numbers of highly susceptible young stock. Under these circumstances, anthelmintic treatment of breeding stock shortly before parturition, or immediately after, affords protection to their progeny by eliminating or at least reducing this rise in the output of potentially infective material.

The above remarks on prophylactic anthelmintic medication refer principally to the control of strongyle worms. The approach to the control of ascarid worms is rather different in that young animals tend to be the chief source of eggs, although their dams also play some part as carriers. Ascarid eggs are remarkably resistant and the large numbers passed by young stock survive long enough to infect later batches of young animals, such infection being acquired, in the main, within the first few weeks of life. The principle to be followed, then, in using anthelmintics prophylactically for the control of ascarid worms is to treat young stock when their ascarid worms are about to begin egg-laying. Accordingly, chickens should be treated with a suitable anthelmintic when they are about 6 weeks of age while young pigs and foals should be treated when aged 2 and 3 months respectively. In all cases treatment should be repeated once or twice at monthly intervals. The aim here is to reduce the amount of infective material to which later generations of young stock are exposed, and if this system is adopted it must become a routine management procedure if satisfactory results are to be obtained. Treatment of sows and mares shortly before parturition is advisable because of the role they may play as carriers.

For reasons which cannot be discussed in this brief review the epidemiology of *Neoascaris vitulorum* infestation of calves is rather different, but it may be noted that treatment of calves as a routine at 1 and 2 months of age is generally adequate in herds where this worm is troublesome.

Flukes or trematodes

In the tropics, fluke infections are found in all species of domestic animals, including poultry. The life cycles of flukes which infect domestic animals involve the use of one or two intermediate hosts. One of the intermediate hosts is invariably a snail, but where the life cycle involves the use of two intermediate hosts the first is always a snail in which development of cercariae, representing the penultimate stage in the development of the parasite outside the final host, is completed. In such cases, the cercariae encyst as metacercariae in or on the bodies of a wide variety of second intermediate hosts such as other snails, arthropods, crustaceans, frogs and fish. The metacercaria is the infective stage for the final host. The type of second intermediate host, where utilized, is related to the food chain of the final host. For example, the first intermediate host of *Dicrocoelium dendriticum*, a trematode parasite of the bile ducts of ruminants, is a land snail while the second intermediate host is an ant which, by the nature of its habits, is likely to be ingested by sheep and cattle grazing on dry terrain. Snails, crustaceans, arthropods and frogs frequently serve as second intermediate hosts for the trematodes of birds.

In many parts of the tropics, particularly in Africa, the Indian subcontinent, Southeast Asia and many of the Pacific islands, *Fasciola gigantica* is economically the most important trematode of domestic animals, affecting cattle and sheep. However, the common liver fluke *F. hepatica*, which is so widely distributed in temperate and sub-tropical regions, also occurs in some parts of the tropics, where it tends to be confined to cool, higher altitude areas. This latter parasite generally, though not invariably, uses a mud snail as an intermediate host so that infection with this species is usually associated with herds and flocks grazing wet, marshy land. On the other hand, *F. gigantica* generally uses a water-snail as its intermediate host. Therefore, infection with this species is associated with stock drinking from snail-infected watering places as well as with grazing wet land which may be seasonally inundated.

The ecology and therefore the control of another group of trematodes known collectively as rumen flukes is similar to that of *F. gigantica*. The latter trematode may be encountered in a variety of domestic and feral animals, but cattle and sheep are the principal victims. Eggs, laid by adult parasites in the bile ducts, are passed in the faeces and provided they reach water motile organisms hatch in 10 days or more. These organisms seek a suitable snail which they penetrate and after a process of asexual multiplication has been completed within the tissues of the snail numerous cercariae emerge some 6 weeks later. The cercariae are very active and swim about in search of a suitable medium such as herbage on which to encyst as metacercariae and as such are infective for the final host. Metacercariae are fairly resistant although they are unable to withstand prolonged desiccation and on very dry herbage die in a matter of weeks. Sheep and cattle become infected by ingesting contaminated herbage or by drinking water containing metacercariae.

The severity of the disease caused by this parasite is largely associated with the number of metacercariae ingested. Where massive infections are suddenly acquired the host may succumb to an acute, rapidly fatal hepatitis characterized by haemorrhagic tracts in the liver caused by the migration of numerous immature flukes throughout the tissues of the organ. In lighter infestations a chronic condition develops as the flukes mature in the bile ducts some 16 weeks after infection, giving rise to a progressive loss of blood. Affected animals develop anaemia, become unthrifty, lose condition and in the terminal stages of the disease they are emaciated and watery swellings may appear on dependent parts of the body.

Control measures may be directed towards preventing access of animals to snail habitats where metacercariae have encysted, towards reducing snail populations or by maintaining the fluke burdens of the final host at the lowest possible level by regular anthelmintic medication.

Removal of stock from snail habitats cannot be relied upon to eliminate infection of the snails because wild species serve as reservoirs of infection. However, if possible stock should be kept away from the margins of slow-running water and from wet places, pools and reservoirs, especially during the dry season when recession of water levels frees previously submerged land for grazing. Theoretically, once such pastures are well dried out they should tend to become safer for grazing stock through the destruction of metacercariae by desiccation.

The use of watering troughs sited on dry ground and fed with water from reservoirs or from deep wells should be considered, but the inlets should be screened to reduce the risk of infected snails being introduced in the water and the troughs should be inspected regularly to ensure that they do not become colonized with snails.

Tapeworms or cestodes

A wide variety of tapeworms occur in all the domestic animals, although in general they are of little pathogenic importance in their adult stages in these hosts.

The tapeworm problems of greatest economic importance in the tropics are *Cysticercus bovis* and *C. cellulosae* infection of cattle and pigs, respectively. They are the intermediate stages of the adult tapeworms *Taenia saginata* and *T. solium* which parasitize the small intestine of man. Cattle and pigs become infected by ingesting eggs released by mature tapeworm segments passed in the faeces of man and they develop eventually into milky-white cysts about 1·0 cm (0·4 in) long situated in the musculature of these animals. Man acquires the adult tapeworm by eating raw or improperly cooked beef and pork.

Both these infestations are prevalent in the tropics and cause economic loss through condemnation or special treatment of affected carcases. In the case of *Cysticercus bovis*, in particular, its high incidence in certain African countries complicates the development of an export trade in beef. As far as the stock-keeper is concerned, control is largely a matter of preventing humans defecating on pasture, avoiding the use of human manure and sewage on the land and encouraging employees and others living on the property to refrain from eating improperly cooked beef and pork.

Young stock are particularly susceptible to infection and as ripe segments of *Cysticercus bovis* are capable of passing through the anus of man of their own volition special care should be taken to see that calf attendants are kept free of infection.

Adult tapeworms are more pathogenic to poultry than to other domesticated animals, and birds are susceptible to many species which may be minute and barely visible to the naked eye or up to 25 cm (9·8 in) long. They utilize various intermediate hosts, including ants, beetles, house flies, slugs and earthworms for completion of their life cycles; consequently, tapeworms are more common in birds on free range and are seldom a problem under semi-intensive or intensive systems of management. Under the former conditions regular treatment with anthelmintics is frequently the only practicable control measure.

Diseases caused by arthropod parasites

Arthropod parasites assume economic significance in two principal ways. Firstly, they impair productivity or cause disease as pests or as direct pathogens. For instance, biting flies such as tabanids may worry stock so much that the animals have to be housed by day and allowed out to graze only after dark. The larvae of the sheep nostril fly, *Oestrus ovis*, which hatches from eggs laid on the muzzle, causes catarrhal inflammation of the nasal passages of sheep and goats. The mange mite, *Demodex bovis*, and other species produce lesions in skin follicles that render vast quantities of hides and skins useless for leather manufacture. Secondly, arthropod parasites assume even greater importance for the part that they play in the transmission of infectious diseases. For example, midges belonging to the genus *Culicoides* transmit the viral diseases blue-tongue (*Febris catarrhalis ovium*) of sheep and African horse sickness (*Pestis equorum*), as well as acting as intermediate hosts for certain nematodes. Mosquitoes transmit Rift Valley fever (*Hepatitis enzootica*) of sheep and other animals, African horse sickness and other important viral infections of animals and man. Horse flies, belonging to the family Tabanidae, are restless feeders and may bite a number of animals in a short space of time. Thus, they are efficient mechanical transmitters of a variety of viral, bacterial and protozoan diseases such as equine infectious anaemia (*Anaemic infectiosa equorum*), anthrax and trypanosomiases. The blood-sucking stable fly, *Stomoxys calcitrans*, also transmits disease mechanically and the common house fly, *Musca domestica*, transmits a variety of bacterial and several viral infections as a result of its feeding on faeces, and on the food of man and animals. Among the arthropods the tsetse fly and ticks are the most important transmitters of diseases of domestic animals.

The tsetse fly is important because of its role in the transmission of trypanosomiasis, or 'nagana', of cattle and other animals in Africa. It is estimated that some $4\frac{1}{2}$ million square miles of tropical Africa are infested with tsetse flies and vast tracts (Fig. 2.1) are literally closed to successful animal husbandry because of trypanosomiasis.

There are over twenty different species of tsetse fly and various groups have particular biological requirements which may be exploited for their eradication or control. For example, riverine species such as *Glossina palpalis* and *G. tachinoides* require the cool, moist environment associated with tree-lined river banks. In certain areas clearing and spraying the heavier vegetation which is often confined to the banks of streams may result in eradication or an effective reduction in fly numbers, provided sufficiently large areas are treated.

On the other hand *Glossina morsitans*, a savanna species, inhabits dry, open parkland through which it ranges widely, and bush-clearing over such large areas would be generally impracticable. This species prefers to feed on big game and in order to survive it must find a suitable host within a few days of emerging from the pupal case. This suggests that the systematic destruction of big game might control *G. morsitans* populations and for some years this action was recommended. This type of control is now considered by many to be unnecessarily wasteful as it has

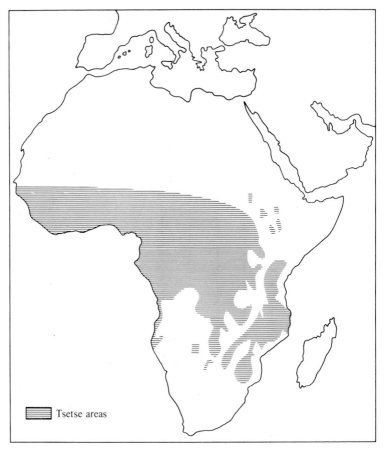

Fig. 2.1   Approximate distribution of tsetse flies in Africa.

not yet been shown that the fly is incapable of adapting itself to other hosts, such as small game which are practically impossible to eliminate.

In the case of some species the breeding places are confined to relatively restricted areas, and as the fly populations rise in these locations a point is reached where dispersion over much larger tracts occurs. Also, during very dry periods savanna tsetse may be forced to retreat to thickets from which they range in search of hosts. Control may be attempted under these circumstances by the wholesale destruction or treatment with insecticides of restricted breeding and resting places and of dry season refuges.

While eradication of the tsetse fly remains the fundamental approach to elimination of trypanosomiasis it is usually an expensive undertaking and requires highly skilled personnel for its direction. Consequently, much attention has been paid to chemotherapy of trypanosome infections, and for many years a number of drugs have been in common use for treatment of established cases. Reinfection presents a problem, but drugs are also available which, in addition to curing existing infections, give protection for up to 6 months against further infection. Such long periods of protection are afforded only under conditions of low fly density; where the challenge is high the period of protection may be drastically reduced. However, the use of these drugs enables cattle to pass through and to use infested bush, but unfortunately their use has also contributed to the development of strains of trypanosomes resistant to a wide variety of these drugs and it is now known that some of these strains can be transmitted by the tsetse. Thus, there is a pressing need to develop new chemotherapeutic agents, unrelated chemically and in mode of action to the existing drugs.

Ticks occur in all parts of the world, and on a global scale they are of even greater importance than the tsetse fly in the transmission of disease. They transmit many of the more serious viral and protozoan diseases found in the tropics and sub-tropics, and their significance in this respect is such that tick control is one of the first requirements for an efficient animal industry in most warm countries. It is thus essential for the livestock owner to be acquainted with the principles underlying tick control. It is so important that it is considered necessary to devote the remainder of this chapter to the subject.

The engorged female tick lays her eggs on the ground in sheltered places, under stones and in crevices, in a single cluster comprising thousands of eggs. She then dies. The eggs hatch in a matter of weeks or months, depending on the species and prevailing temperatures, and the larvae or 'seed ticks' which emerge climb blades of grass and shrubs to reach a favourable position for attaching themselves to a passing host.

Certain species are one-host ticks. That is to say, the ticks spend all their time continuously on the same individual during their larval, nymphal and adult stages, and the females drop to the ground to lay eggs after they have finished their blood meal. *Boophilus decoloratus*, the blue tick, which transmits babesiosis or red-water fever and anaplasmosis or gall sickness of cattle and other diseases of domestic animals is a typical one-host tick. The parasitic stages from larvae to adults require about 3 consecutive weeks on the host. Therefore, spraying or dipping at intervals of 2 to 3 weeks constitutes effective control.

With two-host ticks the larvae and nymphs require to spend about 2 weeks or longer on the host. The engorged nymph falls to the ground, moults and the adult seeks a fresh host on which it remains for 5 or 6 days or more. Since the immature stages are frequently spent on small ground game, action is directed towards the adults and dipping at intervals of 7 days or less is required for the control of these ticks. Finally, in the case of three-host ticks each stage drops to the ground after a feeding period which may last for as short a time as 3 days.

Plate 2.1   A spray race used in the Ankole District of Uganda (Department of Information, Uganda).

Treatment may be required at intervals of a few days for complete control of three-host ticks.

Various measures such as grass-burning, cultivation of land and starvation have been recommended for the control of tick populations, but their destruction on the host by the application of chemical substances is still the most practical and effective method. Application is by dipping or spraying (Plate 2.1).

The essential features of a good cattle-dipping tank are shown in Fig. 2.2. The tank should be sited on well-drained land with adequate space for mustering and holding cattle. A permanent supply of clean water, preferably piped to the tank, should be available. The collecting pen should be easy to clean and the entrance race, at least, should be constructed of concrete to reduce the amount of mud and dung carried into the tank on the feet. Indeed, the construction of a foot-bath at the entrance is advisable since exclusion of organic matter prolongs the effective life of the dip wash, especially where the active principle is one of the synthetic insecticides. This is an important consideration because of the high cost of filling the tank.

The actual swim-bath, excluding the exit ramp, must be at least 4·6 m (15 ft) long so that animals are exposed to the dip wash for an adequate

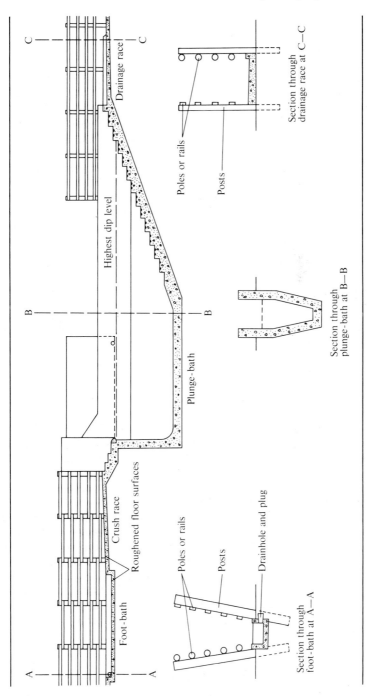

Highest dip level

Drainage race

C — C

Poles or rails

Posts

Section through
drainage race at C–C

Section through
plunge-bath at B–B

B — B

Plunge-bath

Crush race

Roughened floor surfaces

Foot-bath

Poles or rails

Posts

Drainhole and plug

Section through
foot-bath at A–A

A — A

Fig. 2.2 The essential features of a good cattle dipping tank. (Courtesy of The Wellcome Foundation Ltd., London and Berkhamsted, England).

time. The officially recommended South African dips are 7·3 m (24 ft) long at this point. Similarly, the depth must be sufficient to ensure that the cattle submerge completely following the plunge, and it is usual to have an attendant with a forked stick to push down individuals that have learned how to keep their heads dry. Considerable splashing occurs as the cattle hit the surface and the extension of the sides of the tank above ground level as 'splash walls' effects a great saving in dip wash. Another feature essential for economy is the provision of a concrete draining race to hold dripping animals as they leave the tank. It should be sufficiently long to accommodate animals while the surplus dip drains off without interrupting the steady passage of cattle through the tank.

For satisfactory results it is necessary to maintain the dip wash at a constant strength. Precautions must therefore be taken to prevent storm-water from entering the tank from the drainage and entrance races. Similarly, the tank itself should be roofed. Apart from diverting rain-water the roof reduces evaporation which in the tropics can very rapidly raise the concentration of the dip wash. This precaution was formerly very important when arsenical dips were used almost exclusively, because toxic levels of arsenic can easily be reached.

Inexperienced stock may require a little persuasion to take the plunge, so once they start to go through they should be kept moving in a steady stream. Not infrequently individuals experience difficulty in the tank and attendants should be prepared with ropes and halters to deal with emergencies.

For many years arsenic was the most common active principle of dipping solutions and it had the advantage of being cheap and effective. It is, of course, toxic to animals and to man and its use has been pro-hibited in the major meat-exporting countries although it is still used in certain African countries. On account of its toxic properties strict pre-cautions must always be taken to see that the wash is maintained at the correct concentration, and when the tank is emptied the old wash must be disposed of carefully to prevent pollution of food and water. A further disadvantage is that strains of ticks resistant to arsenic have now de-veloped after many years of its use.

Arsenic has been largely replaced by chlorinated hydrocarbons, such as benzene hexachloride and toxaphene and by organo-phosphorus compounds. They are very effective and can have some residual effect, but this varies depending on the chemical employed as well as the species and stage of tick against which they are used. All are toxic to man and animals, therefore recommended dipping strengths should not be ex-ceeded and the precautions issued by manufacturers in connection with dipping and spraying procedures and the general handling of containers and solutions must be heeded.

Unfortunately, in some countries, ticks – especially those belonging to the genus *Boophilus* – have developed resistance to the non-arsenical compounds and it is likely that in time all species of ticks exposed to

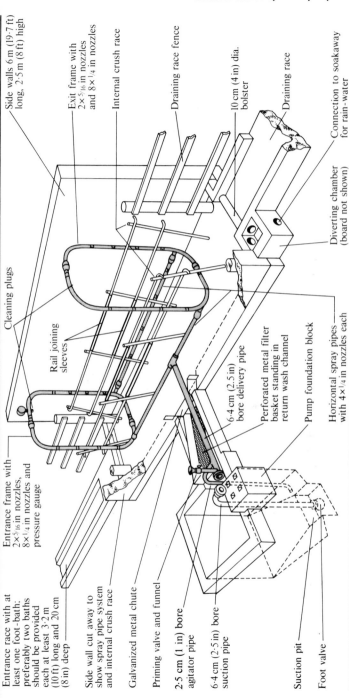

Side walls 6 m (19.7 ft) long, 2.5 m (8 ft) high

Exit frame with 2×5/16 in nozzles and 8×1/4 in nozzles

Internal crush race

Draining race fence

10 cm (4 in) dia. bolster

Draining race

Connection to soakaway for rain-water

Cleaning plugs

Rail joining sleeves

Diverting chamber (board not shown)

6.4 cm (2.5 in) bore delivery pipe

Perforated metal filter basket standing in return wash channel

Pump foundation block

Horizontal spray pipes with 4×1/4 in nozzles each

Entrance frame with 2×5/16 in nozzles, 8×1/4 in nozzles and pressure gauge

Entrance race with at least one foot-bath: preferably two baths should be provided each at least 3.2 m (10 ft) long and 20 cm (8 in) deep

Side wall cut away to show spray pipe system and internal crush race

Galvanized metal chute

Priming valve and funnel

2.5 cm (1 in) bore agitator pipe

6.4 cm (2.5 in) bore suction pipe

Suction pit

Foot valve

Fig. 2.3   The essential features of a good cattle spray race. (Cooper's Improved Spray Race. Patented courtesy of The Wellcome Foundation Ltd, London and **Berkhamsted**, England.)
Note: Imperial measurements only given for the spray nozzles.

regular treatment will become resistant. The stockowner should be conscious of this possibility, and he should see that formulations are not used below the recommended strength and should seek expert advice at once if he has any reason whatsoever to believe that his dipping or spraying is ineffective.

By reason of the high capital cost of dipping tanks – which, if they are to be effective, must be of considerable capacity and are therefore expensive to fill with the newer non-arsenical dips – spray races have tended to replace dipping tanks in many countries in recent years. These consist of an enclosed race in which cattle are exposed to a dense spray delivered at high pressure from a system of appropriately arranged jets (Fig. 2.3; Plate 2.1). The discharged fluid drains to a sump from which it is circulated by a pump operated by a small stationary engine or a tractor power take-off. In addition to being cheaper to install than a dipping tank it uses only a small quantity of wash which can be freshly made up each day. Thus, the risk of using under-strength solutions is avoided and the operator can switch to new formulations without the expense of having to refill a large-capacity tank. Spraying is quicker than dipping and causes less disturbance to cattle.

Other methods of treatment include hand spraying and hand dressing. Hand spraying can give satisfactory results when carried out by an experienced and conscientious operator, but it is impracticable where there are large numbers of animals. In hand dressing, dip washes or even greasy substances, such as used engine oil, are applied to the predilection sites of ticks and it can be a useful last resort in the control of outbreaks of disease, such as East Coast fever (*Theileria parva* infection), in backward areas where facilities of dipping or spraying do not exist and, indeed, where supplies of dip materials may not be readily obtainable.

Finally, it should be appreciated by the livestock owner that the control of ticks is a complex undertaking, and in planning a programme much thought must be given to such matters as the frequency of dipping or spraying, whether such treatments should be seasonal or continue throughout the year, the best formulation to use and the most suitable rate of application. Decisions depend on such considerations as the species and ecology of the ticks in the area and whether the purpose of the programme is merely to reduce tick infestations on the host or to control tick-borne disease. Expert advice, which is generally available locally from government departments, should be sought.

Further Reading

British Veterinary Association. *Handbook of Animal Diseases in the Tropics* (rev. edn).
Brit. Vet. Ass.: London, 1970.

Dunn, A. M. *Veterinary Helminthology.* Heinemann: London, 1969.

FAO/WHO/OIE. *Animal Health Yearbook.* FAO: Rome, 1975.

Hall, H. T. B. *Diseases and Parasites of Livestock in the Tropics.* Longman: London,
1977.

Parker, W. H. *Health and Diseases in Farm Animals.* Pergamon: Oxford, 1970.

Soulsby, E. J. C. *Helminths, Arthropods and Protozoa of Domesticated Animals.* Baillière,
Tindall and Cassell: London, 1968.

Chapter 3

Nutrition and Feeding

[with a sub-chapter on Forage]

One of the ultimate objectives of any livestock industry is the conversion into animal products of feeds which are either inedible by man or surplus to his immediate requirements.

In a world where the ever-increasing human population exercises continual and probably mounting pressure on world feed resources it is inevitable that conventional animal feeds should become increasingly more expensive and that the range of basic feeds available for animal feeding should decrease as more by-products are processed so that they can be directly consumed by man. These handicaps for the animal feeders are reinforced by the fact that the production of animal products inevitably includes a double conversion of basic food constituents. First, soil nutrients are converted into plant products. The latter are then fed to animals for conversion into animal products. One example of this double conversion is that the average efficiency of conversion of fertilizer nitrogen into plant protein is approximately 50 per cent, while the average efficiencies of conversion of plant into animal protein in the temperate zone are approximately 40, 25 to 18, 24, 19 and 11 per cent for milk, eggs, poultry meat, pork and beef, respectively (Table 3.1). For a variety of reasons conversion in the tropics is even less efficient. For example Cuthbertson (1969) has stated that the average efficiency of conversion of plant to animal protein during milk production in the tropics is only 25 per cent. While it may be argued that research during the years ahead will undoubtedly discover new methods of increasing the efficiency of nitrogen conversion it has to be accepted that two steps in the conversion of nitrogen fertilizer into edible protein can never be as efficient as one. This means that it will always be possible to feed more humans per unit of cultivable land by growing crops for direct human consumption than by growing crops for conversion by domestic livestock into edible animal products. Wilcke (1966), for example, has calculated that 0·4 ha (1·0 acre) of productive land will provide for the protein requirements of one man for only 77 days if the crop is beef, but for 2,224 days if the crop is soybean.

What then are the justifications for feeding any livestock? First, most humans demand a mixed diet as man is an omnivorous species and the

Table 3.1 *Approximate efficiency of some domestic livestock in converting the energy and protein of animal feeds into food for man*

Type of animal	Efficiency of conversion (%)	
	Energy	Protein
Cattle		
Milk production during lactation	27	40
Beef production during fattening	11	11
Pigs		
Pork production	27	19
Poultry		
Broiler production	7	24
Egg production	13–17	18–25

Note: The data have been calculated for temperate-zone countries and not specifically for the tropics.
Source: Cuthbertson (1969).

majority are willing to pay higher prices for foods of animal origin than they are for foods of plant origin. Nutritionally, it may be possible for man to exist solely on plant foods, but less total bulk is required of a good mixed diet than of one containing only foods of plant origin. In addition, foods of animal origin are very palatable and usually possess a high protein, fat and mineral content. Secondly, there are many plant foods, particularly forage, that cannot be properly digested by man and that at present can only be processed into foods suitable for man by the feeding of them to ruminant livestock. Thirdly, in the more ecologically stable agricultural systems plants and animals are complementary and the utilization of both as sources of food may increase total food production per unit area of available land. The latter justification may become more important as the necessity increases for the establishment of ecologically stable agricultural systems.

In the past all animal feeds were derived from three sources. These were as follows: crops other than forage, the by-products of crop and animal processing, and natural or planted forage. Today there is a fourth possible source that will probably increase in importance: synthesis from non-biological materials, for example urea from nitrogen or protein concentrate from oil or natural gas.

Most feeds for livestock may be conveniently classified into two major types, roughage and concentrates. Roughages are characterized by the relatively large amounts of crude fibre that their dry matter contains. As a group they can be further sub-divided and classified into dry roughages and succulents, the latter containing large quantities of water. A major source of roughage is forage, whose production and utilization are discussed in some detail in the second part of this chapter. In general only ruminants such as buffaloes, cattle, sheep and goats, camels and llamoids can properly utilize large quantities of roughage feeds. This is because ruminant livestock differ from non-ruminant livestock in possessing complex digestive tracts capable of digesting forage. These differences between ruminant and non-ruminant livestock are fully discussed in the appropriate chapters in Part II. In general, concentrate feeds contain less crude fibre than roughages and relatively large but varying quantities of carbohydrates, crude protein and fat, together with relatively little water. They can be utilized by non-ruminant livestock such as pigs and poultry as well as by ruminants. In addition there are a limited number of feeds that are difficult to classify into either category.

A knowledge of the chemical components of different feeds and of the basic principles of feeding are essential for successful livestock production. The fundamental principles of nutrition are universally applicable, but all aspects of their utilization for all species of livestock in tropical climates are not as yet fully understood. Under these circumstances discussion will include the components of animal feeds and their evaluation and the feeding standards and requirements of different types of livestock utilized in the tropics – as far as these requirements are at present known. One of the major differences is that for some part of the year in the temperate zones a part of the energy content of feed has to be expended to maintain the animal's body temperature, whereas for the major part of the year in all except the montane tropics, the animal's problem is to dispose of surplus body heat. The effect of this basic difference – and other differences that may be induced by climate on the feed requirements of livestock – has not yet been properly evaluated.

Components of food

The food that the animal eats is essentially composed of the same elements that form its body and products. The total amount and the relative proportions of the elements in each food vary greatly, but they are integrated to form compounds or groups of similar substances upon which a classification of food ingredients can be based. Thus, all foods contain water and their dry matter consists of inorganic material or minerals and organic matter. The latter includes three major groups of substances: nitrogenous compounds, carbohydrates and fats or oils, together with a quantitatively small but qualitatively important group of organic accessory foods known as vitamins.

A simple classification of these food constituents gives no indication of their relative importance, either quantitatively or qualitatively. Each must be considered with reference to their function within the animal's body and in relation to each other. Therefore, each will be discussed separately.

Water

Water is more vital for the maintenance of the animal's life than any other food component. It is the main constituent of all body fluids, being essential for the transport of nutrients to body tissues and the excretion of waste products through the urine and faeces. It is also vital for the proper functioning of most enzymic reactions as these take place in solution and involve hydrolysis.

In addition body water plays an all important role in the animal's thermoregulatory mechanism. Evaporation of water from lung and skin surfaces helps the animal to dispose of unwanted heat and the high specific heat of the body water assists the animal to accommodate itself to large changes in heat production with little change in body temperature.

The water content of the animal's body varies with age. New-born animals consist of 75 to 80 per cent water, whereas mature, fat animals may contain only 50 per cent or less. The average animal probably consists of between 55 and 65 per cent water.

Water requirement increases with growth, with an increase in productive processes such as lactation and egg-laying and with increased physical exercise as when animals are worked and when the animal is subject to heat stress. Requirements apparently vary between different species, between breeds or varieties within species and between individuals within breeds. In fact, water requirement appears to be a very individual and specific characteristic. Average water requirements of some livestock in the semi-arid tropics are shown in Table 3.2.

Table 3.2 *Average water requirements of some types of livestock in the semi-arid tropics during the dry season*

Type of livestock	Average daily water requirement		Frequency of drinking
	litre	(gal)	
Camel	60–80	(13–18)	Every 4 or 5 days or longer
Cattle	30–40	(7–9)	Every 1 to 3 days
Sheep	4–5	(1)	Every 1 or 2 days
Goats	4–5	(1)	Preferably once a day

Source: Modifications of data from Baudelaire (1972).

Animals acquire water in three ways. Mainly by drinking free water, but also by utilizing the water that forms part of the food that they consume, and occasionally by manufacturing small quantities of metabolic water obtained by the oxidation of fat within their own body.

Some wild animals, particularly those whose habitat is the desert or desert fringe, appear to be able to survive without access to free water.

They presumably manage on dew, on the small amount of water available in the dry vegetation that they consume and perhaps to a very limited extent on metabolic water. All domestic animals require ultimate access to free water, some daily and some at less frequent intervals. The camel is the outstanding example of a domestic animal which can withstand infrequent watering intervals. An interesting example on how domestic livestock can thrive on the water available in the vegetation, without access to free water, occurs in the desert of northwest Sudan. After a specific set of climatic conditions that do not necessarily occur annually, the nomads are able to graze their camels and sheep for quite long periods across considerable tracts of waterless country. This is because the ephemeral vegetation that occurs, known in the Sudan as the *gizzu*, contains sufficient water to satisfy the normal needs of the livestock.

As stated above, different species of domestic animals differ in their water requirements and these differences are reflected in their respective abilities to withstand dehydration and in their demand for free water. The camel, as stated above, has an exceptional tolerance of heat and water deprivation (see Ch. 9, Pt II), can withstand the loss of up to 27 per cent of its body weight and is able to drink exceptional quantities of water at any one time (Schmidt-Nielsen, 1964). Some breeds of sheep also possess an exceptional tolerance of dehydration (Schmidt-Nielsen, 1964) and it is likely that many breeds of goats are also very tolerant of partial dehydration. Cattle are not generally as tolerant as camels and sheep, but their requirements for free water vary with type, *Bos indicus* breeds requiring less water than most *B. taurus* breeds when managed in the same environment (French, 1956). However, the N'dama, an indigenous *B. taurus* breed from West Africa, is likely to be as tolerant of dehydration as any *B. indicus* breed. Payne (1965) reported that acclimatized East African *B. indicus*-type cattle can lose up to 17 per cent of their body weight between drinking, without apparent harm. Buffaloes and pigs are relatively intolerant of water deprivation.

In the humid tropics the grazing animal's demand for water may be largely satisfied by the high water content of the forage and by the free water remaining on it after rainfall. Indeed, the animal's intake of high-water-content forage may make for difficulties in obtaining a sufficiently high dry matter intake. Nevertheless, daily access to free water is always desirable. All yarded or housed animals in the wet tropics must have access to free water, preferably throughout the 24 hours.

In the dry tropics the direct and indirect effects of low rainfall are additive in their effect on grazing animals during the dry season. The decreasing water content of the available forage increases the animal's demand for water at a time when surface water resources are diminishing and the animal has to walk further to obtain both feed and water. Additional walking raises food and water demand, as increased muscular activity requires additional feed and generates additional heat that has to be dissipated, further depleting the animal's water resources. At the same time ambient day temperatures rise during the dry season, with a consequent further increase in the animal's water requirements. In practice this means that often in the arid or semi-arid tropics livestock are watered only every second or third day. If adequate feed is available this reduces productivity, but experimental work in East Africa (Payne, 1965) has shown that if inadequate feed is available water deprivation, if not too prolonged, can be advantageous to the animal, as it assists in the conservation of nitrogen and possibly of other food constituents in its body.

Water deprivation also conserves water if it is in short supply. In the East African experiments referred to above, water deprivation for 48 and 72 hours reduced total water intake by 10 and 26 per cent, respectively. Withholding water from sheep also appears to have the same sparing effect on total water consumption.

Animals living in the dry tropics are also subject to another hazard. In many regions the mineral content of the only free water available progressively rises as the dry season advances and may become so concentrated as to be unsuitable for drinking. Camels, cattle, sheep and goats can acclimatize themselves to such conditions and become comparatively tolerant of highly mineralized water. For example, Denton *et al.* (1961) stated that livestock adapt to highly mineralized water and that in certain regions in Australia cattle and sheep are known to thrive on water containing 1·5 to 1·9 per cent total solids, respectively.

It would be expected that the consumption of highly mineralized water might have a considerable effect on the mineral metabolism of animals. This appears to be the case. For example, French (1956) reported that the consumption of alkaline water (0·37 per cent sodium carbonate) in the dry regions of East Africa increased sodium and chlorine retention but reduced the retention of calcium, potassium, magnesium and phosphorus.

When water is freely available, housed or yarded animals usually drink at frequent, short intervals, imbibing a small quantity at any one time. Grazing animals tend to drink in the cool of the morning or in the evening if they have a free choice, but usually they are watered only every 24 hours. Often this single watering takes place during the heat of the middle of the day as the animals are grazed to the watering place, watered and then grazed away from the watering place.

The temperature of drinking water is of some importance, cool water being preferable to warm, as drinking cool water assists the thermoregulatory mechanisms of the animal to dissipate body heat (see Ch. 1, Pt I).

As the demand of the individual animal for water is normally very variable only average estimates of water requirements in a specific climatic environment can be given (Table 3.2). French (1956) reported on the water consumption of well-managed and fed East African Zebu cattle and grade European-type cattle in Kenya (Table 3.3) and his data

Table 3.3   *The water consumption of tropical- and temperate-type cattle in Kenya*

| Frequency of watering | Average water consumption kg (lb) per day | | | |
| | 1½ years old | | 3½ years old | |
	Tropical*	Temperate†	Tropical*	Temperate†
Once daily	7·8 (17·2)	18·3 (40·3)	19·3 (42·5)	27·0 (59·5)
Every second day	6·7 (14·8)	16·2 (35·7)	16·9 (37·2)	23·5 (51·8)

* Indigenous cattle.
† Three-quarter grade Ayrshires.
Source: French (1956).

should be compared with those given in Table 3.2. Also in East Africa, Payne (1965) found that the range of water intake of growing, indigenous Zebu cattle managed in a semi-arid environment for 2 years was 3 to 43 kg (6 to 94 lb) per day or 0·2 to 4·0 kg (0·4 to 9 lb) per 45 kg (100 lb) of liveweight. These results are comparable with those published by other workers.

Nitrogenous compounds

The nitrogenous compounds in a feed include the proteins and the non-protein nitrogenous compounds. The latter include amino acids, amines, amides, nitrates and alkaloids, etc. Nitrogenous substances in a feed are usually expressed in terms of crude protein (CP) content.

Proteins

Proteins are complex organic compounds of high molecular weight with many and diverse functions within the animal's body. They are found in all living cells where they participate in all phases of cell activity. They also serve as structural elements in all soft body tissues. All known enzymes, many hormones, the oxygen-carrying pigment of the blood, collagen, antibodies and the chemical units of hereditary transmission are all proteins. They consist of chains of amino acids. Most of these are characterized by having a carboxyl group ($-COOH$) and an amino group ($-NH_2$) attached to the same carbon atom (Fig. 3.1). Also attached to the carbon atom at the position (R) in Fig. 3.1 is the remainder of the amino-acid molecule which will of course vary in composition. Approximately 100 amino acids have been isolated from biological materials, but only 25 of these are generally considered to be components of proteins.

There is, therefore, a great variety of proteins, the characteristics of each depending upon the number and the type of amino acids composing their molecule.

Plants and many micro-organisms are able to synthesize proteins from

Amino acids are characterized by the possesion of a basic nitrogenous group
(-NH2) and an acidic carboxyl group (-COOH) as shown below.

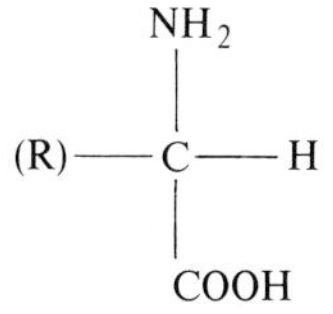

The nature of the (R) group varies with the amino acid. It may be an
hydrogen atom as in glycine;

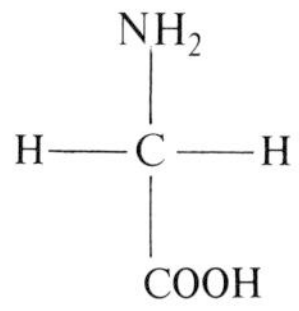

or a more complex group as in isoleucine:

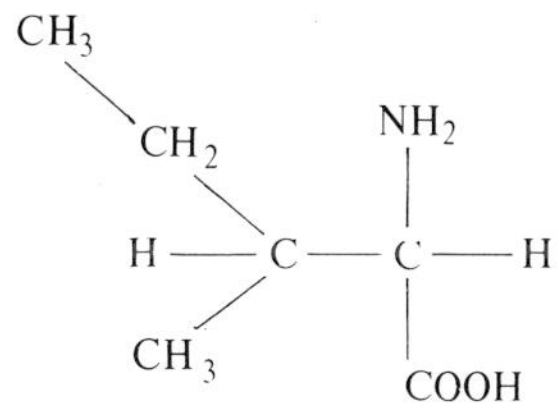

Fig. 3.1 The amino-acid molecule.

simple nitrogenous compounds such as nitrates. Non-ruminant animals
must have a dietary supply of amino acids, but they are able to synthesize
some that they require from others. Those that animals cannot synthesize
are known as essential amino acids. At present it is recognized that growing non-ruminant animals require to ingest ten essential amino acids.
These are:

arginine	methionine
histidine	phenylalanine
isoleucine	threonine
leucine	tryptophan
lysine	valine

Birds, in addition, require to ingest glycine. Arginine and histidine may
not be essential in the adult non-ruminant animal.

Ruminant animals possess biological systems that can synthesize all
the amino acids that they require within their digestive tract. The bacteria
and protozoa in the tract synthesize amino acids (including the essential
ones) from dietary protein and non-protein nitrogen. The microbial
protein so produced is later digested by the animal at a lower point in
the digestive tract with the production of all the amino acids required
by the animal for protein synthesis.

Naturally, those proteins in the ingested food whose amino-acid composition most closely resemble that of the amino-acid composition of the required body protein possess a superior feeding value or a higher protein quality. Food proteins derived from the animal's body, such as the protein in blood meal, can be broken down and synthesized into required body proteins with less waste than the protein of a grain such as sorghum. Blood-meal protein is therefore said to possess a higher *biological value* than sorghum grain protein. The biological value of a protein can therefore be used as an assessment of the relative values of different proteins for non-ruminant animals (Table 3.4). Protein feeds of animal origin usually possess a higher biological value than those of plant origin.

Table 3.4   *The biological value of the protein in selected feeds used in pig feeding*

Feed	Biological value of the protein
Milk	95–97
Fish meal	74–89
Soybean meal	63–76
Cottonseed meal	63
Maize	49–61

Source: Armstrong and Mitchell (1955).

Deficiency of an essential amino acid in the diet of non-ruminants may lead to a failure of growth and eventual death. Different non-ruminants have different requirements for the essential amino acids. In birds glycine cannot be synthesized sufficiently rapidly for adequate feathering since the protein keratin, required for feathering, contains a high proportion of glycine. Lysine, methionine, threonine and tryptophan, in that order, are the most likely amino acids to limit growth and reproduction in most non-ruminants. Their deficiency can be made good by adding them individually to the feed. Thus plant protein diets of low biological value can be supplemented with individual amino acids and their biological value improved to equal that of protein of animal origin. This supplementation technique is now widely used in the manufacture of feeds for pigs and poultry.

Protein requirements.   While the amino-acid content of the protein in the ration is important for non-ruminants and for the pre-rumination period of young ruminants it is of less importance in older ruminants. What is of major importance is the total nitrogenous content of the ration. Thus the protein requirements of adult ruminants are best expressed in terms of *total digestible crude protein*. In feeding practice the quality of the proteins fed to ruminants should not be entirely ignored. It is usually economic to feed a variety of protein concentrates as the pooling of proteins containing different types and quantities of the various amino acids improves the ability of the microbial population in the gut of the ruminant to synthesize rapidly all the amino acids required.

In the case of non-ruminant animals requirement can be expressed in terms of digestible crude protein with the stipulation that the nitrogenous content of the ration should contain x per cent lysine, y per cent methionine, etc. The difficulty of this methodology is that the need for any particular amino acid expressed as a percentage of the total nitrogen ingested may change with the rate and stage of growth of the animal and with the breed.

Calculation of minimal protein requirements involves:

1. assessment of nitrogen retention within the body for growth and other productive purposes and for maintenance (NR);
2. assessment of endogenous urinary nitrogen and metabolic faecal nitrogen losses (NE).

The sum of these, i.e. (NR + NE), is multiplied by 6·25 to provide the minimal protein requirement, i.e. 6·25 (NR + NE). If this figure is divided by the average biological value expressed as a decimal an estimate is obtained of the 'true' digestible crude protein requirement.

As almost all living cells are composed of protein and the cells are continuously undergoing degeneration and distintegration a continuous supply of new protein is required by the body even when it is at rest. Thus every animal must receive a continuous though limited supply of protein if it is to maintain its health and not lose weight and condition. In addition any increase in productivity, with the exception of an increase in work, greatly increases the demand for dietary protein.

Excess protein in the diet will be 'deaminated' in the digestive tract, the excess nitrogen being excreted in the urine and the faeces. The energy component of the protein can then be used by the animal in the normal metabolic manner. This is of course a wasteful process as protein concentrate feeds are usually more expensive to purchase than energy concentrate feeds. In addition the ingestion of excessive quantities of protein may disturb to some extent the normal working of the digestive system.

It is, however, usually desirable to feed rather more protein than the minimal requirements as protein usually improves the palatability of feeds and may thus increase total feed intake. In addition protein is associated in many feeds with desirable minerals and/or vitamins.

The specific protein requirements of the different types of livestock are further discussed in the various chapters in Part II concerned with each type of livestock.

Non-protein nitrogenous compounds

A considerable variety of nitrogenous compounds which cannot be classified as proteins occur in both plants and animals. These include amino acids, nitrogenous lipids, amines, amides, purines, pyrimidines, nitrates, alkaloids and some compounds in the vitamin B complex. In this general text only the briefest mention can be made of some of these.

Amines.   These are often produced from the amino acids – which comprise the major part of the non-protein nitrogen fraction – by micro-organisms. Many thus occur as decomposition end-products and possess toxic properties.

Amides.   A major amide is urea, the main end-product of nitrogen metabolism in mammals.

Nitrates.   Large amounts of nitrates are often found in forage that has been heavily fertilized. Nitrates may be reduced in the rumen to nitrites which possess toxic properties.

Alkaloids.   These occur in specific plants and are of practical interest as many of them possess toxic properties. Well-known examples of toxic or semi-toxic alkaloids in tropical plants are the occurrence of ricinine in *Ricinus communis* (castor) and mimosine in *Lucaena leucocephala.* Other plants contain valuable drugs; for example morphine.

Carbohydrates

The carbohydrates of feeds are generally classified according to the complexity of their structure. There are three major groups.

1. *Monosaccharides.*   These are simple five- or six-carbon sugars. Ribose, for example, has the general formula $C_5H_{10}O_5$, while glucose and fructose have the formula $C_6H_{12}O_6$. They are readily digested and utilized by animals.

2. *Disaccharides.*   These have the general formula $C_{12}H_{22}O_{11}$; examples are sucrose and lactose. They are also normally readily digested and utilized by animals.

3. *Polysaccharides.*   These are complexes made up from the simple sugars and they usually possess a high molecular weight. They include the following:

(a) Starches, the major reserve carbohydrate in plants, and dextrins which are intermediate products in the breakdown or synthesis of starch. Non-ruminant animals can digest and absorb starches.
(b) Pectins, cellulose, lignin, hemicelluloses, pentosans and polyuronides. Of these cellulose and lignin are the most important and abundant, forming part of the structure of most plant cells. Non-ruminant livestock, such as pigs and poultry, cannot efficiently digest most of these compounds. Cellulose is, however, broken down by bacteria

and protozoa in the ruminant digestive tract. The products of cellulose breakdown in the ruminant digestive tract are not simple sugars but the volatile fatty acids (VFA), acetic, propionic and butyric, together with methane and some microbiological starch. The VFA are used by the animal for maintenance and for the synthesis of body fat and milk constituents. Acetic acid is used for the synthesis of milk fat, therefore the percentage of fat in milk depends to some extent on the quantity of acetic acid that is produced in the digestive tract and this depends in turn upon the composition of the diet. For example, dairy cows fed on diets low in roughage tend to produce milk with a low butterfat content. Lignin is not appreciably broken down by the microbia of the digestive tract. Thus the process of lignification, associated with the ageing of the plant, may significantly decrease its nutritive value. When feeds are analysed the residue of lignified material, insoluble in dilute acid and dilute alkali, is known as the *crude fibre*. In a tropical climatic environment the process of lignification in plants appears to commence at an earlier age than it normally would in a temperate climate.

Carbohydrates form the largest constituent of plants and are therefore the major part of the food of domestic livestock. However, very little carbohydrate is found in the animal's body. The reason for this is that after digestion and absorption carbohydrates are either oxidized directly for the production of energy or they are transferred and stored in the form of fat.

Cereals, tubers and roots are the feeds that are richest in sugars and starches, whereas forage, particularly straws, contains less sugar and starch and very large quantities of fibre.

Although crude fibre cannot normally be easily digested, even by ruminant livestock, a certain amount is required in the diet of all animals after they have been weaned. Ruminants, of course, require more than non-ruminants. However, even the pig requires some fibre in its diet. In moderate quantities fibre ensures the proper working of the digestive system and gives a feeling of repletion which is one essential of proper feeding. However, as it is the cheapest feed and as it is usually in such plentiful supply the tendency is to always feed too much. When this occurs the digestion of all food constituents is depressed and the sheer bulk involved may depress total intake below nutritional needs. This often happens when cattle graze old, dead forage at the end of the dry season or when pigs are fed only rice bran.

There are major differences between ruminant species in their ability to utilize roughages. For example, buffaloes are known to thrive on forage that will not support cattle, while camels, llamoids, tropical breeds of sheep and goats all appear to be able to utilize roughages rather more efficiently than cattle. The reasons for this are not as yet well understood.

If a sufficiency of carbohydrate food is not available the animal can use excess dietary protein, or if neither is available it can utilize its own fat reserves as a source of energy.

Fats

When fats are estimated in food not only the true fats or glycerides but also resins, organic acids, essential oils, sterols and plant pigments are extracted and estimated. In general the glycerides possess a higher feeding value than the non-glycerides, but the latter do include essential nutrients such as vitamins A, D, E and K.

In non-ruminants absorption of glycerides takes place in the upper section of the small intestine. If the gut is full of dietary fat some may be absorbed in particulate form. Normally, however, triglycerides are transformed into monoglycerides and fatty acids through the agency of the enzyme lipase. Bile salts then mix with the monoglycerides and fatty acids to form completely dispersed *micelles*. These are absorbed by the mucosal cells of the digestive tract, the bile salts being returned to the lumen of the tract and the monoglycerides and fatty acids being re-synthesized into triglycerides. In ruminants lysolecithin may take the place of the bile salts as no monoglycerides reach the small intestine and bile salts do not form *micelles* with free fatty acids.

The resynthesized triglycerides are utilized directly or they are stored in the fat deposits of the body. As triglycerides are a combination of different fatty acids and glycerol, different species of animals may possess different and specific types of body fat.

Fat is deposited everywhere in the body, either as a protective or as a supporting material. A considerable part of the body fat forms a sub-cutaneous layer which is usually more conspicuous in temperate-type livestock. Ledger (1959) has shown, for example, that in East Africa *Bos taurus* and *B. indicus* cattle exhibit different patterns of fat deposition. At any particular degree of fatness *B. indicus* cattle deposit more fat intramuscularly than subcutaneously compared with *B. taurus* cattle. This is presumably because subcutaneous fat deposits form an insulating layer that creates a barrier to heat flow from the deep body tissues to the skin, thus increasing heat stress. It has also been reported from South America that Criollo-type cattle, which have been acclimatized to a tropical climate for several hundred years, deposit their sub-cutaneous fat in 'blobs' and not as a continuous layer. This also would facilitate heat transfer from the deep body tissues to the outer skin of the cattle. Other types of tropical livestock also deposit surplus fat at specific body sites – camels and Zebu cattle in their humps and fat-tailed and fat-rumped sheep in their tails or rumps. In the past it has been suggested that these fat deposits were useful in times of water shortage as the animal could oxidize the fat in order to obtain metabolic water. However, a simple calculation will demonstrate that the quantity of water thus obtained would be very small. It is more likely that the deposition of fat reserves at specific sites, rather than subcutaneously, is a device that assists the animal to rid itself more easily of surplus heat.

The deposition of fat usually increases with age, and in quick-maturing animals the final deposition takes place between and around the muscle fibres. This process is known as *marbling* and has considerable commercial importance as marbling is associated with tenderness in meat. With present methods of husbandry, marbling is not as common in tropical as in temperate breeds of cattle.

As stated above, different species of livestock possess different and specific types of fat, and both the quantity and the type of fat are influenced by feeding. The quantity of fat that may be stored by the animal depends upon the total quantity of feed that it consumes rather than on how much fat there is in the food. Herbivora normally eat little fat, unless they are fed on oil-cake, as forage usually contains only quite small quantities. Young animals can consume more fat than older animals and the milk consumed by all young often contains considerable quantities of fat. Some breeds of buffaloes, for example, secrete milk that contains as much as 14 per cent fat. Young pigs can consume milk substitutes containing as much as 25 per cent lard. The quality of fat as expressed in terms of hardness can be very easily influenced by feeding. For example, pigs fed large quantities of rice bran exhibit very soft fat, while those fed large quantities of cassava possess very hard fat.

The fat of different species may differ considerably in colour. Species and breeds of animals that convert the food pigments as soon as they are assimilated normally possess white fat, while those that do not rapidly convert the pigments may accumulate them in their fat deposits. For example, buffalo fat is white while the butterfat and body fat of certain breeds of cattle, such as the Jersey, are yellow.

Some fat must be directly consumed by the animal as a deficiency adversely affects carbohydrate metabolism and increases the demand for certain B complex vitamins. Fats are also the source of the fat-soluble A, D and E vitamins. In omnivorous animals fat also retards the emptying of the stomach and delays the onset of the feeling of hunger and restlessness associated with an empty stomach.

Minerals

The inclusion in the diet of a number of mineral elements that possess important metabolic roles is essential. If one or more of these elements are deficient in the diet, animals will ultimately exhibit clinical symptoms of deficiency.

These essential mineral elements may be classified into two groups (Table 3.5). There are firstly the macro-elements: calcium, phosphorus, potassium, sodium, chlorine, sulphur and magnesium which are required by animals in relatively large quantities. Secondly, there are the trace or

Table 3.5 *Essential mineral elements and their approximate concentrations in animal bodies*

Essential				Probably essential	
Macro-elements	(%)	Micro-elements	(ppm)	Micro-elements	(ppm)
Calcium	1·50	Iron	20–80	Fluorine	No data
Phosphorus	1·00	Zinc	10–50	Bromine	No data
Potassium	0·20	Copper	1–5	Barium	No data
Sodium	0·16	Manganese	0·2–0·5	Strontium	No data
Chlorine	0·11	Iodine	0·3–0·6		
Sulphur	0·15	Cobalt	0·02–0·1		
Magnesium	0·04	Molybdenum	1–4		
		Selenium	No data		

Source: McDonald, Edwards and Greenhalgh (1973).

micro-elements which are required by animals only in very small quantities. At the present time the elements iron, copper, cobalt, iodine, manganese, zinc, molybdenum, selenium and fluorine are included in this group. In addition the elements bromine, barium and strontium may also be essential, but the evidence for their inclusion is not yet conclusive.

The total amount of minerals in the animal's body is a very small

Table 3.6 *Macro-element deficiency symptoms and common sources of the element*

Element	Type of animal	Deficiency symptoms	Source of element and/or cure for deficiency
Calcium	Young animals	Rickets	Milk; green plants; fish and meat and bone by-products; ground limestone; steamed bone flour; dicalcium phosphate; rock calcium phosphate (the latter must be free of fluorine)
	Mature animals	Osteomalacia	
	Hens	Soft beak and bones; retarded growth; thin egg shells; reduced egg production	
	Milking animal	Milk fever	Intravenous injection of calcium gluconate
Phosphorus	Young animals	Rickets; stunted growth	Milk; cereal grains; fish and meat and bone by-products; dicalcium phosphate; rock calcium phosphate
	Mature animals	Osteomalacia; low milk yield	
	All animals	Pica (depraved appetite); aphosphorosis; stiff joints; muscular weakness; low fertility; low milk yield	

Table 3.6 – *continued*

Element	Type of animal	Deficiency symptoms	Source of element and/or cure for deficiency
Potassium	All animals	Unlikely to occur in practice	All green plants
	Calves fed on synthetic milk low in potassium	Severe paralysis	
	Chicks fed deficient diets	Retarded growth; tetany	
Sodium	All animals	Retardation of growth	Fish and meat and bone by-products; common salt
	Hens	Reduced growth and egg production	
Chlorine	All animals	Decline in appetite; reduction in growth	As for sodium
	Hens	Feather picking; cannibalism	
Sulphur	All animals	Limits synthesis of the amino acids cysteine, cystine and methionine	Protein feeds; sodium sulphate; elemental sulphur
Magnesium	Calves; milk fed for 50–70 days	Tetany; death	Wheat bran; cottonseed cake; linseed cake
	Mature cattle and sheep	Grass staggers or hypomagnesaemic tetany;* when blood serum Mg 0·5 mg per 100 ml death may result	Injection of magnesium sulphate; prophylactic; magnesium oxide at rate of 50 g per head per day; magnesium fertilizer on the pastures

*The exact cause is unknown; it may be that dietary magnesium is poorly absorbed.

proportion of the total body weight and the major part are found in the skeletal tissue. Nevertheless, small quantities of minerals are found in all parts of the body.

A short account of the metabolic role of each of these essential minerals is given below and in Tables 3.6 and 3.7 the various mineral deficiency symptoms encountered, some feed sources of the minerals and cures for specific deficiencies are listed. The role of minerals in the nutrition of animals is complicated because excess of some of them may also cause toxicities (Table 3.8) and there are, in addition, a number of rather complex interactions between different essential mineral elements.

Table 3.7   *Micro-element deficiency symptoms and common sources of the element*

Element	Type of animal	Deficiency symptoms	Source of element and/or cure for deficiency
Iron	Suckling pigs Hens	Anaemia	Iron dextran injections for pigs Iron is well distributed in green leafy materials
Copper	Cattle and sheep	Anaemia; poor growth; bone disorders; scouring; depigmentation of hair and wool; gastro-intestinal disorders	Plant seeds; copper salts
	Cattle	'Teart', with excess molybdenum and sulphate	
	Lambs	Lesions in brain and spinal column; muscular incoordination	
Cobalt	Cattle and sheep	Emaciation and listlessness occurs when cobalt content of forage less than 0·08 ppm; pining (vitamin B_{12} deficiency)	Cobalt salts; cobalt bullet containing 90% cobaltic oxide; vitamin B_{12}
Iodine	All animals	Endemic goitre or 'big neck'; reproductive failure	Fishmeal; seaweed; iodized salt
Manganese	Cattle grazing sand and peat soils	Poor growth; leg deformities; poor fertility; frequent abortion	Only very small quantities of manganese are required Rice and wheat offals; manganese salts
	Pigs	Lameness	
	Chicks	Perosis or 'slipped tendon'	
	Hens	Reduced hatchability; reduced shell thickness in eggs; head retraction	

Table 3.7 – *continued*

Element	Type of animal	Deficiency symptoms	Source of element and/or cure for deficiency
Zinc	Grazing animals	Unlikely to occur	Widely distributed; yeast; bran and germ of cereal grains
	Pigs; intensively housed and fed on a dry diet	Para-keratosis; sub-normal growth; low efficiency of feed conversion; skin lesions	Zinc at the rate of 40 to 100 ppm in the diet; as zinc carbonate or suphate
	Chicks	Poor growth; poor feathering and calcification; skin lesions	
Molybdenum	All animals	None under practical farming conditions	Molybdenum salts
	Lambs on diets low in molybdenum	Poor liveweight gain	
	Chicks on purified soybean diets	Poor growth	
Selenium	Pigs	Liver necrosis due to vitamin E deficiency	Vitamin E or sodium selenite
	Calves Lambs	Muscular dystrophy due to vitamin E deficiency	Vitamin E or sodium selenite
Fluorine	All animals	Dental caries	Fluorides in very small quantities

Table 3.8 *Toxic mineral elements*

Element or compound	Symptoms	Limits of concentration of element or compound
Potassium	High intake of potassium may interfere with the absorption and metabolism of magnesium	
Sodium chloride	Too high a level of intake causes excessive thirst, muscular weakness and oedema; salt poisoning quite common in pigs and poultry, particularly when water is limited	When water is limited; 4% hens, 2% chicks and 1% turkey poults

Table 3.8 – *continued*

Element or compound	Symptoms	Limits of concentration of element or compound
Iron	Excessive intake causes digestive disturbances	
Copper	Continuous ingestion of excess copper leads to an accumulation in the body tissues; sheep are particularly susceptible; copper poisoning occurs naturally in parts of Australia	
Cobalt	Unlikely to occur under practical farming conditions	40–50 mg daily of Co per 45 kg (100 lb) body weight
Manganese	Toxic in very large doses; toxicity unlikely to occur under normal farming conditions	
Zinc	Depression of feed intake and induction of a copper deficiency; unlikely to occur under normal farming conditions	
Molybdenum	Induces copper deficiency under certain conditions	
Selenium	Causes toxicity in horses, cattle and sheep; known as 'alkali disease' or 'blind staggers' in the United States; dullness; stiffness of joints; lameness; loss of hair; some plants accumulate selenium; *Astragalus bisulcatus* may contain up to 4,000 ppm on a dry-matter basis; the toxic effect is reduced when high-protein feeds are given to the livestock	10–30 ppm
Fluorine	Causes fluorosis; teeth become pitted and worn; intake affected; fluorine is an accumulative poison; the major sources are water, rock phosphates used as a fertilizer, and industrial plant in some regions	> 20 ppm in diet

As it is impossible to consider this subject in depth in an 'introduction' and as the subject is a dynamic one with new information constantly being made available, the reader who is particularly interested should consult specialized texts and the current literature.

Macro-elements

Calcium.   This is the most common mineral element in the animal body. It is a constituent of bone and teeth and most living cells and tissue fluids. It also performs a role in the coagulation of the blood, the normal action of skeletal and heart muscle and in the regulation of the excitability of the nervous system.

The deficiency symptoms described in Table 3.6 may also be caused by a deficiency of phosphorus and/or vitamin D or by an abnormal calcium:phosphorus ratio. Normal ratios are 1:1 to 2:1 in mammals and are rather wider in birds. Calcium metabolism is under the control of a hormone secreted by the parathyroid gland.

Phosphorus.   It is a constituent of bone, phosphoproteins, nucleic acids and phospholipids and has a role in calcium metabolism. Phosphorus deficiency (Table 3.6) is usually more common in cattle than in sheep. Pica (Table 3.6) is not a conclusive symptom of phosphorus deficiency as it may be caused by other factors.

Although cereal grains are a good source of phosphorus, much of what they contain may not be available for non-ruminants if it occurs in the form of phytates. These are more digestible by ruminant than by non-ruminant livestock.

Potassium.   This element has a role, together with sodium, chlorine and bicarbonate ions, in the osmotic regulation of the body fluids, in which it functions primarily as the cation of cells. It also plays a part in nerve and muscle excitability and in carbohydrate metabolism.

Sodium.   Like potassium this element is concerned with the osmotic regulation of body fluids, being the main cation of blood plasma and other extra-cellular fluids.

Chlorine.   The element is associated with potassium and sodium in osmotic regulation and has an important role in gastric secretion in the true stomach of animals.

Sulphur.   Proteins containing the amino acids cystine, cysteine and methionine, the vitamins biotin and thiamine and the hormone insulin all contain sulphur. Wool contains up to 4 per cent sulphur. Small quantities of sulphates also occur in the blood. Deficiency of sulphur normally denotes a protein deficiency. When a non-protein nitrogenous compound such as urea is fed to ruminants additional sulphur may assist microbial synthesis of sulphur-containing proteins.

Magnesium.   This element is closely associated with calcium and phosphorus in the skeletal structure, it is an activator of phosphates and it is also concerned with calcium metabolism. As adult animals possess only a very small available reserve of magnesium in their bodies they are very dependent upon a regular supply of this mineral.

Micro-elements

Iron.   Most iron in the body occurs in the haemoglobin of the red blood cells, but it is also found in a blood serum protein known as siderophilin. This protein is believed to have a role in the transport of blood from one part of the body to the other. Iron is also found in the protein ferritin which is present in the spleen, liver, kidney and bone marrow. It is also a component of many enzymes and some flavoproteins.

The daily requirement of iron by the normal healthy animal is small. Anaemia due to iron deficiency could occur after prolonged haemorrhage, but normally only occurs in baby piglets. This is because sows' milk is particularly deficient in iron. The absorption of iron appears to be to some extent independent of the dietary source.

Copper.   This element is essential for the production of red blood corpuscles and for maintaining their activity. It is a component of many enzyme systems and is necessary for the normal pigmentation of hair, fur and wool. Storage takes place mainly in the liver, but copper is probably present in all body cells. As will be seen from Table 3.6 there are a variety of deficiency symptoms. In Australia a copper deficiency in lambs is known as 'enzootic ataxia' and is associated with the grazing of pasture with a low copper content (2 to 4 ppm Cu in the dry matter). Similar clinical symptoms occur in lambs in the United Kingdom suffering from a condition known as 'swayback' although the copper content of the grazings is normal (7 to 15 ppm Cu in the dry matter). A clinical condition known as 'teart', characterized by unthriftiness and scouring, occurs in cattle in the United Kingdom. A similar condition is known as 'peat scours' in New Zealand. The feeding of copper sulphate to animals controls this condition although the copper content of the pasture may be normal. However, these pastures do possess a high molybdenum content (20 to 100 ppm compared with 0·5 to 3·0 ppm in the dry matter of normal pastures). It is believed that molybdenum affects copper retention by the animal, but limits it only in the presence of sulphate.

Cobalt.   This element is required by microbia in the rumen for the synthesis of vitamin B_{12} and it is an activating ion in certain enzymic reactions. Sheep are more liable to exhibit cobalt deficiency than other types of livestock.

Iodine.   This is a constituent of the hormone thyroxine that controls the metabolic rate of animals. Although a deficiency of iodine in the diet causes goitre, it is not the sole cause. Some feeds contain goitrogenic compounds, particularly *Brassica* spp., soybeans, peas, groundnuts and linseed. These goitrogenic compounds appear to block the absorption of iodine in what would otherwise be an adequate diet.

Manganese. This is important as an activator of enzymic reactions concerned with carbohydrate, fat and protein metabolism. It is found in traces in most tissues. The highest concentrations are in the bones, liver, kidney, pancreas and pituitary gland. Manganese deficiency is not the only factor concerned in the clinical condition known as 'perosis' in chicks (Table 3.7). The condition is aggravated by high intakes of calcium and phosphorus.

Zinc. This element appears to be present in all tissues and is concerned in some enzymic reactions. The clinical condition in pigs known as parakeratosis (Table 3.7) is aggravated by increased calcium levels in the diet and decreased by reduced calcium and improved phosphorus levels.

Molybdenum. This is a constituent of the enzyme xanthine oxidase that has an important role in purine metabolism, of nitrate reductase and of a bacterial hydrogenase.

Selenium. The exact relationship between selenium and vitamin E (Table 3.7) has not yet been determined. Selenium can replace sulphur in the amino acids methionine and cystine found in seleniferous plants.

Fluorine. This is distributed throughout the body but is concentrated in the bones and teeth. The role of this element in the metabolism is not yet fully understood.

Bromine. This element may possess some role in the growth of chicks.

Barium and strontium. Conclusive evidence that these are essential elements is not yet available.

In tropical environments mineral deficiencies may be enhanced by the animal losing considerable quantities of the elements during sweating or by dribbling saliva. For example, Bonsma (1940) stated that unacclimatized bulls may dribble 13 to 18 litres (3 to 4 gal) of saliva a day and lose 51 to 71 g (2 to 2·5 oz) of minerals. However, it is not considered that this is a problem in acclimatized livestock.

Cereals, and to a lesser extent cereal by-products, normally possess a low proportion of calcium and a relatively high proportion of phosphorus. Most forages possess more calcium than phosphorus. Legume forages normally possess a relatively high calcium content and browse is usually relatively rich in all mineral elements. Feeds of animal origin are usually well supplied with minerals.

Our knowledge of mineral deficiencies in tropical regions is very limited at the present time. In Guyana very large areas are known to be deficient in minerals as are extensive areas in Brazil and Central America. There is at present a major project, with headquarters at the University of Florida, that is concerned with ascertaining the extent of mineral deficiencies in tropical America. In Africa it is known that very large areas of range, particularly in East, Central and South Africa, are deficient in phosphorus and that this deficiency reduces the fertility of cattle in these regions. In Kenya and Zaire cobalt-deficient areas have been identified (Suter, 1962). It is likely that the soils in almost all humid tropical regions are deficient to a greater or lesser degree in one or more mineral elements. Obviously a very great effort will be required to map mineral-deficient areas in the tropics. In the interim period the livestock owner can only insure himself against mineral deficiencies by the feeding of mineral supplements.

Nomadic peoples in the tropics have known for a very long time that it was necessary for them to insure against mineral deficiencies, although their livestock range over wide areas thus reducing the risk of mineral deficiency in any one locality. For example, the Baggara people in the western Sudan know which of their ranges are 'salty' and they herd their animals so that they spend as long a time as is possible on the 'salty' range. Nomadic herders also usually carry salt with them for their livestock and/or visit areas where there are edible earths. Certainly earth-eating or *geophagia* is a very common habit of both domestic and wild animals in the tropics. It is interesting that chemical analyses of edible earths from both East and West Africa, although demonstrating the variety of their mineral constituents, have failed to establish direct links between known mineral deficiencies and geophagia (French, 1945). In the humid forest regions of South and Southeast Asia salt has been used to attract wild cattle of the *Bos* (*Bibos*)-type to breed with domestic cattle and it has been suggested that the domestication of *B.* (*Bibos*)-type cattle may have been originally achieved by man attracting the wild cattle by the provision of salt or highly mineralized earths (Simoons and Simoons, 1968).

We suggest that in the tropics all grazing livestock should be fed a simple mineral supplement and that all yarded and/or housed livestock should be fed complete mineral supplements.

A very suitable and simple mineral supplement for ruminant livestock is as follows:

Common salt	40 parts
Ground chalk, limestone or shell	40 parts
Steam bone flour	20 parts

This mixture should be fed *ad lib.* to grazing animals. If concentrates are fed the mixture may be added to them at the rate of 2 to 3 per cent of the total ration. If there is a known mineral deficiency in the region – apart from calcium, phosphate, sodium and chlorine – then a salt of the specific mineral that is known to be deficient should be added to the above mixture at the recommended rate. We do not advocate the indiscriminate feeding of complete mineral mixtures to grazing animals unless the latter are exhibiting some symptoms of mineral deficiency. However, it should be realized that in this context the deficiency symptoms may be sub-clinical in their manifestation, i.e. poor growth and low fertility.

Range livestock may have to be supplemented in the dry season with other nutrients, and where urea–molasses–mineral blocks or liquid feeds are used the animals will be able to obtain their mineral requirements from the block or liquid feed.

Yarded or housed livestock must of course be considered to be in a different category. They should all receive rations containing complete mineral supplements. In most tropical countries the livestock-feeding industry has now developed to such an extent that complete mineral mixtures are readily available. If this is not the case then the livestock owner requiring information on the composition of complete mineral mixtures should consult his local extension adviser.

Vitamins

Vitamins are essential food substances that are required in very small quantities by animals. Those known to be of any importance in animal nutrition are listed in Table 3.9. For convenience they are classified in

Table 3.9 *Vitamins of importance in animal nutrition*

Fat soluble

A	retinol: precursor: carotenoids, the most important being β-carotene
D	there are ten to twelve different forms: only ergocalciferol (D_2) and cholecalciferol (D_3) are of importance
E	collective name for a group of closely related compounds known as tocopherols: α-tocopherol is the most important
K	collective name for a number of compounds: phyloquinone (K_1) is the most important

Water soluble

B complex
    B_1 thiamine
    B_2 riboflavine
          nicotinamide: formerly known as nicotinic acid or niacin
    B_6 pyridoxine: exists in three forms that are interconvertible
          pantothenic acid
          biotin
          choline
          folic acid
    B_{12} cobaltamin: several forms of the vitamin are known
C   1-ascorbic acid

---

two groups: fat soluble and water soluble. Details of the clinical symptoms that deficiencies of these vitamins may cause, together with some of their common sources, are listed in Table 3.10. Brief accounts of the roles that these essential foodstuffs occupy in the metabolism of animals are summarized below.

Table 3.10   *Vitamin deficiency symptoms and common sources of the vitamin*

Vitamin	Type of animal	Deficiency symptoms	Source of vitamin and/or cure for deficiency
A	Cattle	Rough coat and scaly skin; excessive watering of eyes culminating in xerophthalmia; low fertility; abortion	Green, leafy materials; fish-liver oils; synthetic vitamin A
	Pigs	Poor growth; low fertility	
	Poultry	Retarded growth; staggering gait; low egg production and hatchability	
	All animals	Secondary bacterial infections	
D	Young animals	Rickets	Synthesis in the skin of outdoor-managed animals; sun-dried feeds such as hay; fish-liver oils
	Older animals	Osteomalacia	
E	Young cattle and lambs	Muscular dystrophy	Green leafy materials; cereal grains; synthetic α-tocopherol; selenium salts
	All animals	Reproductive failure	
	Chicks	Encephalomalacia; exudative diathesis	
K	Chicks	Delayed clotting time of the blood	Green leafy materials; fish meal
B_1	Chicks	Polyneuritis	Cereal grains; generally wide distribution in feeds
B_2	Pigs	Loss of appetite; severe diarrhoea	Green leafy material; milk; dried whey; dried skim-milk
	Chicks	Curled toe paralysis	
	Hens	Decreased hatchability of eggs	
Nicotinamide	Pigs	Poor growth; enteritis; dermatitis	Any source of tryptophan as nicotinamide can be synthesized from it
	Poultry	Black tongue	

Table 3.10 – *continued*

Vitamin	Type of animal	Deficiency symptoms	Source of vitamin and/or cure for deficiency
B_6	Pigs	Poor growth rate; anaemia; convulsions	Widely distributed in feeds so that deficiencies are unlikely to occur in practice
	Chicks	Poor growth; convulsions	
	Hens	Poor egg production; reduced hatchability	
Pantothenic acid	Pigs	Poor growth; dermatitis; characteristic 'goose-stepping' gait	Widely distributed in feeds; deficiencies unlikely to occur in farm practice
	Chicks	Poor growth; dermatitis	
Biotin		No deficiency symptoms seen under practical farming conditions	Widely distributed in feeds; also usually synthesized in the alimentary tract
Choline	Chicks	Perosis or 'slipped tendon' (see Table 3.7); can be prevented by feeding choline	Widely distributed in feeds and can be replaced with methionine and betaine in the diet
Folic acid	Chicks	Anaemia; poor growth	Widely distributed in feeds; also synthesized by intestinal microbia
B_{12}	All animals	Poor growth	Foods of animal origin; synthesized by intestinal microbia when cobalt is present; also synthesized in poultry litter
C	All animals	None	Farm animals do not require any dietary source of this vitamin as they can synthesize it

Fat-soluble vitamins

Vitamin A. The animal has to synthesize vitamin A from the precursors found in plants. These are known as carotenoids, the most widely distributed one being β-carotene. Vitamin A is a constituent of the pigment of the red cells of the retina of the eye. It is concerned with the maintenance of the mucous membranes of the respiratory tract, intestinal tract, urethra, kidneys and eyes and also plays a role in bone formation.

Species and breeds within species differ in their ability to convert carotenoids into vitamin A. Sheep and buffaloes are efficient converters while some breeds of cattle such as the Jersey are relatively inefficient converters, their butterfat and body fat containing large quantities of the unconverted yellow carotenoids.

Vitamin A is stored in the liver so that deficiency symptoms may not appear for quite a long period after animals are fed on a carotenoid-deficient diet.

In the monsoonal and dry tropics grazing ruminant livestock may suffer from vitamin A deficiency towards the end of prolonged dry seasons. It is unlikely that grazing animals in the wet tropics suffer from a deficiency of the vitamin. All yarded or housed livestock should receive adequate green feed or synthetic vitamin A supplements. Poultry, in particular, are likely to suffer from a deficiency of the vitamin.

Vitamin D. This vitamin facilitates the deposition of calcium and phosphorus in the bones and improves the absorption of these elements from the intestinal tract. Grazing animals in the tropics are unlikely to suffer from vitamin D deficiency as sunlight helps to synthesize it in the skin. Housed animals without access to sunlight should receive supplements.

Vitamin E. The exact biological functions of vitamin E are not yet completely understood, but it appears to be essential for the proper functioning of a number of biological systems including the synthesis of vitamin C. Deficiency of the vitamin can cause a muscular dystrophy in calves and lambs; this can be cured by the administration of either vitamin E or a selenium salt.

As the vitamin is widely distributed, particularly in green leafy material, deficiencies are unlikely to occur in grazing animals in the humid tropics. Housed animals should receive adequate green feed or synthetic vitamin E supplements.

Vitamin K. The complete role of this vitamin has not yet been established although it is known to be necessary for the formation of prothrombin, an essential component of the blood-clotting mechanism. Symptoms of vitamin K deficiency have not been reported in ruminants or pigs under practical farming conditions. A disease of cattle associated with the feeding of spoiled sweet clover (*Melilotus alba*), containing a compound known as dicoumarol, can be cured by the administration of vitamin K. Poultry feed should contain up to 2·5 per cent dried green forage material to ensure that the birds do not develop deficiency symptoms.

Water-soluble vitamins

Vitamin B_1.   A derivative of the vitamin – thiamine pyrophosphate – is a coenzyme involved in the oxidative decarboxylation of pyruvic acid. Ruminants can synthesize the vitamin, and because of the fact that cereal grains are a rich source of the vitamin pigs and poultry are unlikely to suffer deficiencies. In some areas of the humid tropics the feeding of raw fish to livestock could induce a thiamine deficiency as some fish contain an enzyme known as thiaminase that destroys thiamine in the remainder of the feed.

Vitamin B_2.   Riboflavin is an important constituent of the flavoproteins. These are concerned in carbohydrate metabolism. In practice, deficiencies may occur in the diets of pigs and poultry fed mainly on cereals. As poultry excreta is often richer in riboflavin than their diet, the floor brooding of chicks is advantageous when high cereal content diets are fed.

Nicotinamide.   The precursor for this vitamin is the amino acid tryptophan. The vitamin functions as part of two important coenzymes that are involved in hydrogen transfer in living cells. In practice, deficiencies are only likely to occur where pigs and poultry are fed very high maize content diets.

Vitamin B_6.   Pyridoxal phosphate, a derivative of the vitamin, serves as a coenzyme in a number of metabolic reactions. Deficiencies do not normally occur under practical farming conditions.

Pantothenic acid.   This vitamin is a constituent of coenzyme A. Because of the wide distribution of the vitamin in feeds, deficiencies are rarely reported in farming practice.

Biotin.   All the metabolic functions of this vitamin have not yet been ascertained, but it is known to possess an important role in fat synthesis. Deficiencies are rare in farming practice.

Choline.   This vitamin has a role in several metabolic reactions, a derivative of it being important in the transmission of nervous impulses. As it can be replaced in metabolic functions by the amino acids methionine and betaine and is widely distributed in feeds, deficiencies are rare in farming practice.

Folic acid.   The vitamin plays a role in various enzyme systems. In practice only chicks are likely to suffer from deficiencies although the prolonged oral administration of sulpha drugs may induce deficiency symptoms in other livestock due to the depression by the drug of bacterial synthesis of the vitamin.

Vitamin B_{12}. Compounds formed from this vitamin are of importance in many metabolic reactions, particularly in propionic acid metabolism in the ruminant. As long as adequate cobalt is available and its utilization is not blocked, vitamin B_{12} can be synthesized by ruminants and non-ruminants. Synthesis of vitamin B_{12} can also apparently take place in deep litter in poultry houses.

Vitamin C. All domestic livestock can synthesize this vitamin. It has an important role in the oxidation-reduction mechanisms of living cells.

It will be realized from these brief notes that, except under special circumstances, vitamin deficiencies are rare in free-grazing animals. However, the situation with housed animals is different. Non-ruminant livestock and particularly poultry are liable to suffer from vitamin deficiencies if their rations are not supplemented. Commercial poultry rations are usually fortified with adequate vitamins, and farmers who mix their own rations can normally purchase vitamin premixes in most tropical countries. The small pig and poultry farmer with no access to commercial mixed rations or vitamin premixes should always provide some green feed for his livestock. Poultry are less likely to suffer from vitamin deficiencies if they are managed on deep litter.

Additives

Compounders of animal feeds normally add vitamin–mineral supplements to their rations. In recent years they have also been adding specific amino acids, such as lysine, to rations that are considered to be deficient in the amino acids. These constituents can all be considered essential feed additives. In addition, however, compounders have been increasingly adding, in those countries where it is legal, other substances such as antibiotics, hormones, arsenicals, tranquillizers, detergents and – in the case of pig rations – additional copper sulphate.

Antibiotics. These are chemical substances produced by micro-organisms which in minute quantities inhibit the growth of other micro-organisms or even destroy them. Antibiotics can be classified into two groups: broad-spectrum antibiotics that inhibit the growth of a wide range of micro-organisms and narrow-spectrum antibiotics that only inhibit the growth of one or a small number of other micro-organisms.

It has been shown that low-level intakes of antibiotics can improve the productivity of pigs, poultry and young calves.

In pigs the average response to feeding antibiotics has been a 10 to 15 per cent increase in growth rate and a 3 to 5 per cent improvement in the efficiency of feed utilization. The response is greatest where standards of hygiene and management are poor, in young rather than older animals and when all-vegetable protein diets are fed. The optimum level of inclusion of antibiotics is considered to be within the range of 5 to 15 gm per tonne of the rations and it is generally recommended that feeding should continue throughout the life of the fattening pig since abrupt withdrawal may reduce liveweight gain and nullify the initial advantages.

With poultry the degree of response to antibiotics varies with the standards of health and management and the age of the birds. Turkey poults respond better than chicks with increases of up to 15 per cent in growth rate being recorded.

In young calves the inclusion of antibiotics in the diet reduces the incidence and severity of scours and improves growth rates. There is also some evidence that the inclusion of antibiotics in the rations of mature ruminants, fed rations that are composed mainly of concentrates, can be of value.

It is probable that the improvements in productivity achieved by the use of antibiotics are mainly due to the suppression of sub-clinical infections, although there may also be other effects. The disadvantage of using antibiotics in feeds is that resistant strains of micro-organisms may ultimately develop. However, the prolonged use of antibiotics in livestock feeds at the normal recommended levels is unlikely to become a health hazard to the consumers of animal products.

In the United Kingdom and in some other countries recommended inclusion rates of feed antibiotics such as zinc bacitracin have been promulgated by the authorities. Readers interested in maximum and recommended inclusion rates for pig, poultry and calf rations should consult Lucas (1972).

Hormones. Synthetic oestrogenic hormones, such as stilboestrol and hexoestrol, possess growth-promoting properties, while thyroxine can stimulate growth and milk and wool production. Hormones may be administered to farm animals either orally or by subcutaneous implantation. With implantation, pellets are placed at the base of the ear of ruminant livestock, and in the neck in the chemical caponization of cockerels. At slaughter of the livestock the tissues from these sites can be discarded.

The action of hormones in caponized cockerels encourages fat to accumulate in the body tissues. In ruminants the action of the hormones is quite different. The carcases of treated animals contain more muscle, bone and water and less fat than the carcases of untreated animals.

The normal amounts of hormone implanted or fed orally to cattle and sheep are as follows: 45 to 75 mg of hexoestrol implanted or 10 mg in feed per day for beef cattle, and 10 to 15 mg implanted or 2 to 4 mg in feed per day for sheep. The best results are obtained during the final stages of growth when the animals are maintained on a high plane of nutrition. Average increases in liveweight gain can be of the order of 25 per cent.

The use of hormones is a very controversial subject at the present time and their use for implantation purposes or in feeds is illegal in many countries. The most serious criticism is that there is a human health hazard from the possible carcinogenic properties of residues of the hormones in carcases. Excretion from hormone-treated animals could also contaminate pastures and endanger the reproductive cycle of breeding animals grazed at a later date on the pastures.

Arsenicals.   Some compounds containing arsenic, such as arsanilic acid, sodium arsanilate, arsenic acid and arsenobenzene, appear to possess growth-promoting properties. This is probably due to their effect on the intestinal microbia. As arsenic is an accumulative poison very considerable precautions must be taken if these compounds are to be used in feeds, although there is no evidence that the feeding of these compounds produces carcases with unacceptably high tissue concentrations of arsenic.

Tranquillizers.   There is evidence that the feeding of some of these compounds, which are normally used to reduce hypertension and nervousness, may improve liveweight gain.

Detergents.   Evidence for the use of some of these compounds as growth-promoters is contradictory.

Copper sulphate. The use of additional copper sulphate in the diet of pigs is discussed in Chapter 12 (Part II).

There are also a number of other feed additives, such as *nitrovin* – a guanidine derivative – and quinoxaline compounds, that appear to improve the growth rate of some classes of livestock. Coccidiostats used in poultry rations and the drugs used in the treatment of histomoniasis in turkeys also act as growth stimulants.

Apart from the use of mineral–vitamin premixes, the fortification of amino-acid-deficient rations with individual amino acids and the use of feed antibiotics, the feeder in the tropics should be very cautious in his use of the very large number of additives that are available. This is because virtually all investigational work on additives has been conducted in the temperate zone and little is known of the effects of many of them on animals managed in a tropical environment. Readers with a special interest in the subject should consult Lucas (1972).

Evaluation of foods

Although it is possible with modern equipment and methods to determine the individual components of foods, most of the information that we possess on their composition is based on what is known as *proximate analysis.*

In this system of analysis the food is divided into six fractions. These are as follows:

1. *Moisture:* including any volatile acids and bases that may be present;
2. *Ash:* this fraction includes essential and inessential mineral elements;
3. *Crude protein:* this fraction includes protein, amino acids, amines, nitrogenous glycosides, glycolipids, B-vitamins and nitrates;
4. *Ether extract:* this fraction includes fats, oils, waxes, organic acids, pigments, sterols and the fat-soluble vitamins;
5. *Crude fibre:* this fraction includes insoluble cellulose, hemicellulose and lignin;
6. *Nitrogen-free extractives:* these include soluble cellulose, hemicellulose and lignin, sugars, fructosans, starch, pectins, organic acids, resins, tannins, pigments and water-soluble vitamins.

The moisture content is determined by drying food to a constant weight at 100°C (212°F). The ash content by ignition of food at 500°C (1,060°F) until all the carbon has been removed. The CP content is calculated from the nitrogen content of the food, determined by some modification of the Kjeldahl sulphuric acid digestion technique. Where N is the total nitrogen content, $N \times 6.25$ is assumed to be the CP content of the food. The ether extract content is determined by subjecting the food to continuous extraction with petroleum ether for a defined period. The residue after the evaporation of the ether is the ether extract content. The crude fibre (CF) content is determined by subjecting the residual food from the ether extraction to successive treatments with boiling acid and alkali of defined concentration. The organic residue is the CF content. The nitrogen-free extractives content is determined by subtraction of the sum of the percentages of moisture, ash, CF, ether extract and CF from 100.

Digestibility

Although the potential value of a food can be approximately determined by proximate analysis, the actual value of the food to the animal can be determined only if the digestibility is known. Digested food is that portion that is not excreted and which is assumed to be absorbed by the animal.

Digestibility can be measured by the use of *in vivo* or *in vitro* methods.

In *in vivo* methods the food under investigation is fed to an animal and the total input and output of the food constituent are measured. Thus if 'I' represents input and 'O' output of an ingredient the digestibility can be calculated using the following formula:

Percentage digestibility $= \dfrac{I - O}{I} \times 100$

Special methods using indicators have to be used for determining digestibility in grazing animals. Suitable indicators are lignin and chromic oxide. If indicators are used then when 'If' represents the percentage of indicator in the faeces and 'Ir' the percentage of indicator in the ration then

$$\text{Percentage digestibility} = \frac{\text{If} - \text{Ir}}{\text{If}} \times 100$$

The digestibility of the same feed varies according to the species consuming it (Devendra, 1971), as will be seen from Table 3.11. Thus digestibility coefficients for a feed are probably specific for only one type of animal.

Table 3.11   *The range of digestibilities of the dry-matter* (DM) *content of guinea grass* (Panicum maximum) *in cattle, water buffaloes, sheep and goats*

Type of livestock	Range of digestibility of the DM of guinea grass	Site of trials
Cattle	51–60	Uganda, India and the Philippines
Water buffaloes	58–64	Philippines
Sheep	50–59	Australia and Puerto Rico
Goats	57	Malaysia

Source: Devendra (1971).

As any type of *in vivo* digestibility determination is costly and time-consuming, efforts have been made to reproduce in the laboratory the reactions that take place in the digestive tract of animals. As a consequence, *in vitro* methods have been devised that are relatively cheap and rapid to perform. The digestibility coefficients determined by these methods are usually lower than those determined on the same foods by *in vivo* methods so that correction factors must be used. Further correction factors are also probably required in order to equate the data for different species. Nevertheless, these new methods are invaluable for the rapid determination of the digestibility of a large number of food samples. Interested readers should consult standard textbooks and publications for details of the methods employed in both *in vivo* and *in vitro* digestibility determinations.

Energy content

The ability of the food to supply energy is of major importance in the evaluation of its nutritive value. The total energy content of a food is known as the *gross energy*. There are, however, many losses of energy within the body due to defaecation, urination, the production of methane in the digestive tract of ruminants and the heat increment or specific dynamic action of the food. These are shown diagrammatically in Fig.

3.2. That fraction of the gross energy that remains available to the animal for maintenance and productive purposes is known as the *net energy*. The first demand on net energy is for maintenance of the body processes, that remaining may be used for productive purposes. Total heat production – that is the heat released by specific dynamic action of the food, together with the heat resulting from the maintenance of body processes and production – can be a source of major difficulty for the animal in the tropics (see Ch. 1, Pt I).

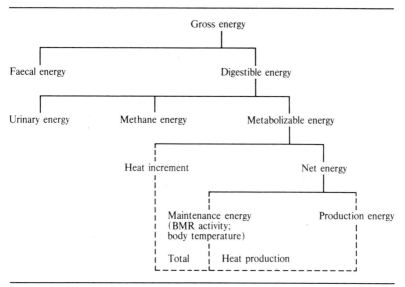

Fig. 3.2 Diagrammatic representation of the utilization of energy in the animal (McDonald *et al.*, 1973).

The two major systems used in practice for the evaluation of food energy in ruminant rations are the *starch equivalent* (SE) system that is used in Europe and many British Commonwealth countries, and the *total digestible nutrients* (TDN) system that is used in the Americas and in some countries in Africa and Asia. The SE system is based on net energy. The value of the food is not expressed in absolute terms but as the fat-producing ability of a food relative to the fat-producing ability of a unit of starch. The SE of a food is therefore:

$$\frac{\text{Weight of fat stored per unit weight of food ingested}}{\text{Weight of fat stored per unit weight of starch ingested}} \times 100$$

The calculation can be expressed on a net energy basis by assuming that 1 g of fat contains 9·5 kcal of energy. TDN, however, is calculated by adding together the quantities in 100 units of food of the digestible crude protein, crude fibre, nitrogen-free extractives and the digestible ether extract multiplied by 2·25. In Table 3.12 calculations are shown of the respective SE and TDN values of barley meal.

Table 3.12   *Calculations of the starch equivalent (SE) and total digestible nutrients (TDN) of barley meal from data on the digestible nutrients*

Constituent	Digestible nutrient in dry matter	SE factor	SE	TDN
Digestible crude protein	12·6	–	–	12·6
True protein	11·3	0·94	10·6	–
Ether extract	1·6	2·12	3·4	3·6
Crude fibre	0·2	1·00	0·2	0·2
Nitrogen-free extractives	65·8	1·00	65·8	65·8
Totals			80·0	82·2

Source: McDonald *et al.* (1973).

It is generally agreed that neither of these major systems achieves an accurate prediction of the effect of food intake on the production of animals. Blaxter (1962) has therefore proposed a new system. This is a more accurate system but greater accuracy is achieved at the expense of simplicity.

Evaluation of foods for pigs is considered in Chapter 12, Part II. Energy values if required are usually stated in terms of TDN, particularly in the Americas. The energy value of poultry foods is now normally expressed in terms of metabolizable energy as this component is relatively easily measured.

Protein content

As stated previously the CP content of a feed measures both the true protein content and the non-protein nitrogen content. In practice this is not very important as in ruminants the non-protein nitrogen fraction can be synthesized into protein by the microbia of the digestive tract and the diet of non-ruminants does not usually contain substantial quantities of non-protein nitrogen. True protein (TP) can be determined chemically. The apparent digestible crude protein (DCP) content can also be determined using the digestibility techniques discussed in a previous section.

Non-ruminants.   As the DCP content of a feed is not an entirely satisfactory assessment of protein value for an animal, because the efficiency with which a protein is used differs according to its source, several other methods of evaluating protein have been devised. The major ones are:

the protein efficiency ratio (PER), the gross protein value (GPV), the protein replacement value (PRV) and the biological value (BV).

The BV is probably the method that is mainly used. It may be calculated from the formula

$$\frac{N-(FN-MFN)-(UN-EUN)}{N-(FN-MFN)} \times 100$$

where 'N' is nitrogen intake, 'FN' is faecal nitrogen, 'MFN' is metabolic faecal nitrogen, 'UN' is urinary nitrogen and 'EUN' is endogenous urinary nitrogen. Some BVs of the proteins of common foods are shown in Table 3.4.

The BV of a food protein depends upon the number and the types of amino acids present in the protein. The closer the amino-acid composition of the food protein approaches to the amino-acid composition of the body protein the higher will be its biological value. It will readily be seen that the BV of a mixture of foods will not be a mean of the individual BVs. In general, animal proteins will possess higher BVs than plant proteins.

Amino-acid estimations can be made by chemical (lysine) or biological methods (methionine and cystine) or by microbiological assay. Relevant textbooks should be consulted as to the methods employed.

In practice a CP estimation is normally used for the evaluation of the protein content of feeds in pig and poultry rations, together with an assessment of the ability of the proteins to supplement the known amino-acid deficiencies of the cereal part of the rations.

Ruminants. Proteins in ruminant rations are normally evaluated in terms of CP or DCP. The concept of protein equivalent (PE) was introduced to allow for the value of the non-protein nitrogen fraction in the CP. The PE was calculated as follows:

$$PE = \frac{\text{Percentage digestible TP} + \text{percentage digestible CP}}{2}$$

or

$$PE = \frac{\text{Percentage DTP} + \text{percentage DCP}}{2}$$

where DTP is the digestible true protein.

There does not appear to be any particular justification for the use of PE rather than DCP in the evaluation of the protein content of ruminant feeds.

Any assessment of protein quality in ruminant feeds is difficult as food proteins are utilized by microbia and transformed into microbial protein. This has a high biological value of approximately 80. Usually the ruminant cannot take full advantage of this situation as some food protein is transformed into ammonia. Although some of this ammonia is used by the microbia most of it will be absorbed into the bloodstream and converted into urea, only a part of which will be returned to the digestive tract via the saliva and other metabolic pathways. The remainder is excreted in the urine. The biological value of food proteins in ruminants therefore depends to some extent on how much ammonia is found in the rumen and how this ammonia is then utilized. The latter will depend upon the availability of an adequate source of energy for the microbia in the digestive tract.

Feeding standards and requirements

Feeding standards for the different classes of tropical livestock, where they are known, are detailed in the chapters concerned with the various types of livestock in Part II of this text. Information on temperate-zone feeding standards, that have at present to be generally used in the tropics, is available in Morrison (1957), Evans (1960), Agricultural Research Council (1963, 1965, 1967), National Academy of Sciences–National Research Council (1966, 1968a, 1968b, 1970, 1971) and McDonald *et al.* (1973).

A major difference in the nutrition of the animal in the tropics is that heat produced within the body generally has to be dissipated, whereas in the temperate zone it can often be conserved in order to maintain normal body temperatures. Thus it might be expected that energy requirements for maintenance would be lower in the tropics. Kehar (1954) suggested that the energy requirements of cattle in India could be as much as 40 per cent less than generally accepted requirements in the temperate zone. A difference of this magnitude is not apparent in practice, but other workers at the Indian Dairy Research Institute have suggested that animals need less energy during the hottest periods of the year. It has also been suggested that the protein requirements of animals may be lower in hot climates, but it is likely that mineral and vitamin requirements will be the same at similar levels of production. Payne (1969) has discussed these and other problems in some detail in a review of the nutrition of animals in the tropics.

Types of feed available

There are obviously many methods that could be used for the classification of animal feeds. One method used in practice is to classify them into groups according to the predominant nutrient or nutrients which each contains. A selection can then be made from feeds within any one group for availability and cost, and the most suitable feed from any one group can be used in a mixed ration. In practice, any food from one group can be substituted in a mixed ration for any other food within the same group without substantially altering the nutrient balance of the mixed feed. It would, however, be a mistake to assume that all feeds within a group possess exactly the same feeding value or that the same feed grown in different parts of the tropics will have exactly the same composition.

One suitable classification by feed group is as follows:

1. *Succulents*. These are feeds whose principal constituent is water. They may be sub-divided into two major sub-groups: green forages and root crops.
2. *Roughages*. These feeds are characterized by their high CF content. Some feeds that can be classified as succulents when they are young would be classified as roughages when they are mature.
3. *Concentrates*. The main characteristic of all concentrate feeds is that they contain relatively large quantities of a major food constituent. They may be sub-divided into concentrates of plant or animal origin, and concentrates of plant origin may be divided into a further two groups – those that are energy-rich and those with a high CP content.
4. *Other feeds*. Some feeds cannot be easily classified in any of the three major groups. This group includes new types of feed that are manufactured from inorganic or organic materials.

In compounding any specific ration the relative quantities of feed used from these different groups will vary according to the species or breed within the species of animal which is being fed, and in accordance with the animal's production. For instance, ruminant animals can utilize food from all groups, but they utilize succulents and roughages more efficiently than other livestock and it may sometimes be wasteful to feed concentrates to them. Non-ruminants require mainly concentrate feeds, as do highly productive milking cows. Some data on the nutrient content of representative feeds from each of the groups are shown in Table 3.13.

Succulents

This group includes practically all growing or fresh vegetation of which forages form a major part. The water content of succulents is always high – usually between 75 and 95 per cent.

Forages. These are of such major importance in the feeding of livestock that they are considered at length in the second section of this chapter. During their growth stage most forages constitute a complete food for ruminant livestock, as long as they are not grown on soils that are deficient in an essential nutrient. Within the forage group, legumes usually possess higher CP, mineral and vitamin contents than grasses. Browse legumes normally possess particularly high CP and mineral contents, though their digestibility may be somewhat less than those of forage legumes.

Table 3.13   *The proximate analyses of some representative feedstuffs*

Group	Feedstuff	Dry matter (%)						On DM basis			
			Ash (%)	Crude fibre (%)	Ether extract (%)	N-free extractive (%)	CP (%)	TDN (%)	Calcium (%)	Phosphorus (%)
Succulents	*Panicum maximum* (guinea); 15 to 28 days' growth	19·4	14·3	30·9	3·4	39·2	12·2	10·2	0·86	0·36
	Centrosema pubescens (centro)	24·2	8·3	31·0	3·9	35·7	21·1	14·9	1·30	0·31
	Manihot esculenta (cassava) roots	37·1	3·0	4·3	0·9	88·3	3·5	31·6	0·26	0·16
Roughages	*Cynodon dactylon* (Bermuda) hay	87·4	10·2	32·0	5·3	39·2	13·2	43·2	0·75	0·23
	Oryza sativa (rice) straw	89·0	17·7	35·7	2·4	38·7	5·4	37·7	0·29	0·36

Concentrates
Plant origin

Energy rich	*Oryza sativa* (paddy)	89·4	7·9	9·5	3·8	68·5	10·2	51·9	0·41	0·50
	Zea mays (maize) cracked grain	87·2	3·3	3·0	3·7	79·5	10·5	66·5	0·20	0·22
	Gossypium spp. (cotton) seed	90·2	5·2	14·6	22·6	36·5	20·8	53·9	—	—
Protein rich	Coconut meal (solvent extracted)	91·1	6·6	13·3	2·4	47·4	21·4	68·6	0·21	0·64
	Sesame meal	93·7	11·6	6·2	9·0	23·6	43·3	71·3	2·02	1·61
	Soybean meal (expeller extracted)	91·0	6·2	5·9	4·9	30·0	44·0	77·9	0·27	0·63
Animal origin	White fish meal	90·7	20·5	0·2	6·8	0·3	62·9	72·4	6·76	3·69
	Meat and bone meal	93·7	28·1	2·2	10·6	3·1	49·7	65·3	10·67	5·27
	Dried skim-milk	93·9	8·0	0·6	1·1	51·1	33·1	79·8	1·28	1·04
Other	Cane molasses	73·4	8·6	0·0	0·0	61·7	3·0	53·7	0·66	0·08
	Wet brewer's grain	23·7	1·0	3·6	1·6	11·8	5·7	16·1	0·07	0·12

Sources: Composite data from Morrison (1957) and McDowell *et al.* (1974).

Roots.   These are grown in large quantities in the monsoonal and wet tropics. The major root crops in the tropics are cassava (*Manihot esculenta*), yams (*Dioscorea* spp.), sweet potato (*Ipomoea batatas*), taro (*Colocasia esculenta*) and arrowroots (*Maranta arundinacea* and *Canna edulis*). Breadfruit (*Artocarpus altilis*), although not a root crop, has approximately the same feed value as the typical root crops. The energy content of the dry matter of root crops is high, the water content varies, but the CP, mineral and vitamin contents are normally low.

Silages made from succulents will vary in nutritive value according to what feed was originally ensiled. The feeding value will always be lower than the fresh material due to wastage during the ensiling process.

Roughages

It is probable that a majority of ruminant livestock in the tropics subsist on roughage for a major part of the year.

Forage roughage.   This includes hay, standing hay and artificially dried forage. Good hay made at the correct stage of growth can be an excellent maintenance roughage feed. Unfortunately, little good hay is made in the tropics. Most of the hay that animals consume is 'standing hay' or forage that has matured *in situ*. Under favourable circumstances, such as occur in the sahel climatic zone of Africa and in some regions of the savanna, standing hay can be a medium-quality roughage. Normally, however, it is fully matured forage with a very low feeding value, containing a high content of indigestible cellulose and lignin. Artificially dried forage may be classified as a roughage or as a concentrate feed, depending on the nutrient content of the original forage and the stage at which it was dried.

Straws and haulm.   The straws of the cereal crops grown in the tropics such as rice (*Oryza sativa*), maize (*Zea mays*), sorghum (*Sorghum vulgare*) and millet (*Pennisetum typhoideum*) are almost universally used for feeding purposes, as are the haulms of legume crops such as groundnut (*Arachis hypogaea*) and the dried stalk materials of such crops as sesame (*Sesamum indicum*) and cotton (*Gossypium* spp.) These roughages generally possess a low feeding value, but livestock grazing them also have access to the weeds in the stubbles and these improve the overall feed value of straws and haulms. Legume straw or haulm possesses a higher feeding value than other straws.

There are other roughage feeds available at specific locations in the tropics such as the waste materials from oil palm processing plants, sisal waste, pineapple waste, bagasse, cocoa pods, coffee hulls, etc. The feeding value of these materials varies, but it is usually low.

Concentrates

There are of course a wide variety of concentrate feeds produced in the tropics, but those that are normally economic to feed are usually the by-products of crop or animal production.

Concentrates of plant origin

These include both energy-rich and protein-rich feeds.

Energy-rich concentrates of plant origin. The major group are the cereals – rice, maize, sorghum and millet. Their SE and TDN are high, CP content medium and CF content low. Their mineral content varies but is often unbalanced. As they are normally the staple human food in the countries in which they are grown it is unusual for them to be used as animal feeds except in restricted quantities in specific regions. If a surplus of cereals is available it is usually most economic to feed it to non-ruminants and in particular to poultry.

Other energy-rich concentrates are sugar and dried roots such as dried cassava, a major product in some parts of Southeast Asia where it is produced for export to Europe. Sugar is not normally fed to live-stock, but when sugar prices are depressed it is an excellent feed to incorporate in the ration of young pigs.

Oil seeds, from which many of the protein-rich cakes are manufac-tured, are high energy content feeds, principally on account of their high fat content. They are not usually used for feeding purposes, the excep-tion being cottonseed.

Protein-rich concentrates of plant origin. Grain legumes, like cereals, are normally used for human consumption, but where there is a surplus they can be fed to animals. The quality of their protein is relatively high.

Oil cakes and meals are the most common protein-rich concentrates. They include groundnut, soybean, sesame, palm kernel, cotton, rubber seed and coconut. Usually they have a relatively high SE or TDN content and a CP content that varies from 15 to 45 per cent. Their feeding value depends partly on the amount and quality of the protein that they con-tain, partly on the amount of fibre and other inedible material retained in the cake after processing of the original plant material and partly on whether they contain any toxic materials after processing. Their oil con-tent varies according to the method of processing. Those cakes pro-cessed by primitive methods will contain quite a high oil content – some-times as much as 10 per cent. Their mineral content varies considerably, but they are often rich in phosphorus. Their vitamin content will be minimal on account of the processing. Some oil seeds, such as cotton and rubber, contain compounds that are toxic to non-ruminants. Cotton seeds contain an aromatic aldehyde known as gossypol, toxic to non-ruminants at low levels, but inactivated by special processing. Rubber seed contains a cyanogenetic glucoside known as linamarin and an enzyme known as limase which hydrolyses the glucoside. The raw cake can therefore be toxic and should be boiled or processed in some other way before feeding.

Concentrates of animal origin

These include the following: the by-products of meat animal processing such as meat meal, meat and bone meal and blood meal, the by-products of fish processing such as fishmeal and shrimp meal, and the by-products of milk processing such as skim milk powder, whey and buttermilk. They are characterized by the relatively large quantities of high-quality protein that they contain and by a high mineral content. The vitamin content of some of these feeds may also be considerable.

In general they are not freely available in the tropics as most animal and fish offals are consumed by the human population and there is insufficient milk available for processing. In some tropical countries there is a waste of these by-products, either because suitable processing plants are non-existent, existing processing plants are inefficient or because of local ignorance of the value of the by-products.

Other, including unconventional, feeds

These include by-product feeds such as sugar and citrus molasses, brewery and distillery by-products like brewer's grains and fermented feeds. The latter are of some importance in certain regions of Southeast Asia.

There is at present in industrialized countries a very considerable interest in new sources of feed. Many of these 'new' feeds could be of value in the tropics.

The possibility now exists for plant breeders to breed plants that are more nutritious. An example is the breeding of high-lysine varieties of maize. Obviously this idea could be of the greatest interest in the tropics where new highly nutritious varieties of all types of crops are urgently required.

The use of waste faecal material for the culturing of chlorella is at present practised only in some countries in Asia, such as Taiwan. The chlorella can then be used as a protein concentrate for pig feeding (see Ch. 12, Pt II).

Possibilities for the processing and utilization of leaf protein or grass juice containing leaf protein are particularly promising in the humid tropics. The leaf protein concentrate with a CP of 60 to 70 per cent could be used for non-ruminant feeding while the discarded material could be used as a roughage for the feeding of ruminants. Readers with a particular interest in this unconventional feed should consult Pirie (1969).

The production of single-cell protein concentrates using specific yeasts from waste carbohydrate materials such as the contaminated flour from cereal processing mills or from paraffins or gas oil is slowly developing. The process that uses waste flour as a substrate produces a high-quality protein suitable for human consumption while that which uses paraffins or gas oil produces a 63 to 70 per cent CP concentrate suitable for feeding to pigs, poultry and calves. In tropical countries where there are by-product carbohydrate wastes or plentiful supplies of natural gas these new processes could be of value.

In the Philippines an edible yeast has been successfully cultured on coconut water, a product that is normally wasted at copra-processing plants. A protein of bacterial origin is already on the market in the United Kingdom.

New ideas are also now current as to how waste wood materials could be hydrolysed in order to break down the cellulose and lignin into feed products that could be digested by animals, and promising new and apparently economic methods are emerging. The possibilities for the utilization of these new methods in the tropics, both for the processing of waste wood in the wet tropics and straws in all regions of the tropics, are obviously immense. Readers who are particularly interested in this subject should consult Bender *et al.* (1970) and Heany and Bender (1970).

A protein known as 'pekiloprotein' obtained by the growth of a fungus on wood pulp substrate is at the pilot stage of production and may also offer considerable possibilities in the tropics.

Storage of feeds

The storage of all feeds is a very considerable problem in the tropics. Some information on the storage of forage as hay or silage is given in the next section of this chapter.

All feeds should be stored in dry, vermin-proof accommodation, in which air can circulate freely and where ambient temperatures can be kept as low as possible. Concentrate feed stores should be regularly treated with an insecticide. The normal method of treatment is fumigation. Protein concentrates are particularly liable to deterioration. The fats in them may undergo oxidative changes and become rancid, making the feed unpalatable. Fungal infection of some concentrate feeds can lead to the feed becoming toxic. This is particularly likely to occur in hot, humid climates.

Forage

It is estimated that 20 per cent of the world's surface is covered with planted pasture or fodder, range plants or some other form of forage.

Figure 1.5 provides some information on the world distribution of the principal plant associations and it can be seen that there is a considerable area of rangeland in the tropics, principally savanna, but also some steppe and desert scrub. In addition there are very large areas of grasslands occurring within other associations, such as the rain-forest or the undifferentiated highland regions.

At present about 10 per cent of man's global supply of food is produced from pasture or range while about 90 per cent comes from cropped land, though it is unlikely that man in the tropics obtains 10 per cent of his food from tropical pasture and range land. Quantitatively, therefore, the contribution of pasture and range to man's food supply is not large, though qualitatively it is important as animal products such as milk and meat have a high dietary value. The contribution of pasture and range to the feeding of man's domestic, ruminant livestock in the tropics is very great, as an extremely high proportion of them subsist on natural grazings. In the tropics, as elsewhere, man utilizes for his ruminant livestock land that cannot be used for any other purpose at the present time; broken hill country, swamps, semi-deserts and heavily leached soils of low fertility. There are some regions, however, such as northern South America and parts of Africa where man at present utilizes areas of good fertile soil as ruminant livestock range. As total population increases and demand for food rises it is inevitable that most of the fertile land now utilized as range will be cropped. In addition, by the drainage of swamps, the irrigation of semi-arid areas and the improvement of less fertile soils by the increasing use of fertilizers, even large areas now considered only economic for use as rough grazings will also be cultivated. Thus, it may be forecast with some confidence that the total area of range available for ruminant livestock in the tropics will diminish in the future.

This situation emphasizes the growing importance of making provision for alternative sources of feed for ruminant livestock. One major alternative is forage, considered as a crop. Forage may be produced from perennial or permanent pastures and/or fodder crops and trees, from short-term pastures or leys, from annual or catch-crop pastures and fodders, as a by-product of other crops such as cereals and pulses or in association with other crops such as fruit, nuts, oil palm and rubber.

Forage, and particularly pasture, could also be important in the cropped area as it could help to restore the fertility of soils that have been worn out by continuous cropping or used to maintain or even improve fertility by alternating it with crops in a rotation. The system of alternating forage with other crops is known as alternate husbandry and this could be a viable system in some tropical countries, particularly in the montane areas. The association of forage with other crops is known as 'integrated husbandry' and is particularly relevant to conditions in the humid tropics where, in the form of pasture, it can be associated with tree crops.

The reasons why forage crops, and particularly mixed forage crops such as pasture, are so useful are complex. The root system of grasses tends to bind the soil together, thus reducing the risk of erosion. At the same time it improves the physical condition or 'tilth' of the soil, adds humus and thus improves both fertility and water-retention properties. In addition, legumes in a pasture mixture will add to the total availability of nitrogenous plant foods in the soil, as bacteria in the nodules on their roots possess the facility to 'fix' nitrogen obtained from the air and make it available to other plants. Finally, the grazing animal returns organic matter to the soil in the form of faeces and its urine appears to possess some special plant growth-promoting properties.

Thus the soil, plant and animal are all components of a biological system that, when manipulated intelligently, can be used to maintain or even raise the fertility of most soils.

Types of forage

Natural grazings or range

Davies (1960) has suggested that major changes in the type and composition of the vegetation occur approximately at latitudes 30°N and S of the equator and that the area between could be conceived as the 'biological tropics'. One-half of the world's natural grazings are found within this area.

Climate, and in particular the total amount and the seasonal distribution of rainfall, is probably the most important factor affecting the use of land for natural grazings. Ranges occur most frequently in regions receiving from 250 to 2,000 mm (10 to 79 in) total rainfall per annum and less frequently in regions of lower and higher rainfall. Topography, soil and the occurrence of natural fires are also factors, but the other most important single factor is undoubtedly the influence of man. Very large areas of range have been derived from forest as the direct result of man's activities.

The major types of natural grazings in the tropics are those associated with rain-forest, dry woodlands, savanna, tropical steppe, semi-arid regions, montane areas, seasonally flooded land and permanent swamps. It is impossible in a brief account to list and describe all the forage species found in these areas, and only a selected few will be mentioned. Readers who have a special interest in specific forage plants or plant associations should consult such general texts as Whyte *et al.* (1953, 1959) and Whyte (1974), or specifically for Australia (Moore, 1970), Africa (Rattray, 1960), the Americas (Beard, 1944; Blydenstein, 1967) and Asia (Whyte, 1964, 1968; Dabadghao and Shankarnarayan, 1972).

Rain-forest grazings

These include evergreen equatorial, evergreen and semi-evergreen monsoonal forests and monsoonal deciduous forests. Annual rainfall in these forests is usually above 1,520 mm (60 in), but in some monsoonal regions moist deciduous forests occur in areas where the annual rainfall may be as low as 1,020 mm (40 in). In virgin forest grasses are either absent or extremely sparse. However, if the forest is clean cleared or 'slash-burn' agriculturists return too frequently to the same area, forest trees are replaced by a mixture of forage plants and shrubs. If these are then burnt annually neither necessarily regenerate and the forest is replaced by an ecologically unstable range association. On account of this process major forests have largely disappeared in the monsoonal regions; in particular the monsoonal deciduous forests are disappearing at an ever-accelerating rate in the equatorial regions of Southeast Asia, Africa and the Americas. Some of the dominant grasses found in grazings derived from these forests are: *Imperata cylindrica, Themeda trianda* (red oat grass), *Dichanthium* spp., *Schima* spp. and *Ischaemum* spp. in South Asia; *Imperata cylindrica* and *Ischaemum* spp. in Southeast Asia; *Andropogon* spp., *Digitaria* spp., *Hyparrhenia* spp., *Pennisetum purpureum* (elephant grass), *Ctenium newtonii* and *Imperata cylindrica* in Africa; *Axonopus* spp., *Bouteloua* spp., *Paspalum* spp., *Hyparrhenia* spp., *Imperata* spp. and *Panicum maximum* (guinea grass) in Central and South America; and *Axonopus compressus* (carpet grass) and guinea grass in the tropical oceanic islands.

Although there are some leguminous tree species in the rain-forests, herbaceous legumes appear to establish themselves rather slowly in the grass–bush associations that replace the forest on account of the activities of man. Nevertheless, conditions can be favourable for legumes as moisture may be more or less continuously available, so that ultimately a considerable number of legumes become established, although they may not make any major contribution to the total quantity of feed available. Commonly found are *Alisicarpus* spp., *Calapogonium* spp., *Centrosema* spp., *Crotalaria* spp., *Desmodium* spp., *Indigofera* spp., *Pueraria* spp. and *Stylosanthes* spp.

In those areas where tree crop plantations have replaced the rain-forest the spread of such legumes as *Calapogonium muconoides* (calapo), *Centrosema pubescens* (centro), *Pueraria phaseoloides* (puero) and *Stylosanthes guianensis* (stylo) has been encouraged by their use as ground cover beneath and between tree crops.

Dry woodland grazings

These occur in regions where the average annual rainfall is within the range 640 to 1,400 mm (25 to 55 in) and where there is a dry season of from 4 to 7 months' duration. The largest area of dry woodland in the tropics is found in Central and East Africa, where it is known as *miombo*. Somewhat similar associations are found in West Africa, Southeast Asia, Australia and Central and South America. In African *miombo* where the rainfall is within the range 890 to 1,400 mm (35 to 55 in) a low tree-high grass, *Combretum-Hyparrhenia* association is dominant, whereas where the rainfall is between 640 and 890 mm (25 and 35 in) trees of the genera *Brachystegia*, *Julbernardia* and *Isoberlinia* dominate, while the ground cover consists of a mixture of tall tussock and fine stoloniferous grass species. The grass cover may include *Hyparrhenia* spp., *Aristida* spp., *Eragrostis* spp. and *Cympobogon* spp.

Dry open woodlands of this type are relatively easily fired during the dry season with the consequence that large areas have been converted to savanna. Where these woodlands persist the relatively sparse ground cover is usually grazed.

Savanna grazings

Savanna is a collective term embracing many different types of open grasslands interspersed with trees. It may have developed as the result of climate or have been derived from rain-forest or dry woodlands. Continuous firing or periodic flooding of forest or dry woodlands may preclude the growth of the majority of trees so that they are replaced by a savanna association. It is often difficult to ascertain whether a specific savanna has developed as the result of natural causes or whether it is a result of the activities of man. In addition this confused situation is compounded by other grassland associations, such as those in the semi-arid thornbush areas or those in floodplains such as the *llanos* of Venezuela and Colombia, being often referred to as savanna.

At present, a major proportion of the range in the tropics may be termed savanna as associations of this type exist in areas where the annual rainfall varies from 508 to 1,520 mm (20 to 60 in), that is from the boundaries of the semi-arid regions to the rain-forest.

Consequently there are many types of savanna association, such as high tree/high grass, high tree/low grass, low tree/high grass and low tree/low grass. Those savannas where the trees are large and relatively well spaced are known as orchard savanna, while those where the trees are usually smaller and generally grouped in clusters are known as parkland savanna.

The grasses and legumes found in savanna are usually similar to those in the association from which the savanna has been derived or to adjacent associations. In general, ground legumes are scarce and the introduction of *Stylosanthes humilis* (Townsville stylo) has been very successful in improving the carrying capacity of many savannas.

Steppe and semi-arid thornbush grazings

Associations of this type are found in regions that generally receive 380 to 760 mm (15 to 30 in) or less rainfall per annum. They are found both within the tropics and more extensively immediately north and south of the tropics. Generally, tropical steppe is found at medium altitudes and semi-arid thornbush at lower altitudes. Thus, in East Africa tropical steppe associations occur at altitudes varying from 1,524 to 2,134 m

(5,000 to 7,000 ft) while semi-arid thornbush usually occurs at altitudes below 1,219 m (4,000 ft).

These are often rather unstable associations. Perennial grass species are rapidly replaced by annuals if tropical steppe is overgrazed, while there is a tendency for bush species to spread in the thornbush areas unless they are restrained by annual burning.

Perennial and annual grasses are medium to short in height, providing an open and sparse cover. Some of the dominant grasses are *Aristida* spp. *Cenchrus* spp., *Eragrostis* spp. and *Themeda* spp. Herbaceous legumes are scarce or absent. There are, however, large numbers of bush legume species in the semi-arid thornbush areas, particularly *Acacia* spp. and *Cassia* spp. in Africa and *Prosopis* spp. in the Americas. As a consequence browse provides a considerable proportion of the forage available for ruminant livestock, particularly in the dry season.

Where the mean annual rainfall is below 250 mm (10 in) the semi-arid thornbush associations merge into desert scrub and true desert. Perennial species disappear on the desert margins and are replaced by ephemerals that grow for a short period after rain.

Montane grazings

Evergreen and/or semi-evergreen tropical montane forests are found at altitudes ranging from 1,070 to 3,050 m (3,500 to 10,000 ft), depending upon the latitude and the climatic environment. Annual rainfall in these forests varies from 1,020 to 5,000 mm (40 to 200 in) and there may or may not be a dry season. In equatorial regions lowland tropical rain-forest gradually merges into humid montane forest, but in the drier tropics the montane forest may resemble a girdle encircling the higher altitude areas, with different ecological associations above and below. In these montane regions there are often tracts of open grasslands completely surrounded by forest. Grasslands of this type have probably been derived as the result of timber cutting and fire, but some may be the result of inadequate drainage. In addition there may be high-altitude natural grazing above the forest and below the snow line, usually at more than 3,050 m (10,000 ft) altitude. These grasslands are characterized by short grasses, few legumes and numerous low-growing herbs.

Grazings associated with montane forests are common in South and Southeast Asia. In Sri Lanka, where they are known as *wet patanas*, they are usually dominated by the grass *Chrysopogon zeylanicus*. In the montane areas of East Africa *Pennisetum clandestinum* (Kikuyu grass) and *Trifolium semipilosum* (Kenya wild white clover) are common in the wetter and more fertile areas, while in the drier areas the grasses *Pennisetum schimperi* and *Eleusine jaegeri* are common. *Loudetia simplex* is a common grass in the montane areas of Rhodesia.

High-altitude natural grazings are of major importance in South America where they are known as *paranas*.

Many temperate grass and legume species will of course thrive and naturalize in the montane regions.

Seasonally flooded and permanent swamp grazings

Where there is seasonal alternation of flooding with dry conditions, growth of trees may be restricted to slightly higher land on the banks of the rivers and streams, where they form 'gallery' forests, or to surrounding higher land. Natural climax grasslands result. In these regions there is normally abundant forage available as the flood waters recede, but it quickly dries out and becomes unpalatable. It is then often burnt to encourage regrowth. This alternation of flooding, drought and burning produces associations in which the species that survive are those that are resistant to flood, drought and fire.

There are very extensive areas of this type of range in South America, particularly in Colombia and Venezuela where they are known as *llanos*. Grasses of major importance in the *llanos* are *Paspalum* spp., *Trachypogon* spp. and *Leersia hexandra*. Smaller areas are also found in other regions of the tropical Americas. In Africa such ranges are found primarily in the Niger and Nile valleys, and around Lake Victora in Uganda and Lake Chad in West Africa where *Echinocloa* spp. are of importance, but smaller areas of the same general type of range are common in East Africa where they are known as *vleis* or *mbugni*. Many large areas are also found in Southeast Asia, particularly in the islands of Borneo and Sumatra and west of the dividing mountain range in eastern sub-tropical and tropical Australia.

Permanent swamps may be grazed on their margins for a part of the year. They are of importance if they can be used during the dry season in association with upland areas of range that are available during the wet season.

Cultivated pasture, fodder and browse

Three major types of cultivated pasture can be differentiated: permanent or perennial pastures, short-term pastures or leys and temporary or annual pastures.

Permanent or perennial pastures

These consist of associations of perennial grasses, with or without legumes and herbs, that are grazed year after year. They may be reseeded at intervals or renovated using a number of different techniques. They are characterized by a high productivity per unit area of land and they can possess a high annual stocking capacity. They are particularly suitably for dairying or for the fattening of livestock. At present there is only a limited area of permanent pasture in the tropics, concentrated mainly in Australia, the Americas, the oceanic islands and certain regions of the African and Asian humid tropics. There are, however, very considerable possibilities for the rapid development of perennial pastures in most wet tropical regions and in some monsoonal tropical regions, particularly in association with tree crops. Perennial pastures are not generally suited to the semi-arid and arid areas unless irrigation is available. When irrigation is available a single species forage crop may be grown. One example is the use of *Medicago* spp. (lucerne or alfalfa) grown under irrigation in the very dry but tropical region of southwest Arabia.

Some of the most suitable grasses to use in perennial pastures in the wet tropics are: *Brachiaria* spp. including *B. mutica* (para) and *B. brizantha* (signal), *Panicum* spp. including guinea, *Digitaria* spp. including *D. decumbens* (pangola), *Ischaemum* spp. and *Echinochloa polystachya* (Aleman). Elephant grass may also be used in perennial pastures, although it has to be managed very carefully. *Melinis minutaeflora* (molasses) and *Hyparrhenia rufa* (jarágua) are also sometimes planted, especially in the American tropics. *Cynodon plectostachyus* (African star grass) is increasingly used in the relatively drier regions of the wet tropics. *Paspalum* spp. are also of utility in specific regions. The major legumes used are centro, puero, calapo, stylo, *Desmodium* spp. such as *D. intortum*, *D. uncinatum* and *Macroptilium atropurpureum* (siratro). *Clitoria ternatea* has also shown promise in some regions. *Indigofera* spp. are widely distributed throughout the tropics and agronomically some species possess excellent characteristics. Unfortunately they contain toxic substances, and the plant breeders are now attempting to produce non-toxic strains. *Mimosa pudica* is also widely distributed throughout the wet tropics. In some countries it is considered a valuable component of pasture and in others a weed. *Aeschynomene americana* is useful in the wetter sub-tropics.

Short-term pastures or leys

These consist of associations of perennial grasses and/or legumes and other forage plants that are grown in rotation with cultivated crops. They may be grazed for from 2 to 5 or more years before they are ploughed and replaced by a crop. The advantage of this system is that the grass ley improves both the texture and the fertility of the soil, particularly if it consists partly of legume species. When the area is ploughed the crops that follow benefit and are more productive. After a few years' cropping, the ley is established once again.

Grass leys can be characterized by a very high level of productivity per unit area of land and are normally associated with high-level farming practices. They can be successful in those regions of the tropics only where it is practical to plant and plough-up pastures easily and where advantage can be taken of the inclusion of pasture in the rotation – that is in those climatic environments that are neither too wet nor too dry. They are usually not suitable for use in the wet or the semi-arid tropics. For example, Meiklejohn (1962) reported that grass leys ploughed up in Ghana did not, as would be expected, improve the yield of the following crops and he attributed this situation to the fact that there was a lack of nitrite-oxidizing bacteria in the soil. This managerial system is likely to be most successful in montane and some monsoonal tropical environments.

The species included in leys must establish easily and quickly and the grasses used must not be stoloniferous, or they will be difficult to eradicate during the cropping period of the rotation. As grass leys are particularly suited to the montane tropics, temperate-type grass and legume species can often be used.

Temporary or annual pastures

These are usually single-species grass, legume or other plants grown specifically as forage within a crop rotation. They are usually characterized by a high yield per unit area of land and a high cost per unit weight of forage compared with that produced from perennial pastures. In the wet tropics the major fodder used is one or the other strain of elephant grass, but *Saccharum* spp., *Sorghum* spp., *Panicum* spp. and *Tripsacum laxum* (Guatemala grass) are also used in specific areas. In the drier tropics the main fodder grasses are *Sorghum* spp. Legumes are not usually grown as annual crops for forage purposes, but certain annual pulses such as *Stizolobium* spp. (Mauritius or velvet bean) may be used for this purpose.

Cultivated browse

Wild trees and bushes, particularly the leguminous species, are a very important source of forage for livestock. They are of major importance in the dry tropics as many of them remain green long into the dry season after the ground vegetation has dried out and their leaves generally possess a high nutrient content. However, the number of trees and bushes specifically planted for forage production purposes is limited. As desirable browse species may be left intact when other bush is cleared it is often difficult to distinguish between cultivated and uncultivated browse.

In the drier regions of Australia the salt bushes *Atriplex* spp. and *Kochia aphylla* are important wild fodder species while *Leucaena leucocephala* is also an important forage, both cultivated and wild, in the oceanic Pacific islands. Roseveare (1948) listed 385 browse species that are utilized in the Americas. Some of these, such as *Gliricidia sepium*, are semi-cultivated as they are used for live fencing. In the drier areas of Africa a high percentage of the trees and shrubs are browsed to some extent by livestock and/or game; in East Africa the percentage is said to be as high as 75. Many trees are also lopped during the dry season (Plate 3.1), so that the leaf material on the branches can be eaten by small stock such as sheep and goats. *Acacia* spp. are particularly useful for this purpose and one species, *A. albida*, even if it is not now considered to be a cultivated plant, is believed to have been planted in the past. It is particularly useful as it remains green throughout the dry season. In the sahel and savanna regions of Africa the tree from which gum arabic is produced, *A. senegal*, is also useful as a browse tree. It might be possible

Plate 3.1   Stripping trees for fodder during the dry season in the African savanna (Dr N. C. Wright).

to integrate gum arabic with livestock production in these regions by planting *A. senegal* as a field hedge or in association with pasture. Browse from trees and bushes is also widely used for livestock feeding in South and Southeast Asia; the Commonwealth Agricultural Bureau (1947) listed ninety-one species that are used for browse in India and Sri Lanka.

Sesbania grandiflora is certainly widely cultivated for use as a browse tree, particularly in Indonesia. *Leucaena leucocephala* is also used everywhere that it grows wild and it is increasingly cultivated in Southeast Asia.

Management of forage

The principal objective in the management of both natural and planted forage should be to maintain, as far as is possible, maximum productivity on a year-round basis of the more desirable species with the intention of obtaining maximum production from the livestock that consume them. The principal problem is an imbalance between forage availability and livestock requirements that is worse on natural than on planted grazings and in dry compared with wet climatic environments. In order to attempt to attain the objective and mitigate the problem the livestock owner must manipulate the complex ecological factors that are involved (Fig. 3.3) to

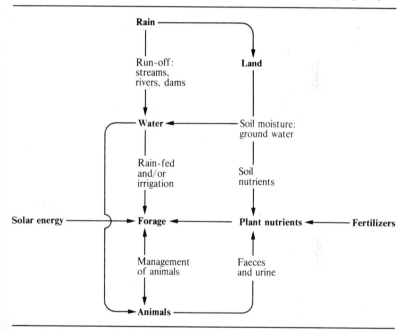

Fig. 3.3   Diagrammatic representation of the major ecological factors involved in forage production.

best advantage. Methods by which the ecological complex can be most economically manipulated will obviously vary from region to region. It is our intention, therefore, to consider some of the more important factors involved in the production of forage under extensive and intensive managerial conditions.

Natural grazings

Natural grazings often provide the only major source of forage available (Plate 3.2). They are often, but not always, the most economical source

Plate 3.2   Nomadic cattle herded on natural grazings in Africa (Shell Photographic Unit).

of forage. The problems of managing extensive natural grazings vary widely from the wet to the semi-arid and arid tropics. In an introduction, however, it is only possible to provide a general outline of managerial requirements.

Rain-forest grazings

Associated grazings, with few exceptions such as the natural stands of elephant grass in Africa, are usually of low productivity. It is often economic to replace them by planted pastures and fodder crops or with integrated tree-crop pastures. The productivity of the *Imperata* spp. grasslands that are so common in Southeast Asia may be improved by the introduction of a legume. The legume generally recommended is stylo. Once the introduced legume has improved the fertility of the soil, improved grasses can be introduced.

Dry woodland grazings

These grazings are only moderately productive. When the available species are young they are readily eaten by livestock, but they soon become rank, unpalatable and of low nutrient quality. The density of the grazings can be improved by thinning of the trees and coarse grasses and bushes can be controlled by the judicious use of fire. In general, the length and severity of the dry season precludes the use of cultivated pasture in these regions.

Savanna, steppe and semi-arid thornbush grazings

These are often unstable associations under grazing conditions. Many of them are dominated by coarse grasses that are palatable and nutritious only when they are very young. If ungrazed they dry out to form low-quality 'standing hay'. There is a general tendency for the grazings to be invaded by shrubs and this is encouraged by the exclusion of fire and by overgrazing. Thus the judicious use of fire is an important managerial tool. In Africa, bush invasion may not only reduce the total availability of forage but may also encourage the spread of the tsetse fly. As total annual rainfall decreases and the dry season lengthens the ground cover may become very sparse, perhaps forming only 5 per cent of the total area, and perennials are replaced by annuals. Supplies of free water may also become very limited, particularly in the dry season, so that livestock may have to travel long distances between watering points.

In some of the savanna areas that are derived from forest and in other areas where rainfall is regular, planted pasture and forage crops may be economic. This is not usually the case in the tropical steppe or semi-arid thornbush areas. The potential and actual carrying capacities are therefore very varied – quite high in the most favoured savanna regions and very low in the semi-arid thornbush regions.

Montane grazings

The productivity of these ranges may be relatively high, but of course it varies with the total and seasonal incidence of rainfall, the fertility of the soil and the species available. High rainfall often causes leaching and increases the acidity of the soils. This is the situation in Sri Lanka where montane pastures require regular applications of lime and other fertilizers. Even if productivity is quite high on the natural range it is often economic to plant pastures and fodder crops in these areas and to practise ley farming.

Seasonally flooded and permanent swamp grazings

Where the grazing of these during the dry season can be combined with the grazing of upland range during the wet season a relatively stable managerial system can be established. There are often many nutritious and palatable perennial forage plants in these ecological associations and if they are properly managed the stocking rate can be quite high. However, uncontrolled grazing will eliminate the superior grasses in seasonally flooded areas. This is essentially what has happened in the *llanos* of Colombia and Venezuela.

Livestock management on natural grazings

Choice of livestock. On unimproved ranges indigenous livestock are likely to thrive better than exotic. In the wet tropics *Bos* (*Bibos*)-type cattle such as the Bali may be particularly valuable. In dry and semi-arid areas Zebu or crossbred Zebu cattle are likely to thrive best. In the tsetse fly infested areas of Africa, trypanosomiasis-tolerant cattle such as the N'dama and the Dwarf Shorthorn must be used. In 'high grass' regions cattle will thrive better than sheep, whereas on 'short grass' ranges sheep will usually thrive better than cattle. In the arid areas goats, sheep and camels will thrive better than cattle. In seasonally flooded and swamp areas water buffalo probably thrive better than cattle. In the montane areas temperate-type livestock can be utilized, while on the highest altitude ranges the llamoids of South America possess special advantages.

It is likely that on most range areas it is a desirable managerial practice to herd two or three different species at the same time. For example, in unstable ecotypes where bush easily replaces grasses a mixed population of cattle and goats may be more satisfactory than grazing either goats or cattle alone. The value of goats under these circumstances has in the past been demonstrated at Mpwapa in Tanzania (Staples *et al.*, 1942). In very dry areas and particularly in those where free water is very scarce wild game may be more productive than domestic livestock (see Ch. 11, Pt II).

Fencing and/or herding. Control of livestock by fencing or herding is as important on range as on planted pasture. Enclosure by fencing is usually more desirable than herding if it is economically viable, but herding is still the main method of controlling livestock on tropical ranges (Plate 3.2). The essential factor is that the livestock should be controlled so that they never graze out all the desirable species, i.e. overgraze. In general, short grasses will withstand some degree of overgrazing better than the tall grasses.

Shade. This is desirable at certain times of the year for almost all types of livestock. Under range conditions shade may or may not be available, depending upon the ecotype that is grazed.

Water. The control of water resources is an essential managerial tool on range. All man-made watering points should be adequately fenced and be subject to overall managerial control. The water requirements of range livestock have been given in a previous section.

Stocking rates. In practice, stocking rates are often too low on range in the wet tropics and invariably too high on range in the dry tropics. As a consequence vast quantities of dry matter are burnt annually and therefore wasted in the wetter areas, while the vegetative cover of the overstocked dry ranges steadily deteriorates both in quantity and in quality. It is now considered by some authorities that chronic overgrazing, resulting in radical changes in the vegetative cover of the range, may so modify the local climate as to cause a decrease in annual rainfall, thus hastening further deterioration of the vegetative cover of the range. What is certain is that badly degraded range recovers very slowly, even after overgrazing ceases.

In the wet tropics stocking rates can be based on the year-round carrying capacity, but in the dry tropics, particularly within enclosed areas such as ranches, they must be based on the dry season carrying capacity. It would be expected that, other conditions being equal, the stocking rates could be somewhat higher under nomadic and transhumant managerial systems where the livestock essentially rotate over vast areas of range.

In assessing the livestock-carrying capacity of a grazing it is usual to express it in terms of the number of livestock units (LSUs) that can be carried by a unit area of the grazing for one year. The LSU denotes a standard liveweight of animal and this standard may vary from country to country, but it is usually within the limits of 300 to 500 kg (660 to 1,100 lb). In order to be able to convert all species of livestock to the same common unit FAO (1974) have used the conversion factors detailed in Table 3.14. These conversion units are recommended for general use.

Table 3.14   *Livestock unit (LSU) conversion factors*

Species	Factor
Camel	1·1
Buffaloes, horses, mules	1·0
Cattle, asses	0·8
Pigs	0·2
Sheep, goats	0·1

Note: The number of the species involved are multiplied by the above factor to obtain the conversion factor, i.e. 100 sheep equal 100×0.1 LSU or 10 LSU.
Source: FAO (1974).

Within any species or type of livestock similar factors can be used to convert the average liveweight of all classes of stock to the common LSU. An example of such a conversion is given in Table 3.15.

Supplementation.   To obtain maximum productivity on range some form of supplementation of the feed supply during the dry season is usually essential. The form that this supplementation should take will depend on

Table 3.15   *An example of the conversion of the average liveweights of different classes of the same species to a common livestock unit (LSU)*

Baggara cattle in southern Darfur, Sudan

Class of cattle	LSU equivalent	
	Males	Females
Calves	0·25	0·25
Weaners and yearlings	0·34	0·34
2–2½ years old	0·80	0·75
2½–3¼ years old	1·00	} 1·00
3¼–4 years old		

Source: Hunting Technical Services (1974).

local ecological and economic factors. Supplementation is dealt with in some detail in the specific chapters concerned with the management of different types of livestock, in Part II of this text.

Other aspects of the management of natural grazings

Forage species utilized.   Although the species that are present are those that have of necessity to be utilized, overall management can influence the type of species grazed by encouraging the desirable at the expense of the undesirable. Overgrazing must be avoided, as must the encroachment of undesirable bush species.

Use of fertilizers.   In all except exceptional cases the use of fertilizers on range forage is likely to be uneconomic. Phosphatic fertilizers may, however, be used under certain circumstances to encourage the growth of oversown legumes. Such managerial practices are most likely to be economic on wet tropical ranges.

Control of bush and weeds.   Mechanical or chemical methods of control are unlikely to be economic except in favoured areas. These are more likely to be in the wet tropics or in some derived savanna regions. In the drier tropics the only economic method of bush control is probably burning and, under special circumstances, biological control.

Burning is a very controversial practice. It is condemned by most foresters, although controlled burning is at present used to clear undergrowth in the coniferous forests of the southern United States, and by the soil conservationists. Nevertheless, it is often the only economic method of controlling bush and weeds on range land.

The major objection to burning is that it wastes organic matter in the soil, particularly if the fire is very hot, and that this encourages erosion. It also kills young trees that may be required for shade, destroys fences and encourages the proliferation of fire-resistant bush species that may not be suitable for browse. These objections may be overcome if the burning is conducted with intelligence and foresight.

In the wet tropics the burn should always be made before the period of major growth. This ensures that the burnt area will quickly be covered with vegetation, thus minimizing the risk of extensive erosion. Precautions should always be taken to see that proper fire-breaks are cut or burnt and fires should not be started when there is a high wind. In order to get a good burn, particularly in the dry tropics, the livestock should be removed from the area to be burnt many months before the burn, so that there will be a dense mat of vegetation that will carry the burn.

Controlled and uncontrolled burning is practised in all tropical regions and the growth of some very desirable species can be encouraged by this practice. For example, in East Africa the dominance of the desirable red oat grass is strongly favoured by burning and in the Pacific islands grasses become dominant in *Psidium guayana* (guava)-infested hill pastures if they are closed and burnt for 2 or 3 successive years. If burning is to be successful it must be accompanied by an intelligent stocking policy. It is of little use to destroy one weed only to replace it by others.

The most spectacular instance of the biological control of bush has been the control of *Opuntia* spp. (prickly pear) in Australia. In 1920 this plant covered some 24 million ha (60 million acres) of fertile soils. In 1926–27 the large-scale distribution of the insect *Cactoblastis cactorum*, whose caterpillars live on the prickly pear, began and the insect established itself so rapidly that by the end of 1931 the bulk of the prickly pear had been destroyed. Mopping-up operations included the introduction of other insect pests and conventional control methods. The prickly pear was completely destroyed in 7 years.

It is unlikely that this spectacular demonstration of biological control can easily be repeated elsewhere, but biological control methods might be used to reduce and weaken invading bush species. The whole subject must of course be approached with the greatest caution.

Cultivated pastures and fodder crops

Although it has been widely demonstrated that grazed forage is the cheapest feed for ruminant livestock and that natural grasslands are necessarily relatively low yielding while cultivated forage can yield more nutrients per unit area than any other crop, the concept of treating forage as a crop is, in general, still a novel idea in the tropics. This is understandable for the following reasons:

- Cultivated forage is generally only practicable and economic in the equatorial, monsoonal and medium-altitude tropics. Without irrigation, the cultivation of forage in the drier tropics is difficult and yields do not usually justify necessary inputs.
- Cultivation requires increased expenditure and the majority of

peasant farmers in the tropics cannot afford to invest in crops that do not provide a direct cash or subsistence return.

● In many regions where forage could be cultivated existing population pressure is intense and is increasing. The average size of holding is very small and often all available land must be used for the production of crops for direct human consumption.

● The cultivation and subsequent utilization of forage require a higher degree of managerial sophistication than the average peasant farmer at present possesses.

● Even if farmers wished to cultivate forage, in most tropical regions there is a lack of knowledge of the most suitable species to use and of satisfactory methods of establishment and management.

● It is often pointless to improve forage productivity unless superior types of livestock can be made available to utilize the improved forage. They are not usually available and in addition the lack of organization of the livestock industry often mitigates against the economic marketing of any additional output of animal products.

Establishment

As the establishment of cultivated pastures is necessarily expensive it is important that it should be carried out as economically and efficiently as possible. Some of the major factors involved are as follows:

Choice of species.   There are virtually no forage species that grow equally well in all tropical environments and even subtle differences in the environment can exert major influences on the growth of the forage species. Generally, pure grass stands can be made more productive than mixtures, but they are often less economic as they require more fertilizer and normally exhibit a more seasonal productivity.

Choice is of course limited by the availability of seed and/or vegetative planting material. The introduction and testing of a large number of forage species are only now beginning in many tropical countries and the most suitable species may not be everywhere available.

If seed or vegetative planting material is freely available then it is important that the forage selected should be high yielding in the specific environment in which it is to be used. Palatability and nutritive value are not so important, as these factors depend primarily on the way in which the forage is managed. Species that produce viable seed are obviously to be preferred to species that have to be propagated vegetatively. The way in which the forage is ultimately to be managed is also of some importance as particular species may be more suitable for cutting than for grazing or vice versa. Topography must also be taken into consideration, as on flat areas mechanization of harvesting may be easy and drainage difficult, while on steep slopes drainage may be easy and mechanization difficult. For grazing species, persistency is important, but if the species is used in a ley it must not be difficult to eradicate. In the wet and dry or the semi-arid tropics species must be able to persist through the long dry seasons.

A list of some of the grass species that may be used in planted pastures in different environments is provided in Table 3.16. Legumes should also be included in planted pastures as at the same stage of growth they normally possess a higher nutrient content than grasses, often possess a different growth cycle, add variety to the diet of grazing animals and, most important, they fix atmospheric nitrogen that eventually becomes available to other plants in the pasture association (Plates 3.3 and 3.4).

Some doubts have been expressed in the past as to the value and efficiency of tropical legumes in symbiotic nitrogen fixation. It is now believed, however, that the comparatively poor results obtained in the past have been due in part to the use of unsuitable species and rhizobium

Table 3.16 *Some grass species that may be used for planted pastures in different tropical environments*

Environment	Common name	Species	Notes
Humid tropics (this includes the monsoonal areas of the tropics)	Elephant or Napier	*Pennisetum purpureum*	Very erect plant with a deep root system
	Para	*Brachiaria mutica*	Also suitable for seasonally flooded land
In general, those grasses listed first will withstand higher rainfall conditions	Signal	*Brachiaria brizantha*	
		Brachiaria decumbens	Forms a dense sward
	Pangola	*Digitaria decumbens*	Stoloniferous
		Ischaemum aristatum	
	Guinea	*Panicum maximum*	Many different varieties
	Jaragua	*Hyparrhenia rufa*	A rather coarse fodder
	Molasses	*Melinis minutiflora*	
	African star or giant star	*Cynodon plectostachyus*	Very suitable for the drier areas of the humid tropics
		Dichanthium caricosum	A good hay grass
		Digitaria pentzii	
	Bermuda or Coastal Bermuda, etc.	*Cynodon dactylon*	Many different varieties
		Setaria splendida	
Seasonally flooded regions	Aleman	*Echinocloa polystachya*	
		Echinocloa pyramidalis	
		Leersia hexandra	
		Panicum repens	

Table 3.16 – *continued*

Environment	Common name	Species	Notes
Dry tropics	Buffel	*Cenchrus ciliaris*	A very great diversity of types
	Rhodes	*Chloris gayana*	Some varieties more stoloniferous than others
		Andropogon gayanus	A good hay grass
	Makarikari	*Panicum coloratum*	Very drought resistant
	Columbus	*Sorghum alnum*	Tall and erect with strong rhizomes
	Sabi	*Urochloa mosambicensis*	Mat-forming species
		Eragrostis curvula	Very drought resistant
Montane tropics	Nandi setaria	*Setaria sphacelata*	A great diversity of forms
		Phalaris tuberosa	
	Kikuyu	*Pennisetum clandestinum*	
	Dallis	*Paspalum dilatatum*	
	Bahia	*Paspalum notatum*	
	Many temperate-zone species		

Note: No attempt has been made to detail all the available and suitable species but only those that are well known and continuously used.

Plate 3.3   Jamaican Red Poll cattle grazing good enclosed pastures.

Plate 3.4   Close-up of a productive grass/legume pasture: *Panicum maximum* (guinea) and *Centrosema pubescens* (centro).

(inoculant) strains, doubtful fertilizer practices and unsatisfactory management. It has been conclusively demonstrated that suitable tropical legumes can fix considerable quantities of readily available nitrogen. Bryan (1962) stated that in grass–legume mixtures in tropical Australia, *Stylosanthes bojeri*, *Desmodium uncinatum* and *Indigofera spicata* yielded 114, 180 and 264 kg per ha (101, 161 and 235 lb per acre) of nitrogen per annum respectively, while Moore (1962) stated that in the humid, tropical region of Nigeria centro in a 2-year-old centro-African star grass mixture yielded 279 kg per ha (250 lb per acre) of nitrogen and that the nitrogen content of the African star grass was raised from 1·8 per cent in a pure stand to 2·4 per cent in the grass–legume mixture. Henzell *et al.* (1966) have shown that in Australia a 4-year-old stand of *Leucaena leucocephala* yielded 578 kg per ha (515 lb per acre) of nitrogen per annum while Townsville stylo yielded 109 kg per ha (96 lb per acre). A

Table 3.17   *Some legume species that may be used for planted pastures in different tropical environments*

Environment	Common name	Species	Notes
Humid tropics	Calopo	*Calopogonium muconoides*	A trailing species; not very palatable
In general, those legumes listed first will with-stand higher rainfall conditions and higher ambient temperatures	Centro	*Centrosema pubescens*	A trailing species; palatable when young
		Desmodium heterophyllum	Wide distribution in natural pastures
	Silver-leaf desmodium	*Desmodium uncinatum*	A sprawling plant
	Green-leaf desmodium	*Desmodium intortum*	A sprawling plant
	Puero	*Pueraria phaseoloides*	A trailing species; not very palatable
	Stylo	*Stylosanthes guyanensis*	Four major varieties in Australia
	Siratro	*Macroptilium atropurpureum*	
		Lucaena leucocephala	A small tree; many different varieties
		Glycine wightii	Three major varieties in Australia
		Lotononis bainesii	Can also be used in montane areas
		Dolichos axillaris	A trailing species
		Desmodium uniflora	An annual species
		Phaseolus aureus	An annual species
		Vigna sinensis	An annual species
Seasonally flooded regions	Phasey bean	*Phaseolus lathyroides*	Does well on heavy soils; an annual
Dry tropics	Townsville stylo	*Stylosanthes humilis*	A profuse seeder; annual
		Stylosanthes hamida	
		Dolichos lablab	An annual
	Pigeon pea	*Cajanus cajan*	Normally used as a food crop
	Lucerne or alfalfa	*Medicago sativa*	Grows well in arid areas with irrigation and some light shade
	Berseem	*Trifolium alexandrinum*	
Montane tropics	White clover	*Trifolium repens*	Grows well when adequate moisture is available
	Kenya wild white clover	*Trifolium semipilosum*	

Note: No attempt has been made to detail all the available and suitable species but only those that are well known and commonly used.

list of legumes that may be used in different environments is provided in Table 3.17.

Choice of land.   Development should proceed in accordance with a plan and the best land should be improved first, as the return on a given investment is likely to be higher on good rather than poor land.

Land preparation.   Cultivated pastures must be treated as a crop and the land prepared accordingly. For seeded pastures the soil should be weed free and consolidated, but the tilth should not be too fine as this may cause 'packing' of the soil once it rains. Where species are to be planted vegetatively the tilth can be rougher.

There are areas of rain-forest, for example in the Amazon basin in South America, where the soils are so poor that after felling the forest and 1 or 2 years' cropping the only possible economic crop is forage. Under these conditions grass and legume seeds should be oversown in the first or second crop or vegetative material planted by hand between the tree stumps. Often the forest should never be felled in such regions.

Time of planting.   It is very important to obtain a good plant cover as quickly as possible. This will occur only if the soil moisture level remains high for several weeks after planting. For rain-fed areas planting should normally take place at the beginning of the rainy season. Where irrigation is available there may be advantage in planting in the middle of the dry season so that a very clean seedbed can be obtained.

In the wet tropics it can be advantageous to sow beneath a nurse crop. If the latter is maize the row spacing should be 1·8 to 2·1 m (6 to 7 ft). There are normally no advantages in planting beneath a nurse crop in the drier areas.

Method of planting.   When using vegetative material the nursery should be sited close to the planting area, and provision must be made for a sufficient quantity of planting material. It has been calculated, for example, that 0·5 ha (1·2 acres) of guinea grass spaced at 50 × 50 cm (20 × 20 in) provides sufficient planting material for 12 to 15 ha (30 to 37 acre) of land if each parent plant is split into four tufts.

There are three major methods of vegetative planting:

1. Using tufted grasses such as guinea the crown of the parent plant can be split. These 'splits' can be 'dibbled' into the ground and consolidated by trampling. It is very difficult to mechanize this operation successfully.
2. In the case of tall, upright fodder grasses such as elephant and Guatemala, short lengths of cane, each with at least two nodes, can be pushed into the ground or the operation can be partially

mechanized by laying lengths of cane in furrows and covering them
with soil in the same way as sugar cane is planted.
3. With stoloniferous or rhizomatous species such as African star grass,
   para or pangola, cuttings can be distributed in plough furrows or
   spread on and disced into the soil. This is a very suitable method to
   employ where irrigation is available and the operation can be completely mechanized.

If seed can be used and it is normally preferable to use seed,
particularly in the drier areas, it may be either broadcast by hand or
sown through a fertilizer distributor or a special seed drill. Viability tests
should be made with the seed before sowing. Seeding rates must be higher
when the seed is broadcast than when it is drilled. Drilling should be
shallow. Very hard legume seeds may require scarification or some other
special treatment before sowing and they should always be treated with
the correct inoculant.

Management during the early stages of growth

Weed control.   This is essential in the early stages of establishment and
is assisted by good land preparation prior to planting.

Weeds may be controlled by chemical methods: either pre-emergence
sprays such as paraquat before the grass is planted or post-emergence
sprays. The latter cannot be normally used where legumes have been
planted. Chemical weed control is usually expensive.

In general, an early mowing to prevent the first weeds flowering, followed by systematic hand or spot-chemical weeding, is likely to be the
most economic form of weed control.

Grazing control.   Early grazing is almost always desirable where
stoloniferous or rhizomatous species are used. Where tufted species are
used in drier areas, too early grazing may result in the animals pulling
out the young plants. In the equatorial and wetter monsoonal areas tufted
species can be grazed quite soon after planting as grazing encourages
them to produce more leaf.

Use of fertilizers.   Farmers should understand something of the fertilizer
requirements of their pastures and fodder crops and if a service is available soil samples from the fields should be taken and analysed. Potash,
phosphate and lime, if considered necessary, should be applied before
planting and nitrogen soon after planting. Phosphatic fertilization is often
essential for the proper growth of legumes and in some regions additional
sulphur may be required. For example, sulphur deficiencies have been
reported in pastures in Uganda and in the Trans-Nzoia area of Kenya.
Lime is not as essential for legume growth in the tropics as it is in the
temperate zone. Heavy nitrogen applications may be economic on fodder
crops but are unlikely to be economic on most planted pastures. As

suggested in a previous paragraph the use of legumes in a pasture mixture should reduce the need for nitrogenous fertilizers. There is now some evidence that certain tropical grass species, such as guinea, can also fix atmospheric nitrogen under certain specific conditions, so that the choice of grass species to be utilized may become of major importance.

Management after full establishment

The aim of the farmer, once he has established cultivated pastures, should be to obtain the maximum quantity and quality of feed from them, to reduce their seasonality of production, to maintain them in a productive state for as long a time as is possible and to ensure the efficient utilization of the forage obtained from them.

Production of the maximum quantity and quality of forage. Dry matter yield of forage per unit area depends upon the species utilized, the amount of solar radiation, the availability of soil moisture and plant nutrients and the method of management. The choice of species has already been discussed in a previous paragraph.

The amount of solar radiation depends upon the total number of hours of sunshine and the cloud cover, etc. Total radiation per annum is almost always higher in the tropics than in the mid-latitude regions and it is usually much higher in the dry than in the wet tropics.

Availability of soil moisture depends upon the total annual rainfall, its seasonality and repeatability and the type of soil. Soils with a high organic matter content normally hold water better than soils with a low organic matter content. In the drier tropics soil moisture content will be a limiting factor in pasture growth for a greater or lesser period during the year, but in the humid tropics it may limit growth for only relatively short periods. If irrigation is economically feasible, then availability of soil moisture ceases to be a limiting factor.

The availability of plant nutrients other than water depends on the inherent fertility of the soil and the rate at which nutrients in the soil become available to the plant. The latter depends on many factors, including the rate at which nutrients are leached out of the soil and the quantities returned to the soil by the grazing animals.

In general, tropical soils are not inherently very fertile, but there are exceptions. Grazed forages certainly require less fertilizer than continuously cut forages. The amount of nutrients removed by grazing animals depends upon their productivity. Approximately 80 per cent of the nitrogen, phosphate and potash consumed by animals are excreted, but much of the excreted nitrogen in the urine and faeces is lost in a tropical environment (Smith, 1965). Even if considerable quantities of nutrients are returned to the soil by grazing animals there is a problem of the poor distribution of excreta on the pasture. This can be improved by an occasional harrowing.

Very large quantities of nutrients may be removed when pastures or

fodders are continuously cut. Vicente-Chandler *et al.* (1964) have produced data (Table 3.18) from Puerto Rico that dramatically demonstrate
this effect.

Table 3.18   *The effect of cutting forage on the removal of nutrients from the soil*

Yield of DM per annum (kg/ha (lb/acre))	Quantity of nutrients removed per annum (kg/ha (lb/acre))				
	Nitrogen	Phosphate	Potassium	Calcium	Magnesium
24,423 (21,800)	314 (281)	52 (46)	408 (363)	119 (105)	79 (70)

Source: Vicente-Chandler *et al.* (1964)

The principal nutrient required by tropical grasses is nitrogen. The
extent to which it is economic to utilize nitrogenous fertilizers depends
upon many factors, not the least being the cost of the nitrogenous
fertilizer. Very detailed experiments have been conducted by Vicente-
Chandler *et al.* (1964) on the response of various tropical grasses to
nitrogen application in Puerto Rico. They found that at the time that the
experiments were conducted molasses grass gave an economic response
when nitrogen was used at the rate of 224 kg per ha (200 lb per acre),
while guinea, para and pangola gave economic responses at the rate of
448 kg per ha (400 lb per acre) and elephant grass at the rate of 896 kg
per ha (800 lb per acre). They also found that the greatest response
occurred when grasses were cut at infrequent intervals, that there was no
advantage gained in splitting the nitrogen application into more than six
parts to be applied in any one year and that the response was greatest in
the 'flush' growth period, thus increasing the seasonality of production.
Irrigation in the drier areas improved the response of the grass to
nitrogen application (Table 3.19).

However, the application of nitrogen to grass–legume mixtures suppresses legume growth. Grasses respond more rapidly than legumes to

Table 3.19   *The effect of irrigation on the DM yield of guinea grass* (Panicum maximum)
fertilized with nitrogen

Total N per annum (kg/ha (lb/acre))	DM yield of guinea grass per annum (kg/ha (lb/acre))	
	Without irrigation	With irrigation
0 (0)	10,883 (9,710)	18,168 (16,210)
225 (200)	13,830 (12,340)	31,664 (28,250)
447 (400)	14,223 (12,690)	42,290 (37,730)

Source: Vicente-Chandler *et al.* (1964).

the nitrogen and the legumes in the mixture suffer from the effect of shading and increased competition for root space, soil moisture and other nutrients. It is possible that creeping legumes such as centro are not so badly affected as those with more upright growth habits.

Under certain circumstances the application of phosphatic fertilizer is essential for the proper growth of legumes. Such action can also raise the phosphorus content of grasses with consequent advantage to the grazing animals in phosphate-deficient areas. Vicente-Chandler *et al.* (1964) recommended the annual application of 74 kg per ha (65 lb per acre) on grasses that are continuously cut and heavily fertilized with nitrogen in the wet tropics.

On grazed pastures animal urine returns potash to the soil, but where grass is heavily fertilized with nitrogen and continuously cut Vicente-Chandler *et al.* (1964) recommended applications of potash.

The response of tropical grass and legume species to applications of lime has been negligible, although lime may be essential under specific circumstances.

Whenever heavy fertilizer applications are used trace elements may also be required.

The method of management depends to a very large extent on the way the forage is to be utilized. Species that are to be continuously grazed should be spaced closer than species that are to be cut, and tufted species require a closer spacing than rhizomatous or stoloniferous species. The manner in which the pasture is cut or grazed determines to a consider-able extent the amount of leaf material present at any one time. Most tropical pastures should be managed so that their average height is some-what above that of similar pastures in the temperate zone. They can be controlled, even when grazed, by the judicious use of the mower. This can prevent flowering, encourage tillering, remove coarse, unpalatable growth and help in the control of weeds.

Reduction in the seasonality of production.   There is not only a problem of seasonality in the growth and total dry matter production but also of variation in nutritive value owing to the effect of the season on matura-tion of the species. Some managerial practices that may reduce seasonality in the quantity and quality of forage are as follows:

1. The well-planned application of fertilizers. These should not be applied during the 'flush' season but before the major growing season begins and perhaps again towards its end.
2. The conservation of excess forage during the 'flush' season and the use of the conserved material at other times. This cannot be achieved without some loss of potential nutrients. This loss has been estimated to average about 25 per cent of the total conserved nutrients. Details of methods of conservation are given in a later section.
3. The implementation of seasonal livestock-breeding programmes so

that the total animal demand for feed achieves a peak at approximately the same time as forage growth is maximal (Fig. 3.4).

4. The use of grass–legume mixtures rather than pure stands of grass. The peak growth of a grass–legume mixture is likely to be somewhat less than that of a pure stand of grass. Generally legumes grow and mature more slowly than grasses so that not only is the overall nutritive value of the grass–legume mixture superior to all except the youngest pure grass stands, but the nutritive value remains higher for a much longer period. Legumes also tend to be deeper rooted than

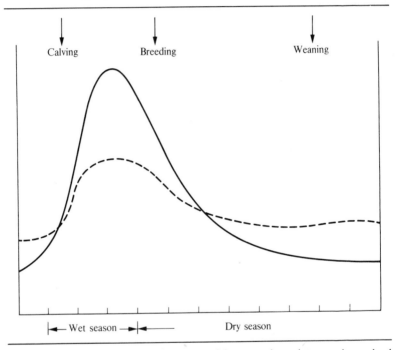

Fig. 3.4 Schematic illustration of a managerial system that relates maximum herd demand for forage to the period of maximum forage production (——— total forage production per unit area; - - - - - herd demand for forage).

grasses and continue to grow in the early stages of a dry season long after their companion grasses have ceased growth.

5. The use of pure stands of legume that could be grazed alternatively with grasses. Under certain environmental conditions this might be an alternative to normal mixed grazings.

6. The use of legume browse in drier areas. Many legume bushes and trees in the dry areas will produce high-quality browse during the dry season. The possibility of the integration of browse production into forage production systems in the dry tropics has not yet been fully investigated.

7. The intensification of weed control during the period of maximum growth. At this time frequent cutting for weed control could have a minimal effect on the growth of the desirable forage species.
8. The use of irrigation.

Maintenance of production. This depends primarily on choice of suitable species and their subsequent management with particular reference to the management of the animals that graze them.

Efficient utilization of forage by livestock. This depends upon the proportion of the total forage grown that is consumed and the efficiency with which the consumed forage is converted into milk, meat or energy for work purposes in the animal's body. Major factors that affect the efficiency of utilization are as follows:

1. *Type of livestock used.* This factor has been discussed in a previous section with reference to the most suitable type of livestock for use on range grazings. Obviously it will depend upon the climatic environment, the type of agriculture practised, the relative demand for different animal products and the species and breeds available. In general, as nutrition should be generally superior on planted pasture to that on natural grazings, it should be possible to use more productive types of livestock on planted pasture.
2. *Palatability of the forage.* Palatability and quality as expressed by digestibility and nutritional value depend upon the species used, the climatic environment and the method and age of utilization. Young forage is always more palatable than older forage, with a higher crude protein and mineral content and a lower crude fibre content. Young forage is not only more palatable, but because its fibre content is relatively low, consumption of large quantities produces less of a 'heat load' on the animal, with the consequence that the animal can increase its intake.

   Thus livestock eat more feed when it is highly palatable even in a tropical climatic environment. However, the availability of forage may determine the level of intake as the total quantity available per animal decreases as the stocking rate increases. At any one grazing it is essential that livestock should eat a high proportion of the forage available so that there will be a minimum quantity of mature forage in the regrowth, as increasing quantities of mature forage reduce the quality of the forage available for the next grazing. In order to ensure that livestock do eat a high proportion of the available forage, the stocking rate must be high and the livestock must graze closely and evenly. However, under these managerial conditions individual animal intake may decline. Therefore if grazing intensity is increased, production per unit area will increase for a time because of the increase in the stocking rate (Fig. 3.5), but the increase in total output is ulti-

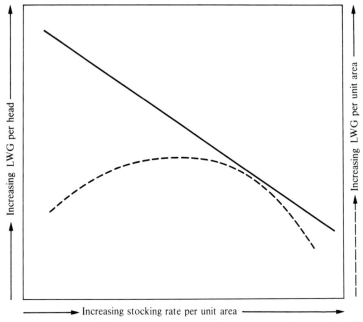

Fig. 3.5   Diagrammatic illustration of the relationship between stocking rate, individual animal productivity and total productivity per unit area (———— LWG per head; - - - - - LWG per unit area).

mately achieved at the expense of a decrease in output of the individual animal. This inherent contradiction in practice is a major problem in assuring the most effective utilization of forage in any climatic environment.

3. *Methods of management of the livestock.* These are discussed in detail in the chapters concerned with specific types of livestock in Part II.

Forage conservation

The unavoidable seasonal nature of range and permanent pasture production means that at one season of the year there is a surplus of feed while at another there is a deficiency. Unless supplementary feed can be fed, or some animals can be removed from the grazings, the stocking rate must be geared to the season of low pasture productivity, and in the season of high pasture productivity a great deal of feed is wasted as there is an insufficient number of animals to consume all the forage available. It is recognized that there must be a wide fluctuation in the yield of forage from season to season in the dry tropics, but it might be thought that in the wet tropics, where growth is continuous, there would be little seasonal fluctuation. Unfortunately, this is not necessarily the case, as will

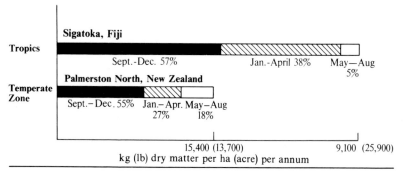

Fig. 3.6 A comparison of seasonal forage production at localities in the tropical and temperate climatic zones (kg(lb) dry matter per ha (acre) per annum).

be seen from Fig. 3.6. At Sigatoka in Fiji, where the average annual rainfall is 1,780 to 2,030 mm (70 to 80 in) and is quite well distributed throughout the year, the seasonal variation in growth of pasture is considerable and is as large as it is at Palmerston North in New Zealand, where forage conservation is a normal practice.

This seasonal fluctuation in the production of forage is a major factor limiting animal production on range and permanent pasture. All over the world millions of tons of dried-out and unused potential animal feed are burnt annually after the 'flush' season. It is obvious that if part of this surplus growth of forage could be preserved for the season when there is insufficient feed, then the annual carrying capacity of range and permanent pasture could be effectively improved.

The preservation of surplus forage is a normal feature of temperate-zone management of range and permanent pasture, but it is hardly practised in the tropics. Forage may be preserved as hay, silage or as an artificially dried product everywhere in the tropics, or as 'standing hay' in the arid tropics.

However, a word of warning is necessary. Forage conservation is an intensive husbandry practice that yields less return on investment than some other improvement practices. It can be argued that only feed that is truly surplus should be conserved. If the grazing area of animals has to be restricted in order to save forage for conservation then the depression in their growth rate during the period of restricted grazing may not be compensated for by an increased growth rate during the period when the conserved material is fed, as there is an inevitable loss of nutrients during the period of storage. This effect has been demonstrated by Smith (1967) in Queensland and some details of his investigations are shown in Table 3.20. Another factor that must also be considered under extensive grazing conditions is that losses in liveweight of meat-producing animals during the dry season will to some extent be made up by compensatory liveweight gain during the wet season. This effect appears to

Table 3.20   *Effect of conservation of forage on liveweight production of cattle*

	kg/ha (lb/acre) liveweight produced per annum	
Stocking rate	0·5 ha (1·24 acre) per steer	0·3 ha (0·74 acre) per steer
No conservation	590 (530)	760 (680)
Conservation and hay feeding	580 (520)	670 (600)

Notes: 1. Reduced growth occurred before feeding-back of the conserved material took place.
2. The pasture was predominantly a *Sorghum almum* – lucerne mixture and the hay that was conserved was predominantly lucerne with a 60 per cent digestibility.

Source: Smith, C. A. (1967).

be due to the fact that animals, and particularly older animals that have been on a low plane of nutrition, eat far more forage when they suddenly find themselves on a high plane of nutrition than animals that have always been raised on a high plane. This phenomenon is further discussed in Chapter 5 (Part II).

Under extensive grazing conditions it could be expedient to conserve some forage for drought or other emergency feeding of breeding stock, but generally forage conservation is a practice that should be used only where the production of animal product per unit area is high and where increased production will justify the necessary increased expenditure, as in dairy farming or in baby beef or fat lamb production.

It will usually be more economic under extensive grazing conditions to attempt to solve the problem of seasonal forage production in other ways: perhaps by using some species whose growth cycle is out of step with the majority of the species used or species which grow for a longer period into the dry season; perhaps by utilizing high fertilizer inputs or by fodder cropping on a limited but improved area of the extensive grazing.

Hay

Hay is generally considered a roughage feed, but forage used for hay should be cut before the plants flower in order to obtain the most nutritious and palatable product. If, as so often happens, the plants are allowed to fully mature and wilt, the hay may still be useful for the feeding of beef cattle if it is properly supplemented, for instance, with urea. In the dry tropics it is preferable under these conditions to leave it standing in the field and not to cut and store it. Hay of medium quality may also be useful for feeding as a supplement in the middle of the wet season when the dry matter intake of grazing animals may be low, owing to the very high moisture content of forage.

Hay can be made in several ways and the choice of method will depend upon local circumstances. The usual method is to cut it in the field, let it dry in the row and to stack it as soon as it is dry. In the semi-arid tropics it may be possible to make hay very rapidly, but in the wet tropics hay can easily be spoiled in the field as it lies in the row. Even in the semi-arid tropics hay may mould in the field as it usually has to be made at the end of the growing season while the humidity is still high. If there is sufficient labour available the forage can be cut and stacked on tripods in the field. This allows it to dry out without spoiling in a wet climate, and hay produced by this method is usually of high quality. Certain new methods, such as crushing of the stalks while cutting or 'fluffing' in the row, may assist rapid drying out in the field and might be useful practices in the tropics. In any event, the cut forage should not be allowed to become sunbleached but should be gathered as soon as it is dry and while it still retains an appreciable amount of colour. Nor should it be exposed unnecessarily to the leaching effect of tropical showers. When it is stacked, or even before it is carted, it may be quite seriously attacked by termites unless it is raised above ground surface.

Despite the fact that it is possible to make satisfactory hay at certain seasons in some tropical countries and there are tropical grasses such as *Dichanthium caricosum* (Antigua hay grass) that are very suitable for hay-making, very little hay is at present made outside the American tropics. There are many reasons for this situation: the generally small size of farms, the lack of suitable machinery, etc., and perhaps most important the fact that even if good hay is harvested it is almost certain to mould during storage in the wet tropics.

Recently, new types of hay-collection machinery have been introduced in temperate countries. These roll the hay into large bundles or gather it into small stacks that can be mechanically handled. Such machinery would be economic on only the largest farms in the tropics.

Silage

Almost any forage can be ensiled, this being a simple method of preservation. There is always some wastage, but good management will reduce it to a minimum.

Forage is ensiled by compacting it in some form of container from which air is excluded. Plant respiration goes on for some time after the silo is filled and the bacteria, yeasts, moulds and enzymes present initiate a fermentation process. The temperature inside the silo rises and acids are released by the fermentation. As the acidity of the silage rises, further fermentation is prevented and the great bulk of the silage is preserved. The quality of silage depends on the following factors: the stage of maturity and chemical composition of the crop ensiled; the ratio of soluble carbohydrates to the mineral base content of the crop; the percentage of moisture in the crop; the rapidity and completeness with which air is excluded during the filling of the silo; and the extent to which the temperature of the forage rises.

Forage of almost any quality may be ensiled, but it should be remembered that to ensile low-quality roughage is hardly likely to be economic, and that the nutrient quality of the silage will always be somewhat less than the nutrient quality of the forage that has been ensiled, as even with the best management there will be some loss of nutrients. Unripe sorghum and maize make excellent silage, but many tropical grasses possess a relatively low sugar content and they should be ensiled using molasses at the rate of 3·5 to 4 per cent of the green weight of the forage. There are many other types of additives that may be used. These include:

1. Those that are a substitute for fermentation such as the mixture of sulphuric and hydrochloric acids used in the well-known AIV method and formic acid;
2. those that enhance fermentation such as enzymes, bacterial cultures and antioxidants; and
3. those that add nutrients such as the molasses referred to above.

As it is unlikely that the majority of farmers in the tropics will have access to acids or special fermentation products the most practical method that they can normally utilize is the addition of nutrients.

A silo should not be filled while it is raining. Succulent fodder should be wilted in the field before filling into the silo, but water may have to be added if the forage is too dry. It is essential that the forage should be well compacted and covered so that air is excluded as much as possible. This means that with the exception of very young, short grass, forage must be chopped in order to ensure adequate compaction and exclusion of air.

The container may be a structure built above the ground such as the tower silos so common in America and parts of Europe or a silage clamp or bunker or it can be a trench or pit in the ground. Some modern tower silos are glass lined and are both efficient and expensive. Sheet plastic is now widely used to cover silage made in bunkers, trenches and pits. Silage can also be stored very successfully in large, evacuated plastic bags and this would appear to be a method that might be used by small farmers in the tropics as the only equipment that is needed to create a vacuum in the silage bag is a small pump. There are difficulties, however, as it has been found that termites attack and puncture the bags. It is not necessary to have any container at all as the silage can be stacked, but the wastage in a stack silo is very considerable.

On large mechanized farms forage is usually cut with a forage harvester that loads the chopped fodder on to a trailer. On smaller farms the forage may be cut with a mower and transported to the silo on a buck-rake mounted on a small tractor. At the silo the forage can be chopped using a portable chaffing machine. On the larger farms it is becoming customary to ensile forage in above-ground, open-ended pits or bunkers. With this type of silo the tractors can run over the silage to help consolidation and the silage can be mechanically loaded when it is required for feeding. Silage bunkers or trenches can also be constructed so that animals can feed themselves. At a self-feeding silo the larger types of cattle can eat up to a height of 2·1 m (7 ft). A barrier such as a wooden fence is needed to prevent burrowing. A feeding width of 17 to 22 cm (7 to 9 in) for each adult animal is required unless feeding time is restricted, when a width of up to 76 cm (30 in) is needed.

The making of silage is equally important but more difficult for the small peasant farmer possessing a few head of stock. A silage pit or trench is the most easily constructed and most economic form of container, but it can be used only in the dry tropics or at a very well-drained site in the wet tropics. In the wet tropics experience has shown that the silage is usually spoilt by water seepage. The pit or trench must be of such a size that to obtain sufficient feed for each day's requirements the exposed surface must be removed only to a depth of a few inches, otherwise much silage becomes mouldy and is wasted. The most difficult operation for the small peasant farmer is the chaffing of the forage during the filling of the silo and this operation is usually essential if efficient compaction is to be ensured, particularly in the drier tropics. This difficulty might be overcome by the cooperative use of small power chaffers.

Supplementary fodder crops such as maize, sorghum or millet are particularly suitable for silage making as are many tall tropical fodder grasses such as elephant, guinea, jaragua and Sudan grass (*Sorghum sudanense*).

Despite the fact that good silage can be made in both the wet and the dry tropics and a major problem of all livestock farmers is the seasonality of the forage supply, little progress has been made in the tropics during the last decade in the development of the concept of conserving surplus forage as silage.

Artificially dried forage

Artificially dried forage is produced by placing forage on some form of drying tray and passing through it a blast of hot air until it is sufficiently dry to store. It may then be baled or milled and the fine milled material may be pelleted before storage. Large forage-drying plants operate on a continuous flow, rather than on a batch system. Machines that harvest, dry and pellet forage in one operation have recently been developed in the United States.

Capital requirements are obviously high, but very considerable improvements have been made in forage-drying machinery during the last decade, and where high-quality forage can be cheaply produced and energy is not too expensive the production of artificially dried forage in the tropics for specialist markets could now be economic. The continuous growth of the livestock feed industry and the development of industrialized pig and poultry industries in some tropical countries has created a continuously expanding demand for dried leaf meal. In addition, if prices can be made competitive, there is the possibility of developing an export market for dried leaf meal in some humid tropical countries.

There are at present some organizations evaluating the economics of producing artificially dried forage in the wet tropics, including a private enterprise group in west Malaysia. Several tropical forage species could be dried to produce leaf meal comparable in quality with lucerne meal, one of these being *Leucaena leucocephala*. It has also been suggested in the Caribbean region that milled, dried young elephant grass with a CP content of 10 to 12 per cent could be used to absorb a mixture of molasses, urea and minerals to produce an economic dairy concentrate feed. A feed of this type could either be produced at existing sugar mills or in association with sugar mills.

Nutritive value of forage

The nutritive value of a forage depends upon its composition, digestibility and intake, or the total amount that any animal will ingest within a specific period.

Total energy intake of the animal ingesting forage is undoubtedly the most important factor determining total output of animal product, as long as protein and mineral requirements are met and the forage contains no toxic substances.

The CP content of forage, though important and a useful indicator of quality, is not of such major significance in ruminant nutrition as was once alleged, as ruminants can utilize non-protein nitrogen as well as protein nitrogen. It is generally accepted that the minimum percentage values of total nitrogen in forage ingested by cattle should be 1·6, 1·6 and 1·9 for maintenance, beef and dairy production, respectively.

If the mineral content of the forage is low, minerals can be provided in the form of a supplement. Indeed, this is the normal practice. It should also be remembered that the mineral content of legumes, herbs and browse trees is usually somewhat higher than that of grasses grown in the same environment. An exception is Townsville stylo. This legume generally possesses a low phosphorus content.

Toxic substances

Several well-known tropical forage plants contain toxic substances. Some of these are: *Leucaena leucocephala*, a small legume tree that contains mimosine, a substance inhibiting cell division; the legume *Indigofera spicata* that produces a dangerous hepatoxin known as indospicine; and species of the grass genus *Setaria* that possess high oxalate contents. As a consequence introduced forage plants should always be screened by the appropriate authority for toxic substances before they are released for general farm use.

Intake and digestibility

The digestibility of forage can be expressed in terms of dry matter, organic matter or energy, or of a single component such as CP. The determination of the digestibility of feeds has already been discussed in a previous section. The digestibility of forage depends above all on its stage of maturity, as will be seen from Table 3.21.

Table 3.21 *The effect of variety and stage of maturity on the digestibility and voluntary DM intake of guinea* (Panicum maximum) *forage in Australia*

No. of days of regrowth	Digestibility of DM (%)		Voluntary DM intake (g/kg $W^{0.75}$)	
	Green panic	Coloniao	Green panic	Coloniao
28	62·0	62·2	69·2	69·2
63	47·4	53·4	47·6	47·6
91	47·7	50·2	42·3	42·3

Notes: 1. Here, DM intake is expressed in terms of the metabolic size of the animal, i.e. g/kg body weight$^{0.75}$.
 2. Green panic and coloniao are two varieties of guinea grass (*Panicum maximum*).
Source: Minson, D. J. (1971).

The voluntary intake of forage by any class of ruminant livestock under specific environmental conditions is greatly influenced by the type of forage ingested and by its stage of maturity. As will be seen from the data in Table 3.21, voluntary intake varies considerably even between varieties of the same forage plant and declines rapidly as the plant ages. In fact the variation in voluntary intake due to varietal differences is much larger than the data shown in Table 3.21 suggest, as the intake of six varieties of guinea grass by individual animals varied from 35·7 to 80·8 g per kg $W^{0.75}$ (Minson, 1971).

Proximate analysis and the determination of the SE and TDN values of tropical forage are said to underestimate their feeding value and it is probable that the approximate nutritive value and digestibility of forage can most easily be determined in the laboratory by measuring the total nitrogen content as an index of quality and the *in vitro* digestibility.

Voluntary intake and digestibility can be determined using live animals either in an animal house or out on grazing. The advantage of using the grazing animal is that measurements are taken on the forage that the animal actually selects and eats. Some details as to how digestibility is determined under such circumstances have been given in a previous section. A further advantage of determinations made on the grazing animal is that pasture measurements, such as the amount and quality of the forage available and the persistence and botanical composition of the pasture, can also be measured. Those requiring further information on the various techniques mentioned above should consult specialized papers and textbooks concerned with this subject.

Effect of climate on nutritive value

The most important climatic factors that limit forage growth, and hence the quantity of feed available, are temperature, effective precipitation, length of daylight and the intensity of solar radiation. The quality of feed depends mainly on effective precipitation and on the intensity of solar radiation. The very real differences in climate that exist between the humid and the semi-arid tropical areas thus present two broadly distinct nutritional problems. These have already been discussed in Chapter 1, Part I.

Nutritive values

It is not possible in an introductory text to present details of the nutritive value of all the different tropical forage species. Fortunately a considerable volume of data has now been collected, collated and analysed, and readers who are interested are advised to consult publications by Morrison (1957), Crampton and Harris (1969), McDowell *et al.* (1974) and Gohl (1975).

References

Agricultural Research Council (1963) The Nutrient Requirements of Farm Livestock. (1) Poultry. *Summary of Recommendations.* ARC: London.
Agricultural Research Council (1965) The Nutrient Requirements of Farm Livestock. (2) Ruminants. *Technical Reviews and Summaries.* ARC: London.
Agricultural Research Council (1967) The Nutrient Requirements of Farm Livestock. (3) Pigs. *Technical Reviews and Summaries.* ARC: London.
Armstrong, D. G. and Mitchell, H. H. (1955) Protein nutrition and the utilisation of dietary protein at different levels of intake by growing swine. *J. Anim. Sci.,* **14,** 49–53.
Baudelaire, J. P. (1972) Water for livestock in semi-arid zones. *World Anim. Rev.* (3), 1–9.
Beard, J. S. (1944) Climax vegetation in tropical America. *Ecology,* **25,** 127–58.
Bender, F., Heany, D. P. and Bowden, A. (1970) Potential of steamed wood as a feed for ruminants. *Forest Prod. J.,* **20,** 36–41.
Blaxter, K. L. (1962) *The Energy Metabolism of Ruminants.* Hutchinson: London.
Blydenstein, J. (1967) Tropical savanna vegetation of the *llanos* of Colombia. *Ecology,* **48,** 1–15.
Bonsma, J. C. (1940) The influence of climatological factors on cattle: observations on cattle in the tropical regions. *Fmg. S. Afr.,* **15,** 373–85.

Bryan, W. W. (1962) The role of the legume in legume/grass pastures. *Bull. Comw. Bur. Past. Fld. Crops,* **46**, 147–60.

Commonwealth Agricultural Bureaux (1947) The use and misuse of trees and shrubs as fodder. *Comw. Agric. Bur. Joint Pub.,* No. 10. CAB: Farnham Royal, U.K.

Crampton, E. W. and Harris, L. E. (1969) *United States–Canadian Tables of Feed Composition.* NAS–NRC, Pub. 1084. NRC: Washington.

Cuthbertson, Sir D. P. (1969) 'The Science of Nutrition of Farm Livestock, in Cuthbertson, Sir D. P. (ed.), *Nutrition of Animals of Agricultural Importance,* Part 1, *Int. Encylp. Food Nutrit.,* Vol. 17. Pergamon: Oxford.

Dabadghao, P. M. and Shankarnarayan, K. A. (1972) *The Grass Cover of India.* Indian Counc. Agric. Res. Sci. Mono. ICAR: New Delhi.

Davies, W. (1960) Temperate and tropical grasslands. *Proc. 8th Int. Grassld. Congr., UK.*

Denton, D. A., Goding, J. R., Sabine, R. and Wright, R. D. (1961) Salinity problems in the arid zones. *Proc. Teheran Symp. Arid Zone Res.,* **14.** UNESCO: Paris.

Devendra, C. (1971) The comparative efficiency of feed utilisation of ruminants in the tropics. *Trop. Sci.,* **13**, 123–32.

Evans, R. E. (1960) Rations for livestock. *Min. Agric. Fish. Food Bull.,* No. 48. HMSO: London.

FAO (1956) *Production Yearbook.* FAO: Rome.

FAO (1974) *Production Yearbook,* Vol. 27, p. 447. FAO: Rome.

French, M. H. (1945) Geophagia in animals. *E. Afric. med. J.,* **22**, 103–10.

French, M. H. (1956) The importance of water in the management of cattle. *E. Afric. agric. J.,* **21**, 171–81.

Gohl, B. (1975) *Tropical Feeds.* FAO: Rome.

Heany, D. P. and Bender, F. (1970) The feeding value of steamed aspen for sheep. *Forest Prod. J.,* **20**, 98–102.

Henzell, E. F., Fergus, I. F. and Martin, A. E. (1966) Accumulation of soil nitrogen and carbon under a *Desmodium uncinatum* pasture. *Aust. J. exp. Agric. Anim. Husb.,* **6**, 157–60.

Hunting Technical Services (1974) *Southern Darfur Land-use Planning Survey.* Annex 3, 'Animal Resources and Range Ecology'. Hunting Technical Services: Boreham Wood, UK.

Kehar, N. D. (1954) *Indian Coun. Agric. Res. Silver Jubilee Souvenir.* Govt. India Press: New Delhi.

Ledger, H. P. (1959) A possible explanation for part of the difference in heat tolerance exhibited by *Bos taurus* and *Bos indicus* beef cattle. *Nature (Lond.),* **184**, 1405.

Lucas, I. A. M. (1972) The use of antibiotics as feed additives for farm animals. *Proc. Nutrit. Soc.,* **31**, 1–8.

McDonald, P., Edwards, R. A. and Greenhalgh, J. F. D. (1973) *Animal Nutrition* (2nd edn). Longman: London.

McDowell, W. R., Conrad, J. H., Thomas, J. E. and Harris, L. E. (1974) *Latin American Tables of Feed Composition.* Univ. Florida: Gainesville, Fla.

Meiklejohn, J. (1962) Microbiology of the nitrogen cycle in some Ghana soils. *Emp. J. exp. Agric.,* **30**, 115–26.

Minson, D. J. (1971) The digestibility and voluntary intake of six varieties of *Panicum. Aust. J. agric. Anim. Husb.,* **11**, 18–25.

Moore, A. W. (1962) The influence of a legume on soil fertility under a grazed tropical pasture. *Emp. J. exp. Agric.,* **30**, 239–48.

Moore, R. M. (ed.) (1970) *Australian Grasslands.* Aust. Nat. Univ. Press: Canberra.

Morrison, F. B. (1957) *Feeds and Feeding* (22nd edn). Morrison Publishing: Ithaca, NY.

National Academy of Sciences – National Research Council (1966) *Nutrient Requirements of Dairy Cattle* (3rd rev. edn). NAC–NRC, Pub. No. 1349. NAC–NRC: Washington.

National Academy of Sciences (1968a) *Nutrient Requirements of Sheep* (4th rev. edn). NAS, Pub. No. 1693. NAS: Washington.

National Academy of Sciences (1968b) *Nutrient Requirements of Swine* (6th rev. edn). NAS, Pub. No. 1599. NAS: Washington.

National Academy of Sciences (1970) *Nutrient Requirements of Beef Cattle* (4th rev. edn). NAS:Washington.

National Academy of Sciences (1971) *Nutrient Requirements of Poultry* (6th rev. edn). NAS: Washington.

Payne, W. J. A. (1965) Specific problems of semi-arid environments. *Qualitas Pl. Mater. veg.*, **12**, 268–94.

Payne, W. J. A. (1969) 'Problems of the Nutrition of Ruminants in the Tropics', in Cuthbertson, Sir D. P. (ed.), *Nutrition of Animals of Agricultural Importance*, Part 2, *Int. Encylp. Food Nutrit.*, Vol. 17. Pergamon: Oxford.

Pirie, N. W. (1969) The production and use of leaf protein. *Proc. Nutrit. Soc.*, **28**, 85–91.

Rattray, J. M. (1960) *The Grass Cover of Africa*. FAO Agric. Studies, No. 49. FAO: Rome.

Roseveare, G. M. (1948) The Grasslands of Latin America. *Comw. Bur. Past. Field Crops Bull.*, No. 36. Comw. Agric. Bur.: Farnham Royal, UK.

Schmidt-Nielsen, K. (1964) *Desert Animals. Physiological Problems of Heat and Water.* Clarendon Press: Oxford.

Simoons, F. J. and Simoons, E. S. (1968) *A Ceremonial Ox of India.* Univ. Wisconsin Press: Madison.

Smith, C. A. (1965) Studies on the *Hyparrhenia* Veld. VI. The fertiliser value of cattle excreta. *J. agric. Sci. (Camb.)*, **64**, 403–6.

Smith, C. A. (1967) Brigalow country. *Rep. Div. Trop. Past., CSIRO 1966/67*, pp. 25–34. CSIRO: Australia.

Staples, R. R., Hornby, H. E. and Hornby, R. M. (1942) A study of the comparative effects of goats and cattle on a mixed grass-bush pasture. *E. Afr. agric. J.*, **8**, 62–70.

Suter, H. E. (1962) Carence en cobalt dans un élevage des bovides au Katanga. *Rev. Élevage Méd. Vét. Pays Trop.*, **15**, 31–41. Abstracted: *Nutrit. Abst. Rev.*, **33**, 1818.

Vicente-Chandler, J., Caro-Costas, R., Pearson, R. W., Abruña, F., Figarella, J. and Silva, S. (1964) The intensive management of tropical forages in Puerto Rico. *Univ. Puerto Rico agric. Exp. Stn. Bull.*, No. 187.

Whyte, R. O. (1964) *The Grassland and Fodder Resources of India* (2nd edn). Indian Counc. Agric. Res., Mono. No. 22. ICTA: New Delhi.

Whyte, R. O. (1968) *Grasslands of the Monsoon*. Faber and Faber: London.

Whyte, R. O. (1974) *Tropical Grazing Lands*. Dr W. Junk: The Hague.

Whyte, R. O., Moir, T. R. G. and Cooper, J. P. (1959) *Grasses in Agriculture.* FAO Agric. Studies, No. 42. FAO: Rome.

Whyte, R. O., Nilsson-Leissner, G. and Trumble, H. C. (1953) *Legumes in Agriculture* FAO Agric. Studies No. 21. FAO: Rome.

Wilcke, H. L. (1966) *Feedstuffs*, **38** (5).

Further Reading

Davies, J. G. Pasture improvement in the tropics. *Proc. Ninth Int. Grassld. Congr Brazil* (1965).

Davies, W. and Skidmore, C. L. (eds.). *Tropical Pastures.* Faber and Faber: London 1966.

Spedding, C. R. W. *Grassland Ecology.* Oxford Univ. Press: London, 1971.

Whyte, R. O. The myth of tropical grasslands. *Trop. Agric. (Trin.)*, **39**, 1–11 (1962).

Chapter 4

Reproduction and Breeding*

Although some of the very first animal-breeding practices must have been initiated when Neolithic man domesticated animals, the major part of modern animal-breeding practice has developed in the temperate zone during the last two centuries.

In some temperate-zone countries, particularly in northwest Europe, the overall environment for livestock had been improved to such an extent by the beginning of the nineteenth century that attention could be directed towards the breeding of improved types of livestock that could take economic advantage of this situation. In addition, in northwest Europe the most adverse effects of climate on livestock could be avoided by the provision of adequate housing. As a consequence, during the nineteenth century spectacular advances were made in livestock breeding, particularly in the United Kingdom. However, these advances, although based on acute observation and limited records, were still very much the result of trial and error, as nothing was known of modern genetic theory.

The science of genetics, based on Mendelian theories of inheritance, began to gain general recognition at the beginning of the twentieth century, and during the last 50 years the application of genetic principles, combined with new knowledge gained on the physiology of reproduction, has revolutionized animal-breeding practices.

These practices are slowly being applied in tropical countries. In the latter, few of the livestock-owning peoples have in the past developed rules or customs concerned with the better breeding of their animals. The majority have allowed their livestock to breed more or less haphazardly and the results have been accepted as a matter of fate and therefore inevitable. Nevertheless, a number of factors have contributed to the evolution of a multiplicity of different breeds of tropical livestock. In the first place the original domestication of most species probably occurred in the tropics and/or sub-tropics. For example, there are three major types of domestic cattle in the tropics, i.e. *Bos taurus*, *B. indicus* and *B. (Bibos)*, together with their crossbreds, while there is only one

* Dr R. S. Temple, Director: Animal Science, International Livestock Centre for Africa, Addis Ababa, Ethiopia, assisted in the writing of this chapter.

145

major type of cattle in the temperate zone, i.e. *B. taurus*. Secondly, the large-scale movement of some livestock-owning peoples within the Euro-Asian–African land mass, followed by periods of isolation due to intermittent warfare and/or the natural hazards of communication of small groups of people in large land areas, meant that livestock were moved into isolated areas where they naturally developed over a long period characteristics that fitted them to their new environment. Some peoples probably also bred their livestock for specific features, and originally this action may have had magico-religious connotations. For example the *B. taurus* breeds of Hamitic Longhorn cattle that were first taken by migratory people from western Asia to the tsetse-fly infested forest regions of West Africa, perhaps some 5,000 years ago, have developed a tolerance of trypanosomiasis that is certainly not possessed by any other major cattle breed originating from western Asia. Not only have both the N'dama and Dwarf Shorthorn breeds developed this tolerance but the tolerance of the N'dama cattle, which were the first to arrive in West Africa, is more developed than that of the Dwarf Shorthorn cattle. On the other hand, there must have been deliberate selection by man for very large horns within cattle of the Ankole breed in East Africa.

Efforts to improve the productivity of livestock in the tropics have moved in a cyclic manner ever since the sixteenth century. At that time when Europeans first discovered and then colonized the Americas, they imported their unimproved domestic livestock with them. These livestock thrived in the temperate but not in the tropical regions of the Americas. However, some of the breeds in the tropical regions did gradually acclimatize. One example is the Criollo cattle of tropical Central and South America. However, the parallel importation of European livestock into Africa and Asia was almost totally unsuccessful except in some favoured tropical islands such as Mauritius. Later, with the advent of a large-scale slave trade between Africa and the Americas some African livestock such as N'dama cattle and Dwarf Forest sheep and goats were imported into the Americas. These livestock were crossed with imported temperate-type livestock and form the basis for some modern American breeds such as the Nelthropp cattle and the Black Bellied Barbados sheep of the West Indies and several sheep breeds in northeast Brazil. In the eighteenth and nineteenth centuries there were also considerable importations of tropical livestock from Asia into Europe, an important example being the Siamese and Chinese pigs which have contributed characteristics to modern British pig breeds (see Ch. 12, Pt II).

During the latter part of the nineteenth century, as it began to be realized that many of the original importations of temperate-type livestock into the tropics were not flourishing there was a considerable importation of Asian cattle into tropical and sub-tropical America.

Improvements in the breeding of European and North American livestock, with the realization that the productivity of the new breeds far surpassed the productivity of any indigenous tropical breeds, led at the end of the nineteenth and at the beginning of the twentieth century to a new cycle of importation of temperate-type livestock into the tropics. The failure of these importations was immediately apparent as by this time governments were monitoring importations and beginning to keep records. It was ultimately realized that until such time as epizootic disease was controlled and nutrition and management improved the possibilities for the successful introduction of highly productive temperate-type livestock into the tropics were poor. A major effort was then made to identify tropical breeds and to initiate selection within them. The result of these efforts has been disappointing and another major effort is now being made to introduce productive, temperate-type livestock into the tropics. The possibilities for success are now much greater than they were in the past, as we possess more knowledge of the characteristics of tropical and temperate-type livestock and we are better able to control and improve the tropical environment.

In order to promote a rapid improvement in the productivity of tropical livestock we must first understand the basic facts of reproduction and the inheritance of characteristics and be able to apply suitable animal-breeding practices that have been developed in the temperate zone.

The development of the livestock industry in the tropics depends upon improvements on a 'broad front', but it is also important that development priorities should be established. In areas where epizootic disease is still prevalent it is obvious that disease control must be accorded some priority. Elsewhere – and in those regions where the major epizootics have already been brought under control – improved feeding and management should be accorded priority. It is axiomatic that it is useless to improve the genetic merit of livestock if environmental factors remain unimproved, and that the upgrading of livestock must be accompanied by the upgrading of management and by improvements in the overall environment. On the other hand, improvements in management and in the environment should not be allowed to outpace improvements in the genetic merit of the animals managed within that environment. It is just as wasteful to provide an environment that cannot be fully exploited on account of the low genetic merit of the livestock used, as it is to provide animals of high genetic merit for a poor environment.

The reproductive cycle

The reproductive cycle begins when the *ovum* or egg of the female is fertilized by the *spermatozoa* or sperm of the male and it ends at parturition.

Male reproductive cells or sperm differ markedly from other body cells

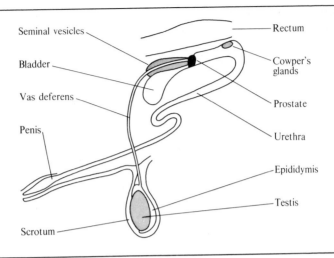

Fig. 4.1   Diagrammatic representation of the male reproductive organs of cattle.

in that they possess a tail-like structure which enables them to move freely. Sperm are produced in the testes, which are encased in and protected by a *scrotum* to form the testicles (Fig. 4.1). The scrotum possesses a muscular attachment which enables a male to lower or raise his testicles. During hot weather the testicles are lowered away from the body, in an effort to ensure that their temperature remains somewhat below that of the remainder of the body, a condition necessary for good viability of the sperm as these are adversely affected by high temperature. In the wet tropics it is not unknown for the testicles of an exotic bull to hang so low that they almost touch the ground. During cold weather the scrotum is contracted so that the testicles receive warmth from the animal's body.

Sperm are produced in vast numbers in the epithelium of the convoluted, seminiferous tubules of the testis and are stored in a retaining reservoir, known as the *ductus epididimis* (Fig. 4.1). The sperm mature during this period of storage, which may be for as long as 1 or 2 months. Thereafter they degenerate and lose their viability.

The male sex hormone is also produced in the testes. This activates the sex instinct and sexual activities of the male. There are also various other glands accessory to the testes which produce the fluid medium in which sperm are conveyed from the male into the genital organs of the female during the act of copulation at mating. The mix of the fluid medium and sperm is known as *semen*. The volume of semen produced at any one time varies considerably as between different species of livestock (Table 4.1) as does the average sperm content of the semen. The period during which sperm retain their viability within the female genital tract varies from species to species. In the cow the average duration is

Table 4.1 *Data on the semen of some domestic livestock species*

Species	Volume of male ejaculate (ml)		Average sperm content of semen (million/ml)
	Range	*Average*	
Buffalo	2·0–13·0	3·0	900
Cattle	2·0–10·0	5·0	1,000
Goat	0·1–3·5	0·7	2,700
Sheep	0·2–3·0	1·0	2,500
Pig	50·0–400·0	250·0	125
Fowl	0·1–1·0	0·2	4,000

30 hours, in the ewe 22 to 24 hours and in the sow up to 35 hours. The spermatozoa of some birds retain their viability for as long as 2 to 3 weeks.

In the majority of species mating can be accomplished only when the female is at a specific stage in her sexual or oestral cycle. That is, when she is in heat. Camels and llamoids are an exception, as in their case copulation induces ovulation (see Chs. 9 and 10, Pt II). After the semen has been deposited in the female's genital tract (Fig. 4.2), depending on where it has been deposited, the sperm move through the cervix and the uterus into one or other of the Fallopian tubes, where fertilization may take place if an egg is present.

The movement of the sperm, from where they are deposited in the female genital tract, to the Fallopian tube usually takes from 2 to 15 minutes and is accomplished partly by their own movement and partly by the aid of other factors, such as rhythmic contractions of the vagina, cervix and uterus. The main site in the female genital tract where sperm are deposited during mating varies from species to species. In cows and

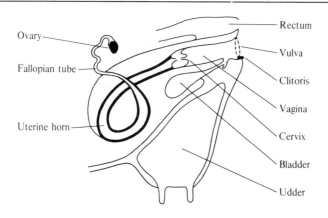

Fig. 4.2 Diagrammatic representation of the female reproductive organs of cattle.

ewes it is usually in the lower part of the vagina, while in sows it is in the cervical canal. Actual penetration of a sperm into an egg is probably the result of the sperm's own powers of movement and the exudation by it of a chemical which helps break down the cell wall of the egg. Several sperm probably play some part in penetrating the outer layer of the egg, but only one actually fertilizes it.

Eggs are produced in the ovaries of the female (Fig. 4.2). The process corresponds to that which takes place in the testes of the male when sperm are produced. Thus the ovary is analogous in its role in the reproductive cycle to the testis. It also produces hormones that activate and regulate the sexual activities of the female. Females normally possess two ovaries, eggs being produced alternately from one or the other. Ovaries are usually only a fraction of the size of the male testes. For example, a cow's ovary is about 2·5 cm (1·0 in) in diameter, though the eggs that it produces are of microscopic size. Eggs are produced in the ovary's outer layer which is composed of germinal epithelium. Within this tissue specialized groups of cells, known as *primary follicles*, are the potential source of the eggs. At sexual maturity, and at specific intervals thereafter, one or more of the primary follicles rapidly mature within a thin, fibrous, capsulated structure known as a *Graafian follicle*. In cows these follicles are of a sufficient size to be visible to the naked eye. With increasing maturity the wall of the follicle becomes thinner and thinner and finally ruptures at the surface of the ovary, releasing the egg into the fibrillated, wide-mouthed end of the Fallopian tube. This process is known as *ovulation*. In the Fallopian tube the egg is held for several hours in a coagulated fluid which is formed from the viscous fluid that is released from the follicle at the same time as the egg. After a period that varies from species to species but is usually a few hours, the coagulated fluid reliquefies, thus releasing the egg and allowing it to move along the Fallopian tube towards the uterus. It is at this stage that fertilization by a sperm can take place.

After ovulation the cavity in the empty follicle on the surface of the mammalian ovary is filled by a yellow cell, variously known as the *yellow body* or the *corpus luteum*. The function of this structure is to secrete hormones that seek to ensure the continuation of gestation and the suspension of further ovulation until after parturition. Should the egg fail to be fertilized it loses its viability within a few hours, the yellow body disappears, the balance of hormones within the female's body changes and the sexual or oestral cycle recommences.

Factors affecting the oestral cycle

Although the oestral cycle of the female is mainly governed by hormones that are secreted internally, there are other factors that exert a considerable influence on it, either directly or indirectly. The extent of their influence varies both between and within species and breeds.

Apart from the abnormality of disease the most important factors affecting the oestral cycle appear to be the plane of nutrition, the length of daylight and ambient temperature.

Nutrition.   The inadequately fed female animal grows slowly and her sexual maturity, and hence the onset of her oestral cycle, is delayed. Very large numbers of tropical cattle have to subsist on a low level of nutrient intake for long periods during the year. As a consequence the first effective heat periods of heifers are often delayed until they are 2 years or older. On the other hand, in some species such as sheep, an abundance of feed during or just before the normal breeding season often increases fertility, as more than one egg is liberated at ovulation with resultant multiple births. Certain individual forage plants can also affect the sexual cycle of the livestock that consume them. For example, there are grasses and legumes that at certain stages of growth contain substances similar in chemical composition to the sex hormones produced by animals. The consumption of these plants may have either a beneficial or an adverse effect, according to the time of the year and the amount consumed. In Australia, Merino ewes consuming considerable quantities of a subterranean clover (*Trifolium subterraneum* var. *Dwalganup*) exhibit infertility and difficulties in gestation and parturition. Pigs fed large quantities of the legume *Leucaena leucocephala* lose hair and often become infertile.

Length of daylight. Changes in the length of daylight may affect the sexual cycle of all domestic livestock, but the effect is only of major importance for sheep, goats and poultry.

In the temperate zones the breeding season of sheep is associated with a shortening day. As a consequence ewes transferred from the northern hemisphere temperate zone to the southern change the months in which they breed. In the tropics, where the length of daylight varies little throughout the year, most breeds of sheep reproduce at any season, although there may still be some seasonal variation in the intensity of breeding. Rams transferred from the temperate to the tropical regions of Australia are usually infertile for the first year after the transfer. Male goats transferred from the temperate region of Australia to Fiji have been reported to behave in a similar manner.

The effect of light periodicity on poultry has been used commercially to increase egg production. This can be raised appreciably by slowly increasing the length of exposure of the birds to natural or artificial light.

Ambient temperature.   There is considerable experimental evidence that high ambient temperatures directly affect the sexual cycle of female livestock (see Ch. 1, Pt I), the libido of males and viability of the sperm of males.

Table 4.2 *Average length of oestral cycle, duration of heat and time of ovulation of some domestic livestock species*

Species	Oestral cycle (days)		Duration of heat (hours)		Time of ovulation (hours)	
	Average	Range	Average	Range	Average	Range
Buffalo	21	very variable	36	12–120	very variable	5–24 after end of oestrus
Cattle	21	16–26	18*	14–22	11	2–22 after end of oestrus
Goats	19	18–21	28†	24–72		12–36 after onset of oestrus
Sheep	17	14–21	26	24–48		24 before end of oestrus
Pigs	21	16–30	48	40–65	36	18–47 after onset of oestrus

* *Bos indicus* cattle often exhibit shorter heat periods as do *B. taurus* milking cattle managed in the tropics.
†Considerably shorter in some tropical breeds.

Managerial considerations

Since, with the exception of camels and llamoids, ovulation occurs at a definite time measurable in hours after the onset of heat and in all mammalian species the egg and the sperm are relatively short-lived, it is very important that mating should be planned so as to coincide with ovulation. As far as is practicable mating should take place about the same time – or somewhat before – ovulation occurs so that the sperm will have the maximum chance of meeting with an egg that is passing down the Fallopian tube. Thus in order to properly plan matings it is important to know the length of the heat period, the duration of heat and the time of ovulation. These vary from species to species. Some details of average data for various species are shown in Table 4.2. The first occurrence of heat is determined mainly by environmental factors, but within the same environment there is considerable individual animal and breed variation.

The occurrence of heat is evident in most species by some form of restlessness on the part of the female and by her seeking out a male. In some species, particularly the pig, there is a slight relaxation of the external genitalia. There may also be characteristic exudations from the external genitalia. However, even within species there is a very wide variation in the manner in which females exhibit the onset of heat. In some females heat is easy to detect and in others it is very difficult. For example, it is well known that heat detection can be very difficult in some breeds of *Bos indicus* cattle while it is particularly easy in the Bali breed of *B. (Bibos)* cattle. What is certain is that the easiest manner of finding out if a female is in heat is to see if she will accept a male.

Fertilization and gestation

When a female accepts a male and he copulates and ejaculates, millions of sperm are deposited in her vagina. Only a portion of these, however, reach the extremity of the uterus and only then if the genital passages are relaxed, are free from inflammation and the secretions in the tract are chemically and physically appropriate. Eventually only one sperm will fuse with the egg. Which one of the many will accomplish this feat is probably a matter of pure chance. That is not to say that only one sperm is necessary for fertilization to take place. On the contrary, it has been well established that there must be a certain concentration of sperm at the site of fertilization if one of them is to be effective.

The process is somewhat different in the case of birds. As no yellow body replaces the ruptured follicle in the ovary and therefore no hormone is excreted to inhibit further ovulation, an egg can be released each day. In the case of the hen, the cock's sperm accumulates towards the end of her Fallopian tube and each egg is fertilized as it moves along the tube.

The fusion of one sperm from the male and the single egg of the female constitutes fertilization and is the only physical link between one generation and another, that is to say that the genetical make-up of the male and the female are combined at the moment of fusion to produce a fertilized egg, called a *zygote*. Shortly after fertilization this zygote begins to divide. The first division is generally completed within 24 hours. As the result of repeated cell divisions and the formation of special structures the embryo of the newly created individual begins to take shape. There are various stages of embryonic development, the length of each depending on the total length of the embryonic period or the length of the gestation period of the species. In cows, for example, the zygote takes about 4 days to reach the eight- to sixteen-cell stage. The next phase in the development of the embryo is further cell division with the formation of a group of specialized cells which become the embryonic membranes, as shown in Fig. 4.3. Three membranes envelop the embryo: the outer *chorion* which directly covers the *allantois*; the outer layer of the allantois which is joined with the chorion to form the *allanto-chorion*; and the inner *amnion*. The amnion, coupled with the inner layer of the allantois, forms the *allanto-amnion*. The allantois and the amnion are filled with fluid and surround the embryo. At an early stage in the development of the embryo, the allanto-chorion makes contact with the developed *uterine mucosa*. At this stage *implantation* into the uterus begins. Implantation is a gradual process. In the cow it begins about one month after fertilization and is completed during the third month. In species with shorter gestation periods, implantation usually takes a shorter period of time. For example, in sows implantation takes place during the second and third weeks of pregnancy.

Implantation takes place so that there can be an exchange of substances between the maternal and embryonic tissues. This exchange takes place

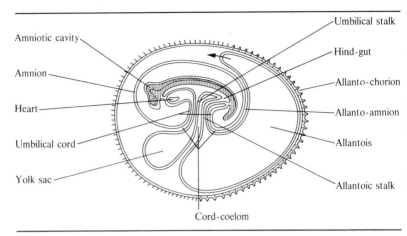

Fig. 4.3 Schematic illustration of the foetus and foetal membranes in the cow about 27 days after fertilization of the egg (Johansson and Rendel, 1968).

through a composite structure known as the *placenta*. It consists of the allanto-chorion, which is the embryonic part, and the mucous membrane of the uterus, which is the maternal part. Different species possess different types of placenta. The placenta of the pig is diffuse, the allanto-chorion making direct contact with the uterine mucosa, while in ruminant species the exchange of materials between the mother and the foetus occurs through 'button'-type structures known as *cotyledons*.

The development of the foetus appears to be very slow during the early stages of gestation, but the pace gradually quickens. In *Bos taurus* cattle, for example, the average 45-day-old foetus weighs approximately 85 g (3 oz), while at 90 days it will weigh approximately 1·0 kg (2·2 lb) and at 200 days approximately 10 kg (22 lb).

There is considerable variation in the length of the gestation period as between species and some variation between breeds and types within species (Table 4.3).

At parturition the placenta is normally evacuated from the uterus after the young animal is born.

Influence of hormones on reproduction

Hormones have a role at all stages in the reproductive cycle, for example the development of the egg in the ovary, the rupture of the follicle and the conditioning of the uterus to receive the fertilized egg are all initiated and controlled by hormones.

Hormones are chemical substances that are produced in ductless glands known as endocrine glands. These secrete the hormone directly into the bloodstream which transports it to the various body tissues on which it acts. Hormones are specific in that they affect particular tissues

Table 4.3   *Gestation periods of some domestic livestock species*

Species	Type	Breed	Gestation period (days) Average	Range
Buffaloes	River	Murrah	308	302–313
		Egyptian	317	313–319
	Swamp		332	301–343
Camels	Dromedary		–	360–390
Cattle	Temperate		280	273–289
		Angus	–	273–282
		Brown Swiss	289	–
		Charolais	289	–
		Friesian	279	–
		Hereford	–	283–286
		Jersey	–	278–280
	Tropical		–	284–288
Goats	Temperate	Saanen	154	–
	Tropical		146	145–148
Llamoids	Alpaca	Huacaya	342	–
		Surti	345	–
	Llama		330	–
Sheep	Temperate	Dorset Horn	–	140–148
		Merino	–	148–152
	Tropical		–	140–160
Pigs	Temperate		114	110–117

that will react only to that hormone. The testes of the male and the ovaries of the female serve a dual role as ductless glands. They not only produce, respectively, male and female sex hormones but also produce the sex cells or *gametes* that transmit characteristics from one generation to the next.

The orchestration or integration of hormone production within the reproductive cycle is conducted from a site in the brain of the animal known as the *hypothalamus* (Fig. 4.4). This controls the pituitary gland, which produces the gonadotrophic hormones, including the follicle-stimulating hormone (FSH), the luteinizing hormone (LH) and the luteo-trophic hormone (LTH) which stimulates the yellow body in the follicle to produce the hormone *progesterone*. The pituitary also produces several other hormones which regulate other specific bodily functions not directly concerned with the reproductive cycle such as the growth hormone (GH) and the thyro-trophic hormone (TSH), etc.

The major hormones concerned in the reproductive cycle are as follows:

Follicle-stimulating hormone (FSH).   The main function of FSH in the female is to stimulate follicular growth in the ovaries and to control the maturation of the egg. In the male, FSH initiates the growth of the testes and induces the production of sperm.

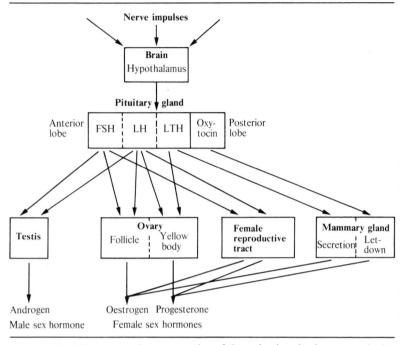

Fig. 4.4 Simplified schematic representation of the endocrine glands concerned with reproduction.

Luteinizing hormone (LH).   In the female LH controls the rupturing of the follicle, thus initiating ovulation. It is also responsible for the production of the yellow body in the ruptured follicle. In the male LH stimulates the production in the testes of *androgen*, the male sex hormone.

Luteo-trophic hormone (LTH).   This hormone controls the production, by the yellow body in the ovarian follicle, of progesterone.

Female sex hormone (oestrogen).   The ovarian follicles produce this hormone while they are developing under the influence of FSH. It is responsible for bringing the female to an excitable stage during heat, so that she will accept the male. It also has an effect on the vagina, causing an increase in the secretion of mucus during heat.

Progesterone.   As stated above, this hormone is produced by the yellow body in the ovarian follicle. It prepares the uterus for the implantation of the foetus and generally ensures the continuation of the normal course of pregnancy. Progesterone, together with oestrogen, also has an effect on the mammary glands of the female, preparing them for the end of pregnancy when they will be required to secrete milk.

Male sex hormone (androgen).   As stated above, this is under the control of LH and is secreted by the testes. It is responsible for stimulating the male in order to increase his libido and for the development of secondary sexual characteristics in the growing male.

The role of hormones in the reproductive cycle is obviously extremely important and in certain cases treatment of reproductive disorders can be affected by the therapeutic use of hormones. It must be emphasized, however, that such treatment is highly specialized and should be conducted only under professional guidance.

Synchronization of the oestrus cycle using hormones has been experimentally performed in recent years in cattle, pigs, sheep and goats. Quantitative relationships between the hormones and fertility are still being intensively investigated and when more is known of their inter-relationships greater success in controlling oestrus can be expected. At present oestrus can be conveniently synchronized in the sheep and goat and the breeding season slightly advanced by the use of 'progestogen'-impregnated intravaginal sponges. Some degree of control of ovulation in yarded cattle is presently possible by the feeding of hormonal compounds which suppress heat and ovulation during the period of their administration. While ovulation is being prevented, the corpora lutea of the ovaries regress as the follicles continue to develop. At termination of the treatment the majority of the cattle come into heat at approximately the same time. Although there is a relatively precise method of controlling ovulation in the sow using a product known as 'otethallibure' – a gonadotrophin-suppressing compound – it is not used extensively and in some countries its use has been prohibited as it has been found that if accidentally included in the feed of pregnant sows it causes the birth of deformed piglets.

The genetic impact and advantage of having a convenient practical method of synchronizing oestrus in farm animals would be through a greater use of artificial insemination (AI) so that a smaller number of sires would be required, thereby considerably increasing the possible selection differential. The best sires could be used on a larger percentage of the total population. Such a practice would, of course, have to be closely supervised by animal breeders so as not to cause any major increase in the level of inbreeding in a breed. Another practical advantage of oestrus synchronization would be the possibility of closer managerial control of the female breeding herd during the breeding season and in producing large groups of marketable animals of about the same age and of similar genetic make-up.

The basis of inheritance

All tissues of the body consist of cells, differing in size and shape in accordance with their bodily function. They contain a substance known as *protoplasm* and among other characteristics they can metabolize nutrients, grow and multiply. A typical cell (Fig. 4.5) is surrounded by a membrane in which the *cytoplasm, nucleus* and *centrosome* can be distinguished. In the nucleus of the resting cell one or more *nucleoli* are present together with a large number of small particles known as *chromatin granules* that at specific stages of cell division appear as thread-like structures or *chromosomes*. These chromosomes occur in pairs. The total number of pairs and the size and shape of individual pairs vary from species to species (Table 4.4). There can also be differences between chromosome pairs within the same species, particularly those that determine the sex of the individual. Chromosomes possess the ability to multiply by division in step with the multiplication of cells while still

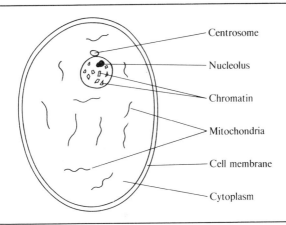

                                             Centrosome

                                             Nucleolus

                                             Chromatin

                                             Mitochondria

                                             Cell membrane

                                             Cytoplasm

Fig. 4.5   Schematic representation of an animal cell.

retaining their individual characteristics. They are of paramount importance because they carry the coded messages or *genes* that transmit inherited characteristics from one generation to the next. The genetically active substance in the genes is *deoxyribonucleic* acid or DNA, which is considered to consist of two chains of nucleolides twisted together in a spiral formation, the sequence of nucleolides in the formation determining the genetic information that is carried in the gene. As the possible total combinations of nucleolides is very large the quantity of genetic information that can be stored in this manner is extraordinary. When a cell divides, the spiral formation of the DNA molecule splits lengthways, one chain of nucleolides going to one cell and the other chain to the other cell. In the two new cells the single chains of the split DNA molecule each act as templates, an exact copy of the single chain being synthesized in order to form a new DNA molecule exactly similar to the one from which the split chains originated. In this way each of the new cells acquires its full complement of chromosomes and genes.

Table 4.4 *The diploid number of chromosomes in some domestic livestock species*

Species	Type	Diploid (2n) number of chromosomes
Buffaloes	River	50
	Swamp	48
Camels		74
Cattle		60
Goats		60
Llamas		74
Sheep		54
Pigs		40
Fowls		78
Ducks		80
Turkeys		82

Cell division

There are two sharply differentiated types of cell in the animal's body. *Somatic cells* that make up the body of the individual animal and are concerned with all body structures and most body functions, and *germ cells* that are concerned with the reproduction of a new generation of individual animals. When somatic cells multiply, the daughter cells are exact replicas of the mother cell, whereas when germ cells are produced the number of chromosomes is reduced to half the number for the species. Somatic cells are *diploid* and possess 2n chromosomes whilst germ cells are *haploid* and possess n chromosomes.

Somatic cell division or mitosis. In mitotic division each daughter cell receives the same chromosome complement as was possessed by the mother cell by the mechanism described in a previous paragraph. Mitosis is a continuing process and it is the means by which the individual animal grows and replaces worn-out cells with new, healthy cells. A schematic illustration of mitosis is shown in Fig. 4.6.

Germ cell division, reduction division or meiosis. The process of meiosis occurs in the same way in both the male and the female of the species. The male and female germ cells are produced in the manner described in the section concerned with the reproductive cycle. It was stated in a previous paragraph that there are differences between chromosome pairs within the same species, in particular those that determine the sex of the individual. These chromosomes are known as the *sex chromosomes.* They also carry many other genes for other characteristics and these are called *sex-linked characteristics.* The other chromosomes in the cell are known as *autosomes.*

   Although the mechanics of meiosis are the same in the male and the female each process will be described separately.

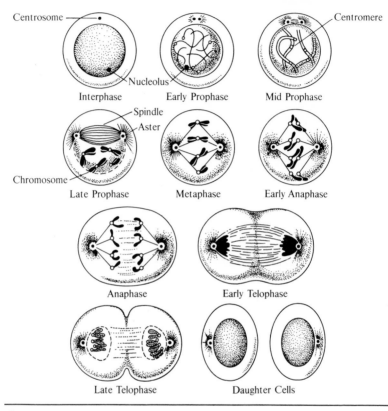

Fig. 4.6   Schematic illustration of mitosis (Gardner, 1960).

In the male the germ cells are found on the inner wall of the seminiferous tubules of the testicles. At sexual maturity these cells are stimulated by hormonal action to produce functional sperm. The process of meiosis begins with the *primary spermatocyte* growing and enlarging and finally dividing into two secondary *spermatocytes*. The division follows a process known as *synapsis* in which the pairs of like chromosomes known as *homologues* – one member of each pair having been derived from each parent – fuse together. During this process filaments of chromatin twist around each other, thus providing an opportunity for the exchange of genes from one homologue to the other. This is one of the mechanisms by which variation occurs, but there is of course no complete interchange of genes between one homologue and another. After synapsis there is a separation of the fused pair of chromosomes, one homologue of each pair moving to one or other side of the cell (Fig. 4.7). After the polarization of the chromosomes is completed a new cell wall is formed with the production of two secondary spermatocytes, each containing one-half the total number of chromosomes normal for the species. The haploid cells containing half the number of chromosomes are not of course identical with the parent cell or with the normal body somatic cells. The two secondary spermatocytes then divide by the process of ordinary mitosis to produce four *spermatids*. After a period of maturation the four spermatids develop into functional sperm with the characteristic tail, body and head. As the cell division proceeds, the mature sperm migrate from the wall of the tubule to the lumen or centre of the tubule through which they exit from the testicle in the manner described in the section concerned with the reproductive cycle.

The process of meiosis in the female is similar to that in the male with the exception that the primary germ cell or *ovacyte* forms one *secondary ovacyte* and one non-functional *polar body* (Fig. 4.7). Each contains one-half the normal number of chromosomes. The polar body differs from the secondary ovacyte in that it has no yoke. The secondary ovacyte and

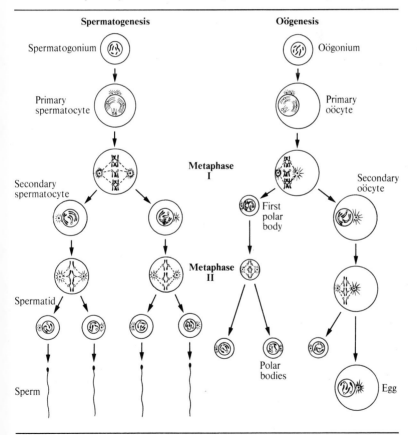

Fig. 4.7 Schematic illustration of meiosis (Gardner, 1960).

the polar body then further divide by the process of mitosis: the ovacyte producing an ovum or egg and an additional polar body and the first polar body producing two polar bodies. The ovum thus produced is capable of being fertilized by sperm. The polar bodies appear to be non-functional and are absorbed.

The function of meiosis is to retain constancy in the chromosome number of the species and to ensure that both the male and female contribute genes to their offspring that are randomly representative of their characteristics. The haploid (n) egg contains half the number of chromosomes of the female parent when it fuses with the haploid (n) sperm that contains half the number of chromosomes of the male, forming a diploid ($2n$) zygote or fertilized egg that contains the number of chromosomes characteristic of the species.

The inheritance of characteristics

As the distribution of chromosomes and consequently of genes in meiosis is at random, this permits new combinations of paternal and maternal characteristics in the offspring. A knowledge of this process and the ability to select individuals through various selection methods provides an opportunity for the selection of animals possessing new combinations of genes that provide desirable characteristics required by man in his domestic livestock. It is also obvious that new combinations of genes may alternatively produce individuals with undesirable characteristics. These animals can be culled before they are allowed to breed and reproduce.

The process of meiosis described above does not necessarily proceed smoothly on all occasions. There can be accidents during the process so that the normal number of chromosomes for the species is not always attained. These accidents may be due to non-disjunction, separation of parts of the chromosomes, abnormal pairing or non-pairing of homologues, etc. In addition, as explained in a previous paragraph, the arrangement of genes on the chromosomes can vary due to crossing over of genes during the process of synapsis. When variations due to these causes occur they will, of course, produce considerable and in some ways abnormal variations in the characteristics of the offspring. These phenomena are discussed in some detail in later sections.

Phenotypic differences – or the difference in the appearance of individuals both within and between species – have been studied and theorized on by naturalists for a long time. In 1900, three botanists working independently – De Vries in the Netherlands, Correns in Germany and von Tschermak in Austria – proposed theories to explain the mechanism of the inheritance of individual characteristics. The work of these three botanists independently substantiated the work of an Augustinian monk, Gregor Mendel, who in 1866 had published papers that reported on data from 8 years of crossbreeding experiments using common garden peas. Mendel's work was known in both Europe and America, but the significance of his findings was not appreciated until De Vries, Correns and von Tschermak published their papers. In his papers Mendel proposed two basic laws on the inheritance of characteristics. These were: (1) the *law of segregation* – that the characteristics of an individual are determined by pairs of genes, but that their germ cells possess only one gene from each pair; and (2) the *law of independent assortment* – that the genes combine at random with each other, both at the formation of germ cells and at fertilization. Since Mendel's original publication there have been many modifications of these laws, but they are still fundamental for the whole science of genetics. The resulting overall interpretation of the laws of inheritance of characteristics is now known as the Mendelian theory of inheritance.

The practical significance of the first two laws of Mendelian theory are of extreme importance when man is selecting for specific traits in plants and animals. They will now be considered with reference to examples from domestic livestock.

As stated in a previous paragraph the chromosomes occur in pairs and each homologue contains identical genes that occur in the same order in each homologue. These identical genes are known as *alleles*. Although the opposite genes are identical in that they affect the same phenotypic characteristic or development process of a character, they do not necessarily influence it in the same way. If both alleles have the same influence on a characteristic the individual possessing them is said to be *homozygous* for that characteristic, but if they differ in their influence the individual is said to be *heterozygous* for the characteristic. If the effect of one allele is stronger than that of the other to the extent that it masks the effect of the other, the masking allele is said to be *dominant*, while the allele that has been masked is said to be *recessive*. For example, in cattle the polled or absence-of-horns trait is dominant over the horned trait. Thus when homozygous horned cattle are mated with homozygous polled cattle the offspring possess one gene for the presence of horns and another for the absence of horns, i.e. they are heterozygous for the characteristic. Since the polled gene is dominant all the offspring are polled (Fig. 4.8).

For graphic purposes, in order to express the actions of such genes, a capital letter is used to denote the dominant allele and a small letter to indicate the recessive allele. Thus, in the example given above the homozygous horned individual would be designated as hh, the homozygous polled individual as HH and the heterozygous individuals resulting from the mating as Hh. The situation could then be expressed in the following manner.

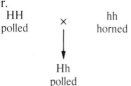

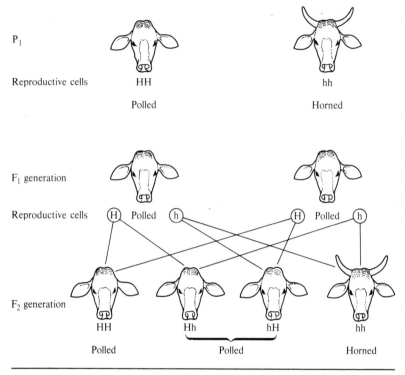

P_1

Reproductive cells   HH   hh

                         Polled   Horned

F_1 generation

Reproductive cells   (H) Polled (h)   (H) Polled (h)

F_2 generation
                    HH   Hh   hH   hh

                  Polled   Polled   Horned

Fig. 4.8 Illustration of the inheritance of the polled trait in cattle.

The phenotypes of the HH and Hh individuals will be the same, but their *genotypes* – or their potential for transmitting characteristics to their offspring – will be different.

In some traits dominance is not complete. If this is the case and dominance is only partial then the offspring may exhibit phenotypic characteristics that are a blend of those of the two parents. A well-known example occurs in the Andalusian breed of poultry in which there are black and white varieties. If a black homozygous individual is mated to a white homozygous individual the offspring possess blue feathers. When an individual is homozygous for a recessive characteristic, such as is the case in the white variety of Andalusian poultry, the phenotype is the same as the genotype since the recessive trait has neither been masked nor modified.

An individual that is homozygous for one pair of genes has only one type of that gene to transmit and therefore breeds true. However, if an individual is heterozygous, it will have two types of the same gene to transmit. As only one of each pair of genes is transmitted to each germ cell at meiosis, any resulting fertilized egg could contain either of the two different types of the same gene. If the example of the transmission of horn or absence of horn characteristics in cattle is reconsidered it will be seen that when the polled herozygotes (Hh) are intermated then, as both parents produce equal numbers of germ cells carrying either allele, the chances of any sperm cell from the male fusing with any egg of the same type or of a different type are equal and so four combinations of the genes are possible. These combinations are HH, Hh, hH and hh (Fig. 4.8).

Thus the result of a random fertilization is on average one homozygous dominant (HH) polled animal, two heterozygous (Hh) polled animals and one homozygous recessive (hh) horned animal. The phenotype grouping is therefore three polled to one horned animal, but since fertilization is at random it must not be expected in practice that among every four progeny of such matings the result will be three polled and one horned animals. This will occur only when a very large number of matings are evaluated. The chance of a recessive trait being exhibited under these circumstances is obviously one in four, and the chance of obtaining a true breeding individual from among those which phenotypically exhibit the dominant trait is one in three. The practical importance of this type of information is considerable when the animal breeder is selecting for specific characteristics.

An example of what happens when dominance is lacking in alleles can be demonstrated by reference to the inheritance of coat colour in Shorthorn cattle. If a red-coated Shorthorn is represented by RR and a white-coated Shorthorn by rr, then when red and white Shorthorns are mated the offspring are of a Rr type and their coat colour is roan rather than either red or white. This may be represented as follows:

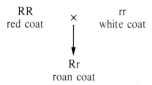

If the roan offspring are intermated then segregation takes place as in the previous example. This may be represented as follows:

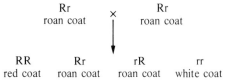

Thus in this case the phenotypic and genotypic ratios are the same – one homozygous (RR) red animal, one homozygous (rr) white animal and two heterozygous (Rr) roan animals and the heterozygotes are distinguished in appearance from either of the homozygotes. This was not the case in the example discussed previously of the inheritance of the polled trait. The genotypes HH and Hh appeared to be phenotypically the same and it would only be possible to distinguish them genotypically by performing a further breeding test, i.e. by mating them with animals of a known genotype and observing the progeny. For example, if the polled HH animals were mated with horned animals then all the progeny would be polled, whereas if the polled Hh animals were mated with horned animals half of the progeny would be polled and half horned.

The examples given above demonstrate the operation of the first Mendelian law on the segregation of inherited characteristics. The second Mendelian law, that of independent assortment, can be demonstrated in an example where the inheritance of two pairs of genes are considered at the same time. For example we can consider two dominant traits, polledness and snorter dwarfism in Hereford cattle. If a homozygous

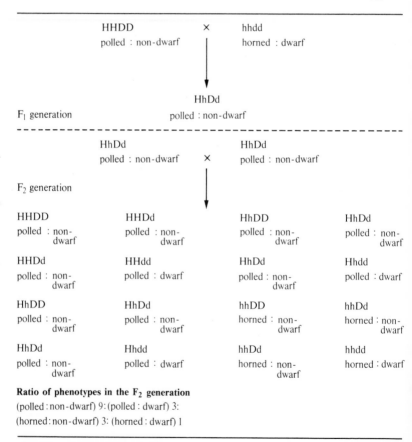

Ratio of phenotypes in the F$_2$ generation
(polled : non-dwarf) 9 : (polled : dwarf) 3 :
(horned : non-dwarf) 3 : (horned : dwarf) 1

Fig. 4.9 Schematic representation of the inheritance of the polled and snorter dwarf traits in Hereford cattle.
Note: H represents the polled, h the horned, D the non-dwarf and d the dwarf traits.

polled, non-dwarf individual with the genotype HHDD is mated to a homozygous horned, dwarf individual with the genotype hhdd then the resulting F_1 progeny will be phenotypically polled and non-dwarf but genotypically HhDd. If the F_1 progeny are then intermated the resulting offspring (F_2) will exhibit four different phenotypes in the ratio of nine polled non-dwarf, to three polled dwarf, to three horned non-dwarf, to one horned dwarf individual. There will be, however, nine different genotypes (Fig. 4.9). The phenotypic ratio of 9:3:3:1 is mathematically the square of the ratio of 3:1, which is the phenotypic ratio when one characteristic is considered. If three pairs of characteristics that all exhibit dominance are considered then a phenotypic ratio of 27:9:9:9:3:3:3:1 will result. The number of possible combinations increases rapidly with an increase in the number of gene pairs. This can be seen from Table 4.5. Thus, in domestic animals where the number of heterozygous gene pairs is very large it is not surprising that no two individuals, with the

Table 4.5 *Combination possibilities in the F_2 generation when F_1 individuals are heterozygous for a specific number of gene pairs*

Pairs of genes	No. of gametes	Combination possibilities	No. of genotypes	No. of homozygous combinations
1	2	4	3	2
2	4	16	9	4
3	8	64	27	8
4	16	256	81	16
10	1,024	1,048,576	59,049	1,024
n	2^n	4^n	3^n	2^n

Source: Johannsson and Rendel (1968).

exception of identical twins, are genotypically or phenotypically completely alike.

Where dominance exists in one pair of genes but is lacking in the other the situation is different. For example, if we consider Shorthorn cattle where the polled trait is dominant and the coat colour trait lacks dominance, then if a homozygous polled red Shorthorn is mated with a homozygous horned white Shorthorn all the F_1 progeny will be heterozygous polled and roan in colour (Fig. 4.10). When the F_1 generation are intermated the following ratio of different phenotypic types of cattle would be obtained in the F_2 generation: three polled and red, six polled and roan, three polled and white, one horned and red, two horned and roan and one horned and white (Fig. 4.10).

From the examples that have been discussed above it will be appreciated that if the mode of inheritance of traits is known then expected ratios of different types of offspring from specific matings can be calculated, as can the probability of obtaining a particular type of

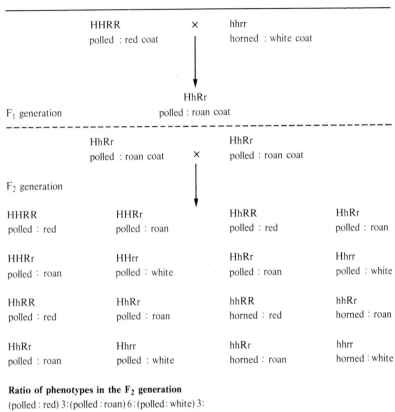

Ratio of phenotypes in the F₂ generation

(polled : red) 3 : (polled : roan) 6 : (polled : white) 3 :
(horned : red) 1 : (horned : roan) 2 : (horned : white) 1

Fig. 4.10   Schematic representation of the inheritance of the polled trait and coat colour in Shorthorn cattle.
Note: H represents the polled trait, h the horned, R red coat colour and r white coat colour.

individual from a specific mating. There are, however, a number of important exceptions to these general rules.

Modifications of the basic Mendelian law may be necessary for a number of reasons. These include, among others, an additive effect of genes, the effect of duplicate recessive genes and the non-linear interaction effects between genes at different loci or *epistasis*. Also important are the effects of *linkage*, *crossing-over*, *multiple alleles* and disturbances in the chromosome mechanism. In general, no sharp distinction can be made between qualitative and quantitative characteristics. A characteristic may be determined by a major gene or *oligogene*, but one or more other minor genes or *polygenes* may cause some variation in the manifestation of the characteristic.

Where gene interaction is between alleles there may be *overdominance* if the heterozygotes are superior in one way or another to both the homozygotes. The occurrence of overdominance is assumed to play an important role in such qualitative characteristics as viability and fertility and will be further discussed in the section on crossbreeding. The effect may be due to one gene having a more advantageous effect than two genes of the same type – i.e. a level of dosage effect – or to the alleles complementing each other in some way.

In epistasis, the effect of a single gene depends upon with which other genes it interacts. The effect on the normal additive situation can be either negative or positive.

An example of linkage is two characteristics that are somewhat related and not completely independent because they are controlled by genes that are located on the same chromosome rather than on different chromosomes. Under these circumstances independent assortment does not occur and the ratios of the phenotypes may be different from those stated above, where it has been assumed that the genes are located on separate chromosomes.

Crossing-over is said to occur when – although the genes are known to be located on different chromosomes – in some way they stay together. It happens if chromosomes do not completely sort themselves independently but somehow a part of one chromosome joins up with a part of its homologue or vice versa.

It has been assumed in the examples of segregation and independent assortment given above that at any given location in the chromosomes there would be two alleles. More than two alleles can, however, be present and this also modifies the normal Mendelian ratios. One of the best-known examples is concerned with the inheritance of blood type in man. In this case there are four blood types derived from combinations of three allelic genes.

The livestock breeder is not of course usually concerned with the inheritance of one or two single traits. What is of major interest is the inheritance of quantitative characteristics such as body size, milk yield, the fat content of milk and the egg production of hens. It is therefore important to realize that although the fundamental laws of Mendelian inheritance still apply, characteristics of this type are strongly modified by environmental variation and that a very large number of genes are involved that may have different degrees of effect and interact in a complicated way with each other.

The inheritance of sex

In the examples of inheritance that have been so far described it has been assumed that the genes were located in the autosomes and not on the sex chromosomes. The latter are different from the autosomes in that they are the primary determinants of sex in the offspring. In mammals the female possesses a pair of homologues known as the X-chromosomes, while the male possesses one X-chromosome and one that is very different called the Y-chromosome. The inheritance of sex can be shown schematically as follows:

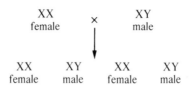

Thus the sex ratio should theoretically be one to one. In farming practice the male:female ratio has been calculated to be 51·5, 52·3 and 49·2 for cattle, pigs and poultry, respectively (Johansson and Rendel, 1968). It is generally assumed that in mammals the male:female ratio at fertilization is considerably higher than 50 per cent, but that the ratio is reduced during the gestation period because males have a higher foetal death rate. The reason why the sex ratio is higher at fertilization could be because for some reason sperms carrying the Y-chromosome are more viable. If there are differences in viability between the sperms carrying the X- and the Y-chromosomes then it might be possible to separate them. This could be the basis for some future method of sex determination.

In birds the male is the homogametic (XX) sex and the female the heterogametic (XY) sex.

Other genes which are located on the sex chromosomes will obviously be linked or associated with sex and will be transmitted to the next generation in combination with sex. The fewer the chromosomes that the species possesses and the larger the sex chromosomes, the more traits are likely to be associated with sex and inherited in a sex-linked manner. To date, no sex-linked characteristics of economic importance have been recorded in mammalian livestock, but there are several in poultry. These include barred compared with dark heads, silver compared with gold down colour and curly compared with late feathering in chicks. Sex-linked inheritance of a colour factor has also been demonstrated in turkeys and geese. Man also demonstrates a number of well-known sex-linked characteristics, including haemophilia and red-green colour blindness. Haemophilia is also sex-linked in dogs.

It was thought at one time that the colour-marking genes could be used for the rapid determination of sex in chicks, but as poultry are bred strictly for their production characteristics breeders could not afford to restrict their breeding programmes to the breeds exhibiting sex-linked colour traits. In any case sexing by examination of the external genitalia of day-old chicks is now commonplace so that the economic need for a colour determinant of sex in the chick has declined. A schematic diagram of the sex-linked inheritance of barring is shown in Fig. 4.11. When a black cock is mated with a barred female, in the F_1 generation all the males are barred and the females are black. After hatching the difference between the sexes can be seen immediately as the male chicks have a light patch on the back of their head and are relatively light coloured on the other parts of the body while the female chicks possess down of an even colour.

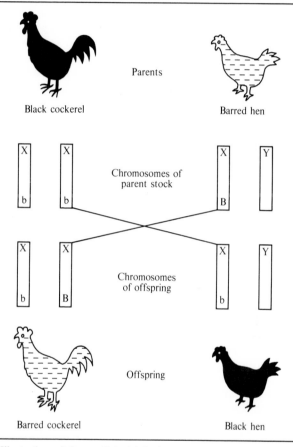

Black cockerel

Parents

Barred hen

Chromosomes of parent stock

Chromosomes of offspring

Barred cockerel

Offspring

Black hen

Fig. 4.11 Illustration of the sex-linked inheritance of the barring trait in poultry (Hammond *et al.*, 1971).
Note: B represents barred and b self-colour (black).

The White Leghorn breed possesses a sex-linked gene for early feathering, an economically desirable characteristic as it is linked with earlier maturity and the chicks are less liable to chill, whereas some of the heavier breeds have a corresponding dominant allele for late feathering. If White Leghorn cocks are bred to the heavier breed hens the female chicks exhibit the early feathering trait.

Autosexing breeds such as the *Legbar* and the *Cambar* have been produced, but they have not been particularly popular as they have not been so productive as some other non-autosexing breeds.

Mutation

There are many examples of the sudden appearance of variants or 'sports' in livestock. The process is known as *mutation*. It may be defined as every change in the heritable sense which is not due to segregation or to a recombination of previously existing genes. This spontaneous change may be due to a variety of reasons, and there is presumably a change in the chemical composition of the gene.

Mutation can take place in both somatic and germ cells; it occurs naturally at all times, but its frequency can be increased by the effect of radiation and certain chemicals. Natural mutations apparently occur at rates ranging from one in 100,000 generations to one in 10 million generations. The majority of visible mutations appear to be generally undesirable as far as the livestock breeder is concerned, but more of them may be advantageous for the breeders of fancy pet animals. It is believed that the majority of the fancy breeds of dogs, cats, rabbits and various species of birds owe their origin to a mutation. If the mutant is a dominant gene the trait that it controls should be exhibited immediately, but if it is a recessive gene the trait may be hidden for generations.

It must be presumed that animals gradually acclimatize themselves generation by generation to a new environment partly on account of mutations that are favourable to them in their new environment.

If a single gene has a multiple effect – a phenomenon known as *pleiotropy* – even mutations that could be considered to be desirable may have other effects that are very undesirable. For example, double muscling in beef cattle might be considered economically desirable, but when the trait is inherited in the homozygous form it is also the cause of unthriftiness and infertility. Another interesting example is the link between polledness and intersexuality of female goats. The polled condition can appear due to a mutation in horned goats, and as it is a dominant character it would be expected that it should be possible to breed hornless goats. This is not the case as homozygous polled females are intersexual and therefore sterile, and homozygotes are required in order to be able to breed for total hornlessness.

Many of the abnormalities common in livestock are due to mutations. Those that cause the death of the foetus are known as *lethal factors*. Others such as cleft palate, hernia, inverted nipples and *atresia ani* in pigs and cryptorchidism in cattle, sheep, goats and pigs cause difficulties after birth. The many types of coat colour in domestic livestock have all been derived by mutation from a more limited number of coat colours in wild animals. Abnormalities are often associated with white colour – such as the underdevelopment of the vagina and uterus in white Shorthorn heifers. Details of known lethal factors in livestock in the temperate zone have been published by Lerner (1944). The majority of abnormalities noted in temperate-type stock are also known to occur in tropical-type livestock.

Domestic livestock can and should be purged of unwanted mutations that cause abnormalities, particularly if male animals are going to be used to mate with a large number of females either naturally or by using AI. If the male is homozygous for the abnormality, then he will normally exhibit it so that his elimination from a breeding programme is simple. If he is heterozygous he may not exhibit the abnormality. He should be mated with two or three females of the same breed that exhibit the abnormality. If he is heterozygous for the trait half the resulting offspring will exhibit the trait; if he does not possess the trait then none of the offspring will exhibit it. Heterozygous males can thus be identified and culled.

Changes in the number of chromosomes

When the chromosome number of a type or species is a multiple of the haploid chromosome number (n) and larger than the diploid number ($2n$) it is usual to refer to it as a *polyploid*. Changes in the chromosome number have been mainly studied in plants and lower animals, and although *polyploidy* may have played a role in the evolution of animal species little is at present known of its incidence in livestock. In this context it is interesting to note than in man possession of an additional X-chromosome, i.e. the male possessing XXY-chromosomes instead of the normal XY, may be one cause of intersexuality.

Genetic–environmental interactions

The suggestion by Hammond (1947), that livestock should be reared and bred in the most favourable environment if maximum improvements are to be made through selection, has been generally accepted in the temperate zone. However, this theory may not be sound if the differences between the environments in which the livestock are bred and used are very great, as they are between temperate and tropical environments. Genetic–environmental interactions may in fact be very important for the livestock breeder in the tropics. They may be defined as the differential response of a specific genotype in different environments.

One obvious effect of the environment on the genotype is on the mature size of domestic livestock. Under natural grazing conditions in high-rainfall areas, where minerals have been leached from the soil, domestic livestock are generally smaller than genetically similar animals managed in drier areas where there is little leaching. An example occurs in East Africa where the semi-arid-area cattle such as the Boran and the Karamajong are on average much larger than the East African Shorthorn Zebu that are found in the more humid areas, although it is highly probable that all these Zebu breeds had a common ancestry. In India virtually all breeds of Zebu hill cattle are on average smaller in size than the Zebu cattle found in the adjacent plains although they almost certainly possess a common ancestry (see Ch. 5, Pt II).

The reasons for genetic–environmental interactions are probably varied. One reason that has been suggested is that the genes affecting a particular trait in an animal may not be the same in two very different environments. It is also possible that the effect of a specific mutation might be very different in different environments. For example, a mutation for additional or longer body hair could be very advantageous to an animal in a cold, temperate climate and very disadvantageous in a hot, humid tropical climate.

What is certain is that the planning of breeding programmes in the tropics depends as much on the magnitude of genetic–environmental interactions as it does on other genetic parameters. Readers who are particularly interested in interactions with regard to specific livestock should consult Pani and Lasley (1972).

Maternal influence

The mother has a very considerable influence on the development of her young during the gestation and suckling periods. Usually the birth weight decreases with an increase in the number of young born. In cattle and sheep the birth weights of individual twins are 25 to 30 per cent lower than the birth weights of singles.

When reciprocal crosses are made between large and small breeds there is no experimental evidence that under most circumstances the maternal influence during the gestation period has any influence on body size at maturity of the offspring. Differences have, however, been noted where the disparities in size are extreme, i.e. between the Shire horse and the Shetland pony and between the Flemish Giant and the small Polish rabbit. Experimental work does not support the idea that the mother has, in the long term, any special influence on the offspring or that the offspring inherit more traits from their dam than from their sire. Differences that occur in the mature offspring of reciprocal crosses of extreme animal types must be considered to be due to carry-over effects of differences in the foetal and suckling environments.

To what extent the age of the mother influences the frequency of congenital defects in domestic livestock is unknown.

It has been shown that there are many instances of congenital malformation in domestic livestock where a change in the environment can have the same effect as a change in the genetic constitution of the animal. This phenomenon is known as *phenocopy*. Phenocopies of a number of genetically determined deformities in the offspring can be obtained by injecting the mother with specific chemical substances during the first part of her gestation period. Deficiencies of vitamins can also induce deformities in the foetus.

In practice, it is suggested that deformities in young livestock should be scrutinized very carefully before they are necessarily attributed to the effect of heredity.

Animal breeding practices

Current animal breeding methods, reviewed by Mahadevan (1970), will be briefly discussed and the ways in which these practices can best be used in tropical environments will be considered.

Selection

In order to improve the average level of a livestock population for any trait by genetic means the population must be subjected to selection for the specific trait or combination of traits required. Some traits are strongly inherited, while others are weakly inherited as their development in the animal is more dependent upon environmental conditions. The intensity of inheritance of a specific trait can be measured. It is known as the *heritability* of the trait, is usually symbolized as h^2, and it may be defined as those phenotypic differences in a trait that can be attributed to inheritance. It has been found that those parts of the animal that develop early in life tend to possess higher heritabilities than those parts that develop later, and that heritability estimates are least variable if they are determined under standardized environmental conditions. Approximate estimates of the heritabilities of a number of selected productive traits in domestic livestock are shown in Table 4.6. It will be seen from this table that carcase traits are generally highly inherited, that liveweight gain and efficiency of feed conversion are moderately highly inherited, that milk and egg production are relatively poorly inherited and that such traits as fertility and viability are very poorly inherited.

Heritability provides an index of the probable efficiency of selection. Where heritabilities are high the most effective programme for genetic improvement of the trait would be mass selection of those individuals exhibiting the desirable trait with little attention being given to ancestry, sibs and other collateral relatives and to progeny tests. Where heritabili-

Table 4.6   *The approximate heritability of selected traits in some domestic livestock*

Type of livestock	Trait	Approximate heritability (% h^2)
Dairy cattle	Butterfat percentage in milk	50–60
	Protein percentage in milk	50–60
	Butterfat production	20–30
	Milk production	20–30
	Reproductive performance	0–10
Beef cattle	Score for tenderness of meat	55–65
	Dressing percentage of carcase	55–65
	Bone percentage in carcase	45–55
	Heart girth measurement	45–55
	Daily liveweight gain	40–50
	Efficiency of feed conversion	35–45
	Birth weight	35–45
	Weaning weight	20–25
Sheep	Daily liveweight gain	50–60
	Staple length of wool	40–50
	No. crimps per unit length in wool	40–50
	Birth weight	25–35
	Weaning weight	25–35
Pigs	Score for leanness of meat	65–75
	Body length	45–55
	Back-fat thickness	45–55
	Daily liveweight gain	40–50
	Efficiency of feed conversion	35–40
Poultry	Thickness of eggshell	35–45
	Egg production	20–30
	Age at first lay	15–25
	Hatchability of eggs	10–15
	Viability of eggs	10–15
	Fertility	0–5

Note: The majority of the estimates have been made in temperate-zone countries.

ties are low, selection should include some form of progeny test and be based on ancestry and the performance of close relatives.

Selection acts by allowing selected individuals to contribute more traits to the next generation than other individuals in the same population. In fact the unselected individuals will have no influence on the next generation as they will not be allowed to breed. The rate at which selection can improve a population depends upon its overall accuracy, its level of intensity and the interval between generations. Accuracy in selection depends upon how well the phenotype reflects the genotype and this can be improved by keeping as many records as is economically practicable. For example, the heritability of milk yield estimated from a single lactation record of a milking cow may be 0·25, whereas when two, three and four lactations are included in the estimate the heritabilities may be 0·33, 0·37 and 0·40, respectively. Stress must, however, be placed on the economic practicability of record-keeping. Multiple and complicated records do not necessarily provide additional information as to how accurately the phenotype reflects the genotype. The intensity of selection depends to a very large extent on suitable replacement animals being available. Thus improvements in overall fertility and mortality improve the possibilities for intensifying selection. The interval between generations depends upon the interval between birth and sexual maturity and the fertility rate. Thus any improvements in the age at first parturition and in overall fertility will help to decrease the interval between generations and thus increase selection pressure.

Four major methods of selection are used in practice: individual or mass selection, pedigree selection, selection on the basis of collateral relatives and progeny testing.

Individual or mass selection and performance testing. This is a most valuable method where a trait is highly inherited and where it can be observed in both sexes. In order to compare animals from different herds and therefore from slightly different environments the animals to be tested must be brought together under the same conditions of feeding and management. An arrangement of this type is called a *performance test.* It can, of course, only be used for selecting for traits that can be measured in the live animal, such as growth rate and efficiency of feed conversion. However, the recent development of ultrasonic carcase measurements has meant that some carcase measurements can also be made, particularly in pigs. The major use of the performance test is for the selection of suitable breeding males.

Pedigree selection. This is a method of selection based on the performance of ancestors. It was, until recent times, the major method by which selection was practised and it spawned a network of pedigree herd societies in the temperate zone. The methods can be of value only if the pedigree information is complete. Today, pedigree information is most useful when no data are available for the individual animal, either because it is too young or because the expression of a trait is sex-linked. The principal use of a pedigree in animal-breeding practice is to avoid too close an inbreeding ratio.

Selection on the basis of collateral relatives. This is most useful when family size is large, when traits are highly inherited, when there is a close genetic relationship between members of the family and when the mean generation interval is short. It is therefore obviously of more use in selecting for productive traits in poultry than in cattle.

Progeny testing.   The assessment of the breeding value of an animal on the basis of the performance of its offspring is known as a *progeny test.* As in most livestock species males produce many more offspring during their lives than females, progeny tests are usually applied to males. It is a particularly valuable method to employ where a trait such as milk production is not measurable in mature animals of both sexes, where the heritability of a trait is low, where the breeding unit is large and where the increase in the generation interval, implicit in the method, is not too pronounced. Selection accuracy is increased at the expense of selection intensity and an increase in the interval between generations. Progeny testing is widely used in order to improve milk production in the temperate zone, but so far this method of selection has not been used to any major extent in the tropics.

Aids to selection

Artificial insemination.   This method of breeding is now used for every species of domestic livestock. Nevertheless, its usefulness is not unlimited and it can be practised successfully only under quite specific practical conditions.

It is generally accepted that the benefits to be derived from AI are that it allows the maximum exploitation of the best sires, the fullest use of a selected sire and a consequent reduction in the total number of sires that have to be maintained. Thus when AI is properly organized there can be a real reduction in breeding costs; AI also minimizes the spread of venereal and other diseases. As AI demands that the farmer should closely observe his female stock, it also probably improves general standards of management. Certainly it is a method by which livestock owners and livestock extension agents are brought into closer contact with each other and it probably stimulates a general increasing interest in livestock improvement.

It is a method that is of particular utility to livestock farmers who wish to use different breeds of sires simultaneously, and is likely to be economic in areas where there are a large number of smallholders, the majority owning one male and a limited number of female stock. It can also be of the greatest use where it is desired to import exotic livestock for crossbreeding and/or upgrading purposes, and where it is doubtful whether exotic sires will thrive.

As AI involves the close handling of animals it cannot be undertaken on an economic scale where the livestock are too wild or too dispersed on the holding. Nor is it normally economic to service widely separated farms, particularly where roads and telephone communications are poor or non-existent.

There are also some special technical problems for AI in the tropics. In most countries the low level of farm recording has been a major handicap in the testing of AI bulls. Obviously little is to be gained and considerable harm may be caused if the sires used in an AI programme are unproven and not known to be superior to most local sires. If they are not proven they could in fact be inferior to some local bulls that would otherwise be used for natural service. Another problem is that many livestock-owning peoples in the tropics rear all their male animals to maturity for meat purposes, so that the use of AI does not reduce their costs in bull maintenance. Perhaps the most serious technical difficulty is that in the females of many tropical breeds – in particular in the females of the Zebu or humped cattle breeds – their heat period is short in duration and often difficult to identify as it usually occurs at night. Under these circumstances many heat periods may be missed and this seriously reduces the efficiency of the AI operation. Short and silent heats are also very frequent in the females of exotic dairy breeds managed in the tropics, and in consequence AI in many exotic dairy herds has tended to become an uneconomic operation.

It is apparent that the organization of an AI service is not necessarily the ultimate answer to livestock-breeding problems in any tropical country. In fact it may be an inefficient method of using scarce resources.

Technological improvements in AI, such as the introduction of deep-frozen semen, may have improved the possibilities of importing the semen of exotic breeds into the tropics and may have solved some of the problems posed by scattered holdings and poor communications, but these new techniques require even more equipment and highly skilled manpower than the old and due consideration should be given to all the relevant factors before they are introduced.

Contemporary comparison test. This is probably the most effective selection method for dairy cattle that has been evolved to date. A sample of the average milk yield of unselected heifers in a number of herds under test is compared with that of contemporaries sired by other bulls. The comparisons are between heifers of approximately the same age and sexual maturity and are made in the same time period. This is therefore a method of testing dairy bulls under farm conditions. It is the standard method used in the United Kingdom and in some other countries. Unfortunately, it is not likely to be of practical importance in most tropical countries as it is only applicable in farming systems where there is a high level of recording.

Testing stations. Special centres for progeny testing have been established for the selection of pigs, poultry, dairy and beef cattle in a number of different countries. At these centres housing, feeding and general management are standardized. For example, in the testing of dairy bulls in Denmark eighteen to twenty daughters of each of the bulls to be tested are chosen at random from different herds without reference to the production of their dams. The heifers must be of approximately the same age and sexual maturity. They are brought together in the testing station at least 3 months before parturition and retained until they have completed one lactation. Comparisons between bulls are then made on the basis of performance of the progeny groups at the test stations.

Progeny-testing stations could be used in most tropical countries where they have the advantage that good husbandry methods can be demonstrated to the livestock owners whose animals are under test. The major problem would be economic, i.e. the cost of such stations in relation to the overall benefit that might be expected.

Selection indexes.   Often the livestock breeder is concerned with selecting for more than one trait in an animal at any one time. There are three major methods by which he may proceed. First, selection of each trait separately and simultaneously. Secondly, selection for one trait at a time in succession, known as tandem selection. Thirdly, selection for all traits simultaneously in accordance with some form of selection index. This latter method can be satisfactory unless there is a high negative correlation between any two of the traits included in the index. An example would be an attempt to select for high milk production and heat tolerance in dairy cattle in the tropics. These two traits are negatively correlated as high milk production automatically reduces heat tolerance. In order to construct a suitable selection index the breeder requires information on the heritabilities of the relevant traits, genetic and phenotypic correlations between the traits and their economic value.

To date selection indexes have mainly been used in the temperate zone in the selection of superior beef cattle.

Selection on the basis of correlated characteristics.   Obviously if a trait could be found that is easily observed and/or measured and that is correlated with productivity, then that trait could be used for selection purposes. One such trait has been noted that can be used for selection purposes in the tropics, particularly when exotic livestock are imported: the trait of woolly-coatedness. It was first reported from South Africa that woolly-coated beef cattle were poorer performers than sleek-coated animals of the same breed in a hot climate and the original observation has since been confirmed elsewhere. Selection for sleek coat can lead to a rapid change in coat type and improvements in growth rate and fertility in beef cattle.

Measurement of genetic change.   If it were possible to measure the rate of genetic change in any livestock population rapidly and accurately, then the livestock breeder would possess a valuable tool by which he could assess the efficiency of any particular method of selection. The degree of genetic change can be measured, but the methods employed require the use of very accurate, complete and numerous herd and flock records. These are not generally available in tropical countries.

The use of selection techniques in the tropics

Although selection has led to immense improvements in the productivity of livestock in the temperate zone it may not be so effective a breeding tool in the initial stages of development as some other breeding practices in the tropics. For example, although it may be relatively easy to increase the number of functional teats in female breeding pigs by culling those that do not possess at least fourteen, it may be very difficult to increase rapidly the milk production of indigenous tropical cattle. Mahadevan (1966) has estimated that the genetic improvements in milk production that have been made in tropical breeds of milking cattle by selection have never averaged more than 1 per cent per annum. If it is accepted that present average milk yields in most breeds are of the order of 680 to 1,360 litres (150 to 300 gal) per lactation, then it will be realized that selection to achieve even medium milk yields could take a very long time. The reasons for this situation are that any improvement programme begins from a low base, superior genotypes for milk production are probably extremely rare in tropical breeds (Mahadevan, 1966) and genetic–environmental interactions are very large (Payne and Hancock, 1957).

Selection techniques must not be ignored in the breeding of more productive tropical livestock. Indeed they cannot be ignored. A search must, however, be made for breeding techniques that will raise overall productivity more rapidly than is possible by conventional selection techniques. Time is not on the side of the livestock breeder in the tropics.

Inbreeding

The mating of close relatives is known as inbreeding. To be strictly correct the term should be used to describe the mating of individuals that are more closely related in descent than randomly chosen mates. The chances are that the closer the relationship the more the individuals will possess characteristics in common. If each has the same parent each will carry, on average, half the genes of each parent. If the relationship is through grandparents the chance of similarity in genotypes is halved, this process proceeding through each receding generation. In farm animals the closest relationship that can be procured will be brother × sister, sire × daughter or dam × son. As would be expected, inbreeding increases homozygosity as the number of genes in common is increased in every generation.

The quantitative measure of the degree of inbreeding is known as the *coefficient of inbreeding*, which measures the amount by which heterozygosity is reduced. As examples, the coefficients of inbreeding of sire × daughter, brother × sister and first cousin matings are 25·00, 25·00 and 6·25 per cent, respectively.

Effects of inbreeding

Both dominant and recessive traits are involved in inbreeding so that success or failure of this system tends to depend upon how many undesirable recessives are carried by the parent stock. This is because the system concentrates in the offspring the bad as well as the good traits of the parental stock. It is for this reason that the system is so often described as dangerous or undesirable. Not only does the concentration of undesirable recessive genes produce an increase in the number of specific abnormalities in the offspring, such as the bulldog condition or recessive achondroplasia in calves, but perhaps more importantly it causes a decrease in size and vigour, a decline in fertility and an increase in the mortality of the offspring, thus leading to a decline in total productivity. Of course it can be argued that if the parent stock is generally free of undesirable recessives then inbreeding will concentrate desirable traits in the offspring. It is, however, now generally accepted that except for the effect of chance in sampling, any breeder who practises inbreeding can be almost certain that there will be some deterioration in his livestock, particularly in vigour. It is also very doubtful whether inbreeding can substantially reduce the range of variation in economically important traits as so much of the within-herd and flock variation is due to environmental factors.

Inbreeding is of course still used to fix a specific trait in a particular group of livestock, such as the polled condition in cattle, but it must be used judiciously. Some measure of inbreeding is also implicit in any progeny-testing programme where AI is used to propagate the progeny of the selected sires. Thus, breeding policy in any large-scale progeny testing and AI programme must be continuously reviewed.

After the success of the maize breeders in crossing inbred lines and producing hybrid corn, the application of their methods to livestock production was considered. The production and crossing of inbred lines of poultry has been commercially successful and most of the new breeds that are available in the tropics today, emanating from the large commercial breeders, are hybrids of one kind or another. Efforts are also being made to develop inbred lines of pigs with the objective of producing commercial hybrids. The extension of this system to the breeding of either dairy or beef cattle is not considered practical at the present time.

Line breeding

Line breeding is the term used to describe the system of inbreeding that ensures that outstanding traits in one ancestor are transmitted to descendants without the undesirable effects normally associated with inbreeding. This is accomplished by ensuring that mating animals are as unrelated to each other as is possible except for their relationship to the outstanding ancestor to which the breeder wishes to line breed his stock. A schematic illustration of line breeding is shown in Fig. 4.12. In tropical cattle breeding perhaps the best-known example of successful line breeding is the use of the outstanding Santa Gertrudis sire 'Monkey' and his sons at the King Ranch, Texas, in the evolution of the Santa Gertrudis breed.

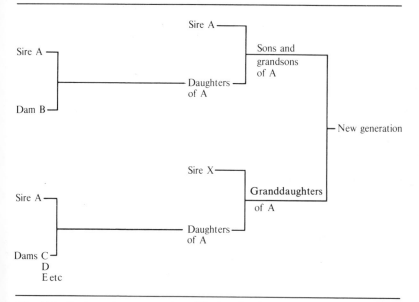

Fig. 4.12 A schematic representation of linebreeding (Mahadevan, 1970).

Crossbreeding

When unrelated livestock are mated the system is known as *crossbreeding*. The progeny of crossbred livestock are heterozygous for those traits that differ in their parents, and the greater the differences between parental traits the greater the degree of heterozygosity in the offspring.

As all crossbred progeny inherit the totality of parental characteristics in more or less the same manner they tend to resemble each other to a greater or lesser degree. A simple example would be the crossbreeding of red and white Shorthorn cattle where all progeny are roan in colour. Also first-cross progeny are usually superior to the inferior parent in productive traits and often to both parents. This phenomenon is known as *heterosis* or *hybrid vigour*. It is probably due to the effect of over-dominance, discussed in a previous section, where the heterozygotes are superior in one way or another to both the homozygotes.

The degree of hybrid vigour exhibited depends on the extent to which the characteristics of the parental stock are complementary. In general, the greater the differences in the parental genetic make-up the greater the degree of hybrid vigour, which in productive traits is expressed mainly in terms of improved fertility, viability and general thriftiness. Hybrid vigour disappears very rapidly when hybrids are mated *inter se* so that new parental stock are continuously required if the livestock owner wishes to exploit hybrid vigour to the utmost.

Crossbreeding, where it has been practicable, has been a constant feature associated with the introduction of exotic livestock into the tropics. In the past, crossbreeding has not been utilized to any extent to improve the productivity of tropical livestock, and where it has been successfully used it has been invariably accompanied by improvements in management and modifications of environmental conditions. One example is the development of a modern poultry industry in most tropical countries depending upon the importation of hybrid chicks from the temperate zone and the adoption of temperate-zone managerial methods. This is of course possible in the poultry industry as the cost–benefit ratio is usually favourable. It may also be possible in the pig industry, as the very rapid development of pig production in some countries in Southeast Asia appears to demonstrate. However, the situation with regard to ruminant livestock has been different. Although the crossbreeding of dairy cattle has been practised in many tropical countries for a long time on an experimental or pilot-scale basis, it is only very recently that crossbreeding has been used on a very extensive scale in India and other countries. Similarly the crossbreeding of beef cattle is now being advocated in the tropical Americas and of sheep for improved wool production in Africa, western Asia and the Indian sub-continent.

Crossbreeding can be useful in three ways to livestock owners in the tropics. First, indigenous low-producing livestock can be upgraded by continuously backcrossing them to more highly productive introduced exotic stock. Secondly, an attempt may be made to create new and more productive breeds by crossbreeding indigenous and introduced exotic livestock, mating *inter se* at either the first generation or after one or more backcross generations and then selecting the type of animal required. Thirdly, advantage may be taken of hybrid vigour by some form of systematic crossbreeding between two or more breeds of indigenous livestock or between an indigenous and an introduced breed.

Upgrading

This is the method of choice when a livestock owner wishes to change radically the characteristics of his animals. A schematic illustration of the upgrading of indigenous (I) stock by imported exotic stock (E) is shown in Fig. 4.13. Males of the exotic type are mated generation after generation to indigenous and crossbred females. It will be seen that by the F_4 generation the livestock are almost entirely of the exotic breed type. In any breed 'grade' animals can be upgraded to 'purebreds' using this technique.

Developing new breeds

The development of a new breed may be accomplished by the crossbreeding of two breeds of a specific type of livestock, followed by backcrossing one way or the other to attain the planned cross of the parent

Generation	Mating types

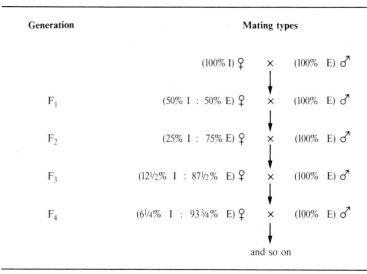

Fig. 4.13 A schematic representation of upgrading.

breeds. At this stage the crossbreds must be mated *inter se* followed by intense selection among their progeny for the type of animal required.

A number of new beef cattle breeds have been evolved using this technique, including the Braford, Brangus, Charbray, Santa Gertrudis and Beefmaster in North America, the Jamaican Red in the Caribbean, the Bonsmara in Africa and the Droughtmaster in Australia (see Ch. 5, Pt II, and Payne, 1970). There has been less success in the evolution of new dairy breeds, although two examples are the Jamaican Hope in the Caribbean and the Australian Milking Zebu in Australia.

The exploitation of hybrid vigour by crossbreeding systems

Two or more breeds of a specific type of livestock may be used in a planned crossbreeding programme in order to exploit the phenomenon of hybrid vigour. A breeding system of this type involves the rotational use of sires of one breed during one generation followed by the use of sires of a second breed during the next generation, and so on. A schematic illustration of such a system is shown in Fig. 4.14, A and B representing the two breeds used in this programme. Any number of breeds could be included in such a programme, but it is generally agreed that nothing is to be gained by using more than three breeds.

The value of a rotational crossbreeding system compared with a system that attempts to develop a new breed is that it may be more productive because it exploits hybrid vigour. Genetically this is because rotational crossbreeding inhibits gene recombination. The disadvantage of rotational crossbreeding is that the breeder must have access to sires or semen from two or more breeds, thus complicating management compared with

Generation	Mating types

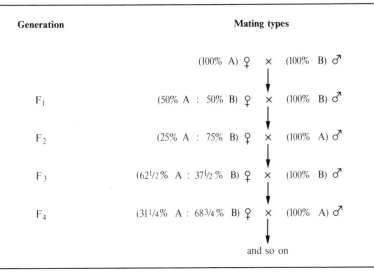

Fig. 4.14   A schematic representation of a criss-cross breeding system designed to exploit hybrid vigour.

the use of one breed. It is very difficult to operate rotational crossbreeding under smallholder conditions and so the use of this breeding system in the tropics is likely to be confined to large holdings. On the latter, however, crossbreeding may have two additional advantages. First, increases in productivity may be achieved with little increase in economic input, and secondly a slowly increasing impact of inbreeding depression in established breeds may be countered by the introduction of a crossbreeding programme.

Breeding livestock for tropical environments

As we already stated in a previous section, livestock development in the tropics can proceed only in an integrated manner and on a broad front.

With regard to the problem of breeding livestock for tropical environments there are three major queries, for which answers are required. First, is there any definite evidence of genetic differences in the performance characteristics of tropical and temperate-type breeds of livestock? McDowell (1967) stated that it would be reasonable to assume that 50 per cent or more of the differences in average dairy merit between tropical and temperate-type dairy cattle could be attributed to differences in their inherent abilities for milk production, and he concluded that the preponderance of evidence indicated that under reasonable environmental conditions there are genetic differences in all livestock in a number of traits of economic importance. Differences in average productivity of dairy cattle in some temperate and tropical countries are shown in Table 4.7.

McDowell (1972), using data from eight breeds in six countries, suggested that traits in cattle that demonstrate large genetic differences are age at first calving, calving percentage, milk yield, length of lactation period, length of dry period, birth weight, rate of daily liveweight gain and mature body weight. In addition he stated that gestation length, generation interval and carcase killing-out percentage demonstrate some

Table 4.7 *Differences in the average productivity of dairy cattle in some tropical and temperate countries*

Country	Climate	Average milk yield of dairy cattle (kg (lb) per annum)
Kenya	Tropical Dry and montane	550 (1,213)
Niger	Tropical Dry	130 (287)
Brazil	Tropical to sub-tropical Humid and dry	820 (1,808)
Colombia	Tropical Humid, dry and montane	680 (1,499)
Trinidad	Tropical Humid	1,778 (3,920)
United States	Temperate Humid and dry	4,631 (10,209)
India	Tropical to sub-tropical Humid and dry	486 (1,071)
Philippines	Tropical Humid	1,237 (2,727)
United Kingdom	Temperate	4,204 (9,268)
New Zealand	Temperate	3,085 (6,801)

Source: FAO (1974).

indications of genetic differences, but that the efficiency of feed utilization depends primarily on the level of feeding; at low nutrient intake levels indigenous livestock usually exhibit superiority while at high nutrient intake levels temperate-type livestock are more efficient.

We suggest that McDowell's conclusions appear to be based on insufficient evidence as in some traits, such as calving percentage, mature body weight and carcase killing-out percentage, some tropical livestock do not exhibit any genetic inferiority, i.e. Bali cattle (Payne and Rollinson, 1973). We further suggest that a great deal more basic information is required on all tropical livestock before this query can be answered with any certainty.

The second query is, how important is the choice of breed and/or breeding method in the tropics? These factors may be more important in the tropics than in the temperate zone, the reason being the multiplicity of different climates, types of stress and methods of utilization of livestock (Table 4.8).

Table 4.8   *Some different systems of utilization of livestock in the tropics*

System	Utilization	Examples
Triple purpose	Work; milk; meat	Subsistence agriculture using buffaloes and/or cattle in Asia
		Nomadic pastoralism using camels in Africa and western Asia
	Milk; meat; manure	Subsistence agriculture using cattle, sheep and goats in Asia
	Wool and/or skins; milk; meat	Subsistence agriculture and nomadic pastoralism using sheep and goats in Africa and western Asia
Dual purpose	Work; meat	Subsistence agriculture using cattle and buffaloes in Southeast Asia
	Milk; meat	Nomadic pastoralism in Africa and Asia
		Ranching in Central and South America
	Wool and/or skins; meat	Sheep and goats in all tropical regions
	Meat; manure	Pigs in Southeast Asia
Single purpose	Meat	Ranching in all tropical regions
	Milk*	Specialized dairy farms in all tropical regions

* This must be qualified as there is a new trend to produce beef from specialized dairy farms in the tropics.

The third major query is what are likely to be the most suitable breeds and the most suitable breeding system to use in any specific region in the tropics? There are three major choices for the livestock breeder:

1. The use of suitable indigenous breeds;
2. The replacement of indigenous by more productive exotic breeds;
3. Crossbreeding and/or upgrading indigenous breeds using exotics (including the evolution of new breeds).

The use of indigenous breeds

The advantages of using indigenous breeds are that they are readily available and that they are acclimatized to the local environment and probably possess desirable genetic traits associated with their acclimatization. The major disadvantages are that natural selection in indigenous breeds in the past has probably been for survival under extreme stress, that this selection is likely to have been at the expense of productive traits and that selection for increased productivity may therefore be a very lengthy process, particularly in large ruminant livestock.

It is suggested that the use of indigenous breeds is likely to be most successful where:

1. Stress on livestock is very severe and genotype–environment interactions are highly significant;
2. Liveweight gain or wool and skin, rather than milk, is the product required;
3. It will be uneconomic rapidly to improve environmental condition, i.e. in many semi-arid regions of the tropics; and
4. The indigenous livestock possess some specific adaptive trait, i.e. the tolerance of trypanosomiasis in N'dama and West African Shorthorn breeds of cattle.

Examples where the utilization of indigenous breeds is at present economically justified and rational and where every effort should be made to improve the indigenous breeds by selection are the use of:

- N'dama and West African Shorthorn breeds of cattle in tsetse-infested regions of West and Central Africa;
- Zebu breeds such as the Boran in East Africa and the Wadara in West Africa for meat production in semi-arid areas;
- Sanga breeds of cattle such as the Mashona, Tuli and Africander for meat production in Central and South Africa;
- A *Bos (Bibos)* breed such as the Bali for work and meat production in the humid areas of Southeast Asia;
- Desert-type sheep for meat production in the semi-arid areas of Africa and western Asia.
- Camels for meat production in the arid areas of Africa and western Asia;
- Water buffaloes for work and meat production in the humid areas of South and Southeast Asia.

Efforts should of course be made to improve the present productivity of these indigenous breeds and species by intense selection, including performance and progeny testing where the use of these methods can be economically justified. In addition it is vitally important that at least limited numbers of all indigenous breeds should be conserved in their specific environments as a future source of genetic variation. Serious errors have already been committed in some tropical countries, where continual upgrading using exotic livestock has almost eliminated indigenous breeds. For example, in Venezuela indigenous Criollo cattle have almost disappeared at a time when experimental breeding is demonstrating that crossbreds between Criollo and Zebu are superior in productivity to Criollo upgraded to Zebu. Many countries in Southeast Asia are about to embark on large-scale cattle upgrading projects and there is a real danger that useful traits in existing Southeast Asian breeds may be lost.

The importation and use of exotic breeds

The present distribution of the world's livestock breeds is almost a historical accident. Primarily it is the result of the movements of human populations with their accompanying livestock and not the result of the deliberate breeding of specific types of livestock for specific environments. If, for example, the northern regions of South America had been colonized by south Asians and not by Europeans then it is likely that the water buffalo would now be of major importance in the Orinoco and Amazon river basins. Instead, the descendants of the European colonizers have only recently realized the potential value of water buffaloes in these environments.

When the importation of exotic breeds into the tropics is discussed it is mainly in terms of importations of livestock from the temperate zone, but it is also essential to consider the importation of exotics from other regions of the tropics.

The advantages of importing exotic livestock are that a rapid improvement in productivity may be achieved if suitable animals are used and/or the local environmental conditions are sufficiently improved, as exotic livestock can be selected that possess desirable traits unavailable in indigenous livestock populations.

The disadvantages are that importation is expensive, that it is difficult to increase rapidly the number of imported livestock so that a long period must elapse before an adequate number of the imported animals can be made available and that the acclimatization of an imported breed may be time-consuming and expensive.

The importation of exotic breeds is likely to be most useful where:

1. Climatic, disease and nutritional stresses are moderate, such as on tropical oceanic islands, montane regions and, in the case of dairy cattle, lowland humid areas where adequate forage can be produced year-round;
2. No indigenous breeds of livestock are available to exploit a specific environment; examples being the use of water buffaloes in the swamp and seasonally flooded regions of tropical Africa and the Americas and Zebu cattle in the semi-arid regions of the Americas and Australia;
3. The managerial system is such that the livestock are more or less unaffected by external environmental factors, i.e. poultry in most tropical regions and, to a lesser extent, pigs.

Examples where the importation and use of exotic breeds can probably be economically justified at the present time are the use of:

● Temperate-type hybrid poultry breeds in all tropical countries;

- Temperate-type pig breeds in those tropical countries where there are adequate supplies of feed;
- European-type dairy cattle in the Caribbean, the Indian Ocean and the Pacific tropical islands and in certain humid tropical areas in central and northern South America and Southeast Asia;
- All types of European livestock in montane areas where disease stress is limited;
- Water buffalo in suitable areas in the Guinea coast, the Congo basin in Africa and the *Sudd* region of the Sudan and in Central and South America;
- Zebu cattle breeds in some regions of Southeast Asia (the indigenous cattle are ancient crossbreds *Bos taurus* × *B. indicus* or *B. (Bibos)* types);
- Additional Zebu breeds in Australia and the Americas, i.e. the possible use of the Boran from East Africa in some regions of Brazil (not possible at present due to quarantine restrictions).

Crossbreeding and/or upgrading of indigenous breeds

As discussed in a previous section the merits of crossbreeding are that the breeder can hope to combine desirable traits from the parental stocks and exploit hybrid vigour. The latter, mainly expressed in traits that are not highly inherited such as vigour and fertility, usually declines with age, is higher in females than in males and is higher under stress conditions.

The major disadvantage of any crossbreeding programme is that two or more different breeds of livestock are required and that this usually means large-scale operations and complicated management. The normal and most suitable practice is to use indigenous female stock and imported males or semen.

On account of the managerial difficulties inherent in the system the use of crossbreeding techniques in the tropics is likely to be limited to poultry and pig production and in ruminant livestock to large-scale ranching operations and possibly government schemes for nomadic pastoralists and large groups of subsistence farmers. Planned livestock crossbreeding schemes could lead to an immediate improvement in productivity in many tropical regions. However, the practical difficulties involved in the planning of such schemes outside the conventional ranching areas are immense. Regions where governments should consider planned cattle crossbreeding schemes are:

- Central and South America where experimental work (Plasse *et al.*, 1969) has already demonstrated the value of Criollo × Zebu crossbreds and where three-way crosses such as Criollo × Zebu × Charolais may be even more productive;
- West Africa where the productivity of three-way crosses between the N'dama, West African Shorthorn and various West African Zebu breeds in tsetse-fly-infested areas should be evaluated;

- Southeast Asia where experimental work (Devendra *et al.*, 1973) has already demonstrated the value of American-Brahman × indigenous crossbreds and where crossbreds between a *Bos* (*Bibos*) breed such as the Bali and a European-type beef breed such as the Red Poll should be evaluated (Payne and Rollinson, 1973).

Similar crossbreeding projects for other ruminant livestock should also be evaluated.

If exotic-type stock are required then obtaining them by means of an upgrading programme, rather than by mass importation, is not only more economical as large numbers of indigenous livestock can be upgraded relatively rapidly and inexpensively (Fig. 4.13) but it also has the very great advantage that the managerial standards of the livestock owners can be upgraded during the same period that the genetic merit of their livestock is upgraded.

The development of new breeds.   Where managerial and other difficulties preclude crossbreeding and where breeders do not wish to completely upgrade their livestock but would like to utilize animals that are intermediate in type between the exotic and the indigenous, then the development of a new breed incorporating as many of the desired characteristics as possible is indicated. As the development of a new breed requires a fairly large-scale breeding programme and highly trained and competent personnel it can be contemplated only by very large, private livestock organizations, by governments or by international agencies.

As stated previously, a number of new beef cattle breeds for use in the sub-tropics and tropics have been developed during this century. Some of these new beef cattle breeds have made important contributions to an overall improvement in productivity in some countries. There has also been some development of new dairy cattle breeds. Some new breeds that are now urgently required in the tropics are:

- Two dairy cattle breeds that are stable and can be used by small farmers. One breed should be stabilized in the range five-eighths to seven-eighths *Bos taurus* × three eighths to one eighth *B. indicus* and the other in the range three-eighths to five-eighths *B. taurus* × five-eighths to three-eighths *B. indicus*. The high-grade *B. taurus* breed is required for well-managed dairy farms in the humid tropics and the lower grade breed for dairy farmers in the drier tropics.
- Dairy goat breeds suitable for use in the humid and dry tropics, respectively. These could be useful for small, subsistence farmers.
- A sheep suitable for meat production in the humid tropics, particularly in rubber, oil-palm and fruit plantations. This could be bred from a cross between West African Dwarf forest sheep or Southeast Asian sheep and a meat-producing temperate-type breed.
- A specialized beef-type water buffalo breed for use in humid regions.

● A specialized beef-type camel bred for use in arid and semi-arid regions.

As it is unlikely that these new breeds will be developed by individual livestock owners it is suggested that international or regional experimental stations should undertake the breeding programmes.

References

Devendra, C., Hassan, M. N., Hodge, R., Choo, T. L. K. and Pathmasingham, M. (1973) Kedah-Kelantan cattle of Malaysia. *Malaysian agric. J.*, **49**, 25–47.

FAO (1974) *Production Yearbook*, Vol. 27 (*1973*) FAO: Rome.

Gardner, E. J. (1960) *Principles of Genetics*. John Wiley: New York.

Hammond, J. (1947) Animal breeding in relation to nutrition and environmental conditions. *Biol. Rev.*, **22**, 195–213.

Hammond, J., Jr., Mason, I. L. and Robertson, T. J. (1971) *Hammond's Farm Animals* (4th edn). Edward Arnold: London.

Johannsson, I. and Rendel, J. (1968) *Genetics and Animal Breeding*. Oliver and Boyd: Edinburgh.

Lerner, I. M. (1944) Lethal and sub-lethal characteristics in farm animals. *J. Hered.*, **35**, 219–44.

Mahadevan, P. (1966) Breeding for milk production in tropical cattle. *Tech. Comm. Comw. Bur. Anim. Breed. Genet.*, No. 17. Comw. Agric. Bur.: Farnham Royal, UK.

Mahadevan, P. (1970) in Payne, W. J. A. (ed.) (1970) *Cattle Production in the Tropics*, Vol. 1. *Breeds and Breeding*. Longman: London.

McDowell, R. E. (1967) Potential for improvement of cattle by linebreeding, inbreeding, grading up and crossbreeding in warm climates. *6th FAO Inter-American Conference on Animal Production and Health, Gainesville, Fla., USA*. FAO: Rome.

McDowell, R. E. (1972) *Improvement of Livestock Production in Warm Climates*. Freeman: San Francisco.

Pani, S. N. and Lasley, J. F. (1972) Genotype × environmental interactions in animals. *Univ. Missouri–Colombia Coll. Agric. Res. Bull.*, No. 992.

Payne, W. J. A. (1970) *Cattle Production in the Tropics*, Vol. 1. *Breeds and Breeding*. Longman: London.

Payne, W. J. A. and Hancock, J. (1957) The Direct Effect of Tropical Climate on the Performance of European-type Cattle. II. Production. *Emp. J. exp. Agric.*, **25**, 321–38.

Payne, W. J. A. and Rollinson, D. H. L. (1973) Bali cattle. *World Anim. Rev.* (7), 13–21.

Plasse, D., Mueller-Haye, B., Gil, R., Koger, M., Butterworth, M. and Linares, T. (1969) Preweaning performance of Criollo and Brahman calves and their reciprocal crosses. *Proc. 2nd World Conf. on Anim. Prod.* Bruce Publ.: St Paul, Minnesota.

Further Reading

Lasley, J. F. *Genetics of Livestock Improvement* (2nd edn.). Prentice-Hall: Englewood Cliffs, NJ, 1972.

Lerner, I. M. and Donald, H. P. *Modern Developments in Animal Breeding.* Academic Press: New York, 1966.

Salisbury, G. W. and Van Demark, N. L. *Physiology of Reproduction and Artificial Insemination of Cattle.* Freeman: San Francisco, 1961.

Part II: Husbandry

Chapter 5

Cattle

Although major changes are occurring, the part played by cattle in the life of the indigenous people of the tropics still differs remarkably from the position accorded to them by man in the mid-latitude zones. In the tropics, as elsewhere, cattle are essential as a source of milk and meat, of work and of many by-products of great value; but for very large numbers of cattle owners these considerations are equal or secondary only to the part cattle play in religion, in social custom, as a reserve of family wealth and as a mark of respectability and status in the community. The nomad would as soon deplete his breeding herd as the family man in Europe or America would his bank account; the religious Hindu would rather starve to death than eat his cow; and in different ways and to different degrees there are few tropical people who have not some regard for cattle quite apart from their immediate economic use. Tothill (1948) thus describes the outlook of the Dinka of the Sudan: 'As a result of living in such close contact with their cattle, their animals have come to assume an almost religious significance with them. Every self-respecting young man possesses a special bullock in which his personality is alleged to be symbolized; these animals are specially fed and groomed, their horns are trained and decorated with tassels, they are lauded in song and regarded with an affection almost amounting to worship.' The subject is further discussed in Appendix 1.

Numbers and distribution

The world's cattle population is increasing more slowly than the world's human population. The total is now more than 1,000 million (Table 5.1) and cattle populations appear to have increased at about the same pace in the tropics as they have in the remainder of the world during the last two decades.

Somewhat more than one-third of the world's cattle population are to be found in the tropics: 11, 14 and 11 per cent of the total in the continents of Africa, the Americas and Asia, respectively. However, only

Table 5.1 *The world's cattle population*

Continent	1951/52–55/56		1973		
	Number ('000)	As percentage of world population	Number ('000)	As percentage of world population	Percentage increase or decrease
Europe	105,773	12	129,294	11	+22
USSR	57,345	7	104,000	9	+81
Africa	107,320	12	149,277	13	+39
Tropics	87,501	10	125,398	11	+43
Other	19,819	2	23,879	2	+20
Americas	278,538	32	381,111	33	+37
Tropics	105,806	12	165,787	14	+57
Other	172,732	20	215,324	19	+25
Asia	292,233	34	348,090	30	+19
Tropics	125,692	15	130,347	11	+4
Other*	114,548	13	154,398	13	+35
China	51,993	6	63,345	6	+22
Oceania	21,516	3	38,736	4	+80
Tropics	4,187	1	7,801	1	+86
Other	17,329	2	30,935	3	+79
World	862,725		1,150,508		+33
Tropics	323,186	38	429,333	37	+33
Other	539,539	62	721,175	63	+33

* Excluding China and the Asiatic regions of the USSR with the exception of Mongolia.
Source: FAO (1974).

1 per cent of the world's cattle population is to be found in the tropical regions of Oceania.

It will be seen from Table 5.2 that within the tropics the largest concentrations of cattle are found in Northeast and East Africa, South America, the Indian sub-continent and tropical Australia. There are, however, major differences in the concentration of cattle per thousand hectares of land area and the number of cattle per thousand inhabitants in the different tropical regions (Table 5.3). For example, stocking rates are very high in the Caribbean and the Indian sub-continent and very low in the humid region of Central Africa, the semi-arid region of western Asia and the humid region of Papua New Guinea. On the other hand, the number of cattle per thousand inhabitants is very high in tropical Australia, where cattle are extensively ranched, moderately high in West, Northeast and East Africa where cattle are often managed in a nomadic or transhumant system, in the offshore islands of Africa where management is usually either transhumant or subsistence and in South

Table 5.2   *The cattle population of various regions of Africa, the Americas, Asia and Oceania*

Continent and region	Cattle population in 1973 ('000)	As percentage of total cattle in the region
Africa		
West (humid)	17,952	12
West (dry)	16,050	11
North (non-tropical)	7,553	5
Northeast and East	68,796	46
Central (humid)	1,473	1
Central (dry)	11,465	8
South (non-tropical)	16,320	11
Offshore islands	9,662	6
Offshore islands (non-tropical)	6	negl.
Americas		
North (non-tropical)	147,543	39
Caribbean	10,731	3
Central	23,728	6
South	131,328	34
South (non-tropical)	67,781	18
Asia		
Western (non-tropical)	21,825	6
Western	1,466	1
Indian sub-continent	103,100	30
Indian sub-continent (non-tropical)	120,954	35
Southeast Asia	25,781	7
China	63,345	18
East (non-tropical)	11,619	3
Oceania		
Australia	7,283	19
Australia and New Zealand (non-tropical)	30,935	80
Papua New Guinea	110	} 1
Pacific Islands	408	

Source: FAO (1974).

America where cattle are ranched. There are small numbers of cattle per thousand inhabitants in the humid region of Central Africa, where tsetse fly is prevalent, in Southeast Asia where the farming system is mainly a subsistence one, and in Papua New Guinea.

It is difficult to find any common interactions between the number and concentrations of cattle and ecological factors and we must conclude that the present concentrations of cattle in different regions of the tropics are the result of many different, and sometimes conflicting, factors.

In a very general way we may conclude that the major concentrations of cattle are found in some of the intensive subsistence agricultural regions and in the natural grassland areas and that there are relatively few cattle

Table 5.3 *The number of cattle per thousand hectares of land and per thousand inhabitants in the various tropical regions in 1973*

Continent and region	No. cattle per 1,000 ha	No. cattle per 1,000 inhabitants
Africa		
West (humid)	69	190
West (dry)	30	645
Northeast and East	110	760
Central (humid)	4	66
Central (dry)	35	390
Offshore islands	162	1,014
Americas		
Caribbean	478	393
Central	167	510
South	93	784
Asia		
Western	8	116
Indian sub-continent	580	301
Southeast	57	81
Oceania		
Australia	38	2,190
Papua New Guinea	2	42
Pacific Islands	44	239

Source: FAO (1974).

in some of the very dry regions and in some of the humid rain-forest regions of the equatorial zone.

Some details of the number of large national cattle herds in the tropics are shown in Table 5.4.

Origin

The family of animals that includes all types of domestic cattle are known as the Bovidae. They are the dominant family of hoofed mammals and one of the most recent to evolve. Within the sub-family Bovinae are found all the varied types of cattle that have been domesticated. Relationships within the Bovinae are shown in Fig. 5.1.

All domestic cattle originate from *Bos taurus* or humpless cattle and *B. indicus* or humped cattle, whose wild ancestors are extinct, and from the wild cattle of Southeast Asia (*B. (Bibos) gaurus* and *B. (Bibos) banteng*), or from crosses of two or all three types. They are all interfertile to a greater or lesser degree.

A very brief description of what is known of the origin of cattle is

Table 5.4   *Tropical countries with a cattle population exceeding 5 million*

Continent	Country	Cattle population (million)
Africa	Ethiopia	26·5
	Kenya	7·4
	Madagascar	9·5
	Nigeria	10·9
	Sudan	15·2
	Tanzania	11·3
Americas	Brazil	85·0
	Colombia	22·1
	Cuba	7·4
	Mexico (tropical regions)	13·3
	Paraguay*	6·0
	Venezuela	8·7
Asia	Bangladesh (tropical regions)	13·0
	Burma	7·7
	India (tropical regions)	88·5
	Indonesia	6·3
Oceania	Australia (tropical regions)	7·3

* Paraguay is considered to be wholly in the tropics for the purpose of these estimates.
Source: FAO (1974).

given below, but the reader seeking further details should consult Payne (1970).

The almost universal distribution of wild species of cattle in the temperate, Mediterranean and sub-tropical climatic zones of the Old World and in some areas of the tropics in the Upper Pleistocene period makes it particularly difficult to discover the original centre(s) of domestication. Some of the earliest evidence of domestication has been found at a site in southern Turkestan where cattle appear to have been domesticated as early as 8000 BC. These cattle were probably the ancestors of the Hamitic Longhorn-type breeds, but there is also evidence from the same site that some 2,000 years later *Bos brachyceros* or Shorthorn-type cattle also originated from this area. The Hamitic Longhorn and Shorthorn types of cattle are believed to be the ancestors of all the *B. taurus* cattle found in the world today. The origin of the Zebu is more controversial. The present evidence of their origin has been discussed by Payne (1970) and he concluded that the known facts appear to indicate that the Zebu originated in western Asia and not, as is so often supposed, in the Indian sub-continent.

There must have been at least two centres of domestication of *Bos* (*Bibos*)-type cattle in South and Southeast Asia. No major archaeological or other evidence is available as to the period when these cattle were domesticated, although very recent archaeological evidence from Thailand suggests that it was earlier than had previously been suspected, but

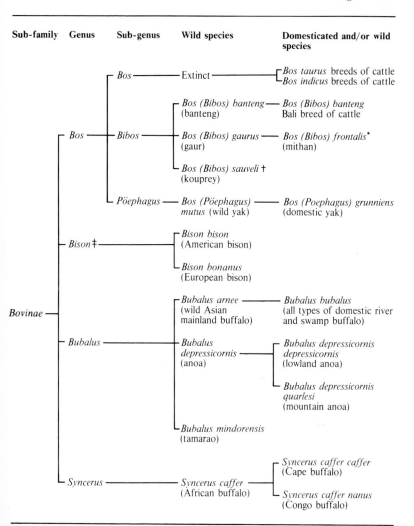

Fig. 5.1 Living relatives of the Bovinae sub-family.
* Listed by some authorities as a separate species.
† May be the result of crossbreeding between *Bos* (*Bibos*) *banteng* and *B.* (*Bibos*) *gaurus*.
‡ Linnaeus includes this genus under *Bos*.

their geographical distribution suggests that it was accomplished by the Indo-Chinese and/or Malaysian peoples.

Hamitic Longhorn-, Shorthorn- and Zebu-type cattle were all imported into Africa within historical times, while cattle have been imported into the Americas and Oceania since the sixteenth century.

Asia

If, as suggested above, cattle were first domesticated in western Asia, the presence of and continuous movement of Semitic, Hamitic-, Vedic Aryan- and Ural Altai-speaking peoples would have provided a unique opportunity for the dispersal and spread of domestic cattle to all parts of Asia, Europe and Africa, and for the mixing and interbreeding of different types of domestic cattle, ultimately resulting in the multiplicity of breeds that exist today.

The first archaeological evidence of the presence of Zebu in the continent comes from Iraq, where it would appear that these cattle were already domesticated by 4500 BC. Zebu are believed to have been brought into India through the northern passes between 2200 and 1500 BC, and thereafter spread along the route taken by their owners, the Vedic Aryan invaders. There is also some evidence that when the Vedic Aryans entered the Indus valley, humpless Shorthorn-type cattle were already present in large numbers.

From a centre of origin in western Asia the large humpless Hamitic Longhorn-type cattle accompanied their migrating nomadic owners towards the eastern Mediterranean littoral where the nomads divided into two major streams, one moving with their livestock northwestwards into Europe and the other southwestwards through Egypt and into Africa (Fig. 5.2). Hamitic Longhorn cattle may also have been taken northwards into Central Asia and south and southeastwards into India, although there are few traces of them in these regions today.

The Shorthorn-type cattle, originating many centuries later, were also taken by migratory people westwards towards the eastern Mediterranean littoral where the nomads, like the Hamitic Longhorn-owning nomads before them, divided into groups, one moving northwards into Europe and the other southwestwards into Egypt and on into continental Africa. The Shorthorn-type cattle were also taken eastwards by migratory peoples and the available evidence from China suggests that the majority of the cattle in that country originated from cattle that were brought from the West (Phillips *et al.*, 1945; Epstein, 1969), and that possibly they were brought to China by the Ural Altaic-speaking people who invaded that country about 2500 BC. The easternmost movement of these cattle was finally to the Philippines, where the present indigenous cattle, known as *Batangas*, are almost identical in conformation and appearance with some of the types of cattle found today around Hong Kong and in western China. It is not known when these cattle were first imported into the Philippines, but it is likely that it was before the Spanish settlement in the sixteenth century. From China these cattle were probably taken by migratory peoples into what are now Burma, Thailand, Vietnam, Cambodia and Laos where they were crossbred with Zebu cattle that had been imported into these countries by migratory peoples from the Indian peninsula. Thus many of the present-day cattle in this area are likely to be descendants of crossbreds between the Shorthorn type and the Zebu

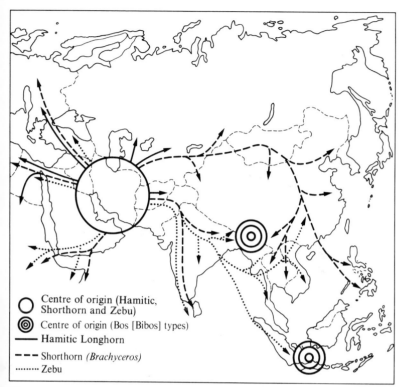

Fig. 5.2 Possible migration routes of domestic cattle in Asia.

and are analogous with the Sanga cattle of Africa. Undoubtedly within China some Zebu accompanied migrants moving from the south northwards, as Phillips *et al.* (1945) and Epstein (1969) have stated that modern cattle in south China exhibit some influence of Zebu genes but that these influences tend to disappear as one proceeds northwards.

There is also evidence that the indigenous cattle of Malaya, Borneo, Sumatra and Java are also of an ancient crossbred *Bos taurus × B. indicus* type. These cattle may have originated from animals imported southwards by migratory peoples from what is now Thailand into Malaysia and Indonesia, or they may be the result of an ancient cross between the Shorthorn-type cattle that were brought into Southeast Asia by migratory people and Zebu cattle from India.

If, as stated above, the Zebu originated in western Asia and not in India, then one would expect to find some Zebu in western Asia today, particularly along the route that cattle-owning peoples must have taken on their way to India. There are, in fact, Zebu breeds in western Asia, particularly the Iraqi and the Aden. It would also appear that once the Zebu was established in India it was used to upgrade local cattle so that virtually all modern cattle in the Indian sub-continent are now of the Zebu type. There are, however, some isolated pockets of crossbred survivors such as the Siri breed of northern India. From India Zebu cattle were apparently taken by migrating peoples southwards into Sri Lanka and eastwards into Burma, Thailand, Vietnam, Laos, Cambodia and Malaysia. It is probable that Zebu were also imported into Indonesia, presumably due to the spread of Hindu culture in that area.

In the northeast of India and in Assam and Burma, Zebu have been crossed with the wild gaur (*Bos* (*Bibos*) *gaurus*) to produce a breed known as the *Gayal*, while in Indonesia Zebu and Shorthorn-type cattle have been crossed with the wild banteng (*B.* (*Bibos*) *banteng*) to form a breed known as the *Madura*.

A domesticated breed of the banteng, known as the *Bali*, has survived in the island of Bali in Indonesia and has been imported into other Indonesian islands, Australia, Hawaii, the Philippines and Malaysia (Payne and Rollinson, 1973). It is the only known domesticated pure breed of the *Bos* (*Bibos*) spp.

Africa

As stated above, domestic cattle were probably first introduced into Northeast and East Africa from a centre of origin in western Asia. Hamitic Longhorn-, Shorthorn- and Zebu-type cattle were taken by migratory peoples into Africa and they are the ancestors of the vast majority of cattle breeds found in that continent today (Payne, 1964). These three types of cattle crossbred at different times and in different ways to create the types known as Sanga cattle that are of considerable importance in Africa today. Although Sanga cattle resulted from crossbreeding at many minor centres in East, North, West and Central Africa, East Africa was probably the main centre of origin of all the Sanga breeds now found in East, Central and South Africa (Fig. 5.3).

Hamitic Longhorn cattle were the first to be brought into Africa. Faulkner and Epstein (1957) stated that the earliest records of their presence in Egypt date from about 5000 BC. Around 2750 to 2500 BC other migratory peoples brought in humpless Shorthorn cattle (*Bos brachyceros*) and the peoples owning the Hamitic Longhorn were forced to migrate or voluntarily migrated westwards and southwards, so that today there are no traces of Hamitic Longhorn cattle in Egypt. There were possibly three main migration routes: westwards along the Mediterranean littoral, southwestwards across the Sahara via the Tibestsi and Tassili highland areas, and southwards up the Nile towards the highland areas of what are today Ethiopia and Kenya.

When the westward migration of Hamitic Longhorn cattle-owning people reached what is now Morocco the stream probably divided, one group proceeding north into Spain, Portugal and beyond, the other west and southwards into West Africa. Curson and Thornton (1936) suggested

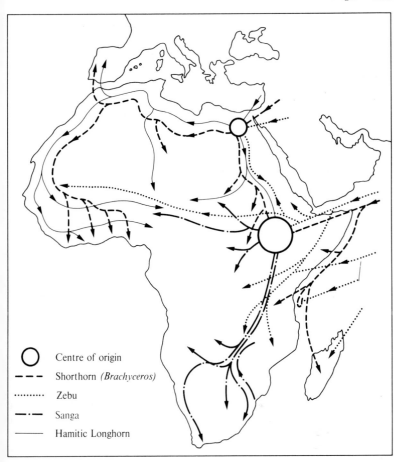

Fig. 5.3   Possible migration routes of domestic cattle in Africa.

that characteristics of the cattle that were taken northwards can be seen today in such breeds as the Raza de Barroza of Portugal and the Andalusian cattle of Spain. Cattle of this type were exported from the Iberian peninsula to the Americas and are represented today in America by the Longhorn and Criollo breeds.

A breed descended from the Hamitic Longhorn cattle that were taken into West Africa still exists as a more or less pure type along the Gulf of Guinea and is known as the N'dama. It has apparently been preserved because it developed a high degree of tolerance to the disease known as trypanosomiasis. A second Hamitic Longhorn breed found in West Africa is the Kuri. This breed probably owes its survival to the fact that it has been isolated for a long period on and around the islands in Lake Chad.

The southward movement of Hamitic Longhorn cattle is not so easy to trace, but early rock paintings and engravings in the Sudan, Ethiopia Somalia and as far south as Mount Elgon in Kenya suggest that the Hamitic Longhorn was the first domesticated animal to be introduced into this region, and the remnant breed known as the Binga in northwest Rhodesia appears to be a dwarf form of Hamitic Longhorn. This suggests that Hamitic Longhorn cattle were taken as far south as Rhodesia. It is of interest that the Binga is also said to exhibit some degree of tolerance to trypanosomiasis.

Peoples owning the Shorthorn-type cattle followed two of the same routes as the Hamitic Longhorn owners – along the southern Mediterranean littoral and southwards along the Nile into Upper Egypt and the Sudan, but not across what is now the Sahara, presumably due to increasing aridity of the region. Modern cattle in Egypt exhibit characteristics that have been inherited partly from these Shorthorn-type cattle, while indigenous breeds in Libya, Tunisia, Algeria and Morocco are almost entirely of the Shorthorn type. The Shorthorn-type cattle-owning peoples probably split into two migratory streams in Morocco. One moved north into the Iberian peninsula and on into France and the British Isles – the modern Jersey, Guernsey and Kerry breeds apparently being partly derived from this ancestral stock. The other stream moved southwards and westwards until the cattle owners arrived at the forest region. Like the Hamitic Longhorn cattle preceding them, the Shorthorn-type cattle apparently gradually acquired a tolerance to trypanosomiasis. Their descendants are known today as the West African Dwarf Shorthorn breed. However, the tolerance to trypanosomiasis of this breed is not as marked as that of the N'dama. Little is known of the southward movement of peoples owning Shorthorn-type cattle, though according to Faulkner and Epstein (1957) small numbers of cattle of this type were still to be found in the Koalib hills in the Nuba mountains of the Sudan in recent times and there is evidence that they existed in Uganda within historical times.

There is also some evidence that Shorthorn-type cattle were introduced independently into the Horn of Africa, the east coast of Africa and the offshore islands, presumably by seafaring people from western Asia.

The chest-humped Zebu is a comparative newcomer to Africa. It is likely that cattle of this type were brought in small numbers by migratory people into Egypt as early as 2000 to 1500 BC and also into the Horn of Africa and possibly East Africa, but it is unlikely that they arrived in large numbers until after the Arab invasion of Africa (*c.* AD 669). Faulkner and Epstein (1957) considered that the neck-humped Zebu was first introduced into Egypt during the period 1580 to 1265 BC, but as Slijper (1951) has shown that crossbreds between humpless cattle and chest-humped Zebu cattle tend to possess neck humps, it is likely that African neck-humped Zebu were the result of crossbreeding within Egypt or within western Asia before they were brought to Egypt and could be described as some of the first Sanga-type cattle to appear in Africa.

Zebu appear to be more tolerant to rinderpest than humpless or Sanga cattle, and are also better adapted to living in arid and semi-arid areas. They have therefore spread rapidly in the semi-arid and arid regions and wherever rinderpest has been endemic. Today they are to be found in West Africa north of 14°N latitude, in Northeast Africa, in East Africa and as far south as Malawi and Zambia. This dynamic expansion has not yet spent itself and the Zebu is still gradually replacing Sanga and other breeds along the borders where they meet in Uganda, northeast Congo and northern Ethiopia.

The term 'Sanga' has been used in the past either to describe a particular breed of cattle such as the West African Sanga or in the broadest sense to describe any breed that is apparently the result of a mixture of Zebu and Hamitic Longhorn and/or Shorthorn cattle. Mason and Maule (1960) suggested that the so-called Zebu breeds with cervico-thoracic or neck humps should be classified as Sanga. We consider that this suggestion should be carried to its logical conclusion and that all crossbreds between humped and humpless cattle in Africa should be termed Sanga. If this definition of Sanga-type cattle is accepted, the possibilities for the formation of different types or breeds of Sanga in Africa, over the period of recorded history, are very great, with tribal migration, raiding and counter-raiding maintaining the gene mixture in a state of continuous flux.

The available evidence suggests that it is likely that East Africa and Ethiopia were major centres of origin of large numbers of the earliest Sanga cattle and that these cattle would have been neck-humped animals. Migration of peoples with their cattle may have taken place northwards, westwards and southwards. There were pressures on the early inhabitants of this region to migrate with their cattle southwards, thus neck-humped Sanga should today be found furthest to the south, as indeed to a considerable degree they are. Choice of migration routes southwards was controlled by the availability of feed and water and the location of tsetse Glossina spp.) infested country, but one or more fly-free corridors undoubtedly existed in the past between East and South Africa (Payne, 970).

The first migration southwards by Hottentot-speaking people and their 'anga-type cattle (c. AD 1400) probably followed a route between Lakes 'anganyika and Nyasa to the Upper Limpopo, then westwards across he Orange river. Ultimately they met the first European settlers advancng north from the Cape, who purchased cattle from them. The Sanga attle owned by these early Hottentot migrants are probably the ancesors of the breed that is known today as the Africander.

Migrating behind the Hottentot people came Bantu tribes, also herdng Sanga cattle of various types. Today the majority of Sanga breeds a Zambia, Angola, Botswana and Namibia are of the Hamitic Longorn × Zebu type, while those of the central region of Zambia and the astern region of Rhodesia are probably derived from Shorthorn pe × Zebu crosses.

In East Africa the Sanga cattle have been displaced by Zebu only in very recent times, and small numbers of Sanga cattle are still to be found in the present mainly Zebu areas.

Western migration of peoples herding Sanga cattle took place from Ethiopia to what is now Uganda and further west along the northern borders of the rain-forest to West Africa, so that today it is likely that the Sanga cattle of West Africa may be derived from two sources: local crosses of introduced Zebu with local Hamitic Longhorn and Shorthorn type cattle, and imported Sanga stock from East Africa.

The Americas

No cattle existed in the Americas when these continents were first discovered by the early European explorers. The first cattle to arrive in the western hemisphere were unloaded in the island of Santo Domingo by Columbus on his second voyage in AD 1493. Twenty-eight years later the first cattle were landed on the American mainland at Vera Cruz in Mexico. Following these importations, large numbers of cattle of the Iberian breeds were introduced throughout North, Central and South America. Modern descendants of these cattle are the Longhorns in Mexico and the United States and Criollo cattle in Central and South America. During the seventeenth century British and other north European cattle were imported into North America and were slowly introduced southwards. In the nineteenth century the first Zebu were imported into the United States. Some detail of the history of these importations has been given by Payne (1970). Zebu were crossed with the British-type cattle and in the southeastern United States it was gradually realized that Zebu and Zebu crossbreds were particularly valuable in those areas where the pure-bred British cattle did not thrive. A new Zebu breed, the American Brahman, and a number of more or less stabilized crossbred breeds, such as the Santa Gertrudis, the Beefmaster, the Brangus and the Charbray, have since been used throughout the southeastern region of North America.

In Central America the majority of cattle are now of mixed Iberian and North European type, but in tropical South America until recently the majority of the cattle were descendants of those originally imported from Iberia, though they are now being replaced very rapidly either by Zebu, Zebu crossbreds or European breeds, according to the severity of the local climatic environment. In Brazil as in the United States, a new breed of Zebu known as the Indú-Brasil has originated from a mixture of Zebu imported into Brazil during the nineteenth and the early part of the twentieth centuries. In addition three more or less purebred Zebu breeds have been retained. Indú-Brasil and other types of Zebu have now almost entirely replaced the indigenous Criollo cattle within Brazil. In the Caribbean islands, similar factors have been operating and the original Criollo cattle have virtually disappeared, being replaced either by Zebu, Zebu crossbreds or European-type cattle. Several interesting crossbred breeds of cattle have been developed in the Caribbean region including the Jamaica Red, Jamaica Black, Jamaica Hope and the Nelthropp.

Oceania

In Australia, as in the Americas, there were no cattle before European settlement. In the early stages of settlement, British-type cattle were imported into tropical Australia, but they never fully acclimatized and in this century the local ranchers realized that they required a type of animal more adapted to the local environment. Observing what had happened in the southeastern United States and in Central and South America, the Australians commenced the importation of Zebu for cross-breeding purposes (Payne, 1970). The number of Zebu and Zebu cross-breds in Australia has consequently grown very rapidly within a relatively short period. It is likely that ultimately, crossbred or purebred Zebu will almost completely replace British-type breeds in the Australian tropics. The Australians have imported more or less stabilized crossbred breeds such as the Santa Gertrudis, Brangus, etc., from the United States and they have also bred their own crossbreds. The *Droughtmaster* and the *Australian Milking Zebu* may be considered as original Australian con-tributions to the growing list of *Bos taurus* × *B. indicus* crossbred breeds.

Types of tropical cattle

There are many types and breeds of tropical cattle. Humpless or *Bos taurus* cattle may either be completely acclimatized and of very ancient origin such as the N'dama and Dwarf Shorthorn of West Africa, the Oksh of western Asia, or the Chinese Yellow of south China; imported into the tropics during historical times and more or less acclimatized, such as the Criollo cattle of the Caribbean, Central and South America and the Mauritius Creole of Mauritius; or imported into the tropics during recent times and more or less unacclimatized, such as Friesian milking cattle in the Caribbean islands or British milking breeds in East Africa. Humped, *B. indicus* or Zebu cattle may also be of ancient origin, as they are in western Asia, the Indian sub-continent and in parts of Africa; imported during historical times, such as the Zebu breeds in many parts of Africa and in some countries of Southeast Asia; or imported recently, such as the Zebu cattle of the Americas and Oceania that include the American Brahman and the Indú-Brasil breeds. The only domesticated *B. (Bibos)* breeds are the Bali of Indonesia and possibly the Gayal of Assam–Burma and these are presumably of ancient origin. In addition there are numerous breeds that are the result of crossbreeding between humpless and humped cattle, either in ancient times or more recently. The older, more or less stabilized crossbred breeds are very numerous in Africa – where as previously stated they are known as Sanga – and also in Southeast Asia. The new crossbred breeds such as the Santa Gertrudis and the Droughtmaster are the result of planned crossbreeding programmes in the Americas and Australia. Finally, in Southeast Asia there are a few breeds such as the Madura, that are the result of crossbreeding between *B. taurus* and/or *B. indicus* and *B.* (*Bibos*) spp. cattle.

There is therefore a greater diversity of cattle breeds in the tropics than in the mid-latitude regions, but little is known as to their existing or potential productivity. Indeed, it is only very recently that a full classification of tropical cattle breeds has been made (Payne, 1970).

Although this classification is only tentative it is reproduced below as a useful first guide to students. Breeds have been classified according to the continent of recent origin, within continents on a regional basis, within regions on a type basis and within type on a 'major characteristics' basis. The major types recognized are humpless (*Bos taurus*), humped (*B. indicus*), crossbreds between these, *B.* (*Bibos*) spp., and crossbreds of humpless and/or humped cattle with the latter. Crossbred types have been sub-divided into three groups. The first (1) includes the more or less established indigenous breeds that are considered to have developed in the past from crosses of the major types. The second group (2) consist of what Mason and Maule (1960) describe as 'intermediate breeds', that may not be particularly recent in origin but are apparently still in the process of formation. The third group (3) includes breeds of very recent origin whose formation has generally been deliberately planned. Classification within type on a 'major characteristics' basis has been restricted to the Zebu of the Indian sub-continent and West Africa, and the Sanga of Central and southern Africa.

Classification of breeds

* It should be noted in this classification that both humpless and cross-bred humpless × humped cattle breeds are known as the Chinese Yellow in south China.

Asia

Western Asia

A   Humpless cattle (Oksh)
B   Humped cattle (Aden, Iraqi)
C   Humpless × humped cattle
   (1) Stabilized indigenous (Damascus, Lebanese, Persian)

India–Parkistan sub-continent and Sri Lanka

B Humped cattle
  (1) Shorthorned Zebu (Bachaur, Bhagnari, Gaolao, Hariana, Krishna Valley, Mewati, Nagori, Ongole, Rath)
  (2) Lateral-horned Zebu (Dangi, Deoni, Dhanni, Gir, Nimari, Red Sindhi, Sahiwal)
  (3) Lyre-horned Zebu (Hissar, Kankrej, Malvi, Tharparkar)
  (4) Longhorned Zebu (Alambadi, Amrit Mahal, Bargur, Hallikar, Kangayam, Killari)
  (5) Small shorthorned or lyre-horned Zebu (Kumauni, Lohani, Ponwar, Punganoor, Shahabadi, Sinhala)
C Humpless × humped cattle
  (1) Stabilized indigenous (Siri)
  (3) Recent (Taylor)
D *Bos (Bibos)* spp. (Gaur, Gayal)

China and Southeast Asia

A Humpless cattle (Chinese Yellow)
B Humped cattle (South Chinese Zebu, Taiwan Zebu)
C Humpless × humped cattle
  (1) Stabilized indigenous (Batangas, Burmese, Indo-Chinese, Kelatan, Sumatran, Thai)
  (2) Intermediate (Chinese Yellow)*
D *Bos (Bibos)* spp. (Bali, Banteng, Gaur, Kouprey)
E *Bos (Bibos)* spp. × humpless and/or humped cattle
  (1) Stabilized indigenous (Madura)
  (3) Recent (Grati)

Africa

North Africa

A Humpless cattle (Brown Atlas, Libyan, Mekne's Black Pied)
C Humpless × humped cattle
  (1) Stabilized indigenous (Egyptian)

West Africa

A Humpless cattle (Dwarf Shorthorn, Kuri, N'dama, N'dama × Dwarf Shorthorn crossbreds)
B Humped cattle
  (1) Shorthorned Zebu (Azaouak, Maure, Shuwa, Sokoto)
  (2) Medium-horned Zebu (Adamawa, Diali)
  (3) Lyre-horned Zebu (Senegal Fulani, Sudanese Fulani, White Fulani)
  (4) Long lyre-horned Zebu (Red Bororo)
C Humpless × humped cattle (Sanga)
  (1) Stabilized indigenous (Bambara, Biu, Borgu)

(2) Intermediate (Kuri × Zebu crossbreds, N'dama crossbreds, N'dama × Dwarf Shorthorn × Zebu crossbreds)

Northeast and East Africa

B Humped cattle (Abyssinian, Boran, Karamajong, Small East African Zebu, Small Somali Zebu, Sudanese)
C Humpless × humped cattle
   (1) Stabilized indigenous or Sanga (Ankole, Danakil, Nilotic)
   (2) Intermediate (Kuri × Zebu crossbreds, N'dama crossbreds, N'dama × Dwarf Shorthorn × Zebu crossbreds)
   (3) Recent (Kasai)

Central Africa

B Humped cattle (Angoni)
C Humpless × humped cattle
   (1) Stabilized indigenous or Sanga
   (a) Longhorned Sanga (Barotse, Tuli, Angolan)
   (b) Medium-horned Sanga (Tonga, Mashona)
   (2) Intermediate (Matabele, Baila)
   (3) Recent (Mateba, Kisantu)

Southern Africa

C Humpless × humped cattle
   (1) Stabilized indigenous or Sanga
   (a) Longhorned Sanga (Bechuana, Ovambo)
   (b) Medium-horned Sanga (Nguni, Basuto)
   (c) Lateral-horned Sanga (Africander)
   (3) Recent (Drakensberger, Bonsmara)

Off-shore islands

A Humpless cattle (Mauritius Creole)
B Humped cattle (Madagascar Zebu)
C Humpless × humped cattle
   (1) Stabilized indigenous (Baria)
   (3) Recent (Rana)

The Americas

North America

A Humpless cattle (Texas Longhorn)
B Humped cattle (Brahman)
C Humpless × humped cattle
   (3) Recent (Santa Gertrudis, Beefmaster, Brangus, other crossbred types)

Central America and the Caribbean

A Humpless cattle (Criollo, Nelthropp)
B Humped cattle (Jamaican Brahman)

C Humpless × humped cattle
    (3) Recent (Jamaica Black, Jamaica Red Poll, Jamaica Hope)

South America
A Humpless cattle (Caracú, Criollo)
B Humped cattle (Indú-Brasil)
C Humpless × humped cattle
    (3) Recent (Canchim, Malabar, Ocampo)

Oceania

C Humpless × humped cattle
    (3) Recent (Australian Milking Zebu, Droughtmaster)

It is not possible in an introductory textbook to describe and discuss all these different breeds of tropical cattle, but in the next section some details are given of representative and important tropical breeds. Readers requiring further details on individual tropical breeds should consult Payne (1970).

Representative and important tropical breeds

Some details of the average performance of some of the breeds described below are given in Tables 5.5 and 5.6. The literature has been exhaustively scanned and the data summarized in order to produce the details in these tables. No references are given as these would be too numerous and the data cited have been obtained by the collation of information from many different sources. Further information on the average performance of tropical cattle breeds not described in this section is provided by Payne (1970).

Asia

Damascus

Synonyms: Aleppo, Damascene, Baladi, Halabi, Halep, Kheisi, Shami (Plate 5.1).

Origin and habitat.   This is a stabilized crossbred between *Bos indicus* and *B. taurus*. The breed appear to have developed in the Ghuta, the oasis of Damascus, and then spread to other areas. Cattle of this type are found today in Syria, southern Turkey, Iraq, Cyprus and Egypt. The habitat is varied and the climatic environment is Mediterranean on the coast and sub-tropical and dry inland.

Physical characteristics.   These animals are of medium size, with a narrow body and long, thin legs. The coat colour is light or reddish to dark brown, males being darker in colour than the females. The skin is medium in thickness and soft, while the hair is short and glossy. The head

Table 5.5 Data on age of first calving and the milk production of some representative tropical breeds

Breed	Age at first calving (months)	Milk production Per lactation (kg (lb)) Normal range	Maximum	Length of lactation (days)	Fat (%)	Calving interval (months)
Asian cattle						
Damascus	—	1,500-3,000 (3,307-6,614)	5,000 (11,023)	190-300	4·0-5·0	—
Hariana	32-72	635-1,497 (1,400-3,300)	4,536 (10,000)	260-320	4·0-4·8	19-21
Ongole	36-51	1,179-1,633 (2,600-3,600)	3,266 (7,200)	300-330	5·1	16-18
Gir	31-51	1,225-2,268 (2,700-5,000)	3,175 (7,000)	240-380	4·5-4·6	14-16
Red Sindhi	30-43	680-2,268 (1,500-5,000)	5,443 (12,000)	270-490	4·0-5·0	13-18
Sahiwal	30-43	1,134-3,175 (2,500-7,000)	4,536 (10,000)	290-490	4·0-6·0	13-18
Tharparkar	24-47	680-2,268 (1,500-5,000)	4,763 (10,500)	280-440	4·2-4·7	14-18
Hallikar	39-69	227-1,134 (500-2,500)		180		14
Thai	—	260-580 (573-1,279)				—
African cattle						
Ndama	27-72	150-270 (331-595)	450 (992)	150-300	6·5-7·0	14-42
Dwarf Shorthorn	30-48	120-360 (265-794)		120-180		12-24
Sokoto	36	454-1,361 (1,000-3,000)		230-283	5·8	15
White Fulani	36-48	635-1,225 (1,400-2,700)	1,940 (4,276)	190-360	5·0-7·5	12-15
Sudanese	24-54	454-2,723 (1,000-6,000)	2,302 (5,075)	168-339	4·7-5·5	12-24
Boran	36-52	454-1,814 (1,000-4,000)	4,659 (10,272)	139-303	4·1-6·8	11-14
Small East African Zebu (Bukedi)	25-61	227-998 (500-2,200)	2,641 (5,823)	223-280	4·7-7·1	11-14
Ankole	42-60	318-817 (700-1,800)	1,941 (4,280)	212-239	3·0-7·0	16-24
Angoni	—	630-800 (1,389-1,764)	898 (1,980)	245-270	5·7	—
Mashona	—	218-499 (480-1,100)		180-270		—
American cattle						
Jamaican Hope	27-33	454-1,814 (1,000-4,000)	9,072 (20,000)	250-305	5·0-5·2	12-14
Australian cattle						
Australian Milking Zebu		1,445-2,647 (3,185-5,835)	4,858 (10,710)	305	4·8-4·9	—

| Breed | Liveweight (kg (lb)) | | | | Height at withers at maturity (cm (in)) | | Approximate carcase dressing percentage |
| | At birth | | At maturity | | | | |
	Male	Female	Male	Female	Male	Female	
Asian cattle							
Damascus	21–42 (46–93)	31 (68)	136–318 (300–700)	136–272 (300–600)	130–160 (51–63)	119–150 (47–59)	—
Hariana	23–25 (51–55)	22–24 (49–53)	363–544 (800–1,200)	356 (785)	132–155 (52–61)	127–140 (50–55)	—
Ongole	27–30 (60–66)	24–27 (53–60)	544–612 (1,200–1,350)	431–454 (950–1,000)	142–155 (56–61)	122–145 (48–57)	—
Gir	25–26 (55–57)	21–24 (46–53)	544 (1,200)	386 (850)	122–142 (48–56)	114–145 (45–57)	—
Red Sindhi	18–22 (40–49)	15–22 (33–49)	318–454 (700–1,000)	249–340 (550–950)	124–145 (49–57)	102–127 (40–50)	—
Sahiwal	22–24 (49–53)	20–22 (44–49)	454–590 (1,000–1,300)	272–408 (600–900)	127 (50)	117–130 (46–51)	—
Tharparkar	22–24 (49–53)	21–24 (46–53)	363–454 (800–1,000)	227–340 (500–750)	127–132 (50–52)	124–127 (49–50)	—
Hallikar	—	—	340 (750)	227 (500)	135–142 (53–56)	119 (47)	—
Thai	—	—	345–500 (761–1,102)		119 (47)	109 (43)	—
Bali	—	—	350–400 (772–882)	250–300 (551–661)	127 (50)	117 (46)	50–58
African cattle							
N'dama	16 (35)	14 (31)	222–419 (489–924)	210–353 (463–778)	94–119 (37–47)	89–112 (35–44)	40–56
Dwarf Shorthorn	25 (55)	23 (51)	120–450 (265–992)	120–350 (265–772)	90–117 (36–46)	79–114 (31–45)	—
Sokoto	25 (55)	24 (53)	499–544 (1,100–1,200)	333 (734)	137 (54)	127 (50)	50
White Fulani	20–25 (44–55)	20–23 (44–51)	250–350 (551–772)	250–350 (551–772)	152 (60)	137 (54)	52–55
Sudanese	23–25 (51–55)	21–25 (46–55)	300–500 (661–1,102)	250–350 (551–772)	142–147 (56–58)	130–137 (51–54)	40–50
Boran	25 (55)	23 (51)	318–680 (700–1,560)	259–454 (571–1,000)	117–147 (46–58)	114–127 (45–50)	54–57
Small East African Zebu							
(Bukedi)	18–20 (40–44)	16–20 (35–44)	254–450 (560–922)	270–318 (595–700)	102–122 (40–48)	99–107 (39–42)	42–53
Ankole	17–22 (37–49)	15–21 (33–46)	350–500 (772–1,102)	200–400 (441–882)	117–147 (46–58)	117–132 (46–52)	45–55
Angoni	20 (44)	18 (40)	272–726 (600–1,600)	181–472 (400–1,040)	124–137 (49–54)	114–135 (45–53)	61–64
Mashona	23 (51)	21 (46)	363–635 (800–1,400)	159–408 (350–900)	—	—	—
Africander	30 (66)	28 (61)	454–907 (1,000–2,000)	363–544 (800–1,200)	130–142 (51–56)	127–135 (50–53)	59–64
American cattle							
Romo-Sinuano		30 (66)	600–800 (1,323–1,764)	500–700 (1,102–1,543)	—		58–60

is long and narrow, the horns small and short, the hump is hardly noticeable, particularly in the female, and the dewlap is relatively well developed. The udder of the female is of medium size and possesses long, thin teats.

Utility.   This is usually considered to be a milking breed with a fair average production (Table 5.5). The breed was used as a source of foundation cattle in the Zionist settlements in Palestine in 1912 and was upgraded using Holstein (Hirsch and Shindler, 1957). It is said that this breed is particularly heat tolerant and that individuals are long-lived. It is not usually used for work purposes.

Plate 5.1   Damascus (stabilized indigenous: humpless × humped).

Hariana (Plate 5.2)

Related types.   Hariana are somewhat similar to the Bhagnari, Gaolao and Ongole breeds, a closely related type being the Shahabadi.

Origin and habitat.   The breed originated in east Punjab, India, north of the tropic. The climatic environment is subtropical and semi-arid, the annual rainfall being 457 mm (18 in).

Physical characteristics.   This is a compact animal of graceful appearance. The coat colour is white or grey, being darker over the hindquarters in the male. The skin is pigmented, fine, thin and tight. The face is long and narrow and there is a well-marked bony prominence at the centre of the poll. The ears are small and somewhat pendulous. The horns are fine

Plate 5.2   Hariana (humped).

and short, and thinner in the female than in the male. The hump is large and well developed in the male but of medium size in the female. The dewlap is moderately well developed but thin in the male and the sheath is short and tight. The navel flap is close to the body. The udder of the female is relatively large and extends well forward. The teats are of medium size, the fore being longer than the hind.

Utility.   This is one of the most important dual-purpose, milk–work breeds in northern India, and indeed cattle of this type are used all over India as the cows are quite good milkers (Table 5.5) and the bullocks make powerful work animals.

Ongole – synonym: Nellore (Plate 5.3)

Related types.   It has considerable conformational similarity with the Gaolao and Bhagnari breeds and blood group data suggest that it is also related to the Hariana.

Origin and habitat.   This breed is found in Madras where the climate is tropical and where there is a low to medium annual rainfall.

Physical characteristics.   They are large, long-bodied animals with short necks and long limbs. The normal coat colour is white, but the male has dark grey markings on the head, neck and hump and sometimes black points on the knees. Red or red and white animals are occasionally seen. The skin is of medium thickness and often shows black mottled markings. The head is long; the ears are moderately long and slightly drooping. The horns are short and stumpy, growing outwards and backwards, and are thick at the base. The hump in the males is well developed and erect. The dewlap is large and fleshy and hangs in folds that extend to the navel flap. The sheath is slightly pendulous.

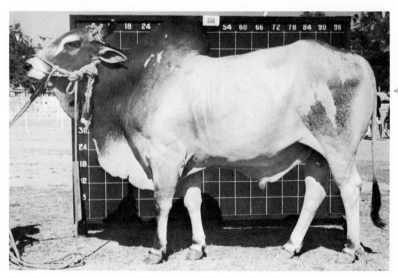

Plate 5.3   Ongole: synonym Nellore (humped) (Indian Council of Agricultural Research, New Delhi).

Utility.   They are primarily used for work, being usually very docile. The cows are fair milk producers (Table 5.5). Animals of this type have been exported to many countries and they have contributed genes to both the American Brahman and the Indú-Brasil breeds. Outside India, they are considered to be good beef animals for use under very adverse conditions. They are rapidly becoming one of the major beef breeds in Brazil.

Gir – synonyms: Decan, Kathiawari, Sorthi, Surti (Plate 5.4)

Related types.   There is definite evidence of Gir blood in the Mewati, Deoni, Krishna Valley and Nimari breeds and blood-grouping data suggest that the Gir is also related to Red Sindhi, Sahiwal and Afghan cattle.

Origin and habitat.   The breed originated in the Gir hills and forest on the west coast of India where the climatic environment is of the monsoonal tropical type.

Plate 5.4   Gir (humped).

Physical characteristics. These cattle are moderately large, heavy animals. The coat colour is characteristic and varies from yellowish red to black or white with dark red or chocolate-brown patches distributed all over the body. The skin is loose, pliable and fine and the hair short and glossy. They possess a very prominent and broad forehead and the ears are long and pendulous. The horns are moderate in size, curving away from the head in a downwards and backwards manner and then inclining a little upwards and forwards, taking a spiral inward sweep and finally ending in a fine taper. The hump is large. The dewlap is only moderately developed while the sheath in the male is large and pendulous.

Utility. These animals are fairly good milkers (Table 5.5) and they are also used extensively for draught purposes. Although they are not used in India for beef production, outside India they have an excellent reputation as beef animals and large numbers have been exported to Brazil from whence they have been introduced to other American countries. Gir are one of the foundation breeds of the American Brahman and Indú-Brasil, and are used as a pure breed in Brazil.

Red Sindhi – synonyms: Malir, Red Karachi, Sindhi (Plate 5.5)

Origin and habitat. The original herd was founded at Malir outside Karachi in Pakistan and they may have derived from hill-type cattle. They are somewhat similar to the Sahiwal and they may be related to the red

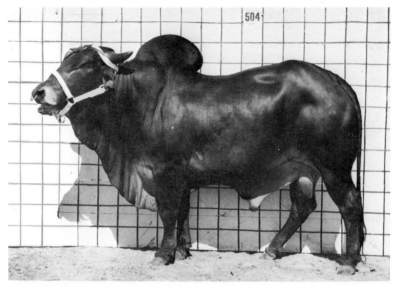

Plate 5.5   Red Sindhi (humped).

Afghan cattle and also possess some mixture of Gir blood. The home base of the breed is now around Karachi, just outside the tropics, where the climatic environment is sub-tropical and semi-arid.

Physical characteristics.   The Red Sindhi is a medium to small animal with a deep, compact frame and round, drooping quarters. The coat colour is usually red, varying from dark red to dun yellow, often with specks of white on the dewlap and the forehead. In the male the colour is darker on the shoulders and thighs. The hair is soft and short; the skin is loose, of medium thickness and usually pigmented. The ears are of moderate to large size and drooping. The horns are thick at the base and emerge laterally, curving upwards. The hump is of medium size though well developed in the male. The dewlap and sheath are pendulous. The udder of the female also inclines to be pendulous and the teats unduly large.

Utility.   It is considered one of the best dairy breeds in the Indian sub-continent (Table 5.5), though it is also used for light work. It has been exported all over the tropical world and used for upgrading indigenous cattle, particularly for milk production.

Sahiwal – synonyms: Lambi Bar, Lola, Montgomery, Multani, Teli (Plate 5.6)

Origin and habitat.   This breed originated in the district of Montgomery

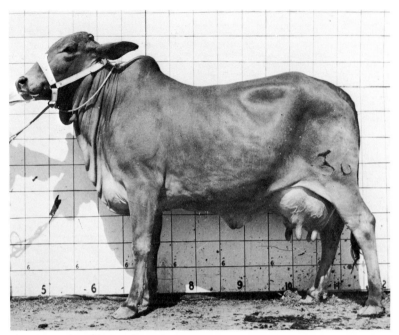

Plate 5.6   Sahiwal (humped).

in the West Punjab, Pakistan, and may have been derived from the Red Sindhi. The climatic environment of the original habitat is sub-tropical and arid.

Physical characteristics.   It is a large, heavily built, long, deep, rather fleshy animal. The coat colour is varied, with reddish dun being rather common. Other coat colours are pale red, dark brown and almost black flecked with white. The skin is frequently unpigmented. The head is broad and massive in the male. The ears are of medium size with black hair on the fringes. The horns are very short and thick and loose horns are common in the female. The hump of the male is massive and frequently falls to one side. The dewlap is large and heavy, the navel flap loose and hanging; the sheath in the male is pendulous. The udder of the female is large and sometimes pendulous.

Utility.   This is one of the most productive of tropical dairy breeds (Table 5.5) and cattle of this type have been exported to many parts of the tropical world. In Jamaica they have been crossed with the Jersey to provide the foundation stock for the breed known as the Jamaica Hope, and in East Africa they have been widely used for upgrading the Small East African Zebu cattle. Although the Sahiwal is basically a dairy breed, cattle of this type can be used for beef and work purposes.

Plate 5.7　Kankrej (humped).

Kankrej–synonyms: Bannai, Gujarati, Nagar, Sanchore, Talebda, Vadhiyar, Wagadia, Wagad, Wadhiar, Wadial (Plate 5.7).

Origin and habitat.　This breed originated in North Gujarat, in the Bombay province of India, where the climatic environment is tropical to sub-tropical and dry.

Physical characteristics.　This is a large animal. The coat colour varies from silver to iron-grey or steel-black. New-born calves are coloured a rusty-red on the poll. The skin is pigmented and the hair is soft and short. The forehead is wide with prominent orbital arches. The ears are large and pendulous. The horns are large and lyre-shaped, and covered in skin to a much higher point than is normal in other breeds. The hump is well developed. The dewlap is thin and pendulous, the males possessing pendulous sheaths.

Plate 5.8 Tharparkar (humped).

Utility. In India this is a dual-purpose milk and draught breed, but it has excellent potentiality for beef production and large numbers have been exported to Brazil where it has been used as one of the foundation breeds of the Indú-Brasil. Some Kankrej-type animals were also included in the foundation stock of the American Brahman. It is also used in Brazil – where it is known as the Guzerat – as a purebred type.

Tharparkar – synonyms: Grey Sindhi, White Sindhi, Thari (Plate 5.8)

Related types. One of the related types is the Cutchi, which originates from the Cutch, on the northwest border between India and Pakistan.

Origin and habitat. The home of the breed is the Tharparkar district of Hyderabad, India. This is an arid area and in drought years cattle have had to be removed to the surrounding regions where they have interbred with Kankrej, Red Sindhi, Gir and Nagori cattle. The habitat is situated just outside the tropics and is very arid. The rainfall averages 203 mm (8 in) per annum.

Physical characteristics. They are strongly built, medium-size animals with comparatively short, straight limbs and good feet. The skin is pigmented and thin, the hair fine and short. The coat colour is usually white or grey with a light grey stripe along the top line. In the male the grey colour may deepen with age, particularly on the face and hindquarters.

Black- and red-coloured cattle are also seen. The head is medium in size, the forehead broad and flat; the ears are long, broad and semi-pendulous. The horns are set well apart and curve gradually upwards and outwards, ending in blunt points that are inclined inwards. The horns of the male are thicker, shorter and straighter than those of the female. The hump is moderately well developed and firm; the dewlap is of medium size; the sheath in the male is of moderate length and semi-pendulous and the navel flap in the female is prominent.

Utility.　This is one of the best dual-purpose work–milk breeds found in the Indian sub-continent. It will milk under very poor feeding conditions and has great powers of endurance and resistance to poor feeding and to drought conditions. Large numbers of these cattle have been exported, particularly to Zaire, Iraq, Sri Lanka and the Philippines.

Hallikar (Plate 5.9)

Origin and habitat.　This is one of the South Indian long-horned Zebu breeds and is found mainly in the State of Mysore. The climatic environment in the area is montane tropical.

Physical characteristics.　These cattle are of medium size, compact and muscular in appearance, with strong legs. The differences between male

Plate 5.9　Hallikar (humped).

and female in size and build are not so well marked as in other breeds as the female has a muscular, masculine appearance. The coat colour is grey to dark grey with darker shadings on the fore- and hindquarters. Frequently, there are light grey markings on the face, dewlap and under the body. The skin is fine and the coat short and glossy. The face is long, the forehead prominent and the ears small. The horns emerge close to each other from the top of the poll and are carried backwards for nearly half their length, and then bend forwards inclining towards their tips which are black and sharp. The hump is moderately developed as is the dewlap. The sheath is very small and close to the body.

Utility.   The Hallikar is one of the best all-round draught breeds to be found in southern India, but like other southern Indian cattle they are poor milkers (Table 5.5).

Thai – synonym: Siamese (Plate 5.10)

Related types.   The fighting cattle of south Thailand are sufficiently distinct to be considered as a related type. They possess more *Bos indicus* genes.

Origin and habitat.   Thai cattle are very similar in conformation to the other breeds of Southeast Asia. Little is known of the origin of these cattle, but it is likely that they are the result of crossbreeding between Zebu imported from India and humpless Shorthorn-type cattle that accompanied nomadic peoples coming from the north by way of China.

Plate 5.10   Southern Thai fighting bull (stabilized indigenous: humpless × humped) (Professor Dr H. Fischer).

This theory receives some support from the fact that the cattle in the south of Thailand appear to possess more Zebu genes than those in the north of the country. In some parts of Thailand the cattle may also possess some genes from the wild *Bos* (*Bibos*) spp. The climatic environment is varied; in the south of Thailand it is humid tropical, while in the north-east it is monsoonal and/or montane tropical.

Physical characteristics. The cattle of the north are of medium size, hardy and relatively long-legged. The coat colour is usually yellow, red, brown or black – lighter shades being preferred by the local farmers. The head is short, the forehead narrow and the ears small. The horns are small, set well apart, and curve upwards and slightly forwards and are pointed. The hump is cervico-thoracic, small in the male and virtually absent in the female. The dewlap is moderately large.

Fischer (1967) has described the cattle in the southern provinces of Thailand. He stated that they are not Zebu, and presumably like the cattle in the northern provinces they are crossbreds, but with a larger admixture of Zebu genes. These cattle are blockier than the cattle in the north with short, strong legs and strong hooves. The coat colour is varied, but black, red and reddish grey are common, as is a speckled colour. The head is short or medium in size, as are the ears. The horns are similar to those of the cattle in the northern provinces and they are particularly well developed in the male. The latter possess a strongly developed cervico-thoracic and pointed hump, the female being more or less humpless. One peculiar characteristic of this breed is the very prominent sex organs in the male.

Utility. The majority of these cattle are used for draught purposes, but in south Thailand some are used for bull-fighting – a local sport. Fighting bulls are selected at 4 years of age and should possess a good strong pair of horns and a well-developed chest, but they are not used until they are 6 years old. After being used for fighting they are then utilized for work and breeding purposes.

Bali (Bos (Bibos) banteng *Wagner*) – synonym: Balinese (Plate 5.11)

Origin and habitat. These animals are unique as they are the only domesticated type of banteng (*Bos* (*Bibos*) *banteng* Wagner). They originated in Indonesia and are found today in Bali, Lombok, Timor, Flores, Sulawesi, East Java and Kalimantan in Indonesia and in small numbers in Sabah. The climatic environment throughout this area is generally humid and tropical.

Physical characteristics. It is a medium-size, deep-chested, fine-legged animal. The coat colour is usually red, though a golden colour and deep brown are known, while being uncommon. The muzzle, feet and switch are black and the legs are white up to the hocks, and there is white

Plate 5.11   Bali (*Bos [Bibos] banteng*). Typical bulls on a smallholding in Bali, Indonesia.

under the thighs and a very distinct white oval patch on the hindquarters. There is always a distinctive black line along the back, commencing at the shoulders and ending above the tail. The male is darker
than the female, the coat colour becoming dark brown to black at
maturity. At birth the calves of both sexes possess a golden to reddish-
brown coat with typical light spots on the back of the legs. The black
colour disappears and the reddish-brown coat colour returns if the male
is castrated. The hair is short, fine and smooth. The skin is pigmented
and fine. The head is broad and short, with a flat poll; the ears are of
medium size and erect. The horns of the male are large, grow sideways
and then upwards, and are pointed. Those of the female are considerably
smaller. The male possesses a definite crest and the dewlap is well
developed in both sexes. The udder of the female is poorly developed
and covered with hair.

Utility.   The breed is used for work purposes, but it is also considered
to be a good meat animal that possesses a high dressing-out percentage
(Payne and Rollinson, 1973). It is more fertile than the Zebu and is considered to be superior to the Zebu as a work animal in humid tropical
climates. It also demonstrates an ability to thrive on feeds of very
low nutritive value. Bali cattle have been exported to Malaysia, the

Philippines and Hawaii and feral animals have become established in Northern Australia.

Africa

N'dama – synonyms: Boenca, Fouta Djallon, Fouta Jallon, Fouta Long-horn, Fouta Malinke, Futa, Gambian Longhorn, Madingo (Plate 5.12)

Origin and habitat.   This is a humpless breed of the Hamitic Longhorn type and the ancestors of this breed were probably the first domesticated cattle in Africa. They are found today in Liberia, Guinea, Gambia, south Senegal, north Ivory Coast, Sierre Leone, north Benin, Upper Volta, Mali and Portuguese Guinea. It is considered that the focal point in West Africa from which the breed spread is the Fouta Djallon plateau in Guinea. The breed has apparently increased in numbers during the last 100 years and has acclimatized to life in or on the edges of the rain-forest of West Africa. The northern limit of distribution of this breed approximates to the northern limit of the tsetse-infested area and to the southern limit of distribution of Zebu. The climatic environment of this area can generally be characterized as humid and tropical.

Physical characteristics.   It is a small, humpless, well-built animal with a straight top line and short, fine limbs. The coat is usually yellow, fawn, light red or dun in colour, although there are black and pied animals

Plate 5.12   N'dama (humpless).

with black or fawn on a white background. The Sierre Leone variety is usually coloured various shades of red. The skin is pigmented, the colour varying from black to light brown, and the hair is soft and short. The head is short and broad, the ears small and horizontal. The horns are lyre-shaped and grow sideways and then forwards and upwards from the poll. In mature cattle they are 45 to 50 cm (18 to 20 in) long, circular in cross-section and white with dark tips. Polled cattle are not uncommon. The dewlap and umbilical fold are not large. The udder of the female is very small and set high between the legs.

Utility. They are poor milkers (Table 5.5), but they can be, and sometimes are, used for draught purposes. They are essentially beef animals producing reasonably good carcases under poor grazing conditions. Their meat is of good quality. Their most unusual attribute is that they are inherently tolerant to trypanosomiasis and that this tolerance appears to be enhanced by exposure to infection (Chandler, 1958) but breaks down under stress. They are also said to be tolerant to piroplasmosis and they have a reputation for longevity.

On account of their tolerance to trypanosomiasis, cattle of this breed have been imported into Ghana, Nigeria and Zaire. They have also been exported to the West Indies where they have been crossed with the Red Poll to form the breed known as the Nelthropp.

Dwarf Shorthorn – synonyms: Dwarf Humpless, Kirdi, Pagan, West African Dwarf Shorthorn, West African Shorthorn (Plate 5.13)

Related types. This breed is also humpless, but it has been developed from the Shorthorn-type cattle that accompanied nomadic peoples into Africa after the Hamitic Longhorns had become established. There are many related types in West Africa including the following:

1. *West African Humpless* – synonym: Taurine.
2. *Nigerian Shorthorn* – synonyms: Maturu, Nigerian Dwarf. Found south of 8°N latitude except in isolated enclaves where they are kept by pagan peoples as far north as 12° latitude.
3. *Lagoon* – synonyms: Mayumbe, Race des Lagunes. Found in the Ivory Coast, Togo and Benin. A very small animal. Mayumbe are the type that have been imported into Zaire.
4. *Gambian Dwarf.* Originally found south of the Gambia river, but becoming extinct (Mason, 1951).
5. *Bakosi* – synonyms: Bakwiri, Kosi. Found in the mountains of the Federated Republic of Cameroun.
6. *Somba.* Found in the Atakora highlands of north Togo and Benin (Doutressoulle, 1947).
7. *Lagone.* Found in Chad.
8. *Manjaca.* Found in the coastal areas north of the Geba and Corubal rivers in Portuguese Guinea.

Plate 5.13   West African Dwarf Shorthorn (humpless).

9. *Gold Coast*. Found in the lagoon area around Keta, Ghana (Stewart, 1937).

Origin and habitat. Today they are found in coastal forest and savanna areas between Gambia and the Federated Republic of Cameroun and to a more limited extent in the interior. The climate of their habitat is mainly humid and tropical, but they are also found in some drier areas such as coastal Togoland, Ghana and Benin where the rainfall is comparatively low.

Physical characteristics. They are small, thickset animals with short, fine-boned limbs. The skin is tight and pigmented and the coat usually black, dark brown or pied in colour. The head is short and broad, the animal possessing a broad poll and short horns that grow sideways and upwards and curve forwards at the extremities. In cross-section the horns are circular in the male and oval in the female. Polled animals are common. There is little dewlap or sheath.

Utility. These cattle are poor milkers (Table 5.5), but they possess a reasonably good conformation and produce fairly good beef. They can be used for working purposes, but their capacity is small and their stamina limited. Like the N'dama they also exhibit tolerance to trypanosomiasis, but this tolerance is not as marked as that of the N'dama and it can more easily be broken down if they are weakened by disease or malnutrition or if they are overworked.

Sokoto – synonyms: Gudali, Sokoto Gudali (Plate 5.14)

Origin and habitat. These cattle are typical of the shorthorned Zebu found in West Africa. In general appearance and conformation they are somewhat similar to the grey-white breeds of Indian cattle. This particular breed is found in Sokoto province of northwestern Nigeria where the climatic environment is semi-arid and tropical.

Physical characteristics. They are medium-size, deep-bodied animals. The usual coat colour is white or cream in the female and light grey or cream with dark shading over the poll, neck, shoulders and tail in the male. There are some males that are coloured dun with blue-grey shading. The hair is short and the skin medium thick, loose and pigmented. They possess pendulous ears. The male has very short, lateral upturned horns while the female has smaller but slightly longer horns. The hump is almost cervico-thoracic and well developed in both sexes. A well-pronounced dewlap and umbilical fold is possessed by both sexes.

Utility. This is essentially a dairy–draught breed, but these cattle are also used for beef production. It is a fair milker under natural grazing conditions and as a work animal it is slow, docile, sturdy and reliable.

Plate 5.14 Sokoto Gudali (humped).

White Fulani–synonyms: Akou (Federated Republic of Cameroun), Bunaji, White Bororo, White Kano, Yakanaji (Plate 5.15)

Origin and habitat. This breed is typical of the West African lyre-horned Zebu owned by the Fulani people. It is found in northern Nigeria and

Plate 5.15 White Fulani (humped).

in the Federated Republic of Cameroun in a climatic environment that is tropical and semi-arid. A related type is the Wodobe which appears to be intermediate in characteristics between the White Fulani and the Red Bororo.

Physical characteristics. They are large animals. The coat is usually white with black points, but a few animals possess coats that are black with blue flecking or red and white. The skin is loose and pigmented and the hair soft. The ears are erect. The horns are medium to long, lyre-shaped and curve outwards and upwards. In some animals there is an outward turn again at the tip. The hump is well developed and often more or less cervico-thoracic in position. The dewlap is large and well developed, possessing many folds. The sheath and navel flap are not large. The udder of the female is well developed with medium-size teats.

Utility. It is a triple-purpose breed, used primarily for milk production (Table 5.5) as milk constitutes the basic diet of the Fulani. These cattle fatten well on natural grasslands and they are good beef animals, possessing a light skeleton. They are good but slow workers. At Shika in northern Nigeria White Fulani have been crossed with the Holstein in an effort to produce a more productive milk animal for use in the region.

Sudanese – synonyms: Arab, Northern Sudan Shorthorned Zebu, North Sudan Zebu (Plate 5.16)

Origin and habitat. There are a number of related types, the major ones being the following:

1. *Kenana* – synonyms: Blue Nile, Fung, Rufa'ai.
2. *Butana* – synonyms: Bambana, Batahin, Hodendowa, Red Butana, Shukria.
3. *White Nile.*
4. *Baggara* – synonyms: Darfur, Kordofan, Kordofani, Western. These cattle are of very mixed origin.
5. *Northern Province* – synonyms: Deleigabi, Dongola, Geigarawi, Shendi.

In general it is difficult to specify distinct types as over wide areas there has been a mixture of these related animals, some of whom closely resemble the Indian-type Zebu in conformation. Of the related types, the Kenana and White Nile are representative of the nomadic cattle of the northern Sudan, their habitat being semi-arid desert scrub where the rainfall is 336 to 457 mm (14 to 18 in). The Northern Province type of cattle come from the riverine region between Khartoum and the Egyptian border and are of somewhat mixed origin, while the Butana are found in the semi-arid area between the Blue Nile and the river Atbara. Baggara cattle have been derived from stock originally introduced from

Plate 5.16   Sudanese bull of the Butana type (humped).

countries further to the west and mixed with many other types. They are found in the savanna regions between the Nile and the western frontier of the Sudan.

Physical characteristics.   The different types vary in size, but much of this variation may be due to environmental influences. The coat colour is also variable. White-grey predominates in the Kenana. In the White Nile there are many colours: red, fawn, white, black and admixtures of these. In the Butana and in the Northern Province cattle the coat is usually red although mixed-colour animals are found. In the Baggara the most usual coat colour is white with red and, less often, black markings, but cattle of many different colours are seen. Kenana calves are born with a red-brown coat that changes to white-grey at 3 to 6 months of age. The coat of the majority of these cattle is short and the skin loose, thin and pigmented. The head is long and coffin-shaped. The ears are fairly long and semi-pendulous. The horns seldom exceed 31 to 35 cm (12 to 14 in) in length, are shorter in the male than in the female, are oval in cross-section and grow from a flat poll in an outward and upward direction. There appear to be a few true polls although loose, hanging horns and scurs are common. The hump is cervico-thoracic to thoracic in position and slopes from front to rear. In Baggara cattle the hump in males is almost always cervico-thoracic and females often possess a very small hump. The dewlap is large and prominent, indeed in some cattle it is often double folded under the chin and may be continuous with the umbilical fold.

Utility. The majority of these cattle are kept by nomadic or semi-nomadic peoples and they are primarily used for milk production (Table 5.5), although surplus males are sold for slaughter. These cattle have a very strong herding instinct, are very docile and are well adapted for living in semi-arid areas. Within the Sudanese breed, the Kenana are considered the best milkers. Northern Province cattle are also used for work purposes. In a small number of Kenana herds the cattle have been especially selected for milk production and the results suggest that this breed is one of the most productive milk breeds in Africa.

Boran (Plate 5.17)

There are three related types:

1. *Somali Boran* – synonym: Avai.
2. *Tanaland Boran* – synonym: Galla.
3. *Kenya Boran* – synonym: NFD.

Origin and habitat. Boran originated from the Borana province of southern Ethiopia, but today the breed is found is southern Ethiopia, Somalia and Kenya. In the latter country the Boran has become an important beef breed on the ranches. The type of Boran cattle now found on the ranches originated from animals sold to the European farmers by Somali traders, and there is no doubt that some of the herds include cattle that possess some temperate-type stock genes, particularly Hereford, as cattle of this breed were imported into Kenya 50 years ago and

Plate 5.17 Boran (humped).

used as foundation stock on the ranches. They were later upgraded using Boran bulls.

The original habitat was tropical and semi-arid, but in the major ranching areas it is montane, tropical and semi-arid.

Physical characteristics.   The Ethiopian Boran is a fairly large, long-legged animal with good body conformation. Some of the Tanaland Boran are inclined to legginess and are rather slab-sided. The coat colour of all types is usually white or grey, but red or pied colours occur. The Somali type is normally white with black points. The Tanaland Boran is also usually white, but shades of fawn occur. The Boran on the ranches in Kenya is typically white with black points, but fawn, red and black animals are seen and cattle in some of the herds are being bred for other colours apart from white. The Kenya Boran and the Somali Boran usually possess a pigmented skin, but the skin of the Tanaland Boran is not always pigmented. The skin of all types is thin, loose and pliable. The head is medium to long. The ears are small and not pendulous. The horns are usually small, thick at the base, pointed and directed forward. In the Tanaland and in the NFD types the horns are variable. Polled animals are not uncommon. The hump is well defined, upright and thoracic. It is sometimes folded on one side and is larger in the male than in the female. The dewlap and sheath are not excessively developed in the Somali Boran but more so in the Tanaland Boran. The improved Boran on Kenya ranches is characterized by a very straight top line and well-developed hindquarters.

Utility.   These cattle are used by the semi-nomadic peoples primarily for milk, and if selected for milk production are moderately good milkers (Table 5.5). On the ranches they have been selected for beef purposes and now appear to be one of the outstanding beef breeds of Africa. Unlike most small East African Zebu, the Boran are susceptible to tick-borne diseases and particularly to East Coast fever (ECF). Because of their reported productive ability and their size they are much in demand in the tick-infested areas and a considerable number of experiments have been made to attempt the pre-immunization of these cattle so that they can be used throughout East Africa. Although some success has been claimed, in general the mortality of these cattle in the tick areas has been high and the immunized stock do not appear to have inherited any tolerance to ECF (Stobbs, 1966).

Small East African Zebu–synonym: East African Shorthorned Zebu (Plate 5.18)

These are the major type of cattle found in most parts of East Africa and they are given different names in different regions. The main related types are as follows:

1. Mongalla – synonyms: Southeastern Zebu, Southern Sudan Hill Zebu

Plate 5.18   Small East African Zebu (humped).

2. Lugware – synonyms: Bahu, Lagware and Lugwaret.
3. Bukedi – synonyms: Eastern Province Zebu, Lango, Nkedi, Teso, Uganda Zebu.
4. Nandi – synonyms: Kavirondo, Kikuyu, Kamba, Akamba, Ukamba, Wakamba.
5. Masai.
6. Tanzania Zebu – synonyms: Iringa Red, Masai Grey, Mkalama Dun, Singida White, Mbulu, Wachagga.
7. Zanzibar Zebu.

Origin and habitat.   Although there are so many different types of Small East African Zebu varying somewhat in size and colour, it is generally accepted that they all have a common origin. Undoubtedly, the total number of these cattle has increased during the last century and it is likely that they are now used in areas where Sanga cattle were previously maintained. The climatic environment of the habitat is very varied and they are managed from sea level to 2,740 m (9,000 ft), but generally they are most numerous in the wetter and more humid areas of East Africa, whereas the larger Zebu, such as the Boran, are more numerous in the drier areas.

Physical characteristics.   The majority are small, stocky animals. Their coat colour varies over a very wide range from white to black. Their hair is short and soft and their skin pliable and deeply pigmented. Their head is of medium length, and although horn shape varies over a wide range, in general horns are short, grow outwards and curve slightly inwards at the tip. Humps are pronounced in both sexes, but are larger in the male than in the female. In the male they often fall over backwards or to one side. Dewlaps vary in size but tend to be small, as are the umbilical folds.

Utility.   Some types of this breed are excellent milkers for their size, particularly the Bukedi and Nandi (Table 5.5). They are all used, however, for draught, milk and meat production and occasionally for ceremonial purposes. Animals that are owned by the semi-nomadic peoples such as the Masai are also used for the production of blood, which is part of the staple diet, and are rarely slaughtered for meat. In general, these cattle are more tolerant of tick-borne disease than the larger types of Zebu.

Ankole – synonyms: Ankole Longhorn, Toro, Wakuma (Plate 5.19)

Related types:

1. Bahima – synonyms: Banioro, Banyoro, Bunyoro, Nsagalla.
2. Watusi – synonyms: Barundi, Kivi, Kuku, Nyambo, Watusi Longhorn.

Plate 5.19   Ankole cattle (stabilized indigenous: humpless × humped).

3. Kigezi.
4. Bashi.

Origin and habitat.   These are Sanga cattle with large or medium-size, lyre-shaped horns and small humps, and the principal owners are two related Hamitic pastoral tribes known as the Bahima and the Watusi. These cattle are found in Uganda in two regions separated by a tsetse belt, in Rwanda, Burundi, in the Kivu district of Zaire and in Tanzania. The climatic environment is very varied, ranging from the hot dry climate of the Ruzizi valley to the cool upland areas of Rwanda.

Physical characteristics.   The Bahima are large, long-legged animals with a straight back. The prominent and favoured coat colour is deep red, but red and white also occur. The hair is short and the skin soft, pliable and pigmented. The distinguishing features are the horns: these are very long and large, curving gracefully outwards and upwards and finally inwards. There is a great deal of variation in type of horn. Some of the cattle have a horn span of 185 to 190 cm (73 to 75 in) while others have shorter, thicker horns and 2 per cent are polled. The total horn weight is often as much as 6·8 kg (15 lb) or 1·7 per cent of the body weight, but there does not appear to be any significant difference in the growth rate of horned and dehorned cattle from birth to 2 or 3 years of age according to Trail and Sacker (1966). The males sometimes have a slight cervico-thoracic hump, but there is usually no hump in the female.

The most common coat colours in the Watusi are brown, fawn, red or black, and combinations of these colours with white. There is a very wide variation in the size and shape of the horn and horn growth is sometimes deliberately stimulated. In Rwanda the *Nyambo* or *Inyambo* strain has exceptionally long horns, up to 2 to 3 m (6·8 to 9·8 ft) between the points, and is held to be sacred. There is also a shorthorned strain known as the *Inkuku* or *Kuku* found in the mountains.

The Kigezi are smaller and finer-boned cattle, paler in colour than the Bahima and with smaller, more upright horns.

The Bashi is also a smaller animal, the common coat colour being red, fawn, black or white or combinations of these. The horns are much shorter and the hump is hardly developed in the male and is absent in the female.

Utility.   These cattle are used primarily for social purposes and for milk production, the Bashi type being the best milk animal (Table 5.5). They do not make particularly good beef cattle and are not normally used for work purposes. They are more susceptible to rinderpest than the Zebu, and in Uganda and Tanzania the total number of these cattle appears to be slowly declining as cattle owners replace them by Zebu-type animals.

Angoni (Plate 5.20)

These are the shorthorned Zebu cattle found in Zambia, Malawi and Mozambique in an area south and west of Lake Nyasa. There are four types, but it is likely that they all have the same origin and that they are descendants of shorthorned Zebu cattle that were introduced from the north.

Related types:

1. Zambia Angoni.
2. Malawi Angoni.
3. Mozambique Angoni – synonyms: Tete, Zulu, Angone Zambesi, Angonia Zebu.
4. Malawi Zebu – synonyms: Nyasa Shorthorned Zebu, Nyasa Zebu.

Origin and habitat.   These cattle represent the southernmost extension of the shorthorned Zebu cattle of East Africa. The habitat is very varied both climatically and topographically, but the climate is generally tropical and dry.

Physical characteristics.   Zambia Angoni are medium-size, light-boned animals. The coat colour is very variable. The hair is short and the skin

Plate 5.20   Angoni (humped) (C. Walker).

thin, loose and pigmented. The ears are of medium size. The horns are usually short and stout, but approximately 15 per cent possess lyre-type horns. The hump and dewlap are well developed in both sexes. Horns of the Malawi Angoni are usually larger, the hump is more variable while the dewlap is generally less developed than in the Zambia Angoni. Mozambique Angoni are smaller animals, their horns are short and stout and their humps are very well developed. The Malawi Zebu is also a small animal very similar to the Small East African Zebu in conformation.

Utility. These cattle are used for draught, milk, meat and ceremonial purposes. The Zambia Angoni appear to possess some beef characteristics and selection for these is taking place at local experimental stations. It has been stated, on the other hand, that the meat of the Mozambique Angoni is dry, coarse and tasteless.

Mashona – synonyms: Amajanja, Ikomo eza Makalanga, Mombe, Makahalanga, Makalanga, Makaranga, Ngombe, Ngombe Dza Maswina, Njanja, Ngombe Dza Vakaranga (Plate 5.21)

Origin and habitat. These cattle are said to have arrived in the region with a people migrating from the north into Rhodesia and they are now found over a wide area although they are named after the Shona people of Mashonaland, located in the eastern part of Rhodesia. During this century they have been extensively crossed with temperate-type and Africander cattle on Rhodesian ranches.

Plate 5.21 Mashona (stabilized indigenous: humpless × humped) (Commonwealth Bureau of Animal Breeding and Genetics).

Physical characteristics.   The general conformation is compact, fine-boned and small. The most common coat colours are black, red, brown with yellow muzzle, brownish black with a lighter back stripe, dun, yellow, cream, black and white, red and white, and brindle, in that order. The hair is short and glossy; the skin well pigmented and of fine texture. The head is short and dished. The ears small and pointed. The horns tend to be of medium size, growing upwards and outwards, though polled animals are quite common. The hump is cervico-thoracic, moderate in size in the male and small in the female. The dewlap is small. The udder is small and is placed well forward and possesses small teats.

Utility.   These are good beef and draught animals, being extremely docile and hardy. They are rarely milked and are not considered to be a milking breed.

Africander – synonym: Afrikander (Plate 5.22)

Related type.   Bolowana – synonym: Izankayi. These cattle have been upgraded with Africander and have now lost their identity as a separate type.

Origin and habitat.   It is generally recognized that this breed originated

Plate 5.22   Africander (stabilized indigenous: humpless × humped).

from the cattle owned by the Hottentots in the seventeenth and eighteenth centuries, but some Portuguese workers consider that it originated from an importation of cattle of the Alentejo breed from Portugal. The early Dutch settlers in South Africa acquired their first herd of Africander cattle in 1652. The climatic environment of the habitat might be described as modified sub-tropical to tropical in the north and Mediterranean in Cape province.

Physical characteristics.   Africanders are large, muscular and hardy. The coat colour is usually a shade of red, often with white marks on the underline. The hair is short and glossy, the skin thick, pliable and amber to yellow in colour. The head is long and the ears small and pointed. The horns are long, wide and have a downwards and backwards sweep where they leave the head. The horns are oval in cross-section and have a characteristic twist. The male has short, strong horns, while those of the female are thinner and more spiral. The hump is cervico-thoracic and prominent in the male. The dewlap is large with loose folds and the umbilical fold is well developed.

Utility.   These cattle were originally developed as draught animals and were considered exceptionally good for this purpose, but more recently they have been developed for beef production. This is the main breed found on South African ranches and it is well adapted to the warmer regions provided that the climate is not too wet or too dry. A breed society was founded in 1919 and the herdbook was closed in 1936. Large numbers of these cattle have been exported to other countries in Africa, to the United States, the Philippines and to Australia.

The Americas.

Brahman – synonym: American Brahman (Plate 5.23)

Related type.   Red Brahman. The only difference between these and other Brahmans is that they possess a red coat.

Origin and habitat.   The breed was developed in the Gulf area of the southwestern United States between 1854 and 1926. It is a Zebu derived from strains of the Kankrej, Ongole, Gir, Krishna Valley, Hariana and Bhagnari breeds. As Mr Edgar Hudgins, a prominent Brahman breeder, has stated, 'the truth of the Brahman breeding will never be known'. The foundation Zebu were either imported directly into the United States or indirectly through Brazil and Mexico.

The climatic environment of the Gulf coast where the Brahman breed was originally developed could be described as humid and sub-tropical, but cattle of this breed are now bred in many regions of the tropical and sub-tropical world.

Plate 5.23   American Brahman (humped).

Physical characteristics.   As might be expected, the breed exhibits some variability in physical characteristics. It is a large animal with a long body of moderate depth, with long to medium-length legs and a straight back. The colour of the coat is normally a very light grey, but it may be red or black. The mature male is usually darker in colour than the female, with darker areas on the neck, shoulders, lower thighs and flanks. Calves often possess a red coat at birth that quickly turns grey. The skin is loose, soft and pliable, of medium thickness and is usually pigmented. The head is normally long. The ears are pendulous. The horns are widely spaced, thick, medium in length, those of the female being thinner than those of the male. The hump is large in the male, smaller in the female. The dewlap is large, but the sheath and navel flaps are not very pendulous. The udder in the female is of moderate size, as are the teats.

Utility.   The Brahman is essentially a beef animal that grows well on poor, dry grazings and also responds to feedlot management. In the United States, Latin America and Australia it has been widely used for crossbreeding purposes, to produce Zebu × temperate-type beef animals that are well acclimatized to tropical or sub-tropical environments and exhibit hybrid vigour. When the Brahman is continuously handled, it is a docile animal, but if it is gathered only occasionally it can be very wild. It appears to have a long productive life, is not unduly troubled by ticks, biting flies and mosquitoes, exhibits considerable tolerance to pink-eye and cancer-eye and is gregarious and a close herder, not responding

Plate 5.24   Santa Gertrudis (recent: humpless × humped).

well to hand mating. The American Brahman Breeders Association was organized in 1924 and Brahmans have been exported all over the world, in particular to countries in the Caribbean, Central and South America, and to Australia, the Pacific islands and the Philippines.

Santa Gertrudis (Plate 5.24)

Origin and habitat.   The Santa Gertrudis is a crossbred, three-eighths Zebu × five-eighths Shorthorn developed on the King Ranch in Texas. The breeding work undertaken in the evolution of the Santa Gertrudis is perhaps one of the best examples of constructive animal breeding in this century and the creation of this breed compares with the work of Robert Bakewell who established the Shorthorn breed in Britain in the eighteenth century. The King Ranch was originally stocked with Texas Longhorns and these were upgraded using Shorthorn and Hereford bulls. In 1910 the first crossbred Zebu were purchased by the ranch and between this date and 1940, by means of a well-planned breeding policy, the Santa Gertrudis breed was developed.

The original habitat is sub-tropical and semi-arid, but the breed has now been exported to many different regions of the tropical and sub-tropical world.

Physical characteristics.   It is a large symmetrical, deep-bodied, strong-boned animal. The coat colour should be a solid cherry-red, the hair short and straight and the skin thin, loose and pigmented red. The head is broad and the animal has a slightly convex forehead. The ears are medium to large and drooping. The horns are usually of the Shorthorn type and polled animals exist. The hump is of medium size in the male but absent in the female. The dewlap is well developed. The sheath and navel flap are of medium size. The udder of the female is of medium size with well-placed teats.

Utility.   This is a beef breed that is said to have cold- as well as heat-tolerance characteristics and to be resistant to ticks. Exports of cattle of this type have made a considerable impact on the beef industries in countries in the Caribbean, Central and South America and in Australia. Some doubts have been expressed as to the fertility of this breed compared with contemporary breeds.

Jamaica Red Poll – synonyms: Good Hope Red, Jamaica Red (Plate 5.25)

Origin and habitat.   The breed has been developed by the upgrading of indigenous Creole and Zebu crossbreds using Red Poll bulls. A Jamaica Red Poll Cattle Breeders Society was founded in 1952 and the herdbook was closed in 1960. The habitat is varied and the climatic environment is tropical and generally humid.

Plate 5.25   Jamaica Red Poll (recent: humpless × humped).

Physical characteristics.   It is a large animal with a good depth of body and medium-size legs. The coat colour should be dark to medium red; the hair sleek and dense; the skin fine; and the animal should be polled.

Utility.   The breed had been developed to produce beef at an early age off pasture and it is particularly well adapted to a humid tropical environment. Cattle of this breed have been exported to Latin American countries and the breed appears to be flourishing, particularly in Venezuela.

Jamaica Hope – synonyms: Montgomery-Jersey, Jersey Zebu (Plate 5.26)

Origin and habitat.   The breed has been developed from a herd founded at Hope, near Kingston, in Jamaica, in 1910. The farm was originally stocked with Creole and imported grade temperate-type cattle originating from Canada and the United Kingdom. In 1912 two Sahiwal bulls were imported from the Pusa herd in India and one was used for cross-breeding purposes. With the facilities available it was impossible to test all the different types of crossbreds produced so that the Ayrshire, Brown Swiss, Red Poll, Guernsey and Holstein crossbreds were discarded, leaving only the Jersey crossbreds. It is estimated that present-day Jamaica Hope cattle have inherited 70 to 75 per cent of their genes from the Jersey, 20 per cent from the Sahiwal and a small percentage from Creole cattle.

In 1952 the herd was 'closed' and the Jamaica Hope was established as a new breed, a society being formed in 1953.

The climatic environment is tropical and humid.

Physical characteristics.   The breed is very similar to the Jersey in conformation although these cattle are usually larger. There is no definite coat colour, it varies from fawn, brown and grey to black.

Plate 5.26   Jamaica Hope (recent: humpless × humped).

Plate 5.27   Romo-Sinuano. A Criollo breed (humpless).

Utility.   The breed has been developed for dairying under humid tropical conditions and it is undoubtedly one of the most productive breeds (Table 5.5) found in the tropics today with individual cows producing up to 9,072 kg (20,000 lb) of milk per lactation. Reproductive efficiency is said to be good. Cattle of this breed have been exported to other Caribbean and to some Central and South American countries.

Romo-Sinuano – synonyms: Coastal Polled, Moruno–Sinuano, Polled Sinú (Plate 5.27)

Origin and habitat.   This is a Criollo breed found in north Colombia around the Sinú river and in the province of Bolivar. They are believed to have originated from crossbreeding between Red Poll and/or Aberdeen Angus and Horned Sinú at the end of the last century. The habitat is either swampy or slightly undulating. The climatic environment is humid and tropical, the rainfall usually exceeding 1,780 mm (70 in).

Physical characteristics.   The Romo-Sinuano is a beefy-type animal. The coat colour is red. The skin colour is deeply pigmented. The hair is scanty and short and many older animals possess a top line and rump completely devoid of hair. The breed is polled but scurs occur.

Utility.   It is a beef breed that possesses a tendency to lay down gobs of fat, a characteristic of the meat that is now considered objectionable. Romo-Sinuano are very docile animals and are easily herded.

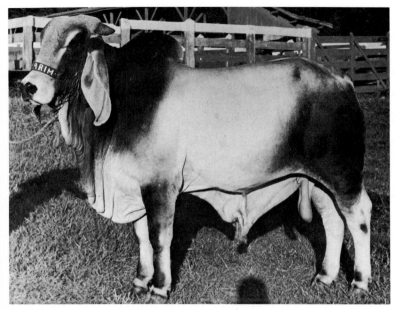

Plate 5.28   Indú-Brasil (humped) (from *Revista dos Criadores*).

Indú-Brasil – synonyms: Indú-Brazilian, Hindu-Brazil, Inubereba (Plate 5.28)
Origin and habitat.   This breed originated from indiscriminate cross-breeding between Indian breeds imported into Brazil; mainly Gir, Kankrej and Ongole cattle.
  The habitat is varied and the climatic environment tropical.

Physical characteristics.   It is somewhat similar to the American Brahman, demonstrating characteristics from the foundation breeds.

Utility. It is a beef breed and some of the best herds are now found in the states of Minas Gerais and Bahia in Brazil.

Oceania

Australian Milking Zebu (Plate 5.29)

Origin and habitat.   This breed is the most recent Zebu crossbred. It has been developed by the Commonwealth Scientific and Industrial Research Organization (CSIRO) in Australia from Sahiwal and Red Sindhi cattle imported from Pakistan and Australian Jerseys. The Australian Milking Zebu Society was formed in 1970. The climatic environment of the area in which they are used varies from warm temperate to tropical.

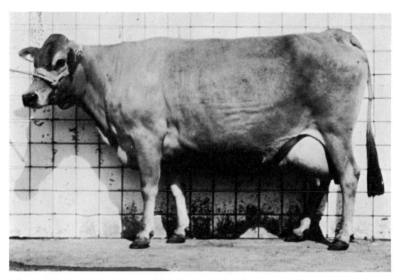

Plate 5.29   Australian Milking Zebu (recent: humpless × humped).

Physical characteristics.   Females are somewhat similar in appearance to Jerseys but are larger. The predominant coat colour is a golden to reddish brown. The bulls possess a cervico-thoracic hump.

Utility.   This is a dairy breed, but the cows produce very acceptable beef carcases. They are more resistant to ticks than British cattle and possess good foraging abilities. Progeny-tested sires are already available.

Droughtmaster (Plate 5.30)

Origin and habitat.   These are crossbred cattle with three-eighths to five-eighths Zebu blood, mainly derived from red American Brahman cattle imported from Texas. There is also some infusion of Santa Gertrudis blood. The temperate-type inheritance has been derived from the Devon, Shorthorn, Hereford and Red Poll breeds, together with some genes from the Shorthorn inheritance in the Santa Gertrudis. A Droughtmaster Stud Breeders Society was formed in 1962.

   The climatic environment of the region in which they are utilized varies from humid tropical on the coast to semi-arid tropical and subtropical in the interior of the continent.

Physical characteristics.   These cattle are large, long-bodied and well fleshed. The coat is short and sleek and the skin loose and pliable. The coat colour is light or dark red. There are both horned and polled individuals. The dewlap and sheath in the male and the navel flap in the female are moderately developed. The udder of the female is of moderate size, possessing evenly placed teats.

Plate 5.30 Droughtmaster (recent: humpless × humped) (from *Queensland Country-Life*).

Utility. This is a beef breed producing excellent-quality meat. Animals of this breed are resistant to tick infestation and appear to be more tolerant to babesiosis than the British breeds. Droughtmaster cattle have been exported to New Guinea and the Solomon Islands.

Dairy cattle

Milk for direct human consumption and for manufacturing milk products is obtained from many kinds of domestic livestock, but it is estimated that approximately 90 per cent of the world's total supply is produced by various breeds of domestic cattle (McCabe, 1955). Although the proportion of the total milk produced by domestic livestock other than cattle is probably higher in tropical than in temperate countries this proportion has probably fallen during the last 20 years and cattle undoubtedly also produce most of the milk consumed in the tropics.

That the production of adequate quantities of milk in tropical countries is a particularly difficult problem is widely recognized. The FAO (1967) stated: 'Output of milk in developing countries scarcely kept pace during the past decade with the increase in their population despite efforts made, with the assistance of international agencies and bilateral aid programmes, to raise production.' As will be seen from Table 5.7 not only was average per capita milk equivalent consumption in 1961–63 low

Table 5.7   *Milk and milk products production and consumption in 1961–63 and projections for 1975*

Region	1961–63		Milk equivalent* 1975		
	Production (1,000 tons)	Per capita consumption (kg/year)	Production† (1,000 tons)		Per capita demand (kg/year)
North America	65,367	309	66,835		264
			Low	High	
Latin America	20,320	91	28,489	31,008	105
Africa	12,670	57	13,988	15,153	65
Asia					
Western	6,405	64	8,653	9,608	73
Indian sub-continent	28,000	50	37,240	40,600	64
Southeast and East	1,596	11	2,211	2,373	15

* Milk and milk products converted into milk equivalent.
† High and low production assumptions.
Source: FAO (1967).

throughout the tropics compared with average per capita consumption in North America, but total production of milk and milk products in Latin America, Africa and the tropical and sub-tropical regions of Asia was little more than the production of North America and represented only 19 per cent of total world population. The demand projection in developing countries for milk and milk products in 1985 is shown in Table 5.8. Even the lowest demand presumed a growth rate in consumption of 3·6 per cent per annum, whereas it is expected that milk production cannot be increased at more than a rate of 2·3 per cent per

Table 5.8   *Consumption of milk and milk products in developing countries in 1961–63 and demand projections for 1985*

	Milk equivalent*					
	Total demand 1,000 tonnes			kg per capita per annum		
	1961–63	1985		1961–63	1985	
		Low†	High†		Low†	High†
Developing countries	71	160	206	51	64	83

* Milk and milk products converted into milk equivalent.
† Based on a high population assumption with low and high income assumptions.
Source: FAO (1967).

annum. Thus according to the FAO, demand will increase more rapidly than supply in developing countries. This situation should create endless opportunities for the growth of dairy industries in milk-deficient countries particularly as the FAO (1967) consider that there will be a tendency for prices to rise and imports to be seriously limited by shortages of foreign currency.

As will be seen from Table 5.7, present levels of consumption of milk and milk products vary from one region of the developing world to another, per capita consumption being almost nine times as high in Latin America as in Southeast Asia in 1961–63. Of course, even within Latin America per capita consumption varies from country to country, and within countries from social class to social class. These local variations in per capita consumption are not necessarily due to the inherent technical problems of milk production but may be due to local dietary and agricultural customs or to special political, economic and social reasons.

It could be argued that if the production of milk presents particularly difficult problems in the tropics, then the simplest solution would be to increase production in the mid-latitude regions and distribute the resulting surplus as condensed, evaporated, dried or long-life milk in tropical countries. The fact is that, even if the economic and political problems of distributing surpluses on a world scale could be solved, there are other very good reasons why the development of a dairy industry should be encouraged in most tropical countries.

Until recently most agriculture in the tropics has been either large-scale plantation, small-scale subsistence or shifting cultivation farming. Shifting cultivation, although efficient in some respects, requires very large areas of forest, and with increasing population is becoming an anachronism. Plantation and subsistence farming have encouraged the exploitation of soil resources and in different ways are often socially undesirable. Under these circumstances new agricultural systems are required. These are likely to be different forms of mixed or integrated farming or specialized forms of farming. Livestock husbandry is likely to become more important in all these systems. Milk production can be readily associated with mixed or integrated farming or it could be developed as a specialized industry. The advantages of developing a dairy industry are that it would create employment; hasten the provision of better services such as roads and electricity in rural areas (these being essential for the industry); provide products that would improve the diet of the local population and save foreign exchange otherwise used to purchase imported dairy products; and increase the supply of meat by the provision of a continuous supply of surplus male calves. The disadvantages of attempting the development of a dairy industry are that it requires inputs not readily available in the tropics and that the industry possesses intrinsic difficulties that have not yet been completely or satisfactorily overcome anywhere in the tropics.

Low milk production in the tropics (Table 5.9) is due to the inter-

Table 5.9 Average performance of groups of dairy cattle in the tropics*

Group	Number of records	Milk yield (kg (lb))	%†	Lactation length (Days)	%†	Calving interval (Days)	%†	Age at first calving (Months)	%†
Indigenous									
Random sample	2,338	631 (1,391)	21	190	57	400	92	41·8	134
Selected	1,464	1,444 (3,184)	49	278	83	437	101	42·4	135
Crossbreds: random sample									
One-quarter temperate type	431	633 (1,396)	21	158	47	393	91	40·5	129
One-half temperate type	990	1,843 (4,063)	62	278	83	414	96	35·0	112
Three-quarters temperate type	210	2,074 (4,572)	70	312	94	441	102	34·9	112
Seven-eighths temperate type	27	2,323 (5,121)	78	295	89	430	99	37·8	121
Exotic temperate type	1,273	2,974 (6,557)	100	333	100	433	100	31·3	100

* Data from forty-eight herds managed at locations of less than 2,000 m (6,562 ft) altitude.

† Percentage of data for exotic temperate-type cattle.

Source: *Improvement of Livestock Production in Warm Climates* by R. E. McDowell. W. H. Freeman and Company. Copyright © 1972.

action of climatic, disease, breeding, feeding and managerial factors, and these vary in their relative importance from country to country and from region to region within countries.The effect of climate on milk production is particularly complicated as climate itself is a complex of so many variable factors, there being a whole range of different climates within the tropics. At medium and high altitudes there are climates in which high-yielding dairy cattle are not unduly stressed, and the possibility of developing a dairy industry at medium or higher altitudes in any specific tropical country should not be overlooked. Climate, of course, has an indirect as well as a direct effect on the dairy industry, primarily on account of its effect on the feed supply, on the incidence of disease and on the transport and storage of milk and milk products. Some aspects of the effects of both climate and disease on milk production have been considered in previous chapters and further pertinent aspects will be discussed in relation to the most suitable methods of the breeding, feeding and management of dairy cattle in the tropics.

Breeding: the most suitable milking breeds to use

There is of course no single breeding policy that is applicable in all tropical countries. Theoretically, dairy farmers could choose one of four possible policies. These are as follows:

1. The utilization of indigenous cattle that are already well adapted to the environment, with selection for high productivity.
2. The importation of highly productive, temperate-type cattle with selection for adaptability to the tropical environment.
3. The importation of highly productive, temperate-type cattle and management of them so that the adverse effects of the tropical environment are ameliorated.
4. The importation of highly productive, temperate-type bulls and/or semen for use in upgrading less productive indigenous cattle. This could be a continuing process or an effort could be made to 'stabilize' one or more specific crossbred types.

In practice, the farmer's choice is limited to the type of cattle that are already available in his country or to what cattle he can afford or is allowed to import. It is also limited by the scale of his operations, by the quality and availability of extension and other services and by his education and managerial skill.

In Asia and Africa, where there are many indigenous breeds, all except the largest producers or governments are likely to use those breeds that are readily available. During the last decades, breeders in many countries in Asia and Africa have attempted to improve the productivity of their indigenous cattle by selection and progeny testing, but the limitations on any improvement in the genetic merit of indigenous tropical breeds must be realized, as it is likely that some characteristics that ensure that these cattle are adapted to their environment adversely affect productivity. As Mahadevan (1966) has stressed, with the exception of a few breeds (Table 5.5) average milk production of indigenous tropical cattle is not much higher than 680 kg (1,500 lb) per lactation so that their average genetic merit for milk production is low. In addition, the intensity of selection that can be practised is likely to be low for a variety of reasons, including long generation intervals and high mortality. Under these circumstances improvement in the milk production of indigenous cattle breeds is likely to be a very slow process. These general conclusions are reinforced by data published by McDowell (1971). He assembled information concerning four tropical breeds: the Blanco Orejinegro and Costeño con Cuernos in Colombia, the Abyssinian Shorthorned Zebu (Horo) in Ethiopia, and the Hariana in India. He found that the large numbers of non-lactating females present in these herds caused low herd efficiency (number in milk/total herd × 100), the herd efficiency percentages being 15·3, 19·6 and 26·5 for Blanco Orejinegro, Horo and Hariana, respectively, compared with 58·8 for Holsteins in the State of New York. He also showed that on account of low herd efficiency the supply of daily feed energy for the maintenance and production of Hariana cattle, producing on average 700 kg (1,543 lb) of milk per day, would be more than four times that of cows producing at a similar level in a herd in the State of New York, and that only 11·5 per cent of the estimated feed energy provided for the Hariana cattle was used directly for production as compared with 43·8 per cent for herds in the State of New York.

Even if the majority of indigenous tropical breeds are unlikely to provide very productive milking cattle and are at present without apparent economic utility, every effort should be made to preserve representative herds. This is a task that can be undertaken only by governments.

Dairy farmers in Australia, the South Pacific and the Caribbean are in totally different situations from those in Africa and Asia. There were no cattle in these regions before settlement by Europeans. This has had some advantages, as indigenous cattle are usually subject to a variety of tropical diseases and countries in the South Pacific, the Caribbean and Australia are often free from tropical disease. Temperate-type dairy stock have been, and still are being, introduced into these regions, and where feeding and management standards are relatively high the exotic cattle thrive and are fairly productive. It has been found that there are wide variations in the ability of high-producing, temperate-type dairy stock to thrive in the tropics and that some individuals thrive very much better than others (Payne and Hancock, 1957). There is no doubt that after importation some degree of natural selection for adaptation takes place, ill-adapted individuals being more likely to die before they reproduce. Selection for production along conventional lines will also lead to selection for adaptability. The practical proof of this thesis is that there are today in Australia, the Pacific islands and the Americas a number of herds of temperate-type cattle that although not yet fully acclimatized produce as well as or better than the very best herds of indigenous tropical cattle in Asia or Africa (Table 5.9). The most common temperate-type breeds found in the tropics are the Holstein, Jersey and Brown Swiss. However, it is generally accepted that if temperate-type dairy cattle are to thrive at sea-level or at moderate altitudes in the tropics, then standards of disease control, feeding and management must be very high. That temperate-type dairy cattle can be productive in a tropical environment is demonstrated by the fact that the average yield of ten leading Holstein herds in Puerto Rico during 1964 was 3,332 litres (733 gal) per lactation (Mahadevan, 1966).

The situation in tropical South America is again different. The indigenous or Criollo dairy cattle are of the *Bos taurus* type. They are the descendants of cattle that were imported more than 400 years ago from Iberia. Previous to their importation there were no indigenous cattle in this continent, so that although the environment is not completely free from tropical cattle diseases, it is relatively free compared with Asia and Africa. The Criollo breeds are also not very productive and crossbreeding with exotic cattle has been widely practised.

Little attention has so far been given to the third policy outlined above. Perhaps it is significant that although the importation of temperate-type cattle into the tropics is now not generally recommended, the importation of temperate-type methods of management have been condoned if not encouraged. It could be that the importation of unsuitable temperate-type management practices have contributed in part to the failure to date to establish any large number of temperate-type cattle in the tropics. There are many methods by which the climatic environment could be ameliorated and not all of them need expensive equipment. For example, little has been done to integrate tree cropping with dairy farming although it is well known that the micro-climatic environment in coconut groves is very different from the climatic environment in open pasture and much more suited to the management of temperate-type cattle. The least expensive ameliorative method would be to utilize the medium and higher altitude regions of the tropics for dairy farming. If the mean annual temperature at sea-level is 26·7°C (80°F), then it is 23·3°C (74°F) at 610 m (2,000 ft) and 18·3°C (65°F) at 1,524 m (5,000 ft) altitude. Obviously, at altitudes above 610 m (2,000 ft) temperate-type cattle thrive considerably better than they do at sea-level and at altitudes above 1,524 m (5,000 ft) the mean annual temperature is optimal for maximum productivity.

The general consensus of opinion is that crossbred dairy cattle are likely to be most economic in those regions of the tropics where management and feeding practices can be improved slowly.

The effect of crossbreeding in increasing productivity is not mainly on account of any hybrid vigour that may be expressed, though there is some effect (Branton *et al.*, 1966), but because the low productivity of indigenous tropical breeds can be very rapidly improved by upgrading them using highly productive temperate-type bulls and/or semen. The farmer in the tropics has a choice of two practical methods of using cross-breeding to improve the productivity of his dairy stock. He can upgrade and then at some stage of the upgrading procedure mate *inter se* or he can use a rotational method of crossbreeding. Whichever system is adopted there are many formidable difficulties involved in operating crossbreeding programmes and it would be most desirable if governments would attempt to produce a stabilized crossbred milking animal that could then be distributed in their dairying areas and used in the first place for upgrading indigenous cattle. As stated previously the Australian government has already produced a new crossbreed between the Sahiwal and the Jersey, known as the Australian Milking Zebu, and this new breed already shows some promise for use in the tropics.

The decision as to whether to utilize low-producing but well-adapted indigenous breeds, high-producing but ill-adapted temperate breeds or crossbreds must depend on a variety of factors. One of the most important of these is the local level of managerial skill. When levels of managerial ability and education are low, then the most suitable dairy animals are likely to be the indigenous breeds. This is usually the situation with peasant producers, but there are countries in the tropical world where the peasant producers are highly literate, such as Sri Lanka, Taiwan and the Philippines, and there are other countries such as Kenya where the extension services are particularly well organized. In these countries it is likely that an upgraded or crossbred animal could be immediately used. This is the present policy in Kenya where the relatively unproductive Small East African Zebu has been upgraded using the Sahiwal (Mahadevan *et al.*, 1962).

Even in those countries where the majority of peasant producers are illiterate and where management is generally poor it should be possible slowly to upgrade indigenous cattle. Indeed, it should be the aim to upgrade the level of managerial ability of the farmers at the same time as their cattle are upgraded. This is now an acceptable policy in many tropical countries, including India.

It is obviously pertinent to ask what the most suitable level of cross-breeding is likely to be. McDowell (1972) has cited evidence, using data obtained from forty-eight herds managed at locations where the altitude is less than 2,000 m (6,562 ft) and scattered throughout the tropical world, that the higher the percentage of temperate-type blood in dairy cattle the higher is the production, the longer the lactation, the earlier the age at first calving and the longer the calving interval (Table 5.9). The first three of these characteristics improve productivity and it would appear from McDowell's data that it is only reproductive efficiency that is poorer in temperate-type cattle. These conclusions of McDowell are at variance with the conclusions of earlier investigators who suggested that the most productive dairy animal in the tropics is a crossbred with one-half to five-eighths temperate-type blood (Amble and Jain, 1967). McDowell's data can of course be criticized on the grounds that all the herds were not managed at sea-level and that it is very likely that the standards of management and feeding varied widely from herd to herd. In fact McDowell's data do not really provide an answer to the original question.

Other interesting data from Thailand on this subject have recently been published by Madsen and Vinther (1975). They have also shown that under exceptionally good managerial conditions milk production

Table 5.10   *The effect of the percentage of* Bos taurus *genes on the length of the first calving interval and second lactation yields of dairy cattle in Thailand*

Percentage of Bos taurus genes	Breed type: foundation females	Number	Length of first calving interval (days)	Second lactation yield (kg)	
				Milk	Butterfat
0	RS and S	36	462	1,000 ± 154	43·04 ± 7·18
37½	T or T₁	7	341	1,193 ± 319	57·21 ± 14·83
50	T	83	383	1,411 ± 114	72·96 ± 5·29
50	T₁	107	391	1,608 ± 106	78·70 ± 4·91
50	RS and S	18	384	2,255 ± 197	101·60 ± 9·18
62½	T or T₁	54	396	1,722 ± 135	77·45 ± 6·28
75	T	72	411	1,996 ± 115	91·57 ± 5·36
75	T₁	156	408	2,210 ± 95	99·89 ± 4·42
87½	T or T₁	53	404	2,238 ± 130	97·39 ± 6·05
100	RD(T)	17	577	2,760 ± 200	114·50 ± 9·31
100	RS(D)	51	544	2,561 ± 199	106·98 ± 9·23

Note: The abbreviations for the breed types are: RS, Red Sindhi; S, Sahiwal; T, Thai; T₁, Thai improved; RD(T), Red Danish born in Thailand; RD(D), Red Danish born in Denmark.
Source: Madsen and Vinther (1975).

increases as the percentage of temperate-type blood in the cattle increases (Table 5.10) and that reproductive efficiency as expressed by the length of the calving interval declines. In addition, they have shown that even where health standards and care are exceptional the percentage of abortions and stillbirths increases as the percentage of temperate-type blood in the cattle increases, as does total mortality up to first calving (Table 5.11).

In the opinion of the authors the answer to the question as to what is the most suitable level of crossbreeding depends entirely on the level of managerial skill available, the availability of feed and the local disease situation. What is interesting about McDowell's data is that they suggest that it is possible to manage highly productive dairy cattle in the tropics, thus confirming the suggestions made in previous paragraphs. The authors believe that where management is fair but endemic diseases are

Table 5.11   *Effect of percentage of* Bos taurus *genes on the mortality of female dairy cattle up to first calving in Thailand*

Percentage Bos taurus genes	Foundation female type	No. heifer calves	Percentage mortality to 6 months	No. replacement heifers	Percentage mortality 6 months to first calving
0	RS and S	58	15·5	37	5·4
37½	T and T₁	450	9·1	243	10·7
50	T	209	3·3	208	2·9
	T₁	183	3·3	181	1·7
	RS and S	85	5·9	53	0
62½	T and T₁	251	8·8	146	9·6
75	T	196	7·7	165	7·3
	T₁	438	7·3	364	9·9
87½	T and T₁	152	9·2	130	20·0
100	RD	96	7·3	93	23·7

Note: RS is Red Sindhi; S is Sahiwal; T is indigenous Thai; T₁ is improved indigenous Thai; RD is Red Danish.
Source: Madsen and Vinther (1975).

still prevalent, the use of no more than half-bred cattle would be indicated, but that where disease is under control and management and feeding conditions are good, three-quarters to seven-eighths temperate-type cattle are likely to be the most productive. This is also the conclusion of Madsen and Vinther (1975) after their analysis of the Thailand data. It is doubtful, however, whether purebred temperate-type milking cattle should be used in most regions of Africa and Asia, as in the authors' experience they tend to suffer from a multitude of minor troubles and management becomes more difficult. Madsen and Vinther's data suggest that disease may be troublesome even where the management is exceptionally good, as it was at the Thai-Danish dairy. In addition, Holstein cattle, in particular, tend to be more difficult to get in calf, as indeed is suggested by the data presented by both McDowell (1972) and Madsen and Vinther (1975).

When governments or large producers organize crossbreeding programmes then it must be most desirable to upgrade using the best possible temperate-type bulls or semen, as the higher the genetic merit from a productivity point of view, the lower the level of temperate-type blood that has to be introduced in order to attain a reasonable level of productivity in the crossbreds. As it is easier to obtain bulls and semen of high genetic merit from the major rather than from the minor temperate-type dairy breeds, and the production of beef from the dairy herd is of importance in the tropics, the breed of choice for upgrading indigenous cattle should probably be the Holstein. However, all European breeds do combine satisfactorily with indigenous tropical breeds.

The Brown Swiss also possess many of the desirable features of the

Holstein and have been widely used in crossbreeding programmes in Latin America, but the overall use of this breed is probably declining due to the relatively small number of sires of high genetic merit available.

In tropical countries where there are no indigenous breeds, where tropical disease is well controlled and where standards of management and feeding are high, the most economic policy may be the importation of high-producing temperate-type stock.

This policy cannot, however, be recommended with any certainty. Even if the disease situation is well under control, the relatively low fertility of high-grade or purebred temperate-type milking cows in a tropical environment, under very good managerial conditions, may necessitate for economic reasons the use of dairy animals possessing a small proportion of tropical-type blood.

If it is decided to import purebred temperate-type stock there does not appear to be any advantage in importing all pedigree cattle. Probably the most suitable policy is to import good-quality-grade heifers and bulls and/or semen of the highest genetic merit.

Managerial systems

Today, there are at least three types of dairy farmer in the tropics: the peasant or subsistence producer; the specialized dairy farmer, sometimes of medium size, but often operating on a very small scale; and the very large-scale producer. The latter may be an individual, a private company, a cooperative or the state.

It must be recognized that the vast majority of milk producers in the tropics are peasant farmers who first satisfy their family requirements and then sell any surplus that they may produce either as liquid milk or as some form of milk product. A survey conducted by the Indian Council of Agricultural Research (ICAR) in 1936–37 in some of the major animal-breeding tracts in India showed that the number of milk cows per holding was 4·2 in Kankrej, 4·1 in Ongole, 1·9 in Bihar, 2·0 in Hariana, 2·3 in Kosi and 3·2 in the Central Provinces. There is no reason to believe that the overall result of a similar survey today would be very different, and good reason to believe that a survey in other peasant communities in the tropics would demonstrate that the small size of the individual herd in India is also normal in many other countries. During the last decade the average annual individual production of milking cows and buffaloes in India has been around 181 kg (400 lb) and 544 kg (1,200 lb), respectively. Of this small production it is generally estimated that at present 40 per cent is used for the making of ghee, 39 per cent as liquid milk, 13 per cent for the manufacture of milk sweets, 6 per cent for the manufacture of butter, 1 per cent as cream and 1 per cent for the manufacture of ice-cream. Apparently the amount used for making ghee and milk sweets is slowly declining, while the amount used in the liquid form or for the manufacture of butter is slowly increasing.

The peasant producer can obviously make available for the liquid milk market only a very small proportion of what is already a very low total product. In fact, a growing proportion of the liquid milk sold in urban areas in the tropics is produced by a small number of relatively large producers, by cooperatives such as the milk colonies of India, is manufactured locally from partially or wholly imported ingredients or is imported as 'long-life' milk.

As the standard of living gradually rises in tropical countries it is likely that there will be some reorganization of land holdings and that liquid milk will increasingly be produced by specialized dairy farmers. It is unlikely that the peasant farmer will be able to apply all the new management, feeding and breeding practices required if productivity is to be improved, but even the smallest peasant dairy farmer should be able to apply some of them.

Specialized dairy farms, unlike specialized beef holdings, do not have to be of considerable size in order to provide a decent standard of living for the farmer. In fact there is intrinsic merit in the intensive dairy farm run by an owner-occupier that must necessarily be relatively small, as one man can handle only a limited number of animals even with the most efficient labour-saving equipment. It is significant that in some of the most productive dairying countries in the temperate zone, such as Denmark and New Zealand, the average size of the specialized dairy farm is relatively small. Statistics do, however, indicate that dairy farms in these countries are steadily growing larger. In areas in the tropics where there are extensive dairy farms, such as northern Queensland in Australia or the northern countries of South America, managerial standards are not usually very high. If milking machinery is to be installed – and this should be the eventual aim in most countries, although it would be completely uneconomic and indeed undesirable because of the surplus of labour in most tropical countries at the present time – then the intensive dairy farmer should keep at least fifteen dairy cows and their followers and in the humid tropics he should be able to do this on an area of 6 to 8 ha (15 to 20 acres) of land.

Large-scale dairy farms can, of course, be intensively managed. There are a small number of these organizations in tropical countries that are privately owned, and there is a movement, particularly in India, to group small producers into large units, where the individual owns and manages the animals while a collective management provides communal services such as housing, feed and veterinary services, and also purchases, processes and markets the milk. There are also an increasing number of state-owned and operated large-scale dairy farms in a number of Asian and African countries.

The subsistence or peasant producer

Peasant producers normally never keep animals solely for milk production. A cow is expected to work and milk during her lifetime, and when she is too old for work purposes if social customs allows she will be sold for slaughter. Feeding will usually be haphazard and management poor. Peasant farmers do not generally understand the value of pasture nor do they normally farm sufficient land to enable them to grow specialized forage crops for their animals. Cows are expected to graze or browse along the roadsides or on stubbles or they are tethered and fed cut forage. They may receive some by-products concentrates such as rice bran, but in many countries such feeds are reserved for the feeding of poultry.

However, any producer is usually responsive to advice if he considers that it is sound and is convinced that it will improve his income. He can be taught the importance of good feeding and shown how to grow legume tree crops such as *Sesbania grandiflora* that will produce high-quality browse in the odd corners of his holding or along paths or on paddy-field bunds; he could be convinced that it is bad practice to tether cows out in the open on hot days; and he can be shown that some of his heifers will let down their milk without the calf suckling at the same time and be persuaded that this is a desirable practice.

The majority of peasant farmers cannot be considered as specialist milk producers within the normal meaning of the term, although it should be recognized that they are an important sector when an assessment is made of the total production of milk in the tropics. If a suitable organization for the collection and processing of liquid milk is available, as it is now in many tropical countries, then the very small quantities of surplus milk that the peasant farmer produces can be channelled to the urban consumer to the benefit of both rural and urban dwellers.

One example of a successful collection scheme is at Mariakani in Kenya. This is an excellent example of dairy development in an area where conditions for milk production are unfavourable and where the local population is extremely poor. The area is semi-arid and the majority of the cattle are of the Boran or the Small East African Zebu type. Milk yields are low and the average lactation period is very short. Milk is collected from a total area of 5,698 km^2 (2,200 miles^2) from 2,300 to 2,400 separate producers. There are approximately 240 collection points and producers are located within a 113 km (70 miles) radius of the plant. Seasonal variation in the volume of milk produced is extreme. In 1966 the largest daily collection was 26,820 litres (5,900 gal) and the smallest 3,910 litres (860 gal). The time taken from loading at the collection points to delivery at the milk plant varies from 2 to 6 hours with the temperature of the milk varying between 24·4° and 33°C (76 and 92°F). In addition the producers' wives or children have already often walked some distance through the bush carrying the milk to the collection points. Despite these very unfavourable conditions the overall loss due to souring has been amazingly low, i.e. 2·9 per cent (Bonscharain, 1964).

Another milk collection scheme that has been very successful and has been built into a huge multi-million-dollar annual sales business is the Kaira District Cooperative Milk Producers Union Ltd in the Anand district of the State of Guzerat in India, some 400 km (249 miles) north of Bombay. The average size of farm in the area is 1·2 ha (3 acres). The scheme commenced in 1946 when 112 small producers formed two village cooperatives. In 1949 the total collection of milk was 227 litres (50 gal) per day, in 1973 it was 772,810 litres (170,000 gal) per day. The latter volume was collected twice-daily from 344,000 cows managed in 800 village cooperatives. These cooperatives included 215,000 farming families, a total of approximately 1 million people, in an area of 6,475 km^2 (2,500 miles^2). The milk supplied comes almost entirely from buffalo cows, each family owning one or two, though some milking cattle are also utilized. The farmers bring their milk to the village collection centres in the morning and evening of each day, where it is tested for adulteration and for fat content. Payment for the milk supplied is made at the next collection and varies according to the fat content of the milk. The minimal standards required are 6·5 per cent butterfat and 9·0 per cent solids-not-fat. The average farmer delivers 3·6 litres (0·8 gal) of milk per day and retains approximately 30 per cent of his total production for his family needs. The quality standard of milk delivered has steadily improved, approximately 3 per cent being graded as sour. This sour milk is processed and used for the production of casein and ghee. All producers receive a uniform price for their milk, irrespective of the distance that their village is from Anand. The Union pays the cost of transport from the collecting centre to the processing plant and hires trucks for transport purposes.

The system of direct daily cash payments to the producers by the village societies is very popular and perhaps partly explains the success of this scheme. The village society is paid twice monthly by the Union. Approximately one-quarter to one-third of the proceeds from milk sales is used by the farmer to purchase concentrate feeds. Producers also receive a bonus once a year, paid from the profits made by their society. The village societies also use part of their profits to finance social schemes, such as the running of libraries and schools.

Perhaps most significant of all, this scheme has demonstrated how successful rural dairy cooperatives and milk-collection schemes can be in generating a development programme in the rural area of a poor country. The Union now organizes AI units, mobile veterinary dispensaries, training schemes for all classes of workers, the largest livestock feed mill in India, credit facilities, an ear-tagging and milk-recording scheme, the prefabrication of cattle housing and extension work in many other fields.

In 1950–51 the AI service conducted 578 inseminations from five centres. In 1973 it owned a stud that possessed 60 tested buffalo breeding bulls and conducted 200,000 inseminations per year, there being one inseminator in each village. Partly as a consequence of better breeding practices, average production per buffalo cow improved by 50 per cent between 1965 and 1973. The Union provided the services of 36 animal husbandrymen and 42 veterinarians in 1973. Veterinary clinics are held weekly in all villages and for a fee of $1·80 the Union guaranteed (1973) that the service of a veterinarian would be available at any village within 4 hours.

In 1973 the Union was delivering 200,000 litres (44,000 gal) of milk per day to the city of Bombay for bottling and retailing through 2,000 government-operated retail sale booths. The remaining 572,800 litres (126,000 gal) of milk were processed at Anand into milk products. The Anand plant at present produces 50 per cent of India's total supply of baby food.

The activities of the Union are still increasing. It is establishing a rice-milling plant, a plant for producing weaning feeds made from soybean for children and a malted milk factory.

Even more encouraging from a development point of view is the fact that the success of the Union has led to the establishment of a National Dairy Development Board with headquarters at Anand. This Board with some assistance from the United Nations is now establishing seventeen similar cooperatives in ten Indian states. Six of these had commenced operations by the end of 1973.

The specialized dairy farmer

The specialized dairy farmer could be potentially the most important milk producer in the tropics. There are today many peasant producers who could rapidly become small specialist producers, but it is unlikely that the larger specialist producers – common in some dairying areas of the temperate zone – will become an important factor in milk production in most tropical countries for a considerable time, if ever.

One major difficulty in organizing specialized milk production is that the size of the average holding in many tropical countries is very small, and even these small holdings are often fragmented, making any form of cattle husbandry difficult. Wilson (1962) stated that grazing enterprises in the West Indies should be at least 8 ha (20 acres) in size, though the data published by Motta (1961) suggested that the output of milk and/or meat per unit area from a small intensively managed unit of pangola grass (*Digitaria decumbens*) in Jamaica could have a value that compared favourably with output per unit area from small farms growing a variety of different crops. Obviously the economic value of the milk and/or meat output from grazing areas compared with the value of the output of crops from the same area will depend upon the relative prices of animal and plant products.

In a limited number of countries, particularly in the Caribbean, governments have recently created incentives and specific projects to encourage the development of family dairy farms. Examples of this type of development can be found in Jamaica, Trinidad and Barbados. These schemes have been moderately successful to date, the most difficult problem being the supply of suitable dairy cattle. Other tropical countries are considering the initiation of similar schemes, often in collaboration with the World Bank (IBRD), regional development banks, FAO/UNDP and bilateral aid organizations.

The Malaysian government is considering the possibility of initiating a project where a central dairy, owned and operated by the government or a government agency, will train the personnel and service satellite, individually owned dairy farms sited in the immediate vicinity of the central dairy farm. This type of development may be very suitable for those areas in which there is no tradition of dairy farming. In Thailand a pilot-investigational dairy farm funded by Denmark has, after some vicissitudes, been moderately successful and is now the centre for a considerable dairying area and a vigorous dairy extension programme.

If the evolution of peasant subsistence farmers into small specialist dairy producers is to proceed rapidly it is essential for the authorities in each country to provide subsistence farmers with organized marketing facilities and efficient advisory and other auxiliary services. Central purchasing and milk-processing plants are required, together with advice on forage production, feeding, disease control and dairy hygiene, and loans for the purchase of the necessary equipment, buildings and stock.

The provision of an artificial insemination (AI) service could be most helpful to the small specialist producer. It could enable him to improve his breeding stock without the necessity of purchasing expensive bulls and to keep an extra cow instead of a bull. The latter practice would increase his total production by a considerable fraction if he has only sufficient land to keep one or two mature cattle. There are, however, inherent difficulties in the establishment of an AI service. Heat detection is often difficult in both exotic and indigenous dairy cattle in the tropics and communications are often very poor. Unless the service is well organized it may be very expensive for the government to operate and do little to assist the small farmer. For example, in one Asian country that one of the authors has recently visited the AI service was so inefficient and so expensive that it would have been more economic for the government to terminate it and give calves free of cost to the small dairy farmers.

The large-scale producer

There are a small number of large-scale private or government-owned dairy farms in most tropical countries. In India, for example, there are many large government dairy farms, about forty military dairy farms producing milk for the armed forces and some large-scale private farms.

Management, feeding and breeding practices on these large farms are usually superior to those on the smaller farms not because they are inherently more efficient units but because of the superior knowledge and resources of the operators. It is unusual, however, for the management of these large units to be of the same standard as that of the best dairy producers in the temperate zone.

The majority of the large producers manage their stock indoors, either in sheds or in yards. Some of them breed their own replacements, indeed many of them are breeding centres for the country in which they are situated, but others purchase replacement heifers. Where replacements are purchased, the culling rate is usually high, sometimes as much as 30 to 50 per cent per annum.

In a few regions of the tropics or the sub-tropics there are either quite large-scale extensive-type dairy farms or moderate to large scale beef ranches that produce milk.

The Atherton table land in Queensland, Australia, is a region where large-scale extensive dairy farms are of some importance. The dairy farmers in this region practice seasonal breeding and normally make no effort to produce milk on a year-round basis. The milk that they produce is therefore relatively inexpensive and is mainly used for manufacturing purposes.

In some countries in Central America and in the northern countries of South America, such as Ecuador, Colombia, Venezuela and the northeastern states of Brazil, many extensive beef farmers select the best milkers in their beef-breeding herds each year and bring them into a milking herd that is managed adjacent to the headquarters of their holding. This is not a new practice, but it has been spreading as the demand for milk in urban centres has increased. It has many attractions for the smaller beef ranchers as it is a system that provides a regular weekly or monthly income, but it is also widely practised on larger ranches. Naturally, it can flourish only where both land and labour are relatively cheap and plentiful. The growth of this system has dictated some changes in the methods of breeding and management of the beef herds. It could be said that there has been a gradual intensification of overall managerial methods and an increasing use of dairy-type bulls in the breeding programmes. Brown Swiss bulls have been widely used and this has given some impetus towards the general utilization of dual-purpose-type cattle. In many of these Central and South American countries milk from the beef herds has become a major source of dairy products for the urban consumer, this milk often being transported over very long distances. For example, in Colombia milk produced in the Sinú valley in the northern coastal region is transported at least 450 km (280 miles) to consumers in the inland city of Medellin.

It is likely that the number of large-scale dairy farms in the tropics will slowly increase in the future, particularly state-owned farms or mixed enterprises. They are unlikely, however, to supplant the small producers as the major suppliers of milk for a very long time.

Management and feeding

It is proposed to discuss the management and feeding of the various classes of dairy cattle from the point of view of the specialized dairy producer, although it is recognized that at the present time the small peasant producers may not be able to apply all or even the majority of the practices discussed. The authors believe, however, that some or most of these methods can be gradually introduced on even the smallest farms in most tropical countries and that it is desirable that ultimately they should be so introduced.

The calf

The first decision that a dairy farmer has to make is what calves he will rear. A breeder will raise almost all his heifer and bull calves, and sell the surplus as breeding stock. Commercial milk producers have a choice of several policies. If they raise single-purpose dairy animals, such as Jersey or Jamaica Hope, they will want to rear all their heifers but may wish to dispose of their surplus bull calves as soon as possible. In the past, in most temperate countries, these surplus bull calves would have been slaughtered and the meat used for manufacturing purposes. Now, most surplus bull calves are reared for beef production, and beef produced from the milking herds has become a major component of beef production in such countries as the United Kingdom. In some tropical countries there is a local market for surplus, live, young calves. For example, in the island of Madura in Indonesia large numbers of young calves are sold in the markets from 6 weeks of age.

If the farmer raises dual-purpose cattle – and this is normal in the tropics as most tropical breeds are dual- or triple-purpose – he can keep all his surplus bull calves and raise and sell them as bulls or steers, either for meat or for work purposes. There is also a third policy that is not widely practised in the tropics. The farmer can keep a beef or work-type bull and use him to serve the poorest producers in the herd, only using the better cows for breeding future dairy replacements. The cross-bred calves, both heifers and bulls, can then be raised for beef or work. This is a very desirable policy, but it cannot usually be practised because calf mortality is often high and the farmer needs all the dairy heifers that he can rear for replacements in his dairy herd.

Calf-rearing systems

Calves can be reared indoors or outdoors or partly indoors and partly outdoors. In cold temperate countries calves are often reared indoors for the first 6 to 9 months of life because of lack of grazing and the cold weather, but in warm temperate countries such as New Zealand calves are usually reared outdoors throughout the year.

In the humid tropics, where temperatures are high all the year round and grass growth is more or less continuous, it might be thought advantageous to follow the New Zealand practice of outdoor rearing. This is not necessarily so, however, for three reasons. First, it is difficult to keep the grass in calf paddocks in a young, palatable stage; tropical grasses grow and mature very quickly and at maturity possess a high fibre and low protein and mineral content and are not suitable for calf grazing. Secondly, a humid tropical environment is ideal for the pro-liferation of internal parasites and it is very difficult to keep the calves free from massive infection if they are grazing. Thirdly, even if the calf grazings are well shaded the calf is exposed to considerable climatic stress at a stage of life when it is least resistant. The combination of low nutrient content forage, parasites and climatic stress is inimical to calf life, and calves raised under these conditions usually have a high mortality rate.

There is, however, some experimental evidence from the Philippines (Payne *et al.*, 1967) that suggests that where management of grazings and cattle are good, dairy calves in the humid tropics grow most rapidly when managed on an indoor–outdoor system (Table 5.12). That is, out-doors at night and indoors during the daytime. Under this system the calves receive considerable protection from climatic stress, and it has been

Table 5.12 *Effect of management and drenching with a vermifuge on liveweight gain and mortality in dairy calves at Los Baños, Philippines*

Group	No. calves	Liveweight gain (kg (lb) per day)	Percentage total mortality
I. Indoor management	28	0·344 (0·758)	3·6
Drenched	15	0·385 (0·849)	6·7
Undrenched	13	0·300 (0·661)	nil
II. Indoor–outdoor management	23	0·404 (0·891)	8·7
Drenched	10	0·435 (0·959)	10·0
Undrenched	13	0·380 (0·838)	7·7
III. Outdoor management	27	0·387 (0·853)	29·6
Drenched	12	0·403 (0·888)	16·7
Undrenched	15	0·369 (0·814)	40·0

Notes: (1) The calves were mixed Sindhi × Friesian crossbreds and high-grade Friesian.
   2. The experimental period was from 13 to 52 weeks of age.
   3. Calves were selected for the groups at random.
   4. Thiabenzole, phenothiazine and promintic were used alternatively as vermi-fuges for two-thirds of the experiment; during the latter third only thiabenzole was used. Drenching was at 14-day intervals.
Source: Payne *et al.* (1967).

found that because the larvae of most internal parasites are phototropic they are more likely to be ingested by calves during daylight grazing than during grazing at night when the parasite larvae have moved down the stems of the forage towards the soil. Calves that are managed on an indoor–outdoor system should never be kept in special calf paddocks but should be rotationally grazed at night on the normal grazings some days before the milking cows so that they can obtain the most nutritious of the available forage; they should never be grazed on poor pastures, and they should be fed indoors during very wet and/or stormy nights. The Philippine data showed that the liveweight gain of the calves was significantly better in the drenched, indoor–outdoor-managed group. There was less mortality in the indoor-managed group, but the differences were not significant. Even allowing for the higher mortality, overall production was superior in the drenched, indoor–outdoor-managed group. What was also significant was the very high (40 per cent) mortality in the undrenched, outdoor-managed group. Of course it is not always possible in some tropical countries to manage calves out of doors at night on account of the activities of human and/or animal predators.

In the arid tropics, the risk of parasitism is less than in the humid tropics, particularly during the dry season, but grass growth is very seasonal and during long periods of the year no suitable grazing is available for calves. They may be reared on an indoor–outdoor system during the period of rapid grass growth, but as in the wet tropics they should not be reared in special paddocks. During the dry season it is likely that they are best reared indoors.

The most practical indoor-rearing system is one in which the calves are reared in a calf shed sited in an earth or gravel yard where they may exercise. The essentials of a good calf house (Fig. 5.4) are that it should provide adequate shelter, should be easily cleaned, and should keep the young calves warm in cool weather and cool in warm weather. It may be no more than a simple roof over a concrete base on a well-drained site. The roof should be at least 3 m (10 ft) in height at the eaves. Side walls are not necessary in the humid tropics as long as the roof has a wide overhang to keep out driving rain. No additional shade is required in the yard as the calves can shelter under the overhang of the roof or in the pens. Under the roof, provision should be made for individual feeding, separate pens, etc. Tubular steel is the most suitable material from which to construct individual calf ties, though hard timber or bamboo will suffice.

The yard must be kept free from all vegetation in order to reduce parasitism. The calves should have access to water, preferably under the shade of the roof, concentrates, good-quality forage and minerals. They should have a dry bed on which to lie, and are best bedded down on straw or sawdust, though this is not essential. It is usual to rear and feed the calves individually for the first few weeks of life and thereafter in batches. The internal layout of the type of calf shed described can

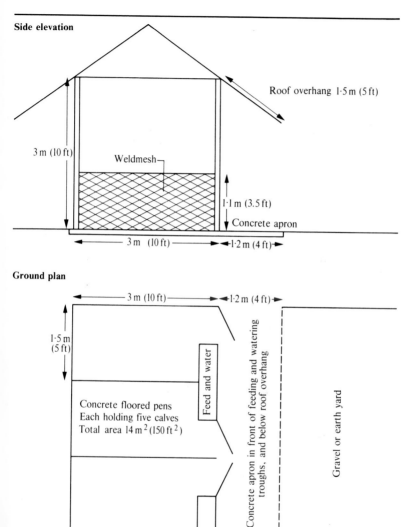

Fig. 5.4 Plan of a simple calf house suitable for a humid tropical environment.

easily be altered to suit particular circumstances. In some tropical countries individual calves are raised for the first few weeks of life in a special calf pen that is raised off the ground and possesses a slatted floor through which the faeces and urine drop (Fig. 5.5). The following conditions should be observed in its construction:

1. The slats can be made of metal or wood and should be spaced at appropriate intervals.

Ground plan

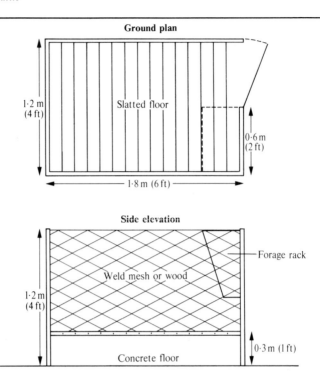

Side elevation

Fig. 5.5   Plan of an individual slatted-floor pen for a young calf.

2. The sides of the pen should be as open as is possible so that air can circulate freely.
3. The pen should be sited on a sloping floor so that faeces and urine can be easily removed. Raising the pen above the floor also assists air circulation and cooling.
4. Water, concentrate and mineral containers can be attached to the walls of the pen at appropriate locations.

This is a good system, but it is more costly and not essential if the conventional calf pens are cleaned daily and kept dry.

Calves that are running in batches often suckle or lick each other after feeding and it is a good practice to keep them in their ties for some time after milk feeding. Hair swallowed by the calves after suckling each other often forms a hard ball in the abomasum and this is a constant cause of digestive disturbances.

If for any reason dairy calves have to be reared entirely outdoors in the tropics, as stated above they should not be reared in special calf paddocks but be rotated round the milking cow grazings. It has been found in New Zealand that the best system is to rotate the calves around the grazings at least 10 days ahead of the dairy herd. In order to practise this system, the farmer needs at least fourteen to twenty separate paddocks.

Whether calves are reared indoors, outdoors or on an indoor–outdoor system it is usual to bring them to one central point to feed milk and concentrates, as it is easier to walk the calves to the food than to bring the food to the calves.

Feeding

The digestive tract of a young calf differs from that of a mature cow and the calf does not function as a ruminant until it is a few weeks old.

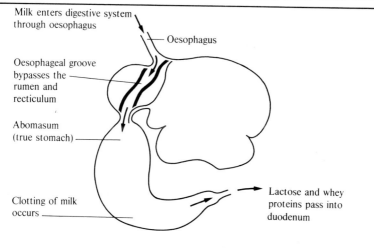

Fig. 5.6 Diagrammatic representation of the digestive system of the very young calf.

In the calf the capacity of the true stomach or abomasum is 70 per cent of all four stomachs, whereas in the mature cow it is only 7 per cent. When the calf suckles, the milk by-passes the rumen and reticulum and passes directly into the true stomach or abomasum (Fig. 5.6), and only if the calf drinks too much does any milk pass into the rumen. The stimulus for the activation of the oesophageal groove 'by-pass' is the presence of fluid in the back of the mouth. Milk going into the rumen of a small calf may curdle and then, because rumination has not yet commenced, putrefy, causing digestive disturbances. Thus it is a better practice to feed the calf small quantities of milk at frequent intervals than large amounts at infrequent intervals. Suckled calves running with their mothers are least likely to suffer from digestive disturbances as they suckle frequently. This is the method by which beef calves are raised, but in the past it has not usually been considered practical or economic to raise dairy calves in this way. There are authorities who now advocate the suckling of calves after twice-daily conventional milking for a period of 4 weeks and then after one milking for a further period of 6 weeks. It is stated that this practice does not decrease overall milk production and that it improves the growth and health of the calf. There is also one other benefit, the incidence of mastitis being reduced in the milking cows. Alternatively, dairy calves can be suckled by raising them on a nurse cow – one, two or three calves being raised according to the milk yield of the nurse cow. This is quite a common practice among breeders of dairy cattle and could be a desirable practice in the tropics where calf mortality is high and general feeding and management practice are poor. Old cows and cows with 'blind' quarters may be used for this purpose.

The majority of peasant farmers in the tropics allow the calf to suckle before milking in order to obtain a let-down of milk. There are many variations of this practice. The most common is for the calves to be shut away from their dams during the night while both cows and calves are held in separate enclosures. In the morning a calf is brought to her dam before milking commences and allowed to suckle for a short while, then the calf is taken away and the milker commences milking. Sometimes, as for instance among many of the nomadic tribes in the savanna regions of Africa, the calf is not taken completely away from the dam but is held by a rope – usually controlled by a child – in front of her dam, who licks the calf while milking proceeds. Other people allow the calf to suckle the front or back teats while they take milk from the remaining teats. Yet others allow the calf to suckle on the one side while they take milk from the other pair of teats. All these peoples insist that their cows will not let down their milk unless the calf has first suckled; and in the past many authorities have stated that cattle of indigenous tropical breeds, particularly the Zebu breeds, will not let down their milk unless they are first suckled. The practice is undesirable as it is both uneconomic and unhygienic and it can be stated quite categorically that it is not essential to suckle the calf of any breed in order to induce the dam to let down her milk. What in fact happens is that a vicious circle is created. The farmer starts the heifer off in this way at first milking and then claims that his cows will not let down their milk unless they are first suckled. If heifers are milked by hand without suckling some of them will let down their milk. Those that will not should be culled at the end of the first lactation. In this manner it is possible to build up a herd of dairy cattle of any breed that will let down their milk without the calves first suckling. There is, for example, a Sahiwal herd of approximately 500 breeding cows at Naivasha in Kenya that 10 years ago was milking with the calves afoot; in 1973 all the cows were milked without pre-suckling and the average yield was 1,630 kg (3,594 lb) per lactation.

If the calf is not suckled but bucket fed – this being the normal practice in dairy-farming countries – then it is better to bucket feed three times a day for at least the first 2 or 3 weeks. Many farmers bucket feed through a nipple as this slows down the rate of feeding. The disadvantage, in the tropics, of bucket feeding through a nipple is that the practice requires more equipment, and that all this additional equipment has to be kept very clean, thus adding to the expense and the difficulties of management, particularly where no piped water supply is available.

Whether the calf is to be suckled or bucket fed it is essential that it should receive the colostrum or first milk from its mother. It should be fed its mother's colostrum for 3 days, but if it is to be bucket fed it should be allowed to suckle its mother for only the first 12 to 24 hours, and after that her colostrum should be fed from the pail. Colostrum contains twice as much dry matter as milk. The protein content can be up to 18 per cent as against 3 to 5 per cent in most milk and it is of a different quality. Colostrum contains very much larger quantities of vitamins and minerals and it is also rather laxative and helps to clear the intestine of the young calf of accumulated faecal material. It also contains *antibodies* needed by the growing calf. These assist the young calf to protect itself against disease. It is particularly important that the young calf should get colostrum within the first 24 hours after birth as its digestive tract can absorb the antibodies during this period, whereas later they cannot be easily absorbed. Surplus colostrum may be fed to the older calves. It is usual to mix it with milk or with water, but this is not essential.

It is sometimes difficult to start a calf drinking from the bucket. The usual method is to starve it for a few hours and then place a hand in its mouth when feeding so that the colostrum laps against the mouth and the calf sucks it up through the fingers, which are then gently withdrawn. The young calf often 'bunts' while being bucket fed; this is quite normal as this is how it starts the 'let-down' of milk in its mother, but it means that the feeding bucket must be secured in some way otherwise the calf will spill its food.

The calf cannot use average-quality tropical roughage extensively until it is 3 or 4 months old and if it is weaned early and fed solely on roughage its growth will be slow. Consequently, it is desirable that calves should be suckled or bucket fed milk and/or a milk starter for as long a period as is economically practical and also fed concentrates and as high a quality roughage as is obtainable. Legume browse roughage is particularly desirable as it is often highly nutritious.

Suckled calves, if raised outdoors, may select what grass they need, but indoors they are usually fed concentrates and cut forage. Bucket-fed calves are usually fed whole milk for a short time, then a whole-milk substitute or skim-milk and finally they are weaned when about 3 to 6 months old. During this period they should also have access to concentrates and cut forage indoors. The 45 kg (100 lb) calf requires food with a nutritive ratio of about 1 : 4, but as it grows it can gradually deal with foods with a higher nutritive ratio.

Early weaning is now practised extensively in temperate-zone countries. Calves are introduced to specially prepared calf starters when they are 10 days old and to good-quality roughage as soon as possible. They are weaned, either abruptly when about 24 days old, after being fed 2·7 kg (6 lb) of whole milk daily, or gradually when they are given 2·7 kg (6 lb) until 10 days old and thereafter 0·5 kg (1 lb) less each week until milk feeding is stopped when the calf is 31 days old. When thus weaned their growth is severely checked, but in due course they recover satisfactorily and suffer no permanent damage. It is necessary to compromise between the needs of the calf and the cost of rearing. In the tropics where conditions are less favourable to the calf it is probably more economic to feed the calf additional whole milk than to attempt to early wean and raise it on the minimum quantity. There are obviously all types of compromise managerial systems between early and late weaning. The choice of system must depend on local circumstances. For example, in the Sahiwal herd in Kenya cited above, the calves are reared on whole milk until they are 9 weeks of age. The possibility also exists of bucket rearing calves on specially prepared synthetic milks, particularly those prepared from soybean products. These types of milk could be cheaper than cow's milk and of particular utility in the tropics.

It is usual to ration the calf to 10 to 12 per cent of its own body weight of milk a day. Some authorities advocate the feeding of up to 15 per cent of the body weight of milk daily, but this is not general and certainly should not be practised in the tropics, where calves usually grow more slowly than in the temperate zone. The milk should be warmed to body temperature and the calf should be fed three times daily during the first week, if that is practicable.

Although it is preferable to first feed a calf whole milk and then skim-milk, this is normally an uneconomic practice, and in the temperate zone milk substitutes are used in place of whole milk from about the second or third week of life. The quantity of milk fed daily is reduced and by the fourth week only milk substitute is fed. Bucket feeding may be discontinued as the calves grow older and they may be collectively fed, using clean, glazed earthenware troughs. In the temperate zone automatic dispensers of milk substitute are being employed and these machines have some advantage, as apart from reducing the cost of labour they ensure that the milk supply is always available and at the correct temperature.

A decision as to whether to feed whole milk for a longer period, skim-milk or milk substitutes must depend on local circumstance. In a dairying area where ghee or butter is produced, skim-milk might be available, and milk substitutes are becoming increasingly available in the tropics as livestock feed industries develop. What must be remembered is that, in general, the environment in most tropical countries is more disadvantageous for the dairy calf than it is in temperate-zone countries and that it may be economic to spend additional money on calf rearing in order to reduce calf mortality and increase calf liveweight gain. It must also be remembered that most dairy calves in the tropics, whether from *Bos indicus* or *B. taurus* breeds, are smaller at birth and grow somewhat slower than would similar calves in the temperate zone. Thus temperate-zone feeding standards are not completely applicable in the tropics and if adhered to are likely to lead to some overfeeding of the calves.

Average tropical dairy calves probably weigh 20 to 27 kg (45 to 60 lb) at birth and during the first week they should be fed no more than 2·8 kg (6·2 lb) of milk a day. By the fourth week this could be raised to 3·7 kg (8 lb) of whole milk or milk substitute per day. Heavier calves should of course receive correspondingly larger quantities. It is likely that the amount of whole milk or milk substitute fed should never exceed 4·5 kg (10 lb) per day as the calves will begin to eat concentrates and forage in increasing amounts as they grow older. Some farmers dilute the milk or milk substitute that they feed to their calves, but this is not necessary.

Although milk is essential for young calves they must not be fed only on milk. Calves fed in this way suffer eventually from magnesium deficiency and they may die.

Calves, however fed, should have access to concentrates from 2 to 3 weeks of age and to the best-quality forage available. The type of concentrate that can be fed obviously depends upon what is locally available. A suitable mixture of feeds that may be available in the tropics is as follows:

Coconut meal	50 parts
Groundnut meal	25 parts
Maize meal	25 parts

Warner (1951) recommended the following mixture for calf rearing in India:

Wheat bran	30 parts
Linseed cake	10 parts
Barley meal	20 parts
Jowar (*Sorghum* spp.) meal	20 parts
Maize meal	20 parts

At 2 months of age average calves in the tropics will eat up to 0·45 kg (1 lb) of concentrates per day, and at 3 months of age at least 0·7 kg (1·5 lb) per day. If the calves are weaned after 3 months of age and are well grown they will soon eat up to 1·4 to 1·8 kg (3 to 4 lb) of concentrates a day as well as forage.

When calves are fed indoors special precautions must be taken to see that they receive adequate amounts of minerals and vitamins. If a commercial vitamin–mineral premix is not available – as it may not be in some tropical countries – it is best to add a little fish-liver oil to the diet and to make available a mineral mixture. The mineral mixture may be fed with the concentrates or alternatively suitable mineral licks are also usually commercially available. Details of a suitable mineral mixture are given in Chapter 3, Part I.

Calves should always have access to water. It is a mistake to assume that they do not require water because they are being fed large amounts of milk or milk substitute.

Special managerial considerations

When a dairy cow is about to calve she should be brought to a place where she can be kept under observation. Some farmers provide special calving pens, but this is not essential unless contagious disease is endemic. Occasionally a cow needs assistance at calving, especially when a tropical-type cow is delivering a crossbred calf got by a temperate-type bull, but help should be given only when it is absolutely essential. After birth the cow will clean the calf by licking it.

Most breeds of dairy cattle are horned and horns are a disadvantage in dairy operations, though the farmer may wish to retain the horns on bull calves to be raised for work or on dual- or triple-purpose heifer calves. Dehorning is best done by cauterizing the horn bud when the calf is a week or two old, either by rubbing the bud with a caustic stick till it is near bleeding, by the use of collodion, or by the use of a cylindrical red-hot iron pressed for a second or two on the rim of the horn bud. The latter operation is usually carried out at 3 to 4 weeks of age. If electricity is available an electric hot iron is most effective. When a caustic stick is used care must be taken that the calf does not carry the caustic to the cow, in suckling for instance, and that the caustic does not spread from the site of the operation, particularly into the eyes. This may occur if the calf is exposed to rain soon after application of the caustic stick.

Castration can be carried out with a knife, with crushers, or with a rubber ring. The rubber ring method is the most suitable for calves up to 2 or 3 weeks old. When the operation is performed by this method on calves that are about 10 days old it causes a minimum of pain or discomfort. The Burdizzo bloodless castrator makes the operation a comparatively safe one at all ages.

It is desirable that calves should be marked at as early an age as possible by one of the methods referred to in Appendix II. If the dairy herd is recorded it is essential that the calves should be marked.

Calf mortality and disease

Calf mortality in the tropics is undoubtedly very high. Often it is as high as 50 per cent, but this almost invariably denotes bad management. In some areas a high death rate is partly due to the fact that unacclimatized temperate or crossbred stock are used for dairying and climatic stress is added to the other hazards of calf life, but it is more usually due to poor feeding and faulty management. The best way to reduce calf mortality is to practise good husbandry. Some common ailments can be treated by the farmer, but once the calf is seriously ill or large numbers of calves are ill, expert veterinary advice should be sought.

The most common disease of calves is 'scouring'. The usual symptoms are a dull appearance of the eyes, listlessness, diarrhoea and sometimes an abnormal rise in temperature and respiration rate. Scouring may be due to purely mechanical causes, nutritive causes or to infection. Calves that drink too rapidly or are fed cold milk or have hair balls in their abomasum often scour. Treatment consists of starving the calf for 24 hours and then feeding small quantities of milk diluted with a little water that has been heated to body temperature. Calves suffering from this type of scour usually recover if treated properly. Scours caused by infection are usually more serious both because there is greater danger of death of the infected individual and because a large proportion of the calves are usually infected. The faeces are often a chalky-white colour and have a very offensive smell. Infection may enter through the mouth, but sometimes enters through the navel cord. Often the calves die within a very short time. The use of antibiotics in the feed of calves undoubtedly reduces the incidence of scours caused by infection.

Pneumonia often occurs when a calf is suffering from scours. The symptoms are as follows: the temperature rises rapidly, the respiration rate increases and the calf 'gasps' for breath. The primary cause is almost invariably an infection predisposed by sudden changes in the environmental temperature and humidity.

The young calf is particularly vulnerable to attack by internal parasites that thrive in the tropics. Calves suffer from roundworms, threadworms, hookworms, lungworms, tapeworms, coccidia and other internal parasites. Symptoms of parasite attack are 'a falling back in condition', a dry rough coat, a pot belly and a swelling under the jaw. Internal parasites are best controlled by good calf-house hygiene, proper rotational grazing and a systematic drenching policy. In the wet tropics it may be necessary to drench the calves at very regular and comparatively short intervals; in the drier tropics it may only be necessary to drench the calves at certain seasons of the year.

The heifer

The rearing period of the heifer from weaning to first calving divides naturally into two stages: one from weaning to first service and the other from first service to calving.

The aim in rearing heifers should be to achieve the maximum growth and development and the earliest sexual maturity consistent with least cost. This ensures that maintenance costs are minimized, that there is the earliest possible return on the investment in the original animal and that the heifer probably produces well during her first lactation.

There is always some check to growth at weaning. If the heifer calf is being rotationally grazed on nutritious pasture, either on an outdoor or an indoor–outdoor system of management, the check will be minimal. However, if she is being raised indoors and is abruptly weaned and suddenly placed outdoors on indifferent-quality pasture, the growth check will be very severe. Although it is now well established that short periods of retarded growth, resulting from sub-optimal feeding, are not likely to have a permanent effect on the future productivity of the heifer they will decrease her growth rate and hence delay sexual maturity. This increases rearing expense and hence decreases profitability.

The feeding of a high-quality roughage such as leguminous browse or the rotation of heifers, managed in the wet tropics, over good grass-legume pastures such as guinea-centro, should ensure that they grow at a reasonable rate; but in the wet and dry tropics or in the semi-arid tropics it may be necessary to supplement their diet during the dry season. Supplements could be good legume or grass hay, silage, molasses–urea–mineral liquid feeds or blocks or cheap protein-rich concentrates such as groundnut or cottonseed meal. Yearling heifers fed 0·25 kg (0·5 lb) per head per day of such concentrates, and maintained on only medium-quality roughage, will materially improve their liveweight gain and shorten the time taken to attain sexual maturity.

Like calves, heifers can be reared indoors or outdoors. As indoor rearing is so expensive heifers are not usually housed in the wet tropics, although in many regions they may be kept indoors until they are 9 to 12 months of age. However, in some wet tropical regions it is essential to rear heifers indoors – particularly in those regions of Africa where the tsetse fly is prevalent, unless cattle tolerant of trypanosomiasis such as the N'dama are being utilized. The latter is unlikely as the indigenous breeds of cattle that are tolerant of trypanosomiasis are poor milkers. Also there are countries such as Mauritius, where biting flies are so numerous that heifers must be housed in screened or dark sheds. There are also regions in Central and South America where cattle are liable to be bitten by vampire bats, the vectors of rabies, and so must be housed at night.

There is no doubt that in the tropics, temperate- and tropical-type cattle do not generally grow as quickly as do temperate-type cattle in the temperate zone, although they may eventually achieve the same mature liveweight. In New Zealand it has been shown that under outdoor conditions growth depends very largely on grazing management. Although the effect of the climatic environment is of some importance in the wet tropics (Hancock and Payne, 1955), grazing management practice is still a major factor in the growth of heifers. They can either be set-stocked or rotationally grazed, rotational grazing being rarely practised. Experimental work in New Zealand has shown that in that country rotationally grazed heifers can weigh 68 kg (150 lb) more than set-stocked heifers at 20 months of age, and unlike set-stocked heifers do not have to be drenched at regular intervals for the control of internal parasites. One reason why set-stocked heifers do not thrive as well as rotationally grazed heifers is that they have to work harder to obtain their feed. In the New Zealand experiments rotationally grazed heifers grazed for 7·5 hours each day, taking forty-eight bites per minute, whereas set-stocked heifers required 9·0 hours of grazing and took thirty-five bites per minute. The significance of these findings is likely to be even greater in the tropics than in New Zealand, as any increase in muscular work in the tropics increases the heat load on the animal with a consequent depressing effect on liveweight gain.

There is no doubt that a major part of the poor growth of heifers in the tropics is due to their poor nutrition, often the result of set-stocking on low-quality pastures or the complete absence of pastures, although in the case of indigenous cattle some part of the poor growth may also be due to inherited characteristics. Another part of the slow growth of both exotic and indigenous heifers (perhaps 10 per cent) is due to the effect of the climatic environment (Hancock and Payne, 1955).

Heifers raised outdoors should be managed as follows. They should always be rotationally grazed around paddocks containing grass of milk-producing quality, or if the quality of the forage is poor they should in addition be fed a supplement. If the milking herd grazings are utilized then the heifers should be rotated 7 to 10 days ahead of the milking cows. A minimum of fourteen paddocks is required in order to exploit rotational grazing techniques. Preferably, more paddocks should be utilized. The heifers should be shifted daily if this is practicable and never grazed on any one field for more than 2 or 3 days. The paddocks should be provided with natural and/or artificial shade and water. A mineral mixture should be available in rain-proof feeders and similar provisions should be made for the feeding of any supplement that may be required.

Heifers raised in yards should have access to cool water, shade, minerals, forage and if necessary a supplement. The shade should be orientated east–west, be approximately 3 m (10 ft) in height and be constructed from suitable materials. Some form of thatch roof on timber uprights may be very suitable, but it could harbour vermin. If corrugated iron is used as a roofing material then it should be painted black underneath and with aluminium paint on the upper surface. Aluminium and asbestos are excellent roofing materials, but they may be too expensive to use.

Heifers raised in yards can be fed cheap roughages and/or crop by-products such as straw, stover, pineapple pulp, sisal waste, etc., but they will also require additional high-quality forage and concentrate supplements. Feeding standards for growing heifers are given in Table 5.13.

As stated previously, the heifers of many tropical and temperate breeds managed in the tropics grow so slowly that sexual and conformation maturity occur at approximately the same age. In the temperate zone, heifers from the smaller dairy breeds are usually first bred at approximately 15 months of age while those of the larger breeds are first bred at about 18 months, although there has been a general tendency to breed

Table 5.13 Feeding standards for heifers. Daily nutrient requirements

Liveweight* (kg (lb))	Feed intake† (kg (lb))	TDN (kg (lb))	Protein‡ (kg (lb))	Calcium (g)	Phosphorus (g)
150 (330)	3·6–4·4 (7·9–9·7)	2·30–2·80 (4·85–6·17)	0·43–0·53 (0·95–1·12)	12	11
200 (440)	4·8–5·6 (10·6–12·3)	2·90–3·40 (6·39–7·50)	0·47–0·57 (1·04–1·26)	13	12
250 (550)	5·8–6·6 (12·8–14·6)	3·30–3·80 (7·28–8·38)	0·57–0·69 (1·26–1·52)	14	13
300 (660)	6·8–7·6 (15·0–16·8)	3·85–4·35 (8·45–9·59)	0·59–0·75 (1·30–1·65)	15	14

* It is assumed that the growth rate during this period will be at a maximum.
† Based on air-dried feed *not* dry-matter content. Intake data must vary according to the composition of the ration and climatic environment and can only be approximate.
‡ It is assumed that approximately two-thirds of this would be digestible.
Source: Mainly from National Academy of Sciences–National Research Council (1966).

Management and feeding 283

them earlier during the last two or three decades, as weight for age has improved. The majority of heifers in the tropics are too small, and hence too sexually immature, to breed at these ages and normally first service does not take place until they are older (Table 5.14). It is recommended that liveweight rather than age should be used as a criterion as to when heifers should be first bred. Adequate liveweights would be 200 to 225 kg (440 to 500 lb) for the smaller and 290 to 315 kg (640 to 700 lb) for the larger breeds.

After the heifer has been bred and conception has taken place she not

Table 5.14 *Average age at first calving of heifers of some representative tropical breeds and crosses between tropical and temperate-type breeds*

Breed	Country	Age at first calving (months)		Reference
		Mean	Range	
N'dama	Sierra Leone	39·4	33·2–48·0	Touchberry (1967)
Kenana	Sudan	38·4	23·0–58·0	Alim (1960)
Kankrej	Brazil	46·9		Pires *et al.* (1967)
Jamaica Hope	Jamaica			
	Experimental herd	34·2		Wellington *et al.* (1970)
	Private herds	35·9		
Red Sindhi	India	51·0		Kumar (1969)
Red Sindhi × Jersey	India	31·7		Kumar (1969)
Hariana	India	39·3		Misra and Kushwaha (1970)
Ongole	India	39·9		Rao *et al.* (1969)
Sinhala	Sri Lanka	44·8		Wijeratne (1970)
Sinhala × Jersey (F_1)	Sri Lanka	36·6		Wijeratne (1970)
Sinhala × Friesian (F_1)	Sri Lanka	36·9		Wijeratne (1970)

only has to continue to grow but also to produce a viable calf and to milk 9 months later. She therefore requires somewhat better feeding than some other classes of dairy cattle, particularly during the last 2 months of pregnancy. It is advisable to bring her into the milking herd at this time. She can then be fed a little extra concentrate in the milking bail and in addition she becomes accustomed to being handled. If the heifer is of a high-producing breed then an additional 1·8 kg (4 lb) of a milk production concentrate ration may be fed. This additional feeding during the pre-pregnancy period is known as 'steaming-up'.

Internal parasite control should be continued throughout the heifer's growth period in the wet tropics and, if required, in other ecological zones. All heifers should be vaccinated with Strain 19 against contagious abortion when they are between 4 and 8 months of age. Where foot and mouth disease is endemic they should be vaccinated twice or three times a year against the indigenous strains of the disease, and in endemic rinderpest areas they should be vaccinated against this disease when they are approximately 8 months of age. In those regions where the diseases are endemic, heifers should also be vaccinated against blackleg and anthrax.

The milking heifer and cow

Management and feeding during breeding

Data from tropical breeds are limited, but it is likely that the normal variation in the gestation period of cows in the tropics is between 275 and 287 days, as in the temperate zone. The normal variation in the period between heats of 18 to 24 days is also similar to that in the temperate zone. There is, however, a major difference in the duration of heat. In the temperate zone the duration of heat averages about 18 hours with a range of from 6 to 30 hours. In the case of temperate-type breeds in the tropics and many indigenous tropical breeds including the majority of Zebu breeds, the average duration of heat is far shorter. In addition the short heat period often occurs at night and 'silent' heats are common. There are exceptions to this generalization as many of the indigenous breeds in Southeast Asia, and particularly the Madura and the Bali, exhibit longer than average heat periods. However, these breeds are not likely to be used for milk-production purposes as they are very poor milk producers, though crossbreds of them with temperate-type breeds might be used.

The short duration of heat and the fact that the heat period so often occurs at night complicates breeding management in the tropics. As a consequence, fertility is often very low in both temperate- and tropical-type dairy cattle unless special managerial measures are employed. This is particularly so in Holstein and high-grade Holstein dairy herds. The use of AI is not recommended unless special arrangements are made for heat detection in the heifers and cows and the general standards of management are high. Even if AI is utilized 'back-up' dairy bulls should be available to breed heifers and cows that are missed during the operation of the normal AI programme. Heat detection may be improved by the use of vasectomized bulls equipped with a head stall, managed with the heifers and cows. These bulls will mark female stock coming on heat. Other heat-detection equipment may also be used such as phials of dye attached to the back of the female that burst when she is mounted, either by another female or by a vasectomized bull.

Dairy cows usually come into heat some 30 to 60 days after calving. In the tropics the most suitable practice would appear to be to breed the cow at her first heat period after calving and not later than 60 days after parturition. If she is not bred at this time the available evidence suggests that she will be more difficult to get in calf. There is also some evidence that the chances of a successful first service are less in the tropics. A percentage of heifers and cows are of course always sterile in all herds, and in the temperate zone the incidence of sterility in females up to 10 years of age varies from 3 to 5 per cent, although when they are older than 10 years the percentage rises rapidly. There is no evidence that the percentage of completely sterile animals is markedly different in the tropics.

Culling for sterility is essential, and persistent culling in a closed herd should gradually improve the fertility of the female stock. It is also possible that culling for short heat periods and 'silent' heats may also be effective in reducing the incidence of these characteristics, although the authors do not know of any experimental work that has been conducted on this subject. It is likely that some considerable part of this phenomenon is due to the effect of the climatic environment so that culling could only be partially effective. In addition the heavy culling of heifers and/or cows for reproductive behavioural defects in tropical dairy herds is often difficult if not impossible on account of high calf mortality, with the consequence that there are only a limited number of heifer calves available annually for replacement purposes.

It is normal to run a bull with the grazing heifers, some arrangement being made for the daily identification of those that he has served. It is, therefore, important that individuals within the groups of heifers should be of approximately the same size and weight. Running a bull with the milking herd is not a very desirable practice. It is more satisfactory to keep the bull adjacent to the milking shed and to take cows that are on heat to him. In order to do this satisfactorily some method of heat detection, as described above, must be employed.

If a cow does not have a dry period between lactations subsequent yield is likely to be reduced. Cows that calve regularly, at approximately 12-month intervals, should be milked for 10 months or for a 305-day period and rested for 2 months. The dry period allows the cow's mammary glands to rest and recuperate and enables her to complete the building up of a body reserve of nutrients ready for the next lactation. For example, one study has shown that a dry period of 55 days resulted in an overall loss of 4·6 per cent of milk compared with no dry period in the current lactation, but a gain of 28·7 per cent in the following lactation, or a net gain of 24·1 per cent in total milk production in the two lactations. Heifers should be allowed longer dry periods than cows, particularly in the tropics where they are likely to continue to grow throughout the first lactation. They should be dried off after approximately 260 to 270 days and given a 90- to 100-day dry period. Undersized heifers should be given a particularly long first dry period, as should cows in a poor condition. In practice, as short lactations are characteristic of both temperate- and tropical-type cattle managed in the tropics the problem that usually confronts the farmer is that the dry period is too long. For example, Mahadevan (1955) stated that 25 per cent of the lactations of unimproved Zebu cattle end before 300 days, so that the lactation yield of these cattle is closely correlated with the length of the lactation. In a later publication (Mahadevan, 1966) it was stated that this correlation also existed in temperate-type dairy cattle managed in the tropics. It is likely that the relatively short lactation periods demonstrated by tropical dairy cattle are primarily the result of environmental factors and that as standards of management and feeding improve the situation may change.

At the present stage of development of the dairy industry in the tropics, as average lactation length is so short, it might be economic to pursue a managerial policy that would increase the total number of milking cows on the holding and systematically dry-off the milkers after a lactation of 240 days, thus increasing both the stocking rate and the proportion of dry cows in the herd. The dry cows could, however, be fed on a low maintenance ration, and this policy would enable the farmer to shift both forage and concentrate feed resources from relatively non-productive to relatively productive animals. Essentially, this policy would mean that the farmer would milk more cows, but that each would be milked for a shorter period and that he would use available feed resources to provide maximum feed during the most productive part of the lactation.

Temperate-breed heifers raised in the temperate zone normally produce, during their first lactations, 70 to 77 per cent of the milk that they will produce when they are mature. Also, cows attain their maximum production at the fourth or fifth lactation, with production declining after the seventh or eighth lactation. Analysis of milk production data from the tropics has suggested that maximum production occurs at an earlier age (Mahadevan, 1966). There is, however, some evidence that this phenomenon may also be due to inadequate feeding and management and may not be an inherent characteristic of dairy cattle managed in the tropics.

A cow or a heifer about to calve should be placed in a pen or in a separate paddock so that she can be kept under observation. The advantage of a special calving box is that the animal can be kept under close observation and that if she does have difficulty during calving assistance can be immediately provided. However, unless calving boxes are kept scrupulously clean there may be more disadvantages in bringing the animal inside than in leaving her out in the field.

She should not be interfered with during calving unless she is obviously in trouble. At calving the heifer or cow loses 8 to 10 per cent of her body weight.

During the calving period the heifer or cow should not be overfed. A small quantity of a laxative concentrate such as rice bran is a useful feed at this time. After calving, concentrate feeding, if not already begun during the previous 2 months, should be commenced immediately and should reach a peak within approximately 3 weeks. The cow or heifer should always be fed a little more concentrate than her milk yield justifies in order to encourage milk production to rise during the first stage of the lactation.

Management and feeding during milking

The aim of good management of dairy cattle in the tropics should be to take all economically justifiable measures that will decrease the total 'heat load' of the animal or help to spread the 'heat load' more evenly over the 24 hours. As temperate-zone methods of management are not based on this premise they are not necessarily suited to the tropics. Within the limits of present knowledge suitable managerial practices would appear to be as follows:

1. The provision of rations that do not exceed optimal requirements with particular reference to total energy and fibre content. Grazing at night but not during the daytime. Concentrate feeding in the early morning and early evening or the spreading of concentrate feeding throughout the 24 hours instead of only feeding during the day.
2. The provision of adequate and cool water supplies both in yards and out on grazings.
3. The siting of yards, milking bails and shelters so that they are open to the prevailing winds but not to driving rain. The provision of adequate natural or constructed shade in yards and out on the grazings. The choice of suitable materials for shelter construction as detailed in previous sections.
4. The clipping of the coats of animals that are sheltered from solar radiation. This is not normally necessary in the case of tropical breeds.
5. The seasonal breeding of heifers and cows to calve down during the coolest season if seasonal milk production is economic.
6. The provision of water sprays, forced air fans and cooled water supplies in the yards, bails and shelters if the use of these practices can be economically justified. This depends primarily on the cost of energy.

Milking cows, like calves and heifers, can be managed indoors or outdoors or on an indoor–outdoor system. It is now generally agreed that in the wet tropics temperate- or crossbred-type animals are more productive than tropical-type cattle if disease control is adequate and they are properly fed and managed. A tropical climate, however, always imposes some degree of stress on milking cattle, and although there will be wide individual variations in yield there is probably a physiological limit to average milk production, the 'ceiling' being lower than it would be for cattle of the same inherent merit managed in a temperate climate (Payne and Hancock, 1957). On the other hand, with good husbandry, total forage production per unit area of land can be maintained at a very high level and it would be logical for the dairy farmer in the wet tropics to aim at a high stocking rate and a high production per unit area rather than for only a high production per animal. Of course, a high production per unit area cannot be attained without relatively high production per animal. In addition, the ability of the dairy farmer to grow forage in the wet tropics is probably well ahead of his ability to utilize it efficiently. All these factors must be considered in any assessment of the most suitable type of managerial system.

The advantages and disadvantages of an indoor system are as follows:

1. The advantages of indoor management in the wet tropics

(a) It is easier to take managerial measures that will decrease the total 'heat-load' if cattle are managed indoors, at least during the day.

(b) Maintenance requirements should be slightly lower and muscular heat production reduced if the cattle are not grazing or walking backwards and forwards twice a day to the milking shed.

(c) Higher carrying capacities can be achieved, according to some authorities, if forage is cut and not grazed. Cut forage will certainly be wilted before it is fed and this may help to maintain a higher dry matter intake.

(d) Grazings will not be spoilt during wet weather.

(e) Manure can be returned to the fields more evenly and by-products such as straw and sawdust can be converted into organic manures in the yards.

(f) Maximum utilization can be achieved of high-growing forage species such as elephant grass (*Pennisetum purpureum*), that are more difficult to manage under grazing conditions and that yield large quantities of dry matter per unit area.

(g) Under circumstances where large quantities of by-products are available for feeding, as when dairying is integrated with citrus, pineapple or sugar production.

2. The disadvantages of indoor management in the wet tropics

(a) Capital requirements are far higher although there would be some savings in the cost of water reticulation to fields, internal fences and roads. The exception would be the very small farmer who tethered one or two dairy cattle beneath trees or who built simple yards. Examples of the latter type of indoor management may be seen in the islands of Bali and Madura, in Indonesia or in Mauritius.

(b) Labour costs are higher. If the cost of labour is low this may not be a a serious disadvantage.

(c) The difficulty of maintaining high-quality forage mixtures, particularly grass–legume mixtures, without grazing. This could mean an increase in fertilizer costs or a decrease in the quality of the feed.

(d) The managerial difficulties of organizing a constant flow of high-quality feed to yard-fed cattle, particularly during very wet periods. This difficulty should not be underestimated.

(e) A general lack of flexibility.

The decision as to whether to adopt an indoor or an outdoor system of management depends primarily upon the ecological conditions. The economics are simple. Will the increased production resulting from an indoor managerial system that ameliorates conditions for the cattle pay for the additional cost of the buildings and equipment required and the cost of bringing feed to the animals and disposing of the waste products? In the wet tropics, although there are some regions where cattle have to be housed on account of parasites, etc., it is likely that in most regions some form of indoor–outdoor system would be most suitable and efficient although it is not known whether it would be the most economic. This could only be determined locally. With an indoor–outdoor system milking cattle could be kept in the yards during the day, when ameliorative measures against the climatic environment could be taken, and grazed on the pasture at night. Surplus forage would be ensiled and fed to the cattle when they were yarded during the day. Some conserved fodder would be fed throughout the year – small quantities when the night grazings were adequate and larger quantities during the very wet or very dry periods when the cattle would be kept off the grazings even during the night. Under this type of management the cattle would not be continuously changing from one type of feed to another but would always receive some conserved fodder whether or not they also grazed. The system would be inherently very flexible.

In the semi-arid tropics it is likely that an indoor system would be a necessity, though this will depend upon whether irrigation is available. The question may in fact be academic as the overall economics of milk production in the semi-arid tropics are doubtful, particularly if irrigation is essential. In the ecological zones between these two extremes the decision will vary according to local circumstances. Unfortunately at the present time there is no objective information on this fundamental question in any ecological zone.

Whether managed indoors or outdoors milking cows exhibit very definite behavioural patterns. They demonstrate a well-established herd order and are very quick to associate pleasant or unpleasant experiences with places and/or persons. They should always be handled quietly and according to a strict routine and if possible by the same person(s).

Cows managed indoors often develop long hooves. These should be trimmed periodically. Cows managed outdoors, particularly in the muddy conditions that occur in the wet tropics, often develop soft pads that are invaded by infectious organisms that cause lameness. It is good practice to walk these cattle through a foot-bath containing a copper sulphate or formalin solution, either at regular intervals or daily as a routine measure, perhaps as they leave the milking bail. Some dairy stock managed indoors develop the habit of suckling each other and odd individuals will suckle themselves. This habit can be prevented by attaching a short length of chain to one or two rings in the nose.

The habit of kicking is usually developed when a heifer is first milked and is due to faulty management. Once acquired it is a difficult habit to break and as kickers disturb the milking shed routine they should be culled. Some cows can become vicious. This is also usually due to poor management. In the early stages the habit may be broken by a few sharp blows on the nose. If this does not effect a cure the cow should be culled.

There is no evidence that grooming improves the health of dairy cattle although it does accustom them to handling. It is a desirable practice if the farmer has spare time. However, it is a very rare individual who has sufficient time to spare for this practice.

Milking technique

The object of milking is to obtain the maximum quantity of milk from the udder. If milking is incomplete there is a tendency for the cow to dry off too soon and total milk production declines. If too long a period is spent on milking the cost per unit weight of milk produced increases. The first essential in milking technique, particularly when milking a heifer for the first time, is to prevent the animal becoming excited or frightened. The second essential is to milk quickly and completely. These objectives apply whether the animal is hand or machine milked.

The let-down of milk is controlled by a combination of nervous and hormonal actions (Fig. 5.7). The cow first needs a stimulus. When the calf suckles, the first pull of the calf on the teat is the stimulus. When there is no calf some other stimulus must be established. It could be the application of a towel during preliminary udder washing or the pressure of the teat cups of a milking machine, etc. Once a stimulus is established the nervous system relays a message to the posterior pituitary gland, which then releases a hormone known as oxytocin. This hormone circulates in the blood, is carried to the udder tissue, and there initiates the let-down process. As the hormone is in circulation for only a short period (up to 4 minutes), the more quickly milking is carried out the more efficient it will be. With both hand and machine milking the establishment of a strong stimulus associated with the preliminaries of milking, that will initiate the let-down reflex, is essential for fast milking. The aim is to produce a single let-down response at such a level that, with normal milking, all the milk can be obtained without the need to induce a second let-down.

The maximum rate of milk flow during the let-down process is a highly inherited characteristic that differs from cow to cow. Of major importance in this respect is the size of the orifice of the teat. Cows possessing teats with small orifices are known as hard milkers. It is desirable to cull this type of cow.

The actual process of milking is accomplished by the application of force to the muscles surrounding the teat meatus so that the orifice of the teat is opened and the milk discharged. In hand milking, the upper part of the teat is closed tightly by the hand to prevent milk flow-

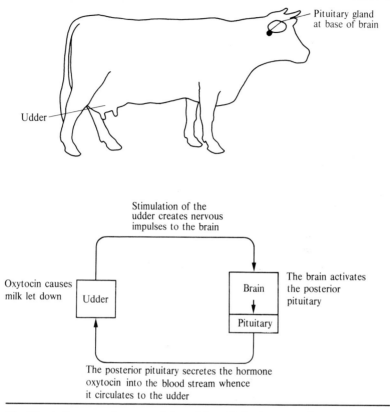

Fig. 5.7 A diagrammatic representation of the milk let-down system.

ing back into the udder cistern while pressure is applied to the milk-filled lower portion of the teat. Increased pressure inside the teat stretches the sphincter muscle and the teat meatus is forced open. In machine milking the pressure on the inside of the teat is unchanged. The pressure inside the teat cup is lowered so that a vacuum is formed and the normal pressure inside the teat in relation to the pressure outside becomes sufficient to force the teat meatus open and allow the milk to flow out. If milk does not flow the vacuum extends inside the teat causing damage to the mammary tissues. This is why the teat cups must be taken off as soon as milk flow ceases.

In hand milking it is better to milk with dry rather than wet hands as wet hand milking is unsanitary. Hand stripping should be completed as quickly as possible, otherwise the cow may become a 'stripper' and only let down her milk very slowly. Cows milked by machine should be machine and not hand stripped.

Cows are usually milked twice daily at approximately 12-hour intervals. However, experimental work in Australia and New Zealand has shown that there is no significant change in the average hourly excretion of milk by cows from 12- and 12-hour to 16- and 8-hour milking intervals. The dairy farmer can therefore exercise some considerable choice in milking interval without endangering the overall productivity of his cows. It is usual to restrict milking gradually in order to dry off a cow. The pressure that develops in the udder soon stops milk production. As stated previously all cows should be dried off at 305 days, even if their milk production is still high, if they are going to calve 12 months after the beginning of their current lactation. Cows should be dried off before 305 days only if they are due to calve or if they produce so little milk that it becomes uneconomic to milk them.

Sometimes a cow's teat leaks milk before milking. This may be due to two causes. The muscles of the orifice may be weak, or there may be a natural fistula or wound in the teat cistern. A wound may be sealed by cauterization or by surgical treatment when the cow is dry. If teats are sore they should be bathed in a warm salt solution and Vaseline applied.

High-producing cows may with advantage be milked more fequently than twice daily, and three times a day milking may increase total milk production by approximately 10 per cent. The increased production obtained by milking three times a day is not due to the cows exhibiting high per hour excretion rates, but to other factors.

Hand versus machine milking

It is generally accepted that machine milking is not quite as efficient a method as is the best hand milking, but that it is generally superior to average hand milking. Cows accept machine milking just as well or even better than hand milking.

Machine milking is likely to be introduced if labour is scarce and expensive, if available labour dislikes the toil of hand milking and if a sufficient number of cows are milked to justify the installation of a machine. None of these criteria apply on small dairy farms in most tropical countries. There is usually a surplus of labour, labour is often cheap and the average size of the herd is small. Even if a farmer manages a large herd and there is no surplus of labour there are other disadvantages in the installation of milking machinery. Machines are more expensive to purchase than they would be in temperate countries, spares are often difficult to obtain and there is usually a lack of skilled mechanics.

As a consequence of this situation only a very small proportion of milking cows managed in the tropics are machine milked. However, it can be assumed that the total will slowly increase. Some information on milking machinery is given in a later section.

Disease

Mastitis is the most common disease in milking cows in both temperate and tropical regions. It is closely associated with the method of management adopted and may be caused by a number of different types of pathogenic bacteria. Mastitis control must be viewed as a continuing process. The disease can be effectively controlled if there is a strict and proper use of the strip cup, so that infection is detected at an early stage, proper washing of the udder and teats, proper hygiene and sanitation in the dairy yards and buildings, good machine stripping, the milking of infected cows either separately or last, the proper treatment of infected teats and/or udders and the segregation or culling of cows suffering from chronic and incurable mastitis.

The vaccination programme recommended for heifers in a previous section should be continued during the life of the milking cow where the vaccinations have to be repeated at definite intervals in order for immunity to be maintained.

Feeding

If dairy cattle are managed outdoors the method of management of the grazings assumes a major importance.

1. *Grazing management in the wet tropics*

Grazings can of course be managed in a variety of different ways. At one extreme they can be set-stocked by using the whole area at the same time, and at the other extreme cattle can be rotationally grazed around very small paddocks or 'folded' across the grazings. The method adopted depends on a variety of circumstances, but the high stocking rates required in the wet tropics make it almost obligatory to use some form of rotational grazing. It has been observed in the Philippines that crossbred dairy cattle, managed under an extremely rapid type of rotational grazing system, grazed for longer periods during the day when the grass was young and succulent. It can be theorized that under these managerial conditions the 'heat-load' due to digestive heat production was minimal so that the cattle could withstand a slightly higher 'heat-load' due to radiation. It has also been noted that when dairy cattle were grazed in a field where the grass growth was sufficient for more than two successive grazing periods, the cows grazed the best grass first, progressively spent less daylight hours grazing and spoilt a great deal of grass by trampling on it when it was long.

It would appear that the most logical method of managing dairy cattle in order to ensure maximum utilization of the fodder available would be to graze them rotationally over as many small paddocks as is practical. The cattle should be grazed in any one field for as short a time as possible, so that they are always able to obtain new and succulent forage. The shortest practical time is that between milkings, i.e. usually 10 to 12 hours, and maximum utilization is obtained by stocking paddocks as heavily as possible for this period. As tropical forage plants grow and mature more rapidly than temperate forage plants under optimal conditions, it is necessary to return the cattle to the same field more rapidly than would be the case in the temperate zone. It is likely that maximum utilization is obtained by rotating cattle around the paddocks once every 10 to 15 days. There are, however, only a limited number of forage species that can withstand this intensity of rotation, and in practice the rotation will probably have to be longer. In order to make certain that every cow receives her fill, slightly more grass needs to be offered than the whole herd is able to consume. This means in practice that some grass is left uneaten after each grazing and that there is a gradual build-up in the proportion of mature grass in the pasture. This can be corrected by utilizing the dry cows to 'eat out' the field every few months and then cutting whatever mature forage remains. After this treatment there should be immediate regrowth, but it is considered desirable to 'spell' the pasture at this stage in order not to reduce unduly the grazing plant's food reserves.

The heavier the stocking rate the more necessary it becomes to correctly apportion available forage between the various groups of cattle. Calves should, as suggested previously, be rotated ahead of the milking herd. Heifers and young bulls should receive the next priority; dry cows, not calving within 2 months, the least priority.

The best grazings should always be reserved for grazing at night, as experimental work has shown that the higher producing cows graze for a longer period at night than during the day.

Grazing is not generally recommended as a managerial method for dairy cows in the dry tropics.

2. Forage conservation

There are several methods of adapting the seasonal supply of fodder to the demands of the dairy herd. The one that is probably most often used is to conserve surplus fodder and utilize it in times of scarcity. It is also possible to reduce the fluctuations in forage production by applying fertilizers at the appropriate time, by irrigation in the dry months or by purchase of extra feeds from outside the farm during the periods of feed scarcity. Under certain circumstances it is possible to adopt seasonal calving so that the cows' maximum demands for feed are equated with maximum seasonal forage productivity. Seasonal calving is certainly suitable for beef operations and for the production of milk for manufacturing purposes, but is not suited for a whole milk supply operation, in which consumption demand does not fluctuate from season to season.

In the dry tropics there is usually a very long dry season, and under some circumstances it may be economic to store surplus feed produced during the wet season, either as hay or as silage. There is usually no difficulty in making hay in the dry tropics and in regions where there is no rain during the dry season the forage can be left standing in the field. Under these circumstances the conserved product is known as 'standing hay'. Pit silage or other forms of silage can usually be made, although much silage that is made in the dry tropics is of rather poor quality. This is probably due to the fact that fodder crops are usually allowed to become over-mature before they are cut and filled into the silo. Over-mature forage of this type is not only unpalatable and of low nutritional value but it is difficult to exclude air from it when being packed in the silo, with a consequent increase in silo losses. In the wet tropics, in particular in the equatorial region, there may be no long dry season. What is more usual are relatively short spells of dry weather. These and perhaps periods of intense rainfall cause fluctuations in the supply of forage, and what is required are relatively small quantities of conserved fodder to feed for short periods. Haymaking is very difficult in the wet tropics, but silage can easily be made, and as long as the forage is not too mature and the weather is not too wet, good silage can be made. One problem is that continuous silage-making may be difficult, so that if silage is made in large bunkers it may be necessary to intermittently close and reopen them, with consequent loss of nutrients. What is probably required on the average farm are a number of relatively small silos that can be filled with the forage cut from a small number of paddocks. Pit silos are not usually practical in wet tropical environments and some form of above-ground silo is usually required. Further details on forage conservation are available in Chapter 3 (Part I).

3. Feeding standards

Once a cow has commenced milking she becomes a mainstay of the farm income and should be treated accordingly. Good milking cows cannot consume as much feed as they are capable of converting into milk following calving and normally they utilize their body reserves at this time. During this period the cow is not only producing the most milk but it is likely that she is producing it more efficiently than at any other time, so she should be offered as much feed as she will eat. Once the cow has passed the peak of lactation and, as stated previously, this may be often a shorter period after calving in the tropics than it would be in the temperate zone, she becomes a less efficient converter of feed into milk and overfeeding will not result in any appreciable increase in production and may mean a waste of feed resources. At this stage the rationing of feed according to production will be most economic.

As tropical forage varies so widely in quality it is difficult to establish basic feeding standards for dairy cattle. In the wet tropics high-producing cows may have some difficulty in obtaining a sufficient quantity of total dry matter because of the low dry-matter content of the forage, and it is generally accepted that for the major part of the year they are more likely to have difficulty in obtaining a sufficient supply of energy than of CP (Hardison, 1967–68). It may be assumed, however, that well-managed pastures in the wet tropics will provide for the maintenance requirements of milking cows and for the production of approximately

Table 5.15   *Feeding standards for milking cows*
I. *Maintenance* (nutrients required per day)

Liveweight (kg (lb))	Starch equivalent (kg (lb))	Digestible crude protein (kg (lb))	Calcium (g)	Phosphorus (g)
363 (800)	2·3 (5·1)	0·23 (0·51)	13	19
408 (900)	2·5 (5·5)	0·25 (0·55)	15	22
454 (1,000)	2·7 (6·0)	0·27 (0·60)	16	23

II. *Milk production* (nutrients required per 1·0 kg (2·2 lb) milk)

Fat content of milk (%)	Starch equivalent (kg)	Digestible crude protein (kg)	Calcium (g)	Phosphorus (g)
3·5	0·60	0·112	2·6	1·8
4·0	0·64	0·123	2·9	1·8
4·5	0·68	0·139	2·9	1·8
5·0	0·73	0·148	3·1	1·8

Note: These are temperate zone standards but should be used in the tropics until such time as other standards may become available.
Source: McDonald *et al.* (1973).

4·5 litres (1 gal) of milk. Cows that are producing more than 4·5 litres (1 gal) of milk a day should be fed concentrates at a rate based on the data given in Table 5.15. In the semi-arid tropics it is likely that pastures will provide only maintenance requirements for part of the year and for maintenance and some part of the milk production during the wet season, unless irrigation is available. At all other times the maintenance requirements will have to be provided by cut fodder, hay or silage fed in the yards or on the pasture, possibly supplemented with molasses–urea–minerals liquid feed or some similar food.

The variety of concentrates available for the feeding of dairy cattle in the tropics is considerable, but in a general treatise it is impossible to recommend different mixed rations produced from the feeds available in all regions.

If it is practical, each cow should be fed its concentrate ration separately, the amount varying according to its production. This may not be an economic practice everywhere, and one alternative is to divide the milking cows into a limited number of groups based on their approximate milk production and date of calving and to feed each group a standard ration. It is normal to feed concentrates at the bail at milking times. For large dairy herds semi-automatic or automatic feeding devices can be installed, but the same reservations apply to the installation of this type of equipment in tropical countries as apply to the installation of milking machines.

Cows should have access to ample supplies of water in both paddocks and yards. It should be noted that the water consumption of dairy cows in the tropics is at least twice that of dairy cows in the temperate zone (Payne and Hancock, 1957) so that the necessary arrangements must be made to see that the cows obtain a sufficient supply.

A complete mineral mix should be added to the concentrate ration or be made available to the cows in separate feeders.

The dry cow

Dry cows not due to calve within 2 months can be considered as non-productive, and every effort should be made to see that their number is kept to a minimum – unless a managerial system is adopted where milking cattle are dried-off early. They must, however, be properly managed during their dry period in order to ensure high productivity in subsequent lactations. Climatic stress will, however, be at a minimum during this period.

As lactating cows utilize energy more efficiently for liveweight gain than do dry cows it is probably more profitable to allow cows to regain the body weight lost in the early stages of lactation during the latter stages of lactation rather than during their dry period.

The aim during the dry period should be to maintain the cows in good condition but not to allow them to fatten. Under grazing conditions dry cows can be used to 'clean up' pastures after the milking herd or to graze the poorer pastures on the farm. They should seldom require concentrate feeds, but they may need to be fed additional minerals. Dry cows managed in yards should be fed medium-quality forage and have access to adequate supplies of water and minerals.

Attention has already been focused on the desirability of 'steaming up' dry cows as from 2 months before calving. Nutrient requirements during the 'steaming-up' period are given in Table 5.16.

Table 5.16 *Nutrient requirements of dry cows during the 'steaming-up' period or the 2 months prior to calving*

Additional to the daily maintenance requirements during the 2 months

Starch equivalent (kg (lb))	Digestible crude protein (kg (lb))	Calcium (g)	Phosphorus (g)
2·3 (5)	0·27 (0·6)	17	9

Source: McDonald *et al.* (1973).

The bull

The selection of a suitable bull is very important as it is said a sire is 'half the herd', i.e. half the inherited characteristics of all the calves are obtained from him. Bulls may be selected by type, by pedigree or by sib or progeny performance. The relative merits of each type of selection have been discussed in Chapter 4, Part I.

The chances are that the average dairy farmer in the tropics has little opportunity to select a suitable bull: he simply accepts what bull is available, irrespective of merit.

However, this situation does not exist in large-scale projects where temperate-type dairy bulls or the semen of temperate-type dairy bulls are used for upgrading purposes. A choice is usually possible. The project organization can adopt one of the following alternatives:

1. Import progeny-tested bulls or semen from progeny-tested bulls. These alternatives are both expensive. As imported, exotic progeny-tested bulls are scarce and expensive and will probably have a high mortality in a tropical environment, it is preferable to import semen and operate an AI service. The organization can then breed either pure or crossbred bulls for distribution to individual farmers. On account of the likely high mortality of purebred bulls it is preferable to distribute crossbred bulls.

2. Import a large number of non-progeny-tested bulls from highly productive herds. If a high wastage rate is acceptable some of the imported bulls will acclimatize. Bulls should be purchased from herds in subtropical or warmer temperate-zone regions such as Florida and Louisiana in the United States or the highlands of Kenya or Israel in order to improve the chances of acclimatization.

3. Attempt to heat-tolerance test suitable bulls from highly productive herds before importation. This procedure will at least ensure that the bulls have a better chance of surviving in the tropical environment into which they are imported. This method was attempted in Fiji in the 1950s with favourable results. Six bulls that were considered to be of approximately equal merit as regards the inheritance of production characteristics were selected and heat-tolerance tested in their country of origin. The bull that demonstrated the highest heat tolerance was imported into Fiji. As far as the authors know no further efforts have been made to develop an importation scheme using these methods. It is also now possible to obtain bulls or semen from pure-bred and crossbred tropical-based dairy herds. Examples are the Australian Milking Zebu stock in Australia and Friesians in Puerto Rico.

Management and feeding

The general management and feeding of young bulls should be similar to that of heifers. Every effort should be made to feed them adequately so that they can be brought into service at as early an age as possible. When fully grown they should be kept in a vigorous physical condition and should not be allowed to get too fat. On peasant holdings it may be necessary for economic reasons to work the breeding bull. This is possible so long as the bull is not overworked.

When mature the bull should receive the same type of roughage rations as the dry cows, together with an extra 0·9 to 1·8 kg (2 to 4 lb) of concentrates. He must also have access to adequate clean water and a complete mineral ration.

Bulls managed in the tropics appear to be quieter and less bad tempered than temperate-type bulls of the same breed managed in the same way in the temperate zone. However, this does not mean that precautions are not needed in the handling of bulls in the tropics. Bull paddocks should always be securely fenced. A copper ring should be inserted in the nose of the bulls by punching a hole in the septum with a special pair of pliers or some other sharp instrument. Peasant producers in most tropical countries punch a hole in the septum of the nose of their bulls and pass a rope through it with a knot at one end that is sufficiently large to prevent the rope slipping through the hole. Dehorning is desirable and will quieten almost any bull, but it may be impracticable when the bull is going to be used for work.

Daily exercise is most important for bulls. If they are managed indoors without access to a paddock they should be led at a good walking pace for some distance, either in the early morning or in the cool of the evening.

Service management

The active breeding life of bulls varies from approximately 5 to 16 years. The age of the bull has no influence on the quality of his offspring. In the temperate zone young bulls can be first used as early as 10 to 12 months of age, but in the tropics bulls are not sufficiently well grown or sexually mature until they are somewhat older. In well-managed herds they might be of use at 18 months of age, but most indigenous bulls are not usually ready for service until they are 2 or more years of age and often do not attain maximum breeding powers until they are considerably older. It is possible, though not proven, that the breeding power of bulls in the tropics does not decline at as early an age as does that of bulls in the temperate zone.

Young bulls can be used once or perhaps twice a week, but older bulls may be used up to five times a week. Mature bulls can serve up to 100 cows a year, but usually a bull is allowed to serve only 50 or 60 cows. The acceptable ratio of breeding females to breeding males is likely to be somewhat lower in the tropics than it is in the temperate zone on account of the effect of the climatic environment on the fertility of the bull.

There is now considerable evidence that the climatic environment *per se* affects the fertility of bulls in the tropics, in particular the fertility of bulls of exotic breeds. Given this situation every effort should be made to ameliorate conditions for breeding bulls by managerial means, using the techniques suggested in a previous section for the proper management of milking cows.

If it is necessary to serve very small heifers or cows using large bulls or vice versa, then special managerial precautions are required. Very large cows should be placed in a shallow pit for service by very young, small bulls, and small heifers and cows should be served in a service crate by very heavy, old bulls. The fertility of breeding bulls should be checked from time to time.

The planning of dairy farms and their equipment

When a new dairy farm is planned the buildings should be sited as far as is possible in the centre of the holding. This ensures that outdoor-managed cattle walk a minimum distance to and from the paddocks and that forage cut in the field for indoor-managed cattle will have to be transported only minimal distances.

A road with a hard surface is required between the perimeter fence and the milking bail, but internal roads can be made of soil, although in the wet tropics they must be well drained on both sides and raised somewhat above the field level or else they are likely to become quagmires. The internal dirt roads should be narrow in order to facilitate the droving of stock, but if the farm is mechanized the road and gateways must be sufficiently wide to allow the operation of tractors equipped with trailers. The road can be relatively narrow even on mechanized farms as long as the gateways are offset.

The farm should be well drained and ditches should be fenced on both sides to prevent their destruction by stock. Double fencing is obviously expensive, but it does have the advantage that shade trees can be planted between the fences so that while the trees are young and vulnerable they are protected from the cattle.

The grazing area should be divided into as many paddocks as is economic. In the wet tropics paddock size should be no more than 0·8 to 1·2 ha (2 to 3 acres) and preferably smaller. In drier areas the economic paddock size will probably be much larger. A minimum of fourteen separate paddocks is required for proper rotational grazing purposes in the wet tropics, although more are desirable. The cheapest type of fence to erect is probably a live fence, although the maintenance costs of such a fence are usually considerable. Some details of common species that can be used to provide 'live posts' are shown in Table 5.17. A four-wire fence is suitable for the enclosure of dairy stock and only the top wire needs to be barbed. The cheapest uprights for a wire fence will probably be termite-resistant, indigenous hardwood posts, but creosote-treated softwood posts, if available, may be equally effective. Concrete and/or steel uprights are usually too expensive to utilize. Some details of species providing suitable timber for fence posts are given in Table 5.18.

Table 5.17   *Some useful common 'live-post' species*

Botanical name	Common name	Notes
Aleurites moluccana	Candle-nut tree	
Aleurites trisperma	Balucanat (Philippines)	Will grow at altitudes up to 1,000 m (3,300 ft)
Ceiba pentandra	Kapok	Produces a useful cash crop
Dracaena menni	Asparagus tree	
Erythrina lithosperma	Dadap	
Erythrina indica	Thorny dadap	
Erythrina senegalensis		
Erythrina umbrosa	Ananca	
Furcraea cabuya		Used at 3,000 to 5,000 m (10,000 to 16,000 ft) in Ecuador
Gliricidia sepium	Gliricidia	Will grow at altitudes up to 1,000 m (3,300 ft)
Hibiscus tiliaceous		
Jatropha curcas	Physic nut	
Lannea nigritana		
Lucaena leucocephala	Wild tamarind	Also cultivated for forage
Moringa pterygosperma	Horse-radish tree	
Pithecellobium dulce	Madras thorn	
Sesbania grandiflora		A very useful forage tree
Spathodea campanulata	African tulip tree	
Spondias mombin		
Sterculia foetida	Wild almond	
Sterculia tragacantha		

Water should be provided in all paddocks if this is practical and economic. It should be possible to devise a fencing layout that allows for one water trough to serve two, three or four paddocks. If water cannot be provided in all paddocks it can perhaps be made available in the field roads that serve a number of paddocks and, of course, at the milking bail.

Shade trees should be planted around all paddocks and along all roads. It should be possible to select species that not only provide shade but also nuts, fruit or browse and timber or firewood. Details of suitable species are given in Table 5.19.

Buildings

The type and number of buildings required will depend upon the managerial practices. If dairy cattle are managed indoors a number of buildings will be required, while if the farm is medium to large in size considerable equipment and machinery will be needed. Details of the general space requirements of different classes of cattle are given in Table 5.20.

Table 5.18 *Some tropical timber trees that can be used for the manufacture of wooden fence posts that will be somewhat resistant to termite attack*

Botanical name	Common name
Artocarpus heterophyllus	Jak-fruit
Artocarpus nobilis	Wild breadfruit
Balanocarpus maximus	Penak (Malaysian)
Bassia longifolia	
Berrya ammonilla	Trincomalee-wood
Brachylaena hutchinsii	
Bridelia retusa	
Cassia siamea	
Casuarina equisetifolia	She-oak
Cedrela toona	Toon tree
Cedrela oderata	Cedar
Chloroxylon swietenia	Satin-wood
Doona zeylanica	Doon
Dryobalanops aromatica	Sumatran camphor
Eucalyptus leucoxylon	Iron bark
Eucalyptus marginata	Jarrah
Eucalyptus robusta	Swamp mahogany
Eusideroxylon zwageri	Billion
Filicum decipiens	
Grevillea robusta	Silky oak
Hemicyclia sepiaria	
Hopea odorata	Thingam
Mesua ferrea	Ceylon iron-wood
Mimusops hexandra	Palu
Myroxylon toluifera	Balsam
Pterocarpus marsupium	
Swietenia macrophylla	Mahogany
Swietenia mahagoni	Mahogany
Tamarindus indica	Tamarind
Tectona grandis	Teak
Terminalia glabra	
Thespesia populnea	Tulip tree
Vitex altissima	

Note: This is a very limited list and the majority of species listed are found in Southeast Asia.
Source: Partly from MacMillan (1952).

Dairy stock managed indoors may be housed, fed and milked in the same building, they may be housed in one building and fed and milked in another, or they may be managed in loafing yards and milked in a separate building. If dairy stock are managed outdoors, only a milking bail and an associated milk room and feed store are required for the milking cows, but other buildings will also be needed such as housing for the small calves and storage space for feed, seeds, fertilizer and machinery.

A building in which milking cows are housed, fed and milked is

Table 5.19 *Some useful tropical shade trees*

Botanical name	Common name	Notes
I. For use in the drier areas		
Albizzia lebbek	Raintree	An evergreen that produces an excellent brown timber
Casuarina equisetifolia	She-oak	
Eucalyptus alba	White gum	
Eucalyptus citriodora	Lemon-scented gum	An evergreen that withstands drought and grows on salty soils
Ficus benjamina	Java fig	
Mangifera indica	Mango	Also produces fruit
Melia azedarach	Persian lilac	
Phoenix dactylifera	Date palm	Also produces a cash fruit crop
Pithecellobium saman	Saman	Useful in the dry and humid areas. Produces sweet pods that are an attractive feed for cattle
Prosopis alba	Algoroba	Produces pods that are relished by cattle
Tamarindus indica	Tamarind	Produces fruit and an excellent red-grained timber
II. For use in the more humid areas		
Anacardium occidentale	Cashew	Also produces a cash nut crop
Artocarpus altilis	Breadfruit	Also produces a food crop
Artocarpus heterophyllus	Jak-fruit	Will grow up to 2,000 m (6,600 ft) altitude and produces fruit and an excellent timber
Chrysophyllum cainito	Star apple	Also produces fruit
Cocos nucifera	Coconut	Multipurpose tree
Leucaena leucocephyla	Wild tamarind	A useful forage
Macadamia tetraphylla	Macadamia nut	Also produces a cash nut crop
III. For use in the montane areas		
Acacia dealbata	Silver wattle	This tree thrives from 1,500 to 2,000 m (4,900 to 6,600 ft). It produces a bark from which tannin is extracted
Acacia decurrens	Black wattle	
Eucalyptus robusta	Iron bark	
Eugenia jambos	Rose apple	Also produces an edible fruit
Grevillea robusta	Silky oak	This tree thrives at from 1,200 to 2,200 m (3,900 to 7,200 ft) altitude
Tecoma leucoxylon	White cedar	

Table 5.20 *The general space requirements of different classes of dairy cattle*

Class	Type of construction	m (ft)	m² (ft²)
Milking cows	Milking stalls (barn)		
	Width single stall	1·03 (3·4)	
	double stall	1·98 (6·5)	
	Length small breed	1·37 (4·5)	
	large breed	1·52 (5·0)	
	Length of feeding manger per cow	0·76 (2·5)	
	Height of floor of stall above dunging passage	0·15–0·18 (0·5–0·6)	
	Width of feeding passage	0·91–1·22 (3·0–4·0)	
	Milking stalls (bail) used with line machine		
	Width of stall	0·76 (2·5)	
	Width of bail	0·60 (2·0)	
	Collection and dispersal yards		
	Area per cow		
	Polled cattle		2·3 (25)
	Horned cattle		3·7 (40)
	Loafing yards		
	Total area per cow		6·5–7·4 (70–80)
	Shade area per cow		3·7–5·6 (40–60)
	Length of feeding manger per cow		
	Access at all times	0·30–0·46 (1·0–1·5)	
	Limited access	0·61–0·76 (2·0–2·5)	
	Loose boxes for calving		
	Area per cow		14·9–15·8 (160–170)
Bulls	Bull houses		
	Area within house per bull		16·7 (180)
	Area outside house per bull		33·5–37·2 (360–400)
Calves	Individual pens for small calves		
	Dimensions	1·83 × 1·22 (6·0 × 4·0)	
	Collective pens: area required		
	Calves up to 3 months of age		1·9–2·8 (20–30)
	Calves 3 to 6 months of age		2·8 (30)

generally known as a dairy barn. The temperate-region type of enclosed dairy barn is not recommended for use anywhere in the humid tropics, but a well-ventilated version could be used in the semi-arid tropics, particularly during the very hot months.

Dairy barns are of two types: single or double range. The double-range barn is more economical for the housing of herds of more than sixteen

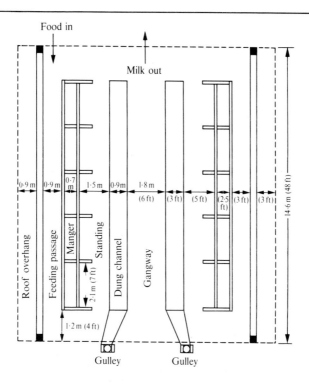

Fig. 5.8   Plan of a typical double-range dairy barn suitable for housing medium-size cows.

to twenty milking cows. Double-range barn standings can be designed so that the cattle face inwards on to a central feeding passage or outwards with feeding passages on either side of the building (Fig. 5.8). It is generally considered that the latter arrangement is more desirable. A building with the same basic plan (Fig. 5.8) but with no walls is suitable for use in the humid tropics. The roof of such a building should have a very wide overhang in order to provide the maximum shade and to prevent the incursion of heavy rain. The floor should be constructed of concrete, which should be left with a rough finish in order to prevent cows from slipping. The standings should be constructed of tubular steel, heavy bamboo or hardwood and the mangers of glazed pipe, if this material is available. If not, specially treated concrete or wood may be used. Water should be available for the cows in every standing, preferably from automatic water devices.

Cow cubicles may be used for housing dairy cattle where they are fed and milked in a separate building. Figure 5.9 illustrates a well-established system of housing which reduces bedding costs, and is useful in areas

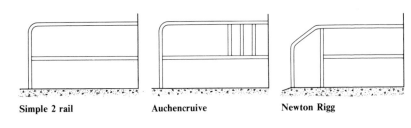

| Simple 2 rail | Auchencruive | Newton Rigg |

Fig. 5.9 Types of cow cubicles.

where bedding is expensive. It gives the animal complete freedom of movement and cows stay cleaner, lessening some of the chores at milking time. This type of housing is suitable only in a semi-arid environment or in montane areas.

Loafing yards do not need to be elaborate structures. They can be concrete, gravel or dirt yards with provision for shade, feeding and watering and the removal of manure. In the wet tropics concrete or gravel yards are essential as even the best-drained earth yards become quagmires. Elsewhere a rammed earth yard will suffice. Shade must be adequate. Water can be provided from automatic devices or from troughs. There should be a number of separate yards for the segregation of milking cows, dry cows, heifers and bulls. The yards may be laid out rectangularly or in a semi-circle. There are advantages and disadvantages in both layouts. Feeding and manure removal can easily be mechanized in yards of this type. In large units the disposal of manure may present problems. Where adequate supplies of water are available concrete yards can be washed down and the resulting effluent pumped or run on to the grazings. In Florida one enterprising feedlot operator, confronted with this problem, is using the manure to produce methane gas and then to culture chlorella that will ultimately be fed back to his cattle. These methods of manure disposal should be seriously considered by large-scale dairy farmers who practise an indoor managerial system in the wet tropics.

The *milking shed, bail* or *milking parlour* may be used by farmers who practise either indoor or outdoor dairying. It is a building used specifically for milking. A milk room, feed store and assembly and dispersal yards are usually associated with it. There may also be a separate yard in which the cows are washed before milking, although this is not recommended.

A number of different layouts are possible, and although all can be used for either hand or machine milking the more elaborate have been specifically designed for releaser machine milking. The most common layouts used in the temperate zone are:

1. Abreast, walk-through types: these can be single or two-level;
2. Herring-bone types;
3. Two-level tandem, walk-through types; and
4. Roundabout types.

In the tropics an abreast, walk-through type is the most convenient for the small dairy farmer and is probably the easiest and cheapest to construct. The other types are only likely to be used by the larger dairy farmers. A choice of type by these must depend on local circumstances and in particular on the availability and cost of labour and the availability of suitable machines, spares and maintenance services.

A plan of a four-stall, single-level, abreast, walk-through type of milking parlour is shown in Fig. 5.10. Where a releaser machine is used the stalls should be 0·7 m (2·5 ft) and the bail 0·6 m (2 ft) wide, whereas when a bucket milking machine is used or hand milking is practised the stalls should be 1 m (3·3 ft) wide. It is usual to have one milking machine unit at each bail, so that one cow can be milked while the cow on the

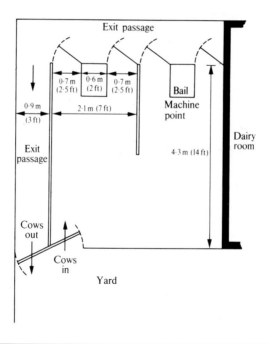

Fig. 5.10   Plan of a four-stall, single-level, abreast type of milking parlour.

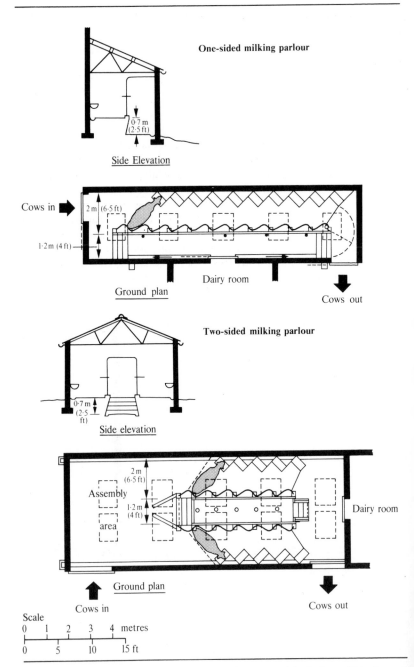

One-sided milking parlour

Side Elevation

Cows in

2 m (6·5 ft)

0·7 m
(2·5 ft)

1·2 m (4 ft)

Ground plan

Dairy room

Cows out

Two-sided milking parlour

Side elevation

0·7 m
(2·5 ft)

Assembly

area

2 m
(6·5 ft)

1·2 m
(4 ft)

Dairy room

Ground plan

Cows in

Cows out

Scale

0   1   2   3   4   metres

0   5   10   15 ft

Fig. 5.11 Herringbone-type milking parlours. (Ministry of Agriculture, Fisheries and Food, Technical Report No. 7. Reproduced with the permission of the Controller of Her Majesty's Stationery Office.)

other side of the bail is being washed. Cold and/or hot water should be on tap at the bail for washing purposes and concentrates can be fed at the bail in a feeding box. Concentrate feeds can be measured out either by hand or by using automatic feed-measuring devices. A two-unit system is the economic minimum. It is considered that for up to a total of fifteen cows a bucket machine is the most economic to use in this type of milking parlour, whereas with more cows a line-type of releaser machine is more economic. The floor should slope away from the bails both in front and behind the cows. The two-level, abreast, walk-through type is a variant where the milker works at a lower level than the cows stand. It does not possess any outstanding advantages over the single-level type.

Some details of herring-bone, tandem and roundabout types of milking parlour are shown in Figs. 5.11, 5.12 and 5.13, respectively. Roundabout milking machines can be of the tandem or herring-bone layout. A rotating platform slowly carries the cows around. Each cow is milked in the time that it takes for the platform to revolve once. As cows which have been milked leave the platform, replacement cows step on. In this way the milking process is continuous and rapid. Readers with a particular interest in milking parlours should consult a dairy extension officer or a representative of a commercial organization concerned with the building and equipping of dairies.

Milking parlours in the tropics do not require walls, only a roof. Provision must be made for shade and water for the cows during the period that they stand awaiting their turn to enter the milking parlour. A fine-

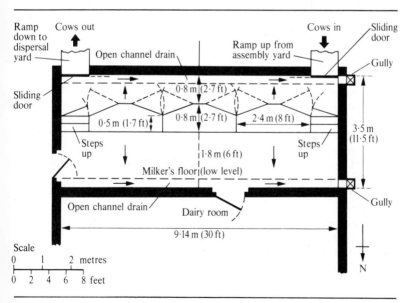

Fig. 5.12 Plan of a typical tandem-type milking parlour.

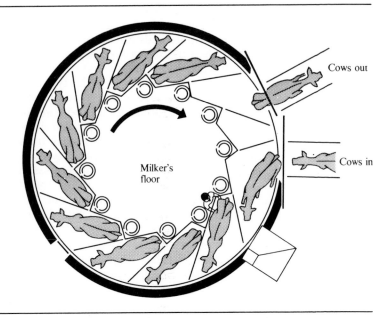

Fig. 5.13   Roundabout-type milking parlour.

spray water sprinkler may be installed in the standing yard to improve the comfort of the cows.

A *milk room* is needed whether the cows are hand or machine milked. If the cows are hand milked or milked with the aid of a bucket machine all that is required is a small room adjacent to the milking parlour. It should be designed so that it is easy to clean and can be screened in order to keep out insects. It should be sited on the side from which the prevailing wind blows and on the other side from the feed store. Milk will be strained and cooled in this room in preparation for sale either to a factory, a wholesaler or through a retail channel. Milk-cooling equipment of some type is necessary and if it is economically feasible this should incorporate refrigeration. Cold and/or hot water should be available as should utensil washing and draining facilities. If the cows are milked using a line-releaser milking machine the milk room should be sited at the end of the line as it will house the releaser and associated equipment.

The size of the *feed store* will vary according to the size of the dairy unit, the types of feed used and the type of equipment utilized. All feed stores, even the smallest, should be constructed so that rodents can be excluded and so that they can easily be fumigated to destroy weevils and other inspect pests.

The essentials of a suitable *calf shed* have already been described in a previous section.

Dairy cattle yards do not have to be so stoutly constructed as beef cattle yards. Details of the space requirements for yarded cattle are given in Table 5.20.

Equipment for milking

The dairy farmer who milks by hand requires only a minimum of equipment: seamless milking pails, washing buckets, teat cups for testing for mastitis and a stool. If milk production is recorded, a simple milk-weighing scale is also necessary. The majority of small dairy farmers in the tropics do not even possess all of this equipment. The aim of dairy extension services in tropical countries should be to assist the small dairy farmer to acquire this minimum of equipment and to teach him how to use and clean it properly.

Considerably more equipment is required for machine milking. There are two main types of milking machine: bucket and line-releaser. The tendency has been for the line machine to increase in popularity as it requires less labour, but as stated in a previous paragraph it is probably most economic to install a bucket machine if fifteen or fewer cows are milked.

The essentials of a milking machine are as follows: a vacuum pump to create the vacuum required; a vacuum tank; a vacuum line to the individual sets of teat cups; and a method of collecting the milk and a pulsator. Vacuum pumps can be of several types and may be operated by an electric motor or by a small internal combustion engine. It is essential to see that there are no leaks in the vacuum system. The normal teat cup is made of metal or plastic and has a rubber inflation or lining. Two types of inflation are in general use: the ordinary rubber liner which collapses and closes under the teat, and the moulded inflation that collapses around the teat and so never obstructs the flow of milk. The pulsator is a device that produces an intermittent vacuum, causing alternate compression and release of the cow's teats through the action of the rubber liner or inflation in the teat cup. First a stimulus is applied to the teat to ensure that the milk is let down and secondly the teat is massaged in order to maintain circulation of the blood. Milking without pulsation causes the teats to swell, makes the cow uncomfortable and thus impedes the let-down of milk. There are several different types of pulsator.

The quality of milk obtained by machine milking depends upon the care taken in cleaning and operating the machine. If the machine is properly cleaned, then the milk will certainly be of as high a quality as that produced by the best hand milking. Milking machines and other dairy equipment may be sterilized by the use of steam or chemicals. Milking machinery acquires a deposit known as milkstone on the metal and rubber parts and fat is absorbed into the rubber. Milkstone is a deposit consisting of milk solids together with mineral constituents from

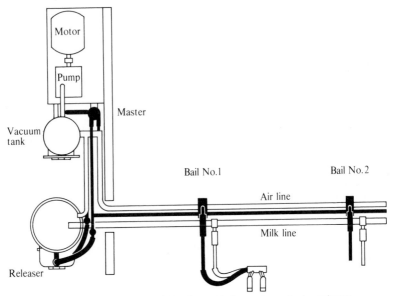

(a)   A sketch showing the layout of the plant with the master and relay pulsator system marked in black.

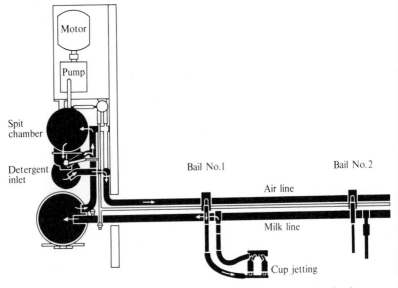

(b)   The path (in black) taken by the washing solution during cycling. The cleaning solutions are drawn in near the vacuum tank. After circulation they are once more released into the bucket for further circulation.

Fig. 5.14 Details of a line-type milking machine suitable for use in the tropics. (a) Sketch showing the layout of the plant with the master and relay pulsator system marked in black. (b) The path (in black) taken by the washing solution during cycling. The cleaning solutions are drawn in near the vacuum tank. After circulation they are once more released into the bucket for further circulation.

the water used in washing the machine. It increases the tendency of the rubber to crack, reduces the efficiency of the rubber rings and harbours bacteria. Fat absorption causes rubber to lose many of its qualities when exposed to light. As a consequence milking machinery must be particularly well cleaned. Line-releaser machines can be fitted with automatic washing equipment (Fig. 5.14) and these are recommended for use in large dairies in the tropics where labour is often unskilled.

The dairy farmer in the tropics requires a machine that is simple in construction and operation, that needs the minimum of cleaning and that is easily cleaned by relatively unskilled labour. Machines that fit these specifications have been available for two decades (Phillips, 1956) and the layout of one is shown in Fig. 5.14. In this machine a milk-flow measuring device indicates to the milker when milking should be ended and stripping begin, and this device has been found to be particularly suitable for use in the tropics where milkers are often relatively unskilled.

Equipment for the milk room

Straining. All milk should be strained immediately after milking is completed. Special strainer pads are the most efficient and hygienic to use for this purpose as they can be discarded after use. However, any type of suitable cloth can be used as long as it is frequently changed and thoroughly washed and sterilized after use.

Cooling and refrigeration. As soon as the cow has been milked the bacteria in the milk start to multiply. Immediate cooling of the milk reduces bacterial multiplication very drastically. In Table 5.21 details of the relationship between temperature and the bacterial count of milk 12 hours after milking is shown. Some bacteria produce chemical changes in the composition of milk, the most common being the formation of lactic acid from lactose or milk sugar. This causes the normal souring of milk. As ambient temperatures are always high in the tropics milk sours easily and quickly unless it is cooled or boiled. Boiling will kill the

Table 5.21   *The relationship between temperature and bacterial count in milk*

Temperature °C (°F)	No. bacteria per ml ('000)
4·4 (40)	4
7·2 (45)	9
10·0 (50)	18
12·8 (55)	38
15·6 (60)	453
21·1 (70)	8,800
26·7 (80)	55,300

bacteria but must be carried out before the concentration of lactic acid in the milk has risen too high.

Thus, if fresh milk is to be distributed in the tropics it should, if possible, be cooled at the farm and then pasteurized or sterilized – either at the farm or at a central processing plant.

The proper cooling of milk at the farm is a very difficult problem as most tropical dairy farmers possess few cows and cannot afford refrigeration even if power was available for this purpose. One solution would be the use of a cooling tower, commonly used on dairy farms in Queensland in the past. This equipment depends upon the evaporation of water having a cooling effect on a second supply of water that can then be used in a milk cooler (Fig. 5.15). Another possibility is the use of solar water coolers, but the technology for this type of equipment is not yet well developed and in any case the initial capital cost of a solar cooler is likely to be too high for utilization by the peasant farmer. The only practical solution at the present time is rapid collection of the milk from individual farmers and cooling at a central collection depot (see Ch. 14, Pt III).

In dairying areas where power is available and the dairy farms are of a sufficient size collection can be made by road tankers, the farmer storing

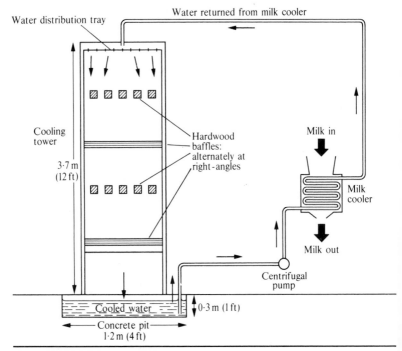

Fig. 5.15 Schematic layout of a Queensland-type evaporative milk cooler (Few, 1946).

his milk from both daily milkings in a refrigerated vat until such time as collection is effected.

Separation.   When, for any reason, milk cannot be sold in the fresh, liquid state it is generally desirable to remove the cream from it. The latter may then be used for the manufacture of butter and/or ghee and the skim-milk can be used for human consumption, for livestock feeding or for the manufacture of a variety of dairy products (see Ch. 14, Pt III).

Fat can easily be removed from the remainder of the milk by reason of the fact that it rises to the surface by operation of the force of gravity. This occurs because fat is lighter than skim-milk, 1 ml of fat weighing 0·9 g while 1 ml of skim-milk weighs 1·036 g.

There are three major methods of accomplishing the separation of fat and skim-milk. These are as follows:

1. *The shallow pan method.* Milk is placed in a shallow pan approximately 10 cm (4 in) deep for a period of 24 to 36 hours. The major part of the fat rises to the top and the cream is removed using a skimmer. The remaining skim-milk usually contains 0·5 to 1·0 per cent butterfat.
2. *The deep pan method.* Milk is placed in a pan 51 cm (20 in) deep, and after standing for several hours the cream is removed using a dipper. Sometimes the milk is diluted with water before being placed in the pan, as it is claimed that dilution lowers the resistance of the milk fluid to the rising milk fat globules. This is a more efficient method of removing butterfat than the shallow pan method, but if it is to work really satisfactorily the deep pan should stand in a bath of cold water. This is often not a practical proposition on small farms where there is no refrigeration.
3. *Mechanical separation.* This is accomplished by applying centrifugal force to the milk. When milk is spun rapidly in a container the force of gravity is increased by about a thousand times so that a difference of 0·136 in the specific gravity of butterfat and skim-milk at rest becomes a difference of 136 as the milk is spun. As a consequence the fat separates very rapidly from the skim-milk towards the centre of the container in which it is being spun. Arrangements then have to be made to remove the fat separately from the skim-milk. Dispersing the milk in the container into thin sheets facilitates separation and all modern milk separators incorporate a series of inverted, cup-like discs inside the bowl, each kept slightly apart. Mechanical separators are now made in almost any size, farm separators usually being made in a range designed to process 46 to 455 litres (10 to 100 gal) of milk per hour.

Beef cattle

Beef is produced in the tropics to a very large extent from cattle managed on free range, grazing natural forage that grows on land which for one reason or another is not used for any other agricultural purpose. The extensive beef producers are either subsistence farmers who manage a small number of livestock on range adjacent to their crop lands, nomads or transhumants who may migrate with their herds over vast areas of open range, or ranchers who manage herds on extensive but enclosed areas of land. In addition to using the range grazings these extensive beef producers may also seasonally utilize crop stubbles and sometimes crop by-products on land farmed either by themselves or by subsistence agriculturists.

The remainder of the beef produced in the tropics comes from the following sources: the working cattle of subsistence agriculturists which incidentally produce beef at the end of their working life; from peasant producers in a few tropical countries who specifically rear cattle under intensive conditions for meat-production purposes; from a few specialist milk producers who raise surplus male calves; and from a very limited number of specialist intensive beef producers who may raise beef either on planted pastures in the humid areas, under ley farming conditions, in integrated systems with tree or field crops, or purchase cattle from other producers and fatten them in feedlots. Thus beef is produced in a variety of ways, although for a majority of the producers production of meat is incidental to other considerations. Subsistence farmers, owning small numbers of cattle, whom we may describe as pastoral-agriculturists, normally keep their cattle primarily for milk production and/or for work purposes. Nomads and transhumants consider their cattle to be a source of milk and/or blood which are major items in their diets; social capital to be used for a variety of purposes; an insurance against disaster; and finally as a source of cash. They are usually willing to sell all surplus male cattle when cash is required or when they consider that they are overstocked, but they do not normally breed cattle specifically for meat production. Only the extensive ranchers and the limited number of intensive beef producers can be considered to be first and foremost beef producers.

It is therefore not surprising that the major proportion of the beef produced in the tropics is not of a very high quality, that the marketing of it is often inefficient and somewhat unorganized and that the introduction of improved production and marketing techniques and the overall development of the industry are slow and laborious.

Beef production systems

As distinct from the situation in the temperate zone there are a multi-plicity of agricultural systems in the tropics, varying from extremely primitive to relatively advanced, and often these contrasting systems coexist within the same country.

Cattle used for beef production, in greater or lesser numbers, may be associated with or be an integral part of the following major tropical agricultural systems:

● Migratory shifting cultivation;
● Sedentary shifting cultivation;
● Sedentary subsistence rain fed and/or irrigated cultivation;
● Ley farming;
● Perennial crop cultivation;
● Nomadic herding;
● Transhumance or semi-nomadic herding;
● Commercial ranching.

In addition there are a small number of specialized intensive beef pro-ducers who cannot easily be classified as part of any of the above systems.

An estimate of the number of bovines used for beef production raised within each of these major tropical agricultural systems is shown in Table 5.22. It will be seen that a far higher proportion are raised under subsistence or nomadic/transhumant systems than under commercial ranching or other specialized beef-producing systems. However, the con-tribution of commercial enterprises to total beef production in the tropics will be somewhat larger than the data in Table 5.22 suggest as generally

Table 5.22   *Estimates of the number and percentage of the total number of bovines reared in the major tropical agricultural systems*

Tropical agricultural system	No. bovines (million)	No. bovines as percentage of total	Type of bovine reared
Migratory shifting cultivation	6	1	Cattle
Sedentary shifting cultivation	30	5	Cattle and buffaloes
Sedentary subsistence cultivation	290	46	Cattle and buffaloes
Regulated ley farming	15	2	Cattle
Perennial crop cultivation	15	2	Cattle and buffaloes
Nomadic herding	32	5	Cattle
Transhumance	63	10	Cattle
Commercial ranching	180	29	Cattle

Note: Bovines include cattle and buffaloes and are expressed as cattle units, with 1·00 buffalo being considered equivalent to 1·25 cattle.
Source: Payne (1976).

the carcase weights of commercially raised cattle are heavier than those of cattle reared in the non-commercial systems and total offtake is invariably higher under the same ecological conditions. In addition buffaloes are mainly owned by subsistence cultivators. If cattle alone were considered, then the percentage of the total in the sedentary subsistence sector would be less and the percentages in the nomadic, transhumant and ranching sectors larger than those shown in Table 5.22.

Extensive systems

Cattle in migratory and sedentary shifting cultivation systems, nomadic and transhumant cattle and ranched cattle may all be considered to be managed under extensive conditions. In addition some cattle in sedentary subsistence systems are extensively managed as they are reared on range adjacent to the sedentary subsistence holdings.

Migratory shifting cultivation

Migratory shifting cultivators normally only raise small stock and poultry and the only major regions of the tropics where cattle are associated with migratory shifting cultivation are:

1. Limited areas of West Africa where trypanosomiasis-tolerant breeds, such as the N'dama and the West African Shorthorn, are utilized;
2. Areas peripheral to the rain-forest in South America, particularly in the Amazon basin.

In West Africa the shifting cultivators herd cattle adjacent to their holdings. In some tropical rain-forest areas of South America, where the pattern of land ownership is very different to that in West Africa, land-owners wishing to clear rain-forest grant shifting cultivators the right to move across their land and then introduce cattle into the cleared areas behind the cultivators.

As far as beef production is concerned the inputs into this system are minimal and the outputs low. The system is unstable and cannot continue once the human population increases beyond a certain limit. As practised in tropical South America it is self-destructive.

Sedentary shifting cultivation

Where land resources are limited, where population is increasing rapidly and where there is the possibility of producing and marketing cash crops, sedentary has replaced migratory shifting cultivation. Some or all of these conditions have occurred in the following regions:

1. The humid forest areas of West Africa and Southeast Asia where perennial tree cash crops have been introduced;
2. The humid forests of Southeast Asia where valley-bottom rain-fed or irrigated rice has replaced hill rice production;
3. Fertile alluvial and volcanic soil areas in the humid savannas of Africa

where population pressure has been intense and cash crops have been introduced;

4. The drier savannas of Africa where cash crops such as cotton and groundnuts have been introduced;

5. The montane areas of Africa, South America and northern India where partial ley systems have developed.

In the humid forests of West Africa and Southeast Asia, shifting cultivation with its cycle of 'fell–burn–plant–abandon' is practised around the villages, but the interval between fellings has of necessity been curtailed on account of increased population and the use of land for perennial tree crops. The result, particularly in Southeast Asia, has been the invasion of the abandoned land by weed grasses such as alang-alang (*Imperata*

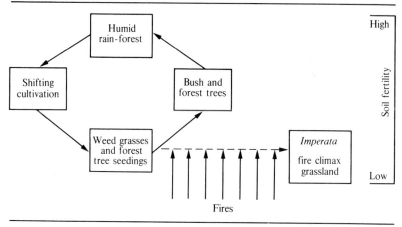

Fig. 5.16 A schematic representation of the degradation process in the Southeast Asian rain-forest.

cylindrica). At this stage shifting cultivators, who previously raised only small stock such as pigs, sheep and goats, have begun to keep cattle and/or buffaloes – not necessarily for work purposes but for beef production and other reasons. These livestock owners burn the weed grasses at frequent intervals in order to provide palatable regrowth feed for their livestock and this practice has effectively prevented the regeneration of tree species. The result is that the forest has been replaced by a low-fertility, unproductive, fire-climax grassland (Fig. 5.16). Millions of hectares of humid tropical forest in Southeast Asia have already been reduced to this status and the area increases annually. In South America, the methods by which landowners utilize migratory shifting cultivators to clear their land has achieved the same result, although the fire-climax grassland that results is sometimes *Hyparrhenia rufa*, a grass of superior feeding value to *Imperata* spp. In most of West Africa the occurrence of the tsetse fly, vector of trypanosomiasis, has limited the raising of cattle unless the farmers have had access to breeds of trypanosomiasis-tolerant cattle.

On these new, low-fertility grasslands livestock carrying capacity is low and often husbandry is almost non-existent. For example, in some areas in Indonesia where sedentary shifting cultivators are growing tree cash crops, but where there are also large areas of *Imperata* grasslands interspersed with forest bush, the cattle and/or buffaloes sleep under their owner's house during the night and at dawn they trek out into the forest or grassland, returning by themselves at night. Vegetable gardens are protected from these wandering livestock by temporary fences. Inputs are minimal and outputs, both per unit area of land and per animal, are low but productivity could be rapidly improved.

In those areas of Southeast Asia where valley-bottom rain-fed or irrigated rice has replaced hill rice production a demand for working animals has been created and farmers have begun to raise small numbers of cattle and/or buffaloes – primarily for work, not for beef production.

On fertile soils in the humid savannas of Africa cultivation is normally by hoe and the major part of the land is cultivated, so that there is no demand for work animals.

Large numbers of livestock are, however, raised in the drier savannas in Africa where cultivation is still mainly by hoe; population pressure has not been too intense in the past and there are large areas of natural grazings available. Cattle are grazed on crop residues, fallows and natural grazings. Unfortunately, a vicious cycle of land and cattle degradation has been initiated in many areas in recent years by the introduction of cash crops and by a rapid increase in both human and cattle populations (Fig. 5.17). These events have resulted in increased cash crop cultivation with a consequent decreasing area of bush-fallow available for grazing. However, in the absence of alternative outlets surplus capital has been invested in cattle, and as forage resources have dwindled cattle numbers have increased. This has led to serious overgrazing in the fallow areas, with resulting erosion and an increase in the population of the bush species that are unbrowsed by cattle. The result is an overall reduction in livestock-carrying capacity, unproductive animals, an increase in the labour requirement for bush clearing and the degradation of the bush-fallow area.

In these drier savannas it has been noted the percentage of females in the herds increases as human and cattle populations increase, and that at least in some areas ownership of livestock is more concentrated than the ownership of crops. In Sukumuland, Tanzania, for example, it has been found that 25 per cent of the families owned 55 per cent of the cultivated crops and 80 per cent of the cattle (Ruthenberg, 1971).

In the drier savannas inputs into beef production are small, but the output is declining. Indeed, it is likely that as the land is degraded the cattle population will have to be reduced and beef production will of necessity decline still further.

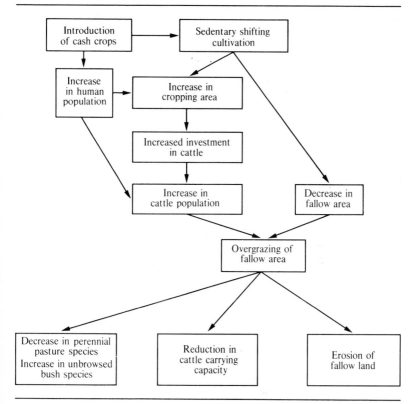

Fig. 5.17 A schematic representation of the degradation process in the dry savanna of Africa.

Unplanned ley systems in montane areas are particularly important in Ethiopia, Kenya, Tanzania and Burundi where crops are rotated with natural grazing. It is likely that the productivity of cattle in these areas could be rapidly improved by the introduction of regulated ley farming and by improvements in the natural grazings. In montane areas of Colombia, Venezuela, Ecuador, Peru and Bolivia, where this system is also practised, cattle are important only at lower altitudes.

Sedentary subsistence: rain-fed and/or irrigated cultivation

Permanent cultivation by subsistence farmers has become established wherever population pressure or other factors have forced the abandonment of shifting cultivation and/or nomadism. Cattle and/or buffaloes are associated with this system in:

1. Some areas of the African savanna, particularly in Senegal, northern Nigeria and Uganda;

2. Monsoonal south and Southeast Asia where buffaloes are often as important as cattle;
3. Irrigated areas in the dry tropics in western Asia and Africa;
4. Tropical islands in the Caribbean, Indian Ocean and the Pacific;
5. Other areas throughout the humid tropics; particularly in Central America and tropical South America.

Within this system cattle may be raised under intensive, semi-intensive or extensive conditions. As the majority of cattle are probably raised in semi-intensive or intensive systems, the problems of cattle in the system will also be discussed in a later section.

In areas of the African savanna where permanent cultivation has been established cattle may be of very considerable importance to the economy. If natural grazings are available adjacent to the cultivated land then the subsistence farmers usually own their own cattle; however, if natural grazings are not available, farmers may invite nomadic or transhumant herdsmen to graze livestock across their crop stubbles. Alternatively, subsistence farmers may own cattle and agist them to the nomads and/or transhumants.

Nomadic herding

This practice is now limited to minor areas in the Indian sub-continent, some areas of western Asia and larger areas in West, Northeast and East Africa. In general, tropical areas where nomadism is still practised are characterized by a dry climate and a sparse population of 0·8 to 10 people per km^2 (2 to 25 per mile^2).

Nomads utilize other livestock besides cattle, particularly camels, sheep and goats. They also usually own donkeys, and in some areas horses. The total amount and the seasonal distribution of rainfall, the availability of free water and the prevalence of disease and parasites determine to some extent what type of livestock is utilized. In Africa cattle are the most important type of livestock raised by nomads, whereas in western Asia sheep are more important.

Some nomads, such as the Baggara Arabs of the western Sudan, may move 'horizontally' (Fig. 5.18). In the dry season they migrate southwards to the higher rainfall region around the Bahr el Arab, while during the wet season they retreat northwards to escape the biting flies and the mud and to graze the ephemeral forage in the semi-arid lands. Others, such as some tribes in Ethiopia and East Africa, move 'vertically' into the more humid higher-altitude country during the dry season, returning to the semi-arid lowlands during the wet season.

Nomadism is normally practised under marginal conditions, carries high production risks and requires large areas of range grazings. In many instances it is a form of large-scale rotational grazing that could be ecologically efficient. Unfortunately, however, a number of factors are contributing to the decay of the system and these are, in large measure,

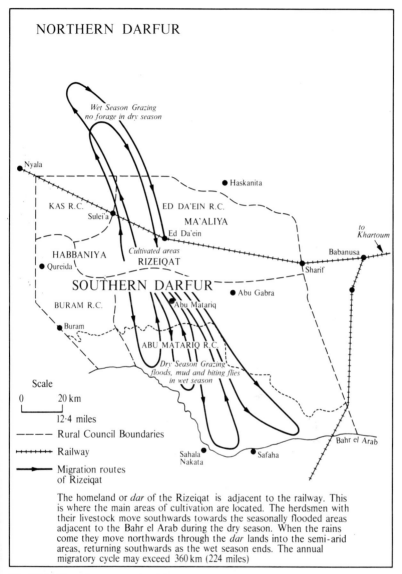

NORTHERN DARFUR

Wet Season Grazing
no forage in dry season

Nyala

Haskanita

KAS R.C.
Sulei'a
ED DA'EIN R.C.
MA'ALIYA
Ed Da'ein

to Khartoum

HABBANIYA
Qureida
Cultivated areas
RIZEIQAT
Babanusa
Sharif

SOUTHERN DARFUR
Abu Gabra

BURAM R.C.
Abu Matariq
Buram

ABU MATARIQ R.C.
Dry Season Grazing
floods, mud and biting flies
in wet season

Scale

0   20 km

12·4 miles

- - - - Rural Council Boundaries

++++++ Railway

→ Migration routes
of Rizeiqat

Bahr el Arab

Sahala
Nakata
Safaha

The homeland or *dar* of the Rizeiqat is adjacent to the railway. This
is where the main areas of cultivation are located. The herdsmen with
their livestock move southwards towards the seasonally flooded areas
adjacent to the Bahr el Arab during the dry season. When the rains
come they move northwards through the *dar* lands into the semi-arid
areas, returning southwards as the wet season ends. The annual
migratory cycle may exceed 360 km (224 miles)

Fig. 5.18 The migratory cycle of the Rizeiqat: a Baggara tribe in the western Sudan
(Hunting Technical Services, 1976).

responsible for the continuing degradation of the sahel and savanna
ecological zones in Africa. These factors include: the private ownership
of livestock but the communal ownership of land; the general increase
in population with consequent increased settlement leading to constant
shrinking of the area of grazings available for the nomads; the introduc-

tion of new technology, and in particular water pumps and veterinary vaccines, without concurrent improvements in the managerial system; the lack of outlets for surplus capital apart from investment in female livestock; and the social attitudes of the people.

The true nomad and his cattle live almost in a form of symbiosis. Cattle are not regarded primarily as a source of income but as a source of food – usually milk and in the case of some non-Moslem people blood, but rarely meat – as a source of social prestige and above all as a means of survival. Survival and prestige depend upon numbers so that the aim is usually to own as large a herd as can be managed by the nomad and his extended family, irrespective of the quality of the animals or the effects of overgrazing on future feed supplies.

Inputs into this system are low, as are outputs per animal and per unit area of land utilized. On the other hand, output per man is relatively high. On account of the nature of the climatic environment outputs per unit area of land could in most instances never be very high, but the nomad's capital assets are usually large and a more rational employment of these is not impossible.

Transhumance or semi-nomadic herding

Semi- and partial-nomadic herding systems are of very considerable importance throughout West, Northeast and East Africa and in the Malagasy Republic. They also exist in western Asia and in the Indian sub-continent.

Transhumants have a village base where they cultivate crops during the wet season, but during the dry season some or all of them move with their herds to areas where they believe that the grazing is superior, returning to their village for the next cropping season.

As an agricultural system, transhumance is not normally superior to nomadism. Indeed, as the herds of transhumants often have less room for manoeuvre the cattle are usually inferior in quality to those of the true nomads. Nevertheless, transhumance has social advantages as the participants can be relatively easily provided with desirable social services such as education and health.

Commercial ranching

Ranching is the commercial alternative to the various types of nomadism. In the tropics large-scale ranches are found in both the semi-arid and humid regions of Mexico, Central America, the Caribbean and South America; in the tsetse-fly-free areas of East and south Central Africa; in Australia and the Pacific islands; and in small numbers in specific locations in Southeast Asia, particularly in the Philippines. It is the preferred use of land that is inherently infertile, semi-arid or inaccesible, and increasingly in Central and South America it is the prime reason for which large areas of primeval rain-forest are being felled.

The form of management adopted depends in the first place on the intensity of stocking; this in turn depends primarily on the climatic environment and above all on the total annual rainfall, the seasonal distribution of that rainfall and the repeatability of these factors. In the humid tropics and particularly in the humid equatorial zone, stocking rates could be as high as one or more cattle units per hectare (2·5 acres). In the arid tropics stocking rates may be very low. For example in Northern Australia stocking rates may be as low as one cattle unit per 259 ha (1 mile²), so that the ranches have to be very large to remain viable economic units.

The major technical objectives of ranch management are to decrease annual fluctuation in cattle numbers and seasonal fluctuations in live-weight, maximize reproductive performance and minimize mortality, and maintain and if possible improve the grazings. All these practices tend to intensify production on the ranch.

In ranching systems outputs generally depend upon inputs, but economic viability may not depend upon maximizing outputs.

The most suitable breeds to use in extensive systems.

This problem has already been briefly discussed in Chapter 4 (Part I).

In the first place breeds must be well adapted to their environment. Some morphological characteristics that assist adaptation to a tropical climatic environment are a pigmented skin with a light-coloured, sleek coat. Under extensive grazing conditions not too short legs are required as the cattle will probably have to range far and wide for feed and water. The animals should be fertile, capable of producing viable calves and rearing them under adverse environmental conditions. They should be responsive in liveweight gain to a favourable nutritional environment; demonstrate a high efficiency of feed utilization; and be capable of producing carcases with the required proportions of fat, muscle and bone, a desirable distribution of fat, a high proportion of the most highly priced cuts and palatable meat. To summarize, what is required are breeds that produce the maximum quantity of high-quality meat in the most economic manner.

Migratory and sedentary shifting cultivators will continue to breed the indigenous cattle that they already possess, and as they are unlikely to be able significantly to improve their management and/or the environmental conditions under which they raise cattle this is a rational policy. In any event, it is likely that both migratory and sedentary shifting cultivation systems will be replaced by more intensive agricultural systems as the population increases.

The problem of suitable cattle breeds for sedentary subsistence farmers is different, but as subsistence systems are likely to become more intensive and/or be partially transformed into cash economy systems the problem of suitable breeds will be discussed in the section concerned with intensive beef production.

Nomads and transhumants are invariably conservative people and it is likely that, left to their own devices, they would continue to use the breeds developed by their forefathers. However, nomadic systems are decaying and whether nomadism evolves into a new and more stable communal system or is replaced by some other system such as individual or group ranching or subsistence crop agriculture, change is inevitable and it is likely that more productive cattle breeds will be required. It is also likely that the requirements will be broadly the same as those for new breeds in ranching systems in similar environments.

As so many of the original settlers in the present extensive ranching areas of the tropical world were of European origin they stocked their new ranches with temperate-type animals, as these were the cattle that they had known in their homelands.

In the Americas, the first extensive area of European settlement, there were no indigenous cattle and temperate-type animals were imported and became established in the tropical and sub-tropical as well as in the temperate regions (see previous section). There must have been considerable losses in the tropical regions, but gradually the imported cattle achieved some form of acclimatization. They slowly evolved in tropical America into the Criollo breeds, discussed in a previous section. More than 100 years ago the first improved temperate-type beef breeds were imported from Europe and efforts were made to upgrade the Criollo breeds. In general these efforts were unsuccessful. At approximately the same period the first tropical-type cattle (Zebu) were imported into tropical America. As they were more resistant to heat, drought and tick-borne disease than the exotic temperate-type breeds, they rapidly increased in numbers.

The present position in the American tropics is that there is an increasing number of high-grade or more or less purebred *Bos indicus*-type cattle available. Three breeds that have originated from a mixture of different Zebu breeds may be identified – the American Brahman, the Indú-Brasil and the Jamaican Brahman. In addition, there are three more or less purebred types of Zebu from India that have been acclimatized and improved by selection in Brazil – the Nellore, Guzerat and Gir. Several 'stabilized' *B. taurus* × *B. indicus* crossbred breeds have also been established – the Santa Gertrudis, Beefmaster and Brangus, etc., in the United States and the Jamaican Red, Jamaican Black and Nelthropp in the Carribbean.

The Zebu and crossbred Zebu breeds that have evolved are now having a very profound effect on the ranching industry in tropical America and they are being exported to many other tropical countries. They have been used on a very wide scale, particularly in Brazil, Venezuela and Colombia, to upgrade Criollo breeds. The first and second crosses between Criollo and Zebu result in cattle that are well acclimatized and yet demonstrate a high productivity compared with the purebred Criollo. The superiority of these crossbreds was attributed to the Zebu *per se*, whereas in reality it was partly due (Table 5.23) to hybrid vigour (Plasse,

Table 5.23 *Estimates of heterosis in a Criollo × American Brahman crossbreeding experiment*

Characteristic	No. observations	Mean of C† and AB purebreds (kg (lb))	Mean of C† × AB crossbreds (kg (lb))	Estimated heterosis (%)
Weaning weight	577			
Males		163 (359)	181 (399)	11·0
Females		150 (331)	164 (362)	9·3
Liveweight at				
18 months of age	390			
Males		236 (520)	277 (611)	17·4
Females		214 (472)	254 (560)	18·7
Average daily				
liveweight gain	577			
Males		0·666 (1·469)	0·720 (1·588)	8·1
Females		0·607 (1·338)	0·661 (1·458)	8·9

† C represent Criollo, AB American Brahman and C × AB Criollo × American Brahman crossbred cattle.
Source: Plasse (1973).

1973). As a consequence upgrading has continued on a vast scale, so that today it is difficult to find any number of purebred Criollo cattle in tropical South America.

In Australia, where there were no indigenous mammalian ruminants, the temperate-type cattle breeds that were introduced spread rapidly into the sub-tropical and tropical areas. They did not thrive as well as was expected, but extensive areas of grazing were available and the incidence of disease and parasites was limited. Some ranchers, realizing the limitations of the temperate-type breeds and aided by the government, imported Zebu and crossbred Zebu breeds from the United States during the first decades of the twentieth century. The advantages of using these cattle were so obvious that their use quickly spread and is still spreading. An indigenous crossbred beef breed, the Droughtmaster, has now been established.

With the exception of South Africa, settlement in Africa occurred much later than settlement in Australia. The temperate-type cattle that were imported into South Africa, where climatic stress was not too marked but disease and nutrient stress were severe, did not thrive too well in many areas so that the early settlers turned their attention to the cattle owned by the Hottentot. These cattle were indigenous *Bos taurus × B. indicus* crossbreds and from these the Africander breed has been developed. This was bred in the first place as a working animal, but with the advent of mechanization the emphasis has been placed on breeding a suitable beef animal and the Africander may now be considered as a beef breed.

The settlers also introduced temperate-type cattle into East and Central Africa, but so many serious diseases are endemic in these regions that introductions into many parts of East Africa were not very successful. Even in the regions of moderately high altitude, some 20 years after the first introduction of temperate-type beef cattle the ranchers realized that they would have to use indigenous cattle. It was fortunate that there was an excellent large Zebu-type animal available: the Boran. In the short period of 40 years, by selection and improved management and feeding, the Boran has been developed into one of the most productive beef breeds in Africa.

In Central Africa, imported temperate-type breeds were used for a longer period and it was not generally until after the Second World War that ranchers began to appreciate the potential value of the indigenous Sanga breeds. Although temperate-type breeds still predominate on ranches in Central Africa, there has been considerable development of the use of Sanga breeds such as the Mashona and the Tuli, and the Africander has been imported from South Africa. American Brahman and Santa Gertrudis cattle have also been introduced from North America.

In Asia, for a variety of reasons, development of the ranching industry commenced later than in the other continents. In general, Europeans who had introduced ranching elsewhere did not settle in Asian countries. There is probably no place in western Asia for an extensive cattle industry. In the Indian sub-continent, where the cattle population is very large, there are social and religious objections to the development of a beef industry. Ranching is most likely to develop in Southeast Asia, particularly in the degraded rain-forest areas mentioned in a previous section. The industry is most advanced in the Philippines, particularly in the large island of Mindanao, but ranches have been created or are being planned in Indonesia, Sabah, Sarawak, west Malaysia and Thailand. It is likely that this is a transient phenomenon as the population is increasing very rapidly in all these countries and most extensive beef cattle systems will inevitable become uneconomic once the land is required for alternative agricultural purposes.

To summarize the available evidence with regard to choice of breed in the extensive beef-production regions. In South America it is likely that 'criss-cross' crossbreds exhibiting hybrid vigour will replace many of the existing upgraded Zebu herds. In Central America 'criss-cross' crossbreds will also increase in number, but it is also likely that there will be more use of the 'stabilized' crossbred breeds. In the Caribbean the use of 'stabilized' crossbred breeds such as the Jamaican Red is likely to increase. In Australia 'criss-cross' crossbreds and 'stabilized' crossbred breeds of cattle are likely to increase in number. In Africa the use of specific indigenous Zebu and Sanga breeds is likely to increase and we believe that their production could be very rapidly improved by intensive selection. In the nomadic areas selection within the indigenous breeds should be the major breeding aim. There are, of course, special situations in Africa. An attempt should be made to breed more productive trypanosomiasis-tolerant cattle for use in the humid areas of Central and West Africa, and as endemic disease is controlled the breeding of exotic × indigenous 'criss-cross' crossbreeds may become possible, in particular in those areas where levels of nutrition and management can be quickly improved. In Southeast Asia, where the Brahman is being imported to upgrade indigenous cattle, there is a danger that what happened in tropical South America will happen once again, i.e. that all the resulting improvement will be attributed to the introduction of the exotic Zebu. In Southeast Asia it is important to ascertain the productivity of the crossbreds before upgrading systems gain too much momentum, and to explore the possibility of introducing other exotic cattle breeds for crossbreeding purposes and the potential of *Bos* (*Bibos*) spp. × *B. indicus* or *B.* (*Bibos*) spp. × *B. taurus* crossbreds.

Finally, it should not be forgotten that in Central and South America, East Africa and in some countries in Southeast Asia, there is undoubtedly a place for temperate-type beef breeds managed at the higher altitudes. In particularly they may be used to provide bulls for 'criss-cross' cross-breeding operations at lower altitudes.

Disease and parasites under extensive managerial conditions

The disease and parasite situation varies from continent to continent and from region to region within continents.

Disease and parasite constraints on productivity are worst in Africa. Not only is a large area of the continent (Fig. 5.19) infested with tsetse flies, the vectors of trypanosomiasis, but there are a larger number of tick-borne diseases than elsewhere, including East Coast fever (ECF), that only occurs in East Africa. A great deal has been accomplished by the rinderpest eradication campaign (JP 15) organized during the last decade and a campaign to eradicate contagious bovine pleuro-pneumonia (CBPP) is about to commence. Nevertheless, foot and mouth disease is still endemic almost everywhere in tropical Africa and the cattle also suffer from the ravages of most of the diseases and parasites found elsewhere in the world. Calving percentages are very low in many regions and this is partially due to widespread phosphorus and other mineral deficiencies in the forage. It may be concluded that in Africa disease and parasites are not only a major constraint on productivity in the extensive beef industry but also on the beef export trade.

In the Americas the situation varies from the Caribbean islands, where disease is not a major constraint to tropical South America where disease and parasites are still a serious constraint, particularly on the meat export trade. In Central America, rabies, which may be carried by vampire bats, can create managerial complications. Otherwise the region is free of the major tropical epidemic diseases. In tropical South America there are still many areas where foot and mouth disease (*aftosa*) is endemic, where

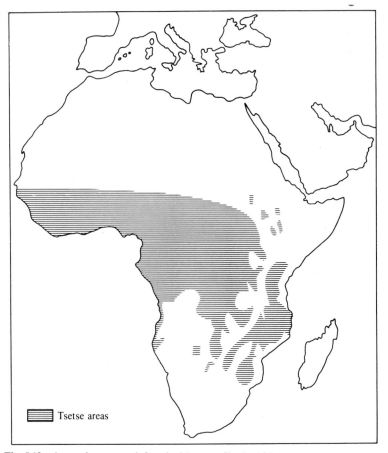

Fig. 5.19   Approximate area infested with tsetse flies in Africa.

calfhood diseases are difficult to control and where the warble fly (*Dermatobia hominis*) known as *nuche* or *torsola* is a major problem.

In Asia rinderpest is under control in most areas and foot and mouth disease has been eliminated in south Thailand, Malaysia and Singapore and in the major part of the Philippines.

Now that CBPP has been eliminated in Australia, that country and the tropical islands in the Pacific are free of the major tropical epidemic diseases.

The overall situation would appear to be that epidemic diseases and some external parasites will continue to be difficult to control under extensive managerial conditions, but that with well-planned eradication programmes, improvements in vaccine production and distribution and improved nutrition and management, disease and parasites will cease to be a major constraint on beef cattle productivity, except perhaps in some regions in Africa. It is of course essential that extensive holdings should have available suitable facilities, such as well-planned and constructed yards where vaccination can take place and dip tanks or sprays for the control of external parasites.

However, some special disease and parasite problems will remain. The incidence of disease and parasites with accompanying mortality will be much higher if the types of cattle used are not acclimatized to their environment. For example, de Pinho Morgado (1961) showed that in Mozambique, under the same conditions of feeding and management, indigenous Landim cattle had a lower mortality rate than introduced Africander cattle, although the latter are indigenous to Africa, and a very much lower mortality rate than introduced Herefords, the differences in the mortality rates being 4·0, 7·5 and 33·3 per cent, respectively. A further interesting observation was that the mortality of crossbred Landim × Hereford cattle, at 5·6 per cent, was lower than that of the Africander cattle.

In the equatorial tropics young calves are very prone to pneumonia in very wet weather. Calf mortality in some areas can be so high that it is worth while considering the erection of cheap shelters on the pastures for use by breeding cows with calves afoot.

Tick-control programmes must always be established. Except under exceptional conditions the complete eradication of ticks is considered unrealistic, but some form of tick control is usually needed everywhere, particularly in those regions of Africa where ECF is endemic. Mortality, even of indigenous cattle, can be very high indeed in ECF areas. Stobbs (1966), who reported on attempts to introduce cattle from tick-free to non-tick-free areas in East Africa, stated that the mortality of purebred Boran, crossbred Boran × Small East African Zebu and purebred Small East African Zebu were 77, 43 and 23 per cent, respectively, despite the fact that Small East African Zebu cattle are indigenous to the non-tick-free areas.

Cattle cannot be herded in tsetse-infested areas without very special precautions and/or the use of prophylactics. The use of the latter is not normally economic.

Management and feeding under extensive conditions

There is no single aspect of herd management the adoption of which would lead to maximum efficiency; one improved management practice leads to another and the integration of all gives the best overall results. The most suitable management practices will also vary according to the climatic environment, some of those found to be most suitable in the humid tropics being necessarily somewhat different from those that should be used in the drier areas, although the same basic principles apply everywhere.

Breeding and reproduction

If productivity is to be maximized under extensive conditions of husbandry it is important that each breeding cow and heifer should produce one calf per year and that this calf should live. Nestel (1965) investigated the relative importance of calving percentage and weaning weight on overall productivity in Jamaica and found that calving percentage was twelve times as important as calf weight in determining output per breeding cow, and that the number of calves weaned per unit area was twenty-five times as important as the average weaning weight in determining the output per unit area of grazing. The number of calves weaned per unit area is, of course, largely influenced by the stocking rate and by the calving percentage, and as the stocking rate is of necessity low under extensive husbandry conditions the calving percentage becomes of paramount importance.

There is a general impression that the calving percentage in many parts of the tropics remains very low and is often little above what is required for replacement purposes. For example, it is generally considered that in Brazil the average calving percentage in beef herds is currently 45 to 50. In nomadic herds in the western Sudan the estimated calving percentage is 50 (Hunting Technical Services, 1974a). In Australia, Chester (1955) stated that less than 50 per cent of all calves born in northwest Queensland survived to slaughter and Donaldson (1962) in a study of 28 extensive holdings over a period of 8 years showed that the number of calves branded as a percentage of the number of cows bred was as low as 46 in the Gulf of Carpentaria region.

What are the factors that influence calving percentage under extensive husbandry conditions in the tropics? They are many, including the utilization of a suitably acclimatized type of cattle, poor nutrition of the breeding females for part or almost all the year, indiscriminate mating, poor fertility of bulls and too high a bull to breeding female ratio.

The type of breed that should be used has already been discussed, and although the advantages of crossbreeding have been stressed, it must be remembered that this practice complicates management. Undoubtedly a greater improvement in a shorter time can be obtained by crossbreeding than by other breeding methods. Nestel (1965) stated that in Jamaica performance testing of existing beef breeds, using the top 1 per cent of all calves born as herd sires, would only improve the genetic merit of the national herd by 1 per cent per annum. Under these circumstances it would take some 20 years of vigorous selection in purebred herds to achieve the same gains that can be made in one year by exploiting heterosis, as crossbred calves wean 15 to 20 per cent heavier than purebreds.

If the breed that is utilized is not fully acclimatized the calving percentage may be low and the mortality high. McCarthy and Hamilton (1964), for example, in a survey of extensive holdings in central Queensland, have shown that calving rate is higher, mortality lower and the age of 'turn off' of Zebu crossbreds significantly lower than that of temperate-type purebred cattle.

The effect of nutrition on calving rates can be very marked in the drier areas of Australia, the Americas and Africa. Low total nutrient intake or a deficiency of protein and/or minerals may so reduce the calving percentage that the cattle may calve only every 2 years or even less often. In areas such as these the feeding of supplements can be a very effective way of improving the calving percentage. Steenkamp (1963) demonstrated that in Rhodesia the calving percentages of supplemented and unsupplemented breeding cows on extensive grazings were 81·3 and 56·7, respectively, and that birth weights were lower in the unsupplemented group, while Bauer (1965) showed that in South Africa supplements to 3-year-old heifers raised the conception rate at 4 years of age from 12·9 to 83·5 per cent.

It is generally conceded that heifers should not be bred too early as this practice may reduce the calving percentage. Indiscriminate mating – which frequently happens when the cattle on a holding are managed as one herd or under nomadic, transhumant and subsistence farming conditions – has been thought to lead inevitably to the early breeding of heifers. Bauer (1965), however, suggested that indigenous cattle in South Africa do not naturally breed until they weigh at least 254 kg (560 lb) liveweight, and that early breeding does not affect the lifetime performance of tropical-type beef cattle if there is a long interval between the first and second calvings. General observations on indigenous tropical cattle managed according to traditional standards tend to support Bauer's thesis. The danger is that when attempts are made to improve the productivity of indigenous herds, earlier matings are encouraged without the provision of alternatives to the compensating factors present within the indigenous managerial systems. When attempting to improve productivity in indigenous beef herds it is necessary to set a weight-for-age standard for the first service of heifers.

Another important consideration is whether the herd bulls are able to serve all the cows and heifers that are likely to come on heat at any one time. Under ideal conditions the fertility of herd bulls should be tested but this is, of course, impossible on most extensive holdings. What is important is to see that there are a sufficient number of bulls available, assuming that some of them may be sterile or lazy. In the temperate zone on most farms it is generally advised that 3 per cent bulls in the herds should be sufficient although on larger properties 5 or 6 per cent may be required, but in the tropics, where the topography may be very rough and the climatic environment stressful, an even higher percentage of bulls may be desirable. If the employment of these additional bulls ensures a high calving percentage, then although the practice may appear wasteful it could in fact be very economic.

As intensification proceeds on extensive holdings the breeding programme should also be intensified. Suggestions from Australia on methods of intensification can be useful in all ranching areas in the tropics. Three stages of intensification have been defined in Australia. First, heifers should be segregated from the other cattle and run as a separate herd for mating purposes. In Australia this operation would be carried out when the heifers are $2\frac{1}{2}$ years of age, but in many other regions it might be carried out when the heifers are somewhat older. Secondly, heifers should be segregated from the main herd when they are weaned and given a choice of better feed so that they can grow more rapidly and be ready for first mating at an earlier age. In the third stage the heifers should be segregated at weaning, fed slightly better than other cattle and mated during a controlled breeding season of 3 to 4 months. A further refinement at this stage would be to pregnancy test the heifers after the mating season and then rigidly cull all non-breeders and at the same time feed all pregnant heifers and cows pre-calving feed supplements.

The advantages of intensifying the breeding system in these ways are that:

1. The nutritional demands of the breeding stock can be synchronized to some extent to the seasonal production of feed;
2. Marking, weaning and dry season supplementation can be simplified because of the uniformity in the stage of pregnancy and lactation of the heifers and cows, and in the age of calves;
3. Heifers can be prevented from calving at too young an age, thus reducing the dry season losses of first-calving heifers and the production of small, underweight calves;
4. After mating bulls can be kept close to the yards where they can easily be fed supplements and where fertility testing can be undertaken and tick control simplified;
5. More or less uniform groups of cattle become available for marketing at specific times;
6. AI techniques can more easily be used for upgrading purposes.

The disadvantages of intensification are as follows:

1. Insufficient information is often available as to the most suitable time for calving so that it is easy in theory but difficult in practice to synchronize the nutritional demands of the cattle with the production of feed. This is particularly true in the very dry areas where seasonal climatic variations may be very marked.
2. There are indications that many cows calve later each succeeding year, requiring more than 12 months between calvings and thus jeopardizing the controlled breeding programme.
3. Bulls that are segregated for 8 to 9 months of the year may not work too well during the early part of the mating season.
4. The system requires more capital. This is, of course, one of the difficulties of any form of intensification.

It is generally thought that in the ranching areas of the Americas and Australia the advantages of a controlled breeding programme outweigh the disadvantages. In Australia it is said that by the use of a controlled breeding programme it is possible to achieve a breeding percentage of 70 to 80 – a far higher percentage than is normally achieved on extensive holdings.

In many tropical regions and particularly in Africa and in Southeast Asia there is at present such a lack of production and other data that controlled breeding programmes should only be introduced after intensive investigations, and then only with caution.

The use of AI techniques for upgrading purposes has been suggested. Although it is difficult to utilize the ordinary AI techniques to any major degree on extensive holdings it is possible to use them with modifications. The most satisfactory method is to gather a limited number of the most productive beef breeding cows on to a small area of the holding, to synchronize their oestral cycles using one of the new techniques, and then proceed to inseminate them over a short period. Using this technique an upgrading programme could proceed very rapidly in a small, specially selected 'nuclear' herd. This 'nuclear' herd could be kept for the production of 'improved' bulls that would subsequently be used with the breeding herds out on the extensive grazings.

Feeding

Major problems encountered in the feeding of extensively managed beef cattle are mainly those that directly result from seasonality in the growth of pastures and fodders. This adversely affects productivity and complicates management in both the dry and the humid tropics.

In the dry tropics seasonality in forage productivity can be very great and often there is no production at all for long periods. This very marked fluctuation in the availability of feed produces the well-known cyclic growth pattern in extensively managed beef cattle (Fig. 5.20). The cattle grow during and immediately after the rainy season, and maintain or lose liveweight during the remainder of the year. (It can be seen from Fig. 5.20 that had the cattle continued to grow at the same rate as they grew in their first 10 months of life, they would have achieved their 40-month-old liveweight at approximately 20 months.) After an exceptionally long dry season cattle may continue to lose weight during the first weeks of forage growth at the commencement of the rains (Fig. 5.21). This phenomenon is known as the 'green-grass loss' and is well known in East Africa where it has been studied (Payne, 1965). Under conditions of cyclic growth there is often accelerated growth when feed becomes abundant during the wet season. This is known as 'compensatory growth', a phenomenon that enables an animal with a retarded growth rate to catch up with the final liveweight of contemporary unretarded animals, often with the advantage of superior food conversion

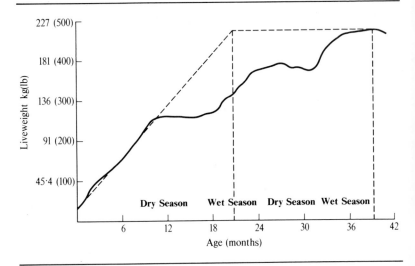

Fig. 5.20   The cyclic growth pattern of extensively managed cattle (Touchberry, 1967).

for the period of most rapid growth. Information on this subject has been reviewed by Wilson and Osbourn (1960).

However, some of this 'compensatory growth' may be more apparent than real. Part of the additional gain may be due to the retention of additional water in the body tissues, just as some of the weight loss during the dry season may be due to loss of water that in the wet season would be retained in the body tissues. Taylor (1959) has show that some of the reported increase in liveweight is due to an increase in the weight of 'fill' in the digestive tract. Nevertheless, Smith and Hodnett (1962) stated that in the natural veld areas of Zambia cattle that have experienced large weight losses in the preceding dry season consume more herbage in the following wet season than cattle that have received supplementary rations during the dry season. This work suggests that some part of the 'compensatory growth' could be real.

There is another factor to consider. As Montsama (1967) has stated, 'compensatory growth' may compensate an animal for loss of weight during periods of under-nutrition, but at the same time the animal ages and becomes physiologically more mature and the normal pattern of growth and development may be disturbed. As might be expected, restriction on growth followed by increases in growth rate will have the most effect on the later maturing tissues, particularly on fat. As a result *Bos taurus* and *B. indicus* cattle may differ markedly in their carcase response to compensatory growth.

Opinions vary as to the age at which compensatory growth is most effective. Montsama (1967) has stated that it is highest in young cattle

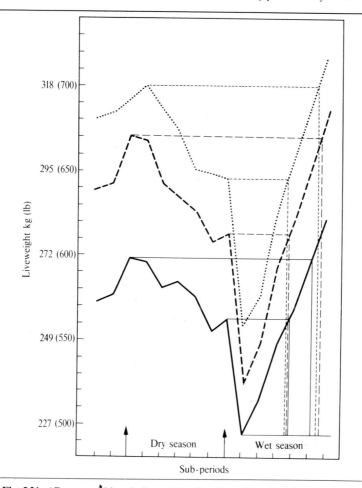

Fig. 5.21 'Green-grass' loss in liveweight of cattle at the end of the dry season (......
control twins; ------ experimental twins; ——— Masai steers) (Payne, 1965).

while Smith and Hodnett (1962) stated that it was least in cattle under
2 years of age.

As far as the effect of breed is concerned it is generally considered
that slower maturing types of cattle respond better in terms of compensatory growth after a period of under-nutrition than do faster maturing types. This suggests that in areas where cattle are subject to periodic
under-nutrition the slower maturing indigenous breeds may have an advantage over rapidly maturing exotic breeds.

The effects of seasonality in forage production on the growth of beef
cattle are fundamentally the same in all those areas of the tropics where
there is a definite dry season. In fact, everywhere except in the equatorial

tropics. The practical results vary in accordance with the length and severity of the dry season. However, even in the humid tropics where planted pastures are grazed, seasonality in production can still create managerial problems.

What are the possibilities of 'ironing out' major fluctuations in the supply of forage on extensive grazings? Any practice that may be adopted must, of course, have an economic basis, and this is a major difficulty as many practices that might be economic on intensive cattle farms are almost certain to be uneconomic on extensive beef holdings. The practices that have been suggested and might be adopted vary both within and between countries according to the climatic environment, the topography, the type of cattle utilized, the intensity of stocking, etc. Methods that have been suggested may be classified into two groups. The first consist of those in which changes in the management of the cattle are necessary and the second are concerned with the manipulation of the feed supply.

Some cattle managerial methods that might assist in 'ironing out' fluctuations in the supply of forage would be the following:

1. Adoption of a seasonal breeding programme designed to correlate the period when there are the maximum number of animals on the holding with the season when the feed supply is at a maximum. As stated previously, a seasonal breeding programme can only be adopted when there is some degree of intensification. It is usually suggested that seasonal breeding should be programmed so that the breeding cows calve just before or just after the wet season commences when the amount of forage present is at a maximum and when the breeding cow's nutrient needs are highest. This appears to be sound advice in those regions where the wet season is short, but in the more humid areas calving at this time might lead to increased internal parasitism and possibly higher mortality in the young calves. In the equatorial regions where there is rain every month it may be very difficult to decide which is the most suitable month to calve.

Another suggestion where seasonal breeding is practised is to arrange the calving period so that the calves are weaned when feed is at a maximum and when their plane of nutrition would normally decline. The difficulty of operating this system is that the breeding cows would then be calving during the dry season and may not milk too well, while they would be dry when feed was most abundant.

(2) The total number of cattle in the herd may be reduced before the dry season commences by culling non-fertile cows and heifers and by selling steers. This may be a good managerial system in some monsoonal areas where the wet and dry seasons are often of almost equal length, but it would not be a very practical system in the very dry areas where the wet season is very short. A major advantage of this managerial practice is that steers are sold before they lose weight, as will inevitably occur during the dry season.

Some managerial methods by which attempts may be made to manipulate the feed supply in order to 'iron out' major fluctuations are as follows:

(1) Grazings may be improved so that they remain green longer into the dry season and grow away faster when the rains come, thus lengthening the period during which feed supplies are adequate. It is probably easiest to do this in the monsoonal and savanna areas as it is often impossible to improve pastures in any economic way in the semi-arid areas. This problem and the managerial methods required are discussed in more detail in Chapter 3 (Part I).

As legumes often continue to grow during the drier periods when grass growth has ceased, the use of legumes, particularly in the monsoonal areas, may reduce seasonability in forage production to a limited extent. Legumes may be encouraged on extensive grazings by dispersing treated legume seeds from aircraft, moving vehicles or from horseback, or if the legume seeds possess a hard outer shell by feeding them to the cattle from strategically located feeding boxes. The cattle will then spread them around the grazings as they defecate.

Another method is to improve a small area of pasture close to a holding area, possibly by the use of irrigation and fertilizers. This is really intensification on a very small part of an extensive area, and in the drier regions the intensive cultivation of grass and/or legume fodder crops can sometimes be a very economic method by which the total amount of forage available to the beef herd can be increased during the dry season. The small area of improved pasture can either be fed off directly, greensoiled or the forage can be made into silage and/or hay and fed when required. The most desirable practice would be to use these small areas for the feeding of those classes of stock that would benefit most for supplementary feeding, such as the weaners. This method is practised in tropical Australia and various reports suggest that it can be very effective in improving the liveweight gain of beef cattle. Sutherland (1959) reported that the feeding of 0·9 kg (2·0 lb) of lucerne hay per day for 100 days to steers during the dry season enabled them to gain an extra 33 kg (72 lb) liveweight over a control group of steers that received no supplement. It has also been reported from Queensland that cattle with access to 2 ha (5 acres) of lucerne between May and August in a 12 ha (30 acre) field gained 39 kg (86 lb) while a control group with no access to lucerne lost 9·5 kg (21 lb) during the same period.

Another desirable managerial practice might be to plant browse for use during the dry season, as browse plants usually retain their leaves and even when the leaves are shed the dry leaf is still good feed and will be picked up and eaten by the cattle. In practice, in the very arid areas, cattle live almost entirely on browse as there is usually no other feed available except for very short periods when annual grasses and herbs thrive during the rains.

(2) The problem of supplementation of rough grazings during dry

periods has received considerable attention in Australia, the Americas and in Central and South Africa, and many suggestions have been made as to how this might best be accomplished. In South Africa, dry pastures have been sprayed with a mixture of urea and molasses, one combination being 27 kg (60 lb) of urea, 182 litres (40 gal) of molasses and 364 litres (80 gal) of water (Van de Vyer, 1954). The cattle were then immediately grazed on the pastures. In Central Africa and in many other regions of the dry tropics, considerable efforts have been made to produce suitable urea blocks that can be fed to cattle to supplement dry season grazings. These blocks may contain approximately 40 per cent urea, together with minerals, molasses and possibly an ingredient such as salt that will assist in the limitation of appetite so that too much urea is not ingested at any one time. Despite the large number of experimental observations that have been recorded Loosli and McDonald (1968), in a review on the utilization of urea for feeding purposes, reluctantly concluded that there is no evidence yet available to support the contention that urea can be profitably employed to enhance the feeding value of low-quality roughages under genuine pastoral conditions. They state that it would be wrong to assume from the magnitude of the commercial enterprise in this sector that the results are favourable in practice, although of course lack of experimental evidence does not preclude the possibility that urea feeding under these circumstances is a desirable practice. In Queensland blocks have been made from meat meal and molasses. These usually contain up to 20 per cent of meat meal and good results from the feeding of them have been reported by Sutherland (1959). Another idea is to feed concentrates in various forms, but it can readily be appreciated that these are unlikely to be an economic form of supplementation on very extensive holdings although they could possibly be economic where intensification has already commenced.

Economic methods of utilizing supplementary feeds would certainly revolutionize beef-production methods in the extensive areas. As will be seen from Fig. 5.20 cattle that would not normally attain a slaughter weight of 400 kg (882 lb) until they were $4\frac{1}{2}$ to 5 years of age could be 'turned off' at a little more than 2 years of age if they were fed supplements during the dry season that enabled them to gain 0·5 kg (1·1 lb) per day. As McDowell (1966) has stated, it is likely that supplementation would be most economic if supplements were fed at the end of the growing animal's second wet season, with the aim of turning them off at 27 to 33 months of age.

Another feeding problem in many parts of the tropics is that cattle on extensive grazings encounter deficiencies of major or minor mineral elements and that these deficiencies are usually intensified during the dry season. Deficiencies can be prevented by the provision of minerals. These may be fed from strategically located boxes that should be provided with a roof to give protection from the rain during the wet season, as ingredients in molasses–urea blocks, or they may be added to the water-supply system by one or other of a variety of methods.

Stratification and stocking rates.   It is desirable to practise stratification, not only between but also within holdings. On large holdings, and elsewhere if possible, the breeding cows with larger unweaned calves afoot, the heifers that are of sufficient age or heavy enough for first mating, together with the non-working breeding bulls should be rotated around the nutritionally poorest sections of the holding. The nutritionally better sections should be reserved for the fattening of steers and for growing-out the younger heifers and bulls. The importance of this strategy is emphasized by the evidence presented by Nestel (1965) that in Jamaica 280 kg per ha (250 lb per acre) of liveweight was produced by the breeding herd compared with 706 kg per ha (630 lb per acre) by fatteners, and that the profit per unit area was correspondingly higher. The reason for this result is that at any one time a large percentage of cattle in the breeding herd utilize feed for maintenance rather than for production purposes.

As the major problems encountered in the feeding of extensively managed beef cattle are mainly those that directly result from seasonality in the growth of pastures, it is absolutely essential that the rancher or pastoralist should make a realistic estimate of the carrying capacity of his land. In the arid and semi-arid tropics this must be determined by carrying capacity in the dry season, while in the humid tropics the stocking rate must be sufficiently high to keep forage growth under control. Experience has shown that this is one of the most difficult estimates to make. In the dry tropics it is almost impossible to determine for a few seasons in advance what the carrying capacity is likely to be in the long term, therefore the cautious grazier should deliberately understock during the first few years of occupancy. In the humid tropics it is only too easy to understock, so that the forage gets away from the cattle and has to be burnt off.

Control of animals, grazings and water.   The grazier must have complete control of his herd, so that they can be handled quickly and efficiently and can properly utilize available feed and water. This means that he must have suitable handling facilities such as yards, races, dips, etc., and that these should be strategically sited and strongly constructed. Some details of suitable types of yards, etc., are given in a later section. Well-planned and constructed handling facilities reduce the number of accidents to cattle and men and improve efficiency of labour utilization.

As intensification of production increases, control of the herds must be improved and this means more separate herds and, consequently more internal fencing and handling facilities. On poorly managed extensive ranches – in the nomadic and semi-nomadic areas, and where settled agriculturalists own relatively large numbers of cattle – there is usually only one herd. This is bad husbandry and considerable improvements can be made in productivity by simply segregating various types of cattle. As stated previously the minimum number of herds should be three, but even this degree of segregation is often difficult to achieve. The very least that can be done is to segregate the weaned heifers and castrate all surplus bull calves. On more intensive holdings, young bulls should be run separately from the steers and old bulls, and the steers should be divided into two or more groups according to age.

The grazier must also develop a grazing system that encourages the production of palatable and nutritive forage species and discourages the growth of weeds or soil erosion. The amount of sub-division required varies according to circumstances, but, in general, much greater subdivision is required in the humid than in the dry areas. Whether the grazier fences or uses herdsmen depends on the availability and cost of labour, but he also has to decide whether he will set-stock or rotationally graze. The general consensus of opinion is that paddocks in the drier areas require 'spelling' or they will deteriorate, and that rotational grazing would appear to be almost obligatory in the more humid areas if the grazier is going to take maximum advantage of the rapid growth of forage. These problems have been discussed in some detail in Chapter 3 (Part 1).

Rotation and the 'spelling' of paddocks have other advantages apart from those concerned with the utilization of forage. In drier areas 'spelling' can improve tick control as ticks can be almost eliminated from a paddock after a minimum period of 4 months without grazing animals. The concentration of cattle in one area also improves the operation of the breeding programme and assists in the efficient handling of stock.

Whether the cattle are fenced or herded, rotationally grazed or set-stocked, every effort must be made to see that they graze evenly over the grazings and do not 'eat out' any one area, particularly around sources of water. The provision of water can itself be used as a method of controlling stocking rate and cattle movement on large holdings and in the nomadic and semi-nomadic tribal areas. Water sources should be separately fenced so that the utilization of water can be controlled.

Nomadic or semi-nomadic graziers can and, during times of drought, have to use the provision of water to control grazing. They spend their lives herding their cattle and can direct them at all times towards available feed and water. In East Africa it is normal practice in the dry season to graze herds away from water for one day then, depending on circumstances, either back to the water on the second day or grazing at some distance from the water on the second day and back to the water on the third day. Thus, cattle are deprived of water for 2 or 3 days at a time. When both feed and water are scarce this is undoubtedly a sound managerial practice (Payne, 1965).

On very extensive holdings it is only practical to gather the cattle occasionally, often only once or twice a year, when calves are weaned, marked, castrated, dehorned, inoculated, dipped, etc.

Weaning. There are different opinions as to the most suitable age for weaning. Some graziers like to wean early, at from 6 to 7 months of age, in order to ensure that their cows breed annually. There is evidence that this may not be a desirable practice in some of the drier areas (Steenkamp, 1963), but it may be a reasonable practice in the humid areas, particularly where the grazings have been improved.

Calves should certainly be weaned by the time they are 9 months of age, but in the herds of some nomadic and semi-nomadic peoples they are often not weaned until a new calf is born, after which the cow usually rejects the older calf. This is not a universal practice and many tribal herdsmen separate the calves from the breeding cows when they are quite young and only allow them to suckle morning and evening. During the day they are grazed separately from their dams. Once calves have been weaned, they should be run as a separate herd and rotated round the best grazings. In the humid tropics, where rotational grazing may be practised, the calves can be rotated in front of the breeding herd. In the drier areas it may be more difficult to ensure that they have a high nutrient intake and it may be necessary to provide supplements during the drier weather. Weaning cannot be controlled in indigenous herds until some segregation of the different types of cattle is practised.

Marking usually takes place at weaning. Different methods of marking are discussed in Appendix II.

Castration. On extensive holdings castration is usually carried out at weaning. Where cattle are herded it could, with advantage, be accomplished earlier. In fact, the earlier the better. In many tropical countries, particularly in India, castration is carried out very late, often when the cattle are 4 years of age. Methods of castration have been described in a previous section.

It has been suggested that in most tropical countries where there is no premium for the production of high-quality beef there are no advantages in castrating bulls that are going to be sold for meat, particularly as bulls normally grow more rapidly than castrates. Macfarlane (1966) investigated this problem in Tanzania using the Small East African Zebu and found that in this breed castration had no positive effect on growth or on carcase composition.

Dehorning. This is usually accomplished at weaning on extensive holdings, though like castration it might better be carried out at an earlier age. There are no advantages in dehorning range cattle unless the horns of the adult cattle are so large that the cattle cannot pass through spray races, etc. Subsistence farmers usually do not wish to dehorn their cattle as the horn is often useful in animals that they may retain for working purposes.

Animal health practices.   The number and type of inoculations and vaccinations required will vary from country to country according to the local disease situation. Drenching of range cattle is not usually required, but when calves are separated from the cows at an early age and only suckled morning and night as they often are under subsistence conditions, internal parasites may become a problem and drenching may be advisable.

Dipping or spraying by machine or by hand is essential in tick-infested areas. The frequency required depends on climatic factors such as humidity and the pattern of rainfall. In the humid areas it could be necessary throughout the year, but in the drier areas it may only be necessary during the wet season. It is usual to endeavour to keep tick infestation under control and not to attempt to eliminate ticks. Where cattle are frequently handled, hand removal of ticks can be a very efficient form of tick control.

Special problems of remote areas

One advantage of the extensive beef cattle industry is that it can economically utilize land in remote areas that would otherwise remain unproductive. However, the very remoteness of many extensive cattle grazings does create special problems for the rancher and the tribal pastoralist. These are mainly concerned with the transport of pastoral requisites to, and fat or store cattle from, these remote areas. Remoteness also creates special social problems which, apart from their effect on the supply of labour to the industry, are generally outside the scope of this text.

In Australia these problems particularly beset the cattle industry in the far north of the country. In South America the problem is continent wide, but particularly affects the industry in the *llanos* of Venezuela and Colombia, and in the interior or Guyana and Brazil. In Africa cattle are raised in the savanna regions that are often remote from centres of population, and separated from them by tsetse fly-infested country. In the Philippines and in Indonesia in Southeast Asia the sea acts as a barrier as cattle may be raised on one island and the major beef consumption centres be located hundreds of miles away on other islands.

Of course the provision of transport is the answer to these problems, but one of the difficulties of providing an adequate road or rail transport system or even adequate sea transport in archipelagos is that the total quantity of goods to be transported is low in relation to the distances involved, and that the number of cattle to be transported fluctuates widely from season to season and from year to year.

Traditionally, cattle have been trekked from the remote areas to railheads or to centres of population. Even when trekking routes with watering facilities are provided by the government this has always been a wasteful method of transport as fat cattle lose considerable weight and condition on their way from production to consumption centres.

This reduces producers' incomes and, consequently, their ability to effect improvements on their holdings as cattle are usually retained until they are over-fat, thereby reinforcing overstocking and low off-take problems.

During the last two decades there has been a revolution in the transport of cattle as the road network has improved and the indigenous peoples have acquired motor transport. In West Africa, for example, increasing numbers of cattle are now trucked from the savanna regions to the coastal centres of population. There is a double advantage in this system as the time to take the cattle from the production to the consumption centres has been dramatically reduced, for example, in Sierra Leone from 15 to 20 days to one day, and the cattle are only subjected to the dangers of exposure to the tsetse fly for relatively short periods of time. The same phenomena can be observed in South America, where in Colombia the trekking of fat cattle from the northern coastal plains to the inland market of Medellin has virtually ceased during the last 10 years and all cattle are now trucked.

This revolution in the transport of cattle is one of the preliminary steps that have to be taken towards the modernization of the beef industry in these regions, and holds the promise that extensive improvements on the grazings and in management will ultimately be considered to be more worth while.

There are, however, some remote areas where the road network may not yet be improved for several decades and where there are no possibilities of transporting by water or by rail. In these areas the slaughter of cattle in the producing areas and the air freighting of carcases to centres of production may be economic. This is at present the procedure in one area of northern Australia where carcases are flown from the Glenroy Works in the Kimberley region. Air freight is, of course, necessarily more expensive than other freight methods, so that producer's receipts are lower, but it may still be cheaper for the producer than the losses occurred on the long treks to railheads or to all-weather roads. Slaughter in the production area also, of course, raises problems of the economic disposal of offals.

In the past the meat industry in developing countries has been less than enthusiastic about any move to locate abattoirs and meat-packing plants close to centres of production. The whole problem should be re-examined and if an economic type of low-throughput abattoir can be designed then slaughter of cattle on a relatively small scale in the production areas may become economic, and the transport problems of the remote areas would be easier to solve.

Intensive systems

As stated previously, some cattle raised within the sedentary subsistence system may be considered to be extensively managed while the remainder are intensively managed. Cattle raised by peasant producers solely for meat production may be classified in the latter group.

Almost all cattle raised in the ley farming and perennial crop cultivation systems are intensively managed. Subsistence farmers, small-scale commercial farmers and large-scale livestock raisers all participate in these systems. Some of the farmers are specialist milk producers, raising male calves for meat production as a by-product. There are also a few specialist dairy farmers outside the ley farming and perennial crop cultivation systems.

The beef fatteners belong to a special category, as they may purchase cattle intended for fattening from either extensive or intensive producers or they may breed and raise them. Whatever method is used they are classified as intensive producers.

There are two major methods of intensive production. The first is to rear and fatten cattle for their whole life out in the field on pasture and/or fodder, while the second is to manage them at some stage of their life under confinement, usually in specially constructed buildings. There can, of course, be many variations and combinations of these two managerial systems and it is likely that the majority of beef cattle that are fattened under confinement are bred and reared outdoors; some, however, in particular those purchased from dairy herds, may be reared indoors while young and fattened later on pasture.

Yard or any other indoor type of feeding management can obviously be classified as intensive, but it is sometimes difficult to decide at what stage beef production off grazings can be so classified. In this text intensive production off grazing is considered to be that form of management where the major part of the pasture and/or fodder on the holding has been specifically planted and managed for beef-production purposes. Thus the majority of specialist beef producers who are ley-farming or integrating their cattle with crop production should be classified as intensive producers.

In general, information on the intensive production of beef cattle within the tropics is still very limited, but interest in new methods of production has noticeably quickened during the last decade. The economics of intensive production depend upon, among other factors, the type of cattle available, the level of managerial expertise in pasture and forage production, the availability and cheapness of concentrate and by-product feeds, the price of beef, whether there is a local or an export demand for quality meat, and what diseases are endemic. Intensive production of pasture or fodder is unlikely to be economic in the drier areas if water for irrigation purposes cannot be provided at low cost. In fact, unless special factors are operating it is unlikely that intensification of production will be very economic in those areas where the annual rainfall is less than 1,020 mm (40 in). As the length and intensity of the dry season decrease the problems of intensification decrease, and where the annual rainfall is as much as, or exceeds, 1,780 to 2,030 mm (70 to 80 in) a high degree of intensification can be achieved by the use of the correct pasture or fodder species, fertilizers, etc. In areas receiving 1,270 to 1,520 mm (50 to 60 in) annual rainfall in East and West Africa and probably in South America and Southeast Asia, there would appear to be some place for alternate husbandry managerial systems where the utilization of pasture and/or fodder crops in a rotation with cash crops would not only provide feed for intensively managed beef cattle but also may assist in the prevention of erosion and the improvement or at least the maintenance of soil fertility. In the equatorial tropics where there is some rain every month intensification is likely to be most economic, but little information is available as to the most suitable managerial methods needed in this ecological zone, although it is likely that integration with tree crops will often be a satisfactory managerial method.

The use of the ecologically most suitable pasture and fodder species (discussed in some detail in Ch. 3, Pt I), fertilizers, irrigation, more intensive sub-division, etc., will undoubtedly usually improve the output of beef per unit area whatever the type of cattle used, and there is increasing evidence from all parts of the more humid areas of the tropics that intensification of beef production on grazings is increasing with a momentum that grows from year to year.

Indoor, yard, lot or stall feeding is at present almost entirely restricted to those areas in the tropics where large quantities of edible by-product feeds are available, particularly on sugar cane, pineapple and sisal plantations. It is therefore an industry that is almost entirely dominated by the large producers. Nevertheless, there are minor areas in the tropical world where peasant farmers have traditionally practised intensive stall feeding of beef cattle. Examples are the area around the towns of Moshi and Arusha on the lower slopes of Mount Kilimanjaro and Meru in Tanzania, northern Nigeria, Batangas Province in the island of Luzon in the Philippines and the island of Madura in Indonesia. In Tanzania indigenous cattle are stall-fed in dark huts, locally produced by-product feeds and fodder grasses cut from the roadsides. The stall feeding of beef cattle in northern Nigeria is particularly interesting as this is a seasonal activity, not practised by the pastoralists (the Fulani) but by the agriculturalists (the Hausa). The latter, using cash realized from the sale of crops, purchase cattle in October or November from the semi-nomadic Fulani, who are at this time returning from their wet season grazings. The Hausa yard-feed the cattle for approximately 5 months on crop residues such as groundnut tops, guinea-corn chaff, bean hulls and cowpea hay, and then sell the cattle when they require money to purchase seeds for the next year's cropping programme. Costing of these operations has shown that Hausa farmers do not make very much profit, but they are able to first hoard and then realize capital to finance their next season's cropping. Batangas cattle in the Philippines are usually kept in small yards and are fed by-product feeds and cut forage. The latter, often elephant grass, may be specifically grown as a feed for the cattle.

The situation on the island of Madura will be discussed in the next section.

Information available with regard to the possibilities for the intensification of beef production, particularly off pasture in the humid tropics, is encouraging. It would appear that despite the relatively unsophisticated nature of the beef-cattle industry in the tropics it is already experimentally possible to produce liveweight yields per unit area in excess of those that could be expected under good managerial conditions in the temperate zone (Payne, 1968). Estimates of the potential yield of beef per unit area, based on published data, are shown in Table 5.24 and it will be seen that intensification could raise liveweight production per unit area very rapidly. It may be predicted that it will ultimately be found that humid tropical pastures, when properly managed, possess more potential for cattle production than pastures elsewhere in the world.

Table 5.24   *Estimates of the potential for beef production from forage in the humid tropics*

Type of forage	Potential productivity under good management (kg liveweight gain per ha per year)	
	Minimum	Maximum
Natural grasslands		
Improved grazing management	10–80	60–100
Oversowing with suitable legumes	120–170	250–450
Cultivated grasslands		
Grass/legume mixtures	200–300	300–600
Grass fertilized with nitrogenous		
fertilizer	300–500	800–1,500

Note: The estimates are of pooled data from many sources.

Sedentary subsistence rain-fed and/or irrigated cultivation.   A very large proportion of the cattle in tropical Asia are raised by subsistence or near-subsistence farmers. Although these cattle are utilized primarily as work animals they also produce considerable quantities of milk, and together with the working buffaloes, almost all the beef available for consumers.

Beef production by the sedentary subsistence farmers in Africa has already been discussed as their methods are generally extensive. In the irrigated areas of western Asia and the rain-fed and irrigated areas of Southeast Asia beef is in large part a by-product of cereal culture. It is produced from oxen and buffaloes that have reached the end of their working life and from culled breeding females.

In the past in Southeast Asia, as the rural and urban populations slowly increased in number demand for rice increased. In order to satisfy this demand new areas of land were brought into cultivation. Expansion of the cultivated area created an increased demand for work animals and ultimately provided increased supplies of beef. Thus the ratio of the human population to the cultivated rice area and to the total number of working cattle and buffalo remained more or less constant, as did the ratio between the quantities of rice and beef that were produced.

During the last two or three decades this equilibrium has been shattered. The urban population has expanded at an unprecedented rate, creating major increases in demand for rice and meat. The increased demand for rice has in large measure been satisfied, not by an increase in the cultivated area but by an increase in yield per unit area. The latter has become possible on account of the introduction of new agrarian technology, including new high-yielding cereal varieties, increased use of fertilizers, etc. The overall result has been that the working cattle and buffalo population has not expanded at the same rate as the human population and rice production. The introduction of mechanization in the rice fields has further decreased the need for work animals.

Thus beef production per capita in Southeast Asia has fallen and urban populations have increased their consumption of pig and poultry meat. These changes are shown diagrammatically in Fig. 5.22. The inevitable result must be that the price of beef will rise more rapidly than the prices of other meat and fish and that new systems of beef production will be stimulated.

Cattle production in Southeast Asia on peasant holdings is therefore at present generally characterized by stagnation, if not by a decline, and it is inevitable that new beef-production systems should evolve.

As rice-growing systems are only seasonally labour intensive the farmers enjoy considerable leisure. As a consequence Southeast Asian farmers often participate in traditional cattle sports. These include bull-fighting in south Thailand and in some districts of Indonesia and bull-racing in the island of Madura in Indonesia.

There are also peasant economies in Southeast Asia where cattle and/or buffalo are specifically raised for meat production, that have been mentioned in the previous section. The system in Madura, an island in Indonesia, is particularly interesting. Madura, an area of 4,497 km^2 (1,736 miles^2) with no pasture, supports approximately 570,000 head of cattle and buffaloes and 150,000 head of sheep and goats. An extraordinary livestock-carrying capacity of 1·3 large bovines per hectare has been achieved by feeding the animals indoors on forage and browse cut from roadside grazings and trees. A major source of browse is the legume tree, *Sesbania grandifolia*.

Irrigation intensifies cropping systems and should therefore increase the demand for work animals. It also introduces the possibility of providing forage on a year-round basis. In most tropical countries, however, irrigated land is too expensive to use for forage production. Irrigation has therefore often generated additional demand for work animals and at the same time aggravated the constant problem of obtaining sufficient feed supplies for them.

350 *Cattle*

Pre-Second World War economy

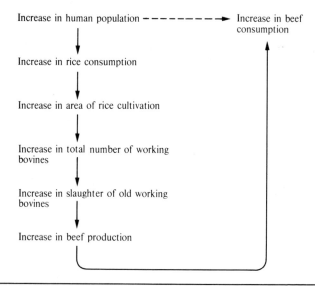

Post-Second World War economy

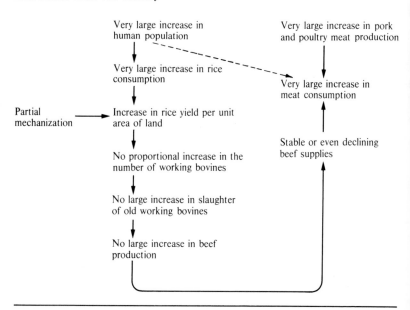

Fig. 5.22 The relationship between human population, rice and beef production in Southeast Asian subsistence agricultural systems.

Ley farming.   Rotation of crops and pastures on which cattle are grazed has developed in some smallholder areas. Examples are the Serere district of Senegal, some montane areas in Ethiopia where teff (*Eragrostis tef*) is cultivated, the Kano plains in Nigeria and the Teso district of Uganda. Ley farming with concentration on dairying has also been widely advocated for smallholder settlement schemes, but generally it has not proved to be a viable system in the lowland tropics.

Large-scale ley-farming systems in the tropics are generally limited to the montane areas of East Africa where beef production has been combined with wheat and pyrethrum production; to tobacco farms in Zambia and Rhodesia where pastures are rotated with tobacco, primarily to control nematodes in the tobacco crop; and to areas in southern Brazil where coffee and milk production are integrated.

There would still appear to be considerable scope for the development of beef production as a by-product of dairying in ley-farming systems in the montane areas of the tropics.

Perennial crop cultivation.   Cattle production may be integrated with perennial field crops such as sugar cane, pineapple and sisal or with perennial tree crops such as coconuts, oil palm, rubber and fruit.

It is the by-products of perennial field crops that are of major importance in cattle feeding. Sugar cane, for example, provides three feed by-products; green tops, molasses and bagasse. The processing of the sisal crop provides sisal waste that may be fed fresh or ensiled, and the pineapple crop waste materials from the canning factories that may be fed fresh or ensiled or be dried to produce pineapple bran. In addition cattle may be grazed in sisal plantations and across pineapple stubbles. Many interesting new ideas on the utilization by cattle of sugar cane and sugar-cane by-products have recently been advocated. One is the peeling rather than the crushing of cane, so that the resulting product can be used either for feeding cattle or for sugar production, depending on the market price of sugar. This idea has not been successfully introduced to the industry. Another is the addition of urea and minerals to molasses to produce a supplement that may be used for the feeding of beef cattle on dry grazings. Preston and Willis (1969) have advocated unrestricted feeding of such mixtures to beef cattle, together with a protein feed of low solubility and high biological value, with restricted feeding of forage either in the feed lot or out on the grazings. Bagasse is being pelleted and used as a source of roughage in beef cattle feedlot rations.

Integration of cattle with tree crop production, although at present only practised to a limited extent, probably offers very considerable opportunities for the expansion of cattle production in the humid tropics. For example, coconut plantations can provide pasture under shade for cattle as well as coconut meal as a by-product feed.

In areas where the rainfall exceeds 1,800 mm (71 in), where the soils are not too heavy and where the farmer is able and willing to provide

adequate inputs, cattle can be successfully managed in coconut plantations at a stocking rate of 2·5 livestock units (LSUs) per hectare (1 LSU
per acre) (Hill, 1969). If cattle could only be managed on half the land
at present planted to coconuts in the humid tropics (Table 5.25) the total
number of cattle could be increased by perhaps 5 million head.

Table 5.25   *Estimates of the area planted to coconuts in humid tropical countries in 1970*

Continent	Country	Estimated area of coconuts × 1,000 (ha (acre))
Africa		310 (766)
Americas		275 (680)
Asia		3,350 (8,278)
	India	780 (1,927)
	Indonesia	785 (1,940)
	Malaysia	205 (507)
	Philippines	1,110 (2,743)
	Sri Lanka	410 (1,013)
	Remainder of Asia	260 (642)
Oceania		290 (717)
Humid tropics		4,225 (10,441)

Source: Payne (1976).

Oil palm and rubber plantations, in which legume mixtures are
invariably sown between the rows of trees, can provide varying quantities
of forage during the crop's life cycle and by-product feeds such as oil
palm kernel cake and rubber seed cake. For example, in a crop of rubber
with an average life cycle of 40 years, potential forage production will be
maximal during the first 3 years, decrease to a low level by the tenth
year, remain at a low level for a further 10 years and then slowly increase
The major problem in the integration of cattle with oil palm and rubber
production is to devise an economic method of utilizing the fluctuating
forage supply.

Specialized cattle production systems.   As stated previously, the total
number of intensive specialized cattle operations in the tropics is very
limited. There are three major types of operation:

1. Large, specialized milk producers, who grow out and fatten their own
   surplus male calves.
2. Specialized beef producers using intensively managed planted pasture
   and/or planted pasture under trees. The majority of these could be
   classified within either the ley-farming or the perennial crop cultivation systems.
3. Specialized beef producers purchasing cattle from other producers and

growing them out and/or fattening them in feedlots. Although there may be no place for the feedlot managed in the traditional manner in the majority of tropical countries, it could be of considerable economic importance in the sahel and savanna ecological zones in Africa and in some other regions. In the nomadic and transhumant areas of the sahel and savanna of Africa productivity could be radically improved by the removal of young cattle from the grazings for growing out and/or finishing on crop by-product feeds or forage cultivated in specially favoured locations. Pilot-scale investigational work in Kenya (Creek, 1972) has suggested that such systems can be economic when world demand for beef is at a high level.

The most suitable breeds to use in intensive systems

The major difference between extensive and intensive beef production is that intensive production requires as complete a control of the major environmental factors – climate, nutrition and disease – as it is economically possible to obtain. It is therefore essential that the type of cattle utilized should be able to respond to any improvements in the environment that might be made, and in particular to improvements in the level of nutrition, although some experimental evidence from East Africa suggests that in the absence of climatic stress feed is digested and utilized equally efficiently by *Bos taurus* or *B. indicus* cattle (Rogerson *et al.*, 1968). There is also an increasing volume of experimental evidence from all parts of the tropical and sub-tropical world suggesting that in general *B. indicus* cattle are not as capable as temperate-type *B. taurus* cattle of responding to improvements in their plane of nutrition. In East Africa, Ledger (1968) has shown that at Muguga, where climatic stress is limited as it is situated at an altitude of approximately 2,134 m (7,000 ft), Hereford out-produced Boran cattle from weaning to slaughter both when out on grazings and when stall fed high nutrient content rations (Table 5.26). According to Rogerson, *et al.* (1968) the superiority of the Herefords was due to their higher feed intake per unit of body weight. In Uganda, Joblin (1966) stated that the Teso variety of the Small East African Zebu managed on grazings at Serere did not respond to the provision of moderate supplements of concentrates, consisting of sorghum,

Table 5.26   *Relative growth rates of* Bos taurus *and* B. indicus *cattle at Muguga, Kenya*

Type of cattle	Liveweight gain per day from weaning to slaughter	
	On grazing (kg (lb))	Stall fed (kg (lb))
Bos taurus (Hereford)	0·50 (1·08)	0·84 (1·86)
Bos indicus (Boran)	0·28 (0·62)	0·33 (0·72)

Source: Ledger (1968).

cottonseed cake and cooked or raw cassava. Stobbs (1969), also working at Serere, stated that the grazings had been so improved that it was now essential to utilize cattle with a greater growth potential than the Small East African Zebu. Stobbs (1969) also showed that over a 2-year period crossbred Small East African Zebu × Hereford and Small East African Zebu × Aberdeen Angus produced 36 per cent more lightweight per unit area of grazing than did purebred Small East African Zebu managed in the same way under similar environmental conditions.

Thus available evidence suggests that the most suitable cattle to utilize under intensive grazing management will be temperate-type *Bos taurus* × *B. indicus* crossbreds. These will probably be more productive than purebred *B. indicus*, tropical-type *B. taurus* such as the N'dama or the Criollo, and ancient *B. taurus* × *B. indicus* stabilized crossbreds such as the Sanga cattle of Africa and the indigenous cattle of Southeast Asia.

In Southeast Asia crossbreds between *Bos (Bibos) banteng* and *B. taurus* and *B. indicus* should be tested as these may be more suitable for the humid areas of Southeast Asia than any other type of purebred or crossbred cattle.

We suggest, therefore, that crossbreds should be the cattle of choice for all intensive grazing systems in the tropical regions of all continents. It will of course be necessary to experiment in each region in order to find out what proportion of temperate-type *Bos taurus* blood is most suitable. Francis (1970) has suggested that with improving conditions of husbandry and disease control approximately 50 per cent of *B. taurus* blood would appear to give the most productive animals in many tropical countries.

In perennial tree crop cultivation systems it should be possible to manage cattle with a higher proportion of temperate-type *Bos taurus* blood than on open grazings. In the same climatic environment ambient temperatures are invariably less under the shade of the tree crops and the trees may also have other ameliorative effects. In coconuts the fronds produce local air currents.

The use of stabilized crossbred breeds such as the Santa Gertrudis should also be considered under intensive grazing conditions, particularly on small holdings.

In those tropical countries where there are extensive highland areas – and the continental montane areas are surprisingly large (Table 5.27) – and endemic disease is well controlled, there would appear to be no reason why purebred temperate-type *Bos taurus* beef breeds should not be utilized. They could perform a dual purpose – produce beef and provide bulls to be used for crossbreeding purposes at the lower altitudes. Consideration might also be given to the economics of the transport of feed from the lowland to the montane areas if feeds are going to be used more efficiently by temperate-type *B. taurus* breeds managed at the higher altitudes.

Table 5.27   *The montane areas in each continent as percentages of the total continental areas*

Continent	Percentage total continental area		
	Altitude		
	<153 m (500 ft)	153–914 m (500–3,000 ft)	>914 m (3,000 ft)
Africa	10	65	25
Americas			
North	27	52	21
South	38	43	19
Asia	21	46	33
Europe	54	39	7
Oceania	23	75	2

Source: W. S. Woytinsky and E. S. Woytinsky, *World Population and Production: Trends in Outlook.* © 1953 by the Twentieth Century Fund, New York, p. 13, Table 4.

Under yard- or stall-feeding conditions, where cattle are purchased from breeders, it would appear probable that the higher the percentage of *Bos taurus* blood in the cattle the more they will respond to higher levels of nutrition. This could possibly stimulate crossbreeding as crossbred cattle would probably command a premium price.

As it has been recommended that the dairy industry in the tropics should mainly depend upon the use of crossbred cattle, bull calves and surplus heifers could be a useful source of beef animals for the feetlot industry. If these animals were collected and transported into areas of higher altitude they could be used for the production of 'baby-beef'. Crossbred dairy calves used for 'baby-beef' production should not be castrated unless castration is mandatory in the country, as it has been shown that generally bull calves are 10 to 12 per cent more efficient converters of high nutrient content rations than are steer calves (see also previous sections).

Where producers own small herds it would be necessary to organize and maintain an efficient AI service in order to produce crossbreds. It would also be desirable if the production and marketing of beef by small producers could be organized by an authority that would provide financial and technical services. A description of a proposal of this type in South Thailand has been published by Hunting Technical Services (1974b).

Disease and parasites under intensive managerial systems

It should be easier to control disease under intensive rather than under extensive conditions, but in general the problems are identical. There are, however, a few special problems associated with intensive management of beef cattle. These are as follows:

1. Although cattle may not be grazing, tick control is still absolutely essential in non-tick-free areas and should not be neglected.
2. Similarly, control of internal parasites is still essential, particularly in the younger animals, as many internal parasites may be brought into the yard on forage harvested from the fields.
3. All classes of cattle are likely to be more subject to mineral and vitamin deficiencies when not managed on natural grazings. Special attention should be given to the feeding of minerals and to the possibility that the cattle may not obtain sufficient vitamin A.
4. Baby-beef production provides special problems because of the nature of the feeding system. Cattle fed large quantities of concentrates and relatively small amounts of roughage are prone to digestive upsets, bloat and urinary difficulties due to the deposition of mineral salts in the urethra. In the temperate zone cattle kept under these conditions are also specially prone to coccidiosis and to clostridium infections. It is not known whether this is also the case in the tropics.

Management and feeding under intensive conditions

Intensive management of beef cattle under grazing conditions is more or less similar to that of dairy cattle, and the intensity of operations of course depends primarily on the methods by which the pasture or fodder is managed. Intensification of fodder production has been discussed in Chapter 3 (Part I).

There is, of course, ample information available in the temperate zone as to the most suitable feeds and methods of feeding and managing cattle indoors or in yards. To some extent temperate-zone experience may be used as a guide as to what may be possible in the tropics. We recommend that readers consult Preston and Willis (1970) and Dyer and O'Mary (1972).

The most intensive method of yard or indoor feeding of beef cattle is where the cattle are fed high levels of concentrates for the production of baby-beef. The demand for meat of this type has expanded with the expansion of supermarkets and changes in consumer preference. Baby-beef has a bright red appearance and contains minimum quantities of fat and bone and maximum quantities of lean meat. It is usual to slaughter cattle that have been fed for the production of baby-beef at about 386 to 408 kg (850 to 900 lb) liveweight, as above this liveweight feed conversion rates decrease.

The normal method of feeding is to give the cattle large amounts of grain which, in the tropics, could be maize, sorghum, rice, etc., plus a minimal quantity of good-quality hay or straw together with a protein concentrate, minerals and vitamins. Holsteins stall-fed this type of ration will grow at the rate of 1·6 kg (3·5 lb) per day. The grain used in these rations should be rolled, crushed or bruised, hay intake should be restricted to 0·9 to 1·8 kg (2 to 4 lb) per head per day after 12 weeks of age, and if silage is used instead of hay then the intake should be restricted to 1·8 kg (4 lb) dry matter per head per day. The protein of the concentrate ration should be of a type that will not rapidly break down in the rumen so that excessive nitrogen is not lost before utilization can take place. Water should always be provided *ad lib.*

Except under very special circumstances this type of feeding for beef cattle is likely to remain uneconomic in tropical countries until such time as there is a large surplus of feed grains available. As previously stated, however, less intensive feeding of limited amounts of concentrates and/or by-products might be economic under certain specific conditions.

Some new ideas on the use of sugar-cane by-products in beef cattle feeding have already been discussed in the section concerned with perennial crop cultivation systems.

Molasses has been used for a long time in the liquid form as a supplement for beef cattle, and either alone or mixed with urea and minerals it can be absorbed into a cheap base such as bagasse and fed as a dry concentrate.

In the West Indies it has been proposed that sugar companies could grow and dry elephant grass and use the milled meal as a base on which to absorb a molasses–urea–mineral mixture. This idea would appear to have considerable merit and feasibility studies suggest that an excellent concentrate could be produced at a relatively low price. In East Africa some experimental work has been completed on the absorption of molasses–urea–mineral mixtures on low-cost by-product feeds such as rice and maize bran.

Molasses may also be mixed with concentrates to provide additional energy and to act as a 'binder'. Attempts are also being made to dry and pellet molasses, but the technological difficulties are formidable.

In Jamaica rations for intensively managed beef cattle have been made from dried citrus pulp, dried brewer's grains and coconut meal, and experiments are in progress in Colombia to evaluate the utilization by fattening beef cattle on corn or sorghum silage and cottonseed meal.

The wider use of urea or other forms of non-protein nitrogen such as diammonium phosphate in the feeding of intensively managed beef cattle is being explored. The utilization of these products has been reviewed by Loosli and McDonald (1968). They state that the available experimental evidence suggests that when fattening beef cattle have been fed high-grain rations satisfactory results have been obtained where urea has provided 25 per cent of the nitrogen in the ration, but that at higher levels than this the palatability of the ration has decreased, causing intake problems. They further state that in the total ration the amount of urea should not exceed one per cent.

Yards and buildings. Where cattle are intensively managed in yards it is essential that the design of the buildings should be such as to save labour in feeding and handling and reduce heat stress on the cattle to a minimum. It should be emphasized that requirements are somewhat different in the dry as opposed to the humid tropics. Whereas in the dry tropics buildings should, in general, be oriented along an east–west axis in order to reduce heat stress to a minimum, in the more humid tropics it is preferable to orient them along a north–south axis in order to ensure that there is some drying out of the floor area on account of the sunlight travelling over the area of shade for some part of the day. It is also important to remember that water should always be available *ad lib.* in either the dry or the humid tropics. Further details on yards and buildings are given in a later section.

Weaning.   The intensive producer is not often concerned with weaning as he is usually not a breeder. However, in the case of producers in montane regions who are interested in baby-beef production, they should purchase calves that have been weaned at as early an age as possible and preferably those that are 5 to 6 weeks of age. At this age Holsteins, the preferred breed that could be available in montane areas, should weigh 64 to 73 kg (140 to 160 lb). Marking would normally be completed before the cattle are intensively fed.

Castration.   Under feedlot conditions castration should be delayed as long as is legally possible, as bulls grow faster and produce leaner meat in the feedlot than do steers (see previous sections).

Dehorning.   Yarded animals should be dehorned.

Animal health practices.   Tick control is necessary in non-tick-free areas, although the frequency of operations can probably be radically reduced compared with that required on grazings.

Planning and development of beef enterprises

Few extensive or intensive holdings in the tropics are well planned. In general, very little attention has been paid to this aspect of cattle husbandry. On subsistence holdings the layout is usually completely haphazard.

Layout

Unless there is a rational layout on extensive holdings it is impossible to maximize labour productivity or to be able to plan efficiently for future intensification. On intensive holdings a well-planned layout is required in order to maximize gains in productivity that are made possible by the use of improved pastures, genetically superior cattle and better overall pasture and animal management. The advantages of well-planned feedlots are obvious.

On large and small holdings the first step towards the attainment of an integrated and efficient layout is a master plan. This should not be sacrosanct but continuously updated in the light of experience and economic circumstances as the development of the holding proceeds. A survey plan is the ideal to use as a starting point for the master plan, but this is not often available. Aerial photographs can be of considerable assistance.

Roads and drainage

On extensive holdings the building of roads may not be a major problem as fully formed roads are almost certain to be uneconomical and there is usually ample space to make a new track if the old one becomes impassable. However, a good all-weather access road is usually required to run from the entrance to the headquarters of the holding.

In hill country, drainage of roads need not be expensive as the roads can be strategically placed so that water runs away from them without the provision of expensive culverts. As far as is possible roads should be planned to run along ridges. Comparatively cheap ranch roads can be easily and rapidly built using a bulldozer or grader. It is usually desirable to have a perimeter track running inside the perimeter fence, if only to give access to the fence for repair purposes. Such a road can also act as a fire-break.

On intensive holdings in the humid tropics it is important that access roads should be usable during the wetter periods. It is better to build a road on top of an existing grass cover and raise the level above that of the fields and then use gravel or road metal for the surface. On intensive holdings a minimum road width between fences is 5 m (16 ft), with access to every field for cattle and machinery. This can be achieved by offsetting the gates; a 3·4 m (11 ft) gateway is usually of sufficient width for cattle and machinery to pass.

Adequate drainage must be provided on both sides of roads on intensive holdings in the wet tropics. These should be waterways built so that they can be maintained using mechanical equipment.

Fencing and shade trees

On both extensive and intensive holdings expenditure on fencing normally represents a high proportion of the total capital expenditure. There is thus every incentive to plan and build fencing as economically as possible. The smaller and the more intensive the holding the greater the length of fencing required. For example, in a large square-shaped 900 ha (2,224 acre) holding divided into six paddocks, 0·023 km (0·014 mile) of fencing per hectare would be required, whereas on a small 30 ha (74 acre) holding divided into thirty paddocks, 0·24 km (0·15 mile) of fencing per hectare would be necessary. Thus close fencing of the small farm would be ten times as expensive per unit area as limited fencing on the large farm.

The number of paddocks required on any holding will depend primarily on the type of management. In principle, the more numerous the paddocks the greater the flexibility in terms of intensity of stocking and the number of different classes of cattle that can be managed. Like all desirable objectives, however, sub-division can be overdone. Little can be expected from additional sub-division beyond what is necessary for efficient grazing practice.

In arid areas the number of internal fence divisions may be very limited. Indeed it may be more economical to herd livestock than to fence. However, on extensive holdings in the humid tropics there is evidence to suggest that field size should be as small as is practicable. Square fields have the lowest fencing cost per unit area.

As cattle prefer to graze walking up steep slopes, fences running across the slope should be avoided.

1. *Wire fences.*   The price of wire is closely related to its weight. Provided it is sufficiently strong for the purpose envisaged, it is most economical to purchase wire that provides the greatest length for a given weight. Approximate lengths of wire per 45·4 kg (100 lb) weight are:

No. 8 gauge plain	462 m (1,516 ft)
No. 12 gauge barbed	425 m (1,393 ft)
12½ gauge high tensile	1,205 m (3,953 ft)

Barbed wire costs more per unit length and has a shorter life than plain wire. High-tensile wire is most economical but is difficult to tie and has little elasticity. It requires particularly good strainer posts.

Staples used in fastening wires to wooden posts should be galvanized. All types of wire will last longer in drier areas. Wire in fences close to the sea will only have one-third of the life of wire on fences located inland.

Posts may be made of green timber, treated timber, concrete or steel, or live posts may be used. Some details of tropical timber trees that can be used for the manufacture of wooden fence posts are given in Table 5.18. In many parts of the tropics the cheapest posts will be those manufactured from treated, non-durable timber. Common preservatives are coal tar, creosote and pentachlorophenol. Full details of methods of post preservation, of which there are several, are given by the CSIRO (1955). The life of treated posts varies according to the climatic environment. Strohman (1957) stated that in Hawaii untreated eucalyptus fence posts lasted from 2 to 4 years, whereas with cold soaking treatment they lasted from 4 to 8 years and with hot and cold soaking treatment or pressure treatment they lasted 10 to 20 years.

Concrete posts are expensive to make, costly to handle and easily broken. They have the advantages of being fire resistant and long lasting. These posts can be made on the farm using a suitable mould. A 1·2 m (4 ft) high fence requires posts that are at least 1·8 m (6 ft) long and

15 × 15 cm (4·5 × 4·5 in) thick at ground level. Strainer posts should be at least 2·4 m (8 ft) long and 19 × 19 cm (7·5 × 7·5 in) thick. A suitable concrete mixture to use consists of one part of cement, two parts of sand, one part of clean shingle and one part of crushed rock. Reinforcing is essential, and four 0·6 cm (0·25 in) diameter steel rods wired together at 46 cm (18 in) intervals to make a frame is satisfactory. Thin bamboo may be used, but it is a poor substitute for steel.

The advantages of steel stakes are that they are easy to transport and to install, but they usually have to be imported and they easily rust. In order to minimize rust they may be painted with an asphalt-based paint.

Live posts are the cheapest, but their use is limited to the more humid areas. The great disadvantage of live fencing is high maintenance cost. They do have an added advantage that they can also be allowed to grow and act as shade trees and suitable species can also provide browse. Some useful common live-post species are detailed in Table 5.17.

For details on erection procedures the reader is referred to some of the several good bulletins that have been published on fencing techniques (Rodda, 1956; Philipp, 1961; Bishop, 1961–62; Reynolds, 1968).

The major points to note when erecting fences are as follows:

(a) That the strainer post or strainer assembly must be well installed. If there is a distance of 100 m (328 ft) or more between strainer posts then these should be buried at least 1·2 m (4 ft) in the ground and held in position by 2·1 m (7 ft) long by 10 × 10 cm (4 × 4 in) stays.
(b) The intermediate posts should be exactly in line and well erected. For cattle it is normal to space the intermediate posts 5 m (16 ft) apart and they should be 1·2 m (4 ft) above ground level. In a five-wire fence the top wire should be 112 cm (44 in) above the ground and the other wires spaced at 25, 25, 20 and 20 cm (10, 10, 8 and 8 in) intervals. The top of the post should be 10 cm (4 in) above the top wire. If it is a four-wire fence the wires should be 30, 30 and 25 cm (12, 12 and 10 in) below the top wire. If the distance between inter-mediate posts is more than 5 m (16 ft) then the fence must be pro-vided with battens or droppers. The top of these should be more or less level with the top wire and the bottom at least 8 cm (3 in) from the ground. Droppers can be made of wood, wire or strip steel.
(c) The wires must be kept tight and straight.
(d) The procedure should be first to erect the strainer post and stays, then to attach two plain guide wires to them, one at the top and one at the bottom. This should be followed by the erection of the guide posts and then the remaining intermediate posts should be installed. Finally the wires should be attached to the posts.

When a fence has to cross a steep gully it should be carried straight across from one bank to the other with the bottom wire just above the level of known floods. A swinging gate should be attached to the bottom of the wire that can close when the gully is empty, but rise with the flood water.

If posts are very expensive they can be spaced further apart and anchors or foots can be used in the fence instead of posts. These fences are known as swinging or suspension fences, and high-tensile wire should be used in their construction.

2. *Stone walls.*   These are common in the West Indies and in Hawaii and are occasionally used in other parts of the tropics such as northern Nigeria. The advantage of a stone wall is the low maintenance cost. The disadvantages are the high initial cost of construction and the lack of skilled stone-wall builders. In Hawaii dry stone walls are 0·9 to 1·2 m (3 to 4 ft) high and 0·9 to 1·2 m (3 to 4 ft) wide at the base.

3. *Hedges.*   These are not at present generally used for enclosure in the tropics though they are common in some parts of East Africa and in some regions of the Americas and Southeast Asia. There are a number of suitable species (Table 5.28). Hedges have the advantage of low initial cost, but maintenance can be labour intensive and consequently expen-

Table 5.28   *Some useful tropical hedge species*

Botanical name	Common name
I. For use in the drier areas	
Acacia modesta	
Agave americana	American aloe
Agave sisalana	Sisal
Caesalpina sepiaria	
Carissa grandiflora	Natal plum
Dodonea viscosa	Pichou
Euphorbia tirucalli	Milk hedge
Jatropha curcas	Physic nut
Opuntia dillenii	Prickly pear
Pithecellobium dulce	Madras thorn
Zizyphus spina-christi	Crown of thorns
II. For use in the wetter areas	
The majority of species listed in Table 5.17 as suitable for use as 'live posts' can also be used for hedges.	
Casuarina equisetifolia	She-oak
Duranta plumieri	Duranta
III. For use in the montane areas	
Aberia caffra (will grow up to 2,500 m (8,202 ft) altitude)	Kei apple
Berberis arista	Berberry
Dodonea viscosa (will grow up to 2,000 m (6,552 ft) altitude)	

sive. This may be no disadvantage on subsistence farms in the humid tropics where available labour is often underemployed during some seasons.

4. *Log fences.* When land is cleared a bush or log fence may be built. In the dry tropics thornbush laid in lines will make a stockproof fence that will last 2 or 3 years. These are common in the sahel and savanna ecological zones in Africa. In the humid tropics a log fence can be built from felled trees, using a bulldozer during clearing operations. Fences of this type can be quite stockproof and may last from 2 or 3 to 10 years.

5. *Electric fences.* These can be cheap to erect and one type is easily moved. The disadvantages of electric fences are that they need regular inspection and maintenance and are therefore only really useful on intensive holdings. There are two types: the high voltage/high impedance and the high current/low impedance. The first type is used over short distances where cattle are rotationally grazed and the fences are frequently shifted. The second type is used for more extensive multi-wired fencing and is said to operate satisfactorily over quite long distances.

6. *Field gates.* Hanging gates can be made of wood, steel or aluminium or some combination of these materials. Provided it is well angle-braced a 1·2 m (4 ft) high hanging gate can be made 4·6 m (15 ft) long. If the gate is longer than 4·6 m (15 ft) then additional support must be provided from the top of the strainer post or two gates must be used.

Wire gates are cheaply constructed and quite satisfactory if they are properly constructed, but they are more tedious to open and shut (Fig. 5.23). An inexpensive 3·7 m (12 ft) pole and chain gate is also illustrated in Fig. 5.23.

7. *Shade.* Shade trees are important in both the wet and the dry tropics. However, overall requirements for shade depend on the type of cattle utilized and managerial policy. When a choice is made of the most suitable shade trees to use it should be possible to combine the provision of shade with the production of fruit, nuts, browse, firewood or saleable timber. Some details of suitable shade trees are given in Table 5.19.

8. *Shelter belts.* These are not normally required at lower altitudes in the humid tropics, but may be of great utility in the drier areas and in the montane tropics. An ideal shelter belt consists of tall trees planted in the centre, surrounded by shorter species with shrubs or very small trees on the outside of these. Shelter belts should generally be planted at right angles to the prevailing winds and the species used should preferably possess a dense and evergreen foliage, a strong tough wood and be capable of natural regeneration from suckers or seeds. Some suitable species are recommended in Table 5.29.

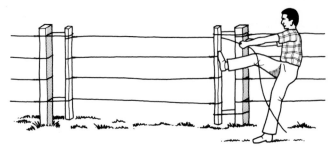

(a) Making a wire gate

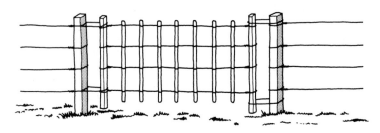

(b) The completed gate

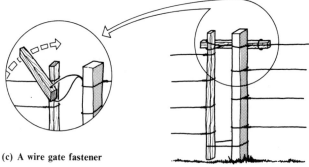

(c) A wire gate fastener

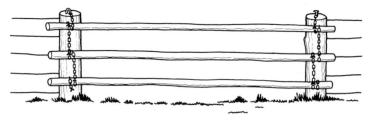

(d) A pole and chain gate

Fig. 5.23   Some details of wire gates and of a pole and chain gate. (a) Making a wire gate. (b) The completed gate. (c) A wire gate fastener. (d) A pole and chain gate.

Table 5.29 *Some suitable tropical shelter-belt species*

Botanical name	Common name	Preferred environment
Acacia dealbata	Silver wattle	Montane; > 1,829 m (6,000 ft) near the equator
Acacia decurrens	Green wattle	Grows on poorer soils than *A. dealbala* and *A. mearasii*
Acacia mearasii (synonym *A. decumens* var. mollis)	Black wattle	As *A. dealbata*
Andira inermis	Bastard mahogany	Lowland, humid
Bixa orellana	Annatto	Lowland, humid, useful when used with larger species
Cedrela serrulata		Montane; at medium altitude
Cinnamomum camphora		Montane; at medium altitude; humid
Eucalyptus spp.	Eucalyptus	Many species; one or the other suitable for lowland or montane; humid or dry; widely grown in montane areas
Eugenia jambos	Rose apple	Lowland: humid
Grevillea robusta	Silky oak	Montane; at medium altitude; dry
Pinus patula		Montane
Pinus radiata		Montane
Pinus caribaea		Lowland
Tamarindus indica		Lowland; dry to humid
Tecoma leucoxylon		Lowland

Water supplies

The first essential is to estimate what the total consumption of water is likely to be on the holding. Some details of average consumption of water by cattle are given in Table 5.30. Water for direct human and cattle consumption should be free from disease-producing organisms and should not contain excessive quantities of organic or inorganic materials in suspension or excessive dissolved mineral salts.

Water may be obtained from natural sources (rivers, streams, springs, rockholes and waterholes), from underground water resources (shallow and deep wells) or from catchment areas (roofs, rocky hills, field tanks and dams).

1. *Natural sources.* The suitability of the water depends upon activities upstream or around the natural source. Springs should be fenced and the water run into a drinking trough. Cattle should not be encouraged to drink from rivers if the banks are steep.

2. *Underground water resources.* Shallow wells should be no less than 9 m (30 ft) deep and be sunk on a hillock rather than in a hollow in

Table 5.30   *Estimated daily water requirements of different classes of cattle in the tropics*

	Daily water requirement per animal	
	Wetter regions (litre (gal))	Drier regions (litre (gal))
Milking cows	65–75 (14–17)	75–85 (17–19)
Dry cows, heifers and steers	50 (11)	55 (12)
Bulls	50–65 (11–14)	55–70 (12–15)
Fatteners	65 (14)	70 (15)
Calves	18–32 (4–7)	21–36 (5–8)

Note: Under range conditions 50 per cent should be added to these allowances in order to offset wastage.

order to minimize surface pollution. It is preferable for the top of the well to be lined with brick, timber or brushwood. It is usual throughout many of the drier areas of Africa and Asia to construct shallow drinking troughs in clay alongside the wells (Plate 5.31).

Deep wells are usually dug with drills whose maximum diameter is no more than 20 cm (8 in). They may be artesian or sub-artesian. Artesian water is often hot and must be cooled before being used for drinking purposes. Deep wells are expensive and are normally provided by a government authority. They should be closely controlled.

3. *Catchment areas.*   A major difference between field tanks or *hafirs* and dams is that tanks only collect catchment water and cannot be washed away, as they are constructed in depressions that may or may not have outlets, whereas dams catch flowing water and can be washed away by heavy rains unless they are properly constructed. Useful information on the construction of field tanks and dams in the tropical areas of Australia is provided by Beattie (1962).

4. *Water-supply systems.*   These may be classified as gravity, hydropneumatic and pneumatic. The choice of system depends upon local circumstances. Specialized texts should be consulted for details of these systems.

5. *Pumps.*   There are a multiplicity of types available and professional advice should be sought as to the most suitable pump to use in any specific location.

6. *Reticulation systems.*   On extensive holdings or in nomadic or transhumant areas short lengths of pipe may be used to deliver water from a pump located at a river, stream, rockhole, waterhole, shallow or deep well or a tank or dam to watering troughs. Otherwise piped systems are not generally required. In the humid tropics under intensive conditions

Plate 5.31 A typical shallow drinking trough made from soil.

piped supplies may occasionally be justified. In areas where the water table is high and labour plentiful, such as the northern coastal regions of Colombia, it may be economic to sink shallow wells and provide hand pumps adjacent to each watering trough. There is now a choice of galvanized and plastic pipe. The latter is less costly and cheaper to install.

7. *Water troughs.* Water troughs can be constructed of galvanized iron or concrete. They should be sufficiently large to allow the cattle to drink freely without congestion. Circular and square tanks ensure that the maximum number of cattle can drink per unit length of the rim of the tank. The normal height of tanks is 38 to 46 cm (15 to 18 in). As mentioned previously clay tanks can also be constructed. They are cheap to construct but usually only last one season. These usually have a rim only 15 to 23 cm (6 to 9 in) above the ground (Plate 5.31).

Buildings and yards

Beef farms, whether extensive or intensive, usually only require handling yards and the minimum of buildings. Large holdings may require some buildings for offices, storage, etc. We will only discuss handling yards and auxiliary equipment in this text.

1. *Handling yards*

These should normally be centrally located, on well-drained land where drinking water is available. Their location may of course determine their layout.

The size of the handling yard will be determined by the number of cattle that have to be worked at any one time. On very large holdings it is usually both more practical and economic to build several handling yards than to bring very large numbers of cattle to one very large handling yard.

Handling yards usually include assembly, holding, drafting and work yards, with forcing pens and crushes. Equipment may include a veterinary crush, a dip or spray and a weighing crush. There can of course be many and varied designs incorporating some or all of these features.

Whatever the design, there are certain considerations applicable to all. The most important are that the yard be located on land that can stand the constant wear of a multitude of cattle hoofs; that the containing fences be strong enough to withstand the shock of bunched cattle trying to break through and high enough to prevent a beast from jumping over – to contain large, active Zebu cattle the fence needs to be at least 1·7 m (5·5 ft) high in the main yards and 1·8 m (6 ft) high at the approaches and around the crush; and that the fences are free from projections which may cause damage to the cattle or to the workers.

Wire fencing is not suitable for such yards. Materials that are strong and that are seen to be strong are needed. Substantial sawn timber, preferably hardwood, is satisfactory. Rails should be 20×8 cm (8×3 in) sawn timber where the cattle are very large and are likely to be wild. Otherwise 15×5 cm (6×2 in) timber rails can be used. Tubular metal is the ideal material if cost is of secondary consideration. Water pipe is usually available and in some areas, particularly where there are sugar factories, old boiler pipes may be obtainable. Concrete posts are not usually very satisfactory as under intense pressure they may snap at the junction with the ground. They are, however, sometimes used. Stone walls or other solid structures are objectionable, because they hinder the worker's movements and obstruct his sight, and they are usually uncomfortably hot to work in during daylight hours. Uprights should be no more than 2·1 m (7 ft) apart and be set at least 0·8 m (2·5 ft) in the ground. When 15 cm (6 in) timber rails are used for a 1·7 m (5·5 ft) high fence, four are required. From the ground upwards these should be spaced at 25, 23, 23 and 36 cm (10, 9, 9 and 14 in) intervals, the top of the top rail being 167 cm (66 in) from the ground. With a higher fence an additional bar may be required.

The plan of a conventional yard designed to handle 100 head of cattle is shown in Fig. 5.24. This type of yard has been found to be satisfactory when numbers of cattle have to be worked and passed through quickly.

Where large numbers of cattle have to be handled by a very small labour force considerable ingenuity has been displayed in the design of handling yards. One very labour-saving innovation is the control of all

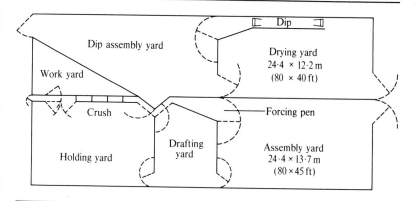

Fig. 5.24 Plan of a handling yard which will accommodate up to 100 head of cattle.

the doors in the sorting pens from a central point, using some form of compressed air system.

Useful plans of different types of handling yards are described and illustrated in detail by Beattie (1962).

2. Cattle crushes

The design essentials in a crush are that it should be sufficiently strong to restrain any cattle likely to be driven into it; that cattle should not be able to damage themselves while in it; and that it should provide the necessary facilities for handling the animals, using the minimum of labour.

A common fault in the design of crushes is to provide too much room for the individual animal. This encourages struggling, attempts to jump out and crowding up by one animal on the animal either in front or behind. It also makes any type of operation on the animal difficult, if not dangerous.

The average width of a crush for large tropical-type cattle should be no more than 70 cm (27·5 in), although the sides of the crush do not have to be vertical and it is desirable that the standing space in the crush should be narrower. Standing space does not need to be more than 53 cm (21 in) wide. The height of the crush does not have to be more than 152 cm (5 ft). The length will depend upon how many cattle the operator wishes to retain in the crush at any one time. Five or six are a suitable number.

The crush may be constructed of tubular metal, sawn timber or roughly dressed timber. Tubular metal is most satisfactory.

The work to be done in the crush may take only a few seconds for each animal, such as in sorting, or it may occupy a longer period as when animals are inoculated. There are also occasions when the work to be done may take a considerable time – as in dehorning or in a veterinary examination. Thus the crush needs to be very versatile. When the holding

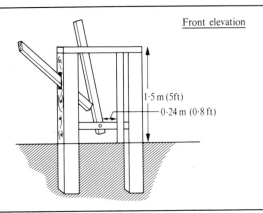

Fig. 5.25   A simple type of head restraint for cattle.

time is short a holding arrangement is required that can be quickly applied or removed so that the flow of cattle through the crush is not impeded. At the end of the crush the control can be a 'drop' or sliding gate, while within the crush and between animals it can be single poles, somewhat wider than the crush and about 10 cm (4 in) in diameter, slipped through brackets on the race or between uprights. These poles can be slotted in behind each animal in order to prevent them from moving backwards. This arrangement can effectively restrain cattle for a short period. For longer periods some form of head restraint is required.

The most suitable arrangement is to have what is essentially two types of crush in one unit. The type of crush described above would have a more elaborate holding arrangement at the exit end where the animal could be restrained by the head and body and where operative work such as dehorning could be conducted. The essentials of this section of the crush are a head restraint (a simple type which could be constructed by any small livestock owner with access to a minimum of tools is illustrated in Fig. 5.25); a length of no more than 1·9 m (6·3 ft); some form of back restraint; and a hinged gate on one side (Plate 5.32) that allows easy access to any part of the animal's body. Details of the design of a suitable crush of this type are shown in Fig. 5.26. It is possible to purchase manufactured standard crushes of this type that can be attached to the end of a locally built crush.

The whole length of the crush should be floored with concrete, and where practicable the concrete should be built up to a height of 0·6 m (2 ft) on either side of the race. This forms a supporting base for the uprights, a protection for the feet and legs of the stock and a platform for the workers.

3. *Buildings for small-scale cattle fatteners*

As stated previously small-scale beef fattening is conducted in certain

Plate 5.32 Crush and walk-through bail unit with a hinged gate (Department of Agriculture and Stock, Brisbane).

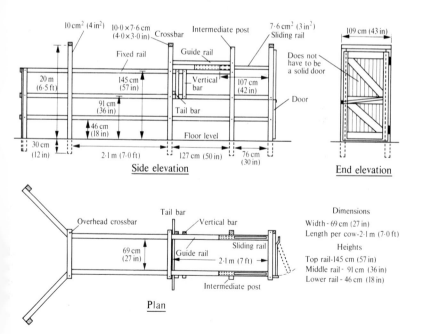

Fig. 5.26 Plan of a suitable cattle crush.

specific areas of the tropics. The cattle are usually stall-fed in a hut, often in almost total darkness. Occasionally they are fed outside in small, shaded yards.

The walls of the hut are usually made of mud and the roof of thatch. A small space is left at the eaves for ventilation, but there are normally no windows, simply an open door. There is something to be said in favour of this primitive structure; it discourages flies, it effectively excludes direct exposure to the sun and reduces the inflow of hot air, it is conducive to rest, and while it restrains the animal it allows movement sufficient for comfort. Its chief defect is that by stopping practically all air currents it does not permit advantage to be taken of the very considerable relief they can afford to fattening animals.

The standing is insanitary, but accumulation of manure is an important sideline of the business and probably no other form of stable can so effectively promote the collection and decomposition of excrement and litter. A fattening ox produces about 4·1 t (4 tons) of solid manure and about 1·54 t (1·5 tons) of liquid manure per annum.

Defects of this simple type of building can be corrected by redesigning the walls so as to permit the free passage of air at all levels. Ventilating spaces can be opened at appropriate heights or, if the wall is made of brick, by leaving sufficient spaces it can be constructed in the form of a screen rather than as a solid wall. When timber is available, rough uprights spaced a few inches from each other can be substituted for the mud wall.

Such walls are satisfactory in a humid climate where there is no great difference in the temperature throughout the 24 hours; however, where there is a great variation between the maximum and minimum daily temperatures the solid walls are less objectionable than they might at first appear and are often preferable to semi-open ones. In any case, the roof, preferably thatched, should amply overlay the walls by a distance of at least 0·6 m (2 ft).

The most economical size of such a building is one with a diameter of 3·7 m (12 ft) which will comfortably hold two mature bullocks of the larger breeds. If built of mud or sun-dried bricks, the wall should be 2·4 m (8 ft) high and at least 23 cm (9 in) thick.

4. *Feedlots*

Feedlot design is a specialized operation. We suggest that interested readers should consult Preston and Willis (1970) and Dyer and O'Mary (1972). Space requirements for yarded beef cattle are given in Table 5.31. In all feeding yards or feedlots in the tropics shade must be incorporated. Approximately 3·7 m^2 (40 ft^2) per adult animal is required. Water and feed troughs should be shaded.

Table 5.31   *The general space requirements of yarded (feedlot) beef cattle*

	Area of yard per head $(m^2\ (ft^2))$	Area of shade per head $(m^2\ (ft^2))$	Height of shade $(m\ (ft))$
Earth yards			
Medium-size yards holding <150 head			
Drier areas	7 (75)	2·5–4·5 (27–48)	3·0–3·7 (10–12)
Wetter areas	<37 (400)	2·5–4·5 (27–48) with concrete base*	3·0–3·7 (10–12)
Slatted floor houses†			
Small yards holding <15 head	1·9–2·3 (20–25)		

Feeding troughs

Length of trough per head: 15 cm (6 in)
 (on assumption that feed is always available)
Width of concrete apron in front of the feeding trough: 1·8–2·4 m (6–8 ft)

Watering troughs

Length of trough per 10 head: 30 cm (12 in)‡
 (on assumption that water is always available)
In houses one automatic water bowl should be provided for every 10–15 head

*If the area below the shade is not concreted a larger shade area will be required.
†If the slatted floor is in a yard and not in a building shade will be required.
‡A concrete 'apron' is also desirable in front of the water trough.

Transport of trade stock

There are few beef-raising areas in the tropics which are served with adequate transport facilities and seldom has the stockowner a choice of how his cattle should be conveyed to market; they might, however, go by one of four ways, namely, on the hoof, by road, by rail or by air transport.

Movement on foot

Cattle which are almost continually on the move in search of food should not be much inconvenienced by moving in one direction for the same distance as they do on their feeding range each day. Thus it might be thought that droving would in all circumstances be the most economical way of moving livestock. For short distances, it undoubtedly is, but over long distances such a categorical statement about it cannot be made because many considerations are involved.

Droving may well be the least expensive method when an adequate supply of food and water can be arranged at suitable points along the route or when a herd can be watered night and morning, and where during the interval it can move at leisure from one post to another while grazing on the way. These happy conditions are seldom found, at least after the herd has joined the main route. On these tracks feed soon becomes scarce, particularly in the dry season, and as one drove follows another it well-nigh disappears. For a time feed can be obtained by skirting the tracks, on land where there is no objection to roving, but such grazings eventually lie too far away to permit of their use if the cattle are to make a reasonable rate of progress to the destination. More often, the owners of the land in the vicinity of the track will not permit grazing.

As well as these reasons why trade cattle must be kept to a well-defined track, there is one other, i.e. the danger that the wandering cattle may spread contagious disease in the country through which they pass. As long as they are kept to defined routes it is possible for the authorities to check their health from time to time, to control disease if it should appear and to give protection to those in danger.

As a controlled, danger-free, unimpeded passage of trade cattle through a country may confer as much benefit to the general community as it does to the owners and because they are often a necessity, trade routes are usually the concern of governments.

Ordinarily it is the location of water which decides how the route will run and also the rate at which the stock will move along it. Where watering points are plentiful, movement is at the discretion of the drover, but where they are located at long intervals, he has no choice but to cover the distance before extreme thirst decimates his stock. For the cattle to travel under such stress results in serious loss of liveweight which, in West Africa has at times been estimated to be as much as 50 per cent. In West Africa, as in other regions of Africa, cattle which have successfully transversed country where scarcity of water is the hazard have to face another danger in the form of a 'tsetse-fly belt' through which, if they are not protected, they must pass very quickly. Even under more favourable conditions in other parts of the world, a shrinkage of up to 20 per cent of liveweight is common and 10 to 15 per cent would be accepted as normal. Only mature cattle are fit to undergo long journeys on foot under these conditions.

Indigenous cattle can manage fairly well when water points are located 19 to 24 km (12 to 15 miles) apart, but in many countries that is not possible. Intervals of over 32 km (20 miles) have to be accepted and sometimes a 2-day journey separates water points. If finished cattle are not to suffer serious liveweight shrinkage water should be available at no more than 8 km (5 mile) intervals, and there should be facilities for grazing or for obtaining conserved forage *en route*. This statement is particularly valid for any temperate-type or crossbred cattle.

The supply of feed offers almost as great a problem as that of water in certain seasons of the year. In localities where a satisfactory fodder reserve can be accumulated at each post for the feeding of trekked cattle, 4·5 kg (10 lb) per head will allow the cattle to continue trekking and the route to be kept open, but it will not prevent the cattle losing weight.

The loss from death which may be expected on a given route is unpredictable, but depends chiefly on the prevailing cattle diseases and the weather, and upon what facilities are afforded to withstand them. Where beef is acceptable in any condition, much of the loss to the owner is avoided by emergency slaughter and sale of the meat at a village or township along the route.

Transport on hoof entails loss from shrinkage, loss from death as well as drovers' pay, taxes, tolls and extortions.

Rail transport

Over long distances rail transport effects saving on maintenance and handling changes, tolls and other incidental expenses as well as from shrinkage and deaths. Loss from shrinkage under the worst conditions of rail transport may be as high as 10 per cent, but should normally range between 3 and 5 per cent on a journey of of up to 72 hours. That does not, of course, take into account losses arising before entrainment. Loss from bruising may be considerable. It has been observed in Kenya that rail transport resulted in down-grading of some 7 to 8 per cent of carcases and that it could be greatly reduced as the following data indicate:

	Bruising observed	Not observed	Total	Percentage with bruising
Horned cattle	271	378 }	788	41·8
Polled cattle	28	111 }		20·1
Exotic cattle	176	118 }	685	59·9
Indigenous cattle	152	239 }		38·9
Bedding used	82	156 }	915	34·5
Bedding not used	454	223 }		67·0
Sexes mixed	78	206 }	915	27·5
Sexes not mixed	83	548 }	348	13·2

It would appear from these observations that a single-sex group of polled, indigenous cattle that were provided with bedding would suffer the least bruising.

Railway trucks which are to carry livestock should be roofed, provide for free passage of air and have battened or non-slip floors. If they are not designed for end-to-end loading they should have movable partitions to facilitate side loading and to help cattle to keep on their feet while the train is moving. Cattle should be packed in a truck close enough to prevent them being thrown about during transit. They should be grouped so that those of approximately the same size and condition are trucked together. Horned cattle should be secured by their horns to the truck side; they should stand head to tail so that alternate animals face in the opposite direction.

The stock should be watered every 24 to 27 hours and, when practicable, should also be fed at these intervals. On journeys of more than 3 days' duration, offloading of the cattle for feed and rest should be compulsory, not only for humane reasons but also to prevent undue loss in body weight.

At the railhead, arrangements must be made for watering, feeding and resting the stock before subjecting them to the rigours of a train journey under tropical climatic conditions. If grazing is not adequate and accessible, a supply of forage must be made available for hand feeding. A minimum of 9 kg (20 lb) of forage per head per day is desirable. Water should also be freely available in troughs, whose approaches and surroundings should be able to withstand constant trampling and wear. The minimum requirement for water would be 23 litres (5 gal) per animal per day.

Where a large number of cattle are regularly loaded a reception yard with crush and sorting facilities should be constructed of a size suitable for the number of cattle expected at any one time. The sorting pen should lead to pens sufficiently large to hold one truckful of cattle, and these to loading pens, which in turn should lead by a ramp, with a gradient of not more than 1:2, to a loading platform on a level with the floor of the truck. These yards should be built according to the specifications given for cattle yards in a previous section. Discarded rails or sleepers make very suitable material for yard construction. If additional horizontal rails are added to the lower half of standard cattle yard fences so that there is no more than 13 cm (5 in) gaps between rails, the yards can be used for the holding, sorting and loading of small stock as well as cattle.

Animals should not be loaded more than one hour before the rail journey commences.

Road transport

As stated in a previous section transport of stock by road is increasing very rapidly in many tropical countries. The major constraint is a lack of all-weather roads. For example, in the western savanna region of the Sudan, a major cattle-producing region, there are at present few all-weather roads between the Nile and the Tschad border. Consequently, cattle are still mainly trekked to Khartoum, very limited numbers being transported by rail. Unformed roads are not only liable to be impassable during the rainy season but the maintenance of vehicles is so expensive that livestock transport becomes prohibitively expensive, and in addition the cattle are likely to be badly bruised or even more seriously hurt during transit.

The advantages of transporting cattle by road, where there are all-weather roads, are obvious. The cattle can be loaded at the farm or at the holding yard out on the range and directly transported to their destination without serious shrinkage loss.

Air transport

This method of transporting live animals is too expensive to allow of its use in the marketing of fat cattle. It is, however, a method that is growing in importance for the transport of breeding cattle from one country to another.

However, under special and specific conditions, it is an economic method of transporting meat and some details of the air transport of carcases have been given in a previous section.

Beef quality

It is impossible to define a universal standard of beef quality. Consumer preference, that depends to some extent on a specific cooking culture, may vary from country to country, or from one social class to another within a country. It can also gradually change within a country or a social class in accordance with changing economic circumstance or the dictates of fashion. For example, in most Western industrialized societies, until comparatively recent times the production of high-quality beef required a well-finished carcase with a high fat content. However, consumer preference has changed and present demand is for lean beef with a minimum fat cover, although with some fat within the muscle or 'marbling'.

The contrasts in consumer preference occurring in the tropics are typified by the differences in consumer demand in Southeast Asia and East Africa. In Southeast Asia very lean meat is required and beef from *Bos* (*Bibos*) spp.-type cattle is preferred where it is available. On the contrary, fat meat is still demanded by the majority of African consumers in East Africa, and carcases possessing a degree of fatness unacceptable to the Southeast Asian consumer are considered to produce quality meat and are highly prized.

A major difference between present consumers in most industrialized societies and consumers in most tropical countries is that the latter prize offals and consider them to be of high quality, whereas consumers in the industrialized societies eat less and less offals and generally consider them to be of inferior quality. As a consequence of these attitudes, cattle of similar liveweight and carcase composition will provide more animal protein and perhaps more high-quality animal protein per head of population in the tropics.

In most tropical countries the average consumer still demands fresh meat, as chilled and frozen meat is unacceptable. This preference has certainly delayed rationalization of the livestock and meat-marketing systems in many of these countries.

If fresh meat is demanded by the consumer then killing usually takes place during the night, the fresh meat being available in the market by dawn and retail sales being completed early in the morning.

In the Philippines, where some of the major beef-production areas are located far from the major centres of consumption, attempts to rationalize the beef industry by siting abattoirs close to the production areas and shipping chilled beef to the major consumption centres have not been very successful. There has been very considerable resistance to this innovation as the majority of indigenous consumers wish to see the meat that they will purchase 'twitching' on the market stall. They consider that under these circumstances it cannot be contaminated.

Although the ageing of beef is considered essential in Western societies, as this process improves tenderness, aged beef is often regarded with suspicion in Southeast Asia as it tends to possess the same colour as buffalo beef. Southeast Asian consumers have no aversion for buffalo beef – indeed they are major consumers of this commodity – but they expect to pay a lower price than they would for cattle beef. Hence it is very difficult to sell high-quality aged beef.

Despite the present major differences in consumer preference from country to country it can be assumed that as tropical countries industrialize and urbanize, and under the stress of economic and technological change, preferences will slowly change and become more uniform.

It is likely, however, that in the long term acceptable beef quality will be equated with that type of meat that the beef industry can produce most economically and that can be used in the food culture practised by the consumer. This means that there are always likely to be some differences between different communities in their definition of quality in beef, but that slowly chilled, frozen and processed meats will become more generally acceptable to tropical consumers and that beef quality will be more or less generally equated with leanness and tenderness.

The policy of imposing Western, and in particular American, meat-grading standards in tropical countries is thus of very doubtful value. It could even be a retrogressive action. This does not mean that grading standards of some kind are not required, but they must be equated with the average consumer's concept of quality meat requirements. The evolution of grading standards in most tropical countries will take time, and considerable investigation of the carcase attributes of locally produced cattle and average consumer preferences will be necessary.

Working cattle

For centuries work animals have been used for transport and cultivation purposes in all tropical regions of Asia and they were initially used by

European colonists in the American and Australian tropics. However, except in those areas where they were introduced by Europeans, they have not been used for cultivation purposes in tropical Africa.

The introduction of powered vehicles is very rapidly removing the burden of road transport from animals throughout the world. As yet, however, power machinery has not effectively displaced work animals in the fields of tropical Asia, although the small hand tractor is now widely utilized in the rice fields of Southeast Asia. During the last half-century many attempts have been made to introduce power mechanization in tropical African agriculture, both collectively and on individual farms. In all except a few cases, however, these attempts have completely or partially failed in their major objective. It is now understood in Africa that power mechanization can only become economically viable if the necessary capital is available, the users of the machinery are sufficiently competent and the necessary infrastructure exists. So often none of these conditions can be fulfilled. Because of this situation agriculturists in many African countries are now concentrating on the introduction of draught animals to replace hand labour in the field, the training of farmers to use these draught animals and the design of improved animal-powered cultivation implements. It will be seen from the data given in Table 5.32

Table 5.32   *The number of hours worked per hectare in the production of groundnuts in Senegal*

Practice	No. hours worked per ha		
	Man	Draught animal	Tractor
Manual labour	480	–	–
Manual and draught animals	311	53	–
Manual and partial mechanization	179	–	13
Complete mechanization	30*	–	12

* Operation of machines only.
Source: FAO (1972).

that although animal power cannot reduce human toil to the same degree as mechanical power it can still substantially decrease the number of hours that a farmer has to spend on cultivation. If, in addition, the purchase of the animal is within the financial capacity of the farmer and the animal provides manure throughout its working life and meat at the end of it, then the benefits to be obtained by the introduction of animal power are substantial and worthwhile.

Judging from the available evidence it is reasonable to suppose that working cattle will continue to be used in South and Southeast Asia for the foreseeable future, although they may be rapidly replaced in the drier lands of western Asia, where energy in the form of fossil fuel is now relatively cheap. However, the nature of the work performed by cattle in South and Southeast Asia may change. It is likely that the heavy cultivation work will increasingly be completed using tractors, but that the lighter work will be left for draught animals to perform, particularly if the cost of fossil fuel continues to increase. As in South and Southeast Asia the water buffalo was often used in the past for cultivation work on heavy soils, the major result of the introduction of tractors may be a decline in the use of buffaloes, with working cattle being retained for light cultivation.

In Burma an interesting situation has developed during the last two decades. On account of land reform and restrictions on the importation of tractors the demand for working buffaloes and cattle has risen so rapidly that the resulting shortage has increased their value very considerably.

In Africa it is likely that there will be an initial major increase in the number of working cattle used for field cultivation purposes, but that ultimately the same trends will develop that are appearing in Asia today.

Thus the future of working cattle in tropical Asian and African agriculture appears to be assured for the foreseeable future. However, the type of cattle required in South and Southeast Asia is changing as smaller, relatively short-legged, nimble animals are most useful for light cultivation work.

The working ability of cattle

The total work that cattle can perform depends upon many factors, including breed, sex, size and liveweight, training, management, feeding and health. Heavier animals are able to perform more work than lighter animals, all other factors being equal.

Under a given set of conditions, each animal is capable of carrying out a certain amount of daily work which cannot be exceeded if the animal is to be kept in a good working condition. For example, Mukherjee *et al.* (1941) stated that Hariana bullocks are capable of drawing loads varying from 310 to 540 per cent of their body weight during a 6-hour working day. There is also, of course, a direct relationship between energy output for work purposes and energy intake in the ration (see later section on nutrition).

Experimental data confirm that working cattle develop maximum power when a relatively low traction effort is made at a relatively high speed. This suggests that working cattle are probably most economic to use for light and relatively fast cultivation work, so that the present trend towards the use of cattle for this purpose, forecast previously, is likely to be economically desirable.

It has also been shown that by reducing the duration of work, the intensity of effort demanded of the animal can be increased. In practice, working cattle in the tropics should be worked for no more than 5 to 6 hours per day, except under exceptional circumstances, and preferably for a somewhat shorter period (see later section on management).

If cattle are harnessed together in order to increase the total traction effort there is a loss of efficiency in the utilization of energy by two animals of approximately 7·5 per cent compared with the use of one. As more animals are harnessed together the loss in efficiency increases.

Some examples of what might be expected from working cattle are given below.

1. Joshi and Phillips (1953) reported that a pair of Hariana cattle harnessed in a cart can pull 1·02 t (1 ton) for 32 km (20 miles) at a speed of 3·2 km (2 miles) an hour.
2. One pair of good working cattle should be able to perform all cultivation work on a 8 ha (20 acre) holding during the year or all work on a 6 ha (15 acre) holding.
3. Pulling a 20 cm (8 in) mouldboard plough, a pair of good working cattle should be able to plough 0·4 ha (1 acre) of land in 6·5 hours, assuming that a speed 3·2 km (2 miles) per hour can be maintained. In practice, of course, this speed cannot be maintained for the total period and it would probably take almost 2 days to plough 0·4 ha (1 acre) of land.
4. In the Chilean forests, i.e. in the cool temperate climatic zone, a pair of oxen can haul 30 m² (323 ft²) of round timber measuring 2·4 m (8 ft) in length over 60 m (197 ft) of medium and gentle slopes for a 9-hour day. The oxen are worked for 250 days of the year and haul 0·4 m² (4·3 ft²) of 2·4 m (8 ft) length timber per load. In tropical forests the number of working hours per day would have to be less.

Choice of animal

As the demand for animals for transport purposes declines buffaloes and cattle form an increasingly large proportion of the total working animal population. The advantages of buffaloes and cattle are that they work slowly but unflaggingly in the fields; they are hardy, strong and easy to feed; their harness is simple and can be made locally; females can be used for light work even if they are being milked; and all animals can be sold for meat at the end of their working life. As the demand for animals for heavy cultivation work declines it is expected that cattle will demonstrate some advantages over buffaloes.

There are good working cattle of all shapes and colours, but the majority conform to certain physical specifications. These are a compact, sturdy body with well-developed muscles, particularly on the back and the hindquarters; a broad deep chest; strong, short legs; and large, sound, hard feet. When choosing working cattle, if one cannot have the advantage of a work test, one can, with a considerable amount of confidence, select the most suitable animal by conformation. The most likely source of error is an inability to judge the temperament of an animal without a prolonged test under the yoke. An unsuitable temperament will belie the promise of even the best conformation, while a suitable temperament will minimize, if not entirely overcome, the drawbacks inherent in an animal with a poor conformation. Temperament is not to be judged on short acquaintance. An exhibition of nervousness or fierceness, for instance, which at first may appear to be evidence of an unsuitable temperament may actually be a symptom of the spirit that all good working cattle require. In fact, it has been our experience that it is often those cattle that are initially the most difficult to handle which eventually prove to be the best workers.

Powerful shoulders, a muscular, short neck and a well-developed hump facilitate the fitting and use of the yoke. Some of these bodily characteristics are associated with the mature bull rather than with the bullock or the cow. In particular, the development of the hump is linked to masculinity. It is primarily for this reason that farmers in many regions of the tropics delay castration of bulls until they are fully grown, or never castrate them. This practice is often at variance with the policy of government livestock departments. They normally advise and encourage the early castration of all bull calves not selected for breeding purposes, with the object of preventing indiscriminate mating. Early vasectomy of males not required for breeding would appear to be one method of solving this problem.

Bullocks, i.e. castrated or vasectomised males, generally make the most satisfactory working animals. Bulls are sometimes unmanageable and cows lack the strength of bullocks and cannot be used at certain periods. There is no reason why cows should not be worked as long as they are properly fed, used for a limited time for light work and not used for a few months both before and after calving. Indeed, the experimental evidence suggests that the working for 4 hours per day of productive temperate-type cows in Western Europe only reduces milk yield very slightly (Kliesch and Neuhaus, 1948; Haring et al., 1956) and the working of less productive indigenous cows in China has no effect on milk yield (Shu et al., 1964).

In some tropical regions, particularly in certain countries in Southeast Asia, cows are the main animals used for field cultivation purposes. This is because the majority of bull calves surplus to breeding purposes are fattened and sold to butchers. Cows are rarely used for transport purposes in any region of the tropics.

Management

The age at which cattle are fit to start work depends upon their weight-for-age, and this depends upon the breed utilized, the climatic environment, management and feeding during growth and freedom from disease and parasitism.

Cattle selected for working purposes can be handled from the earliest age and used for light work when their bones are well grown, but should not be used for heavy work until their bones are strongly knit, i.e. at the attainment of mature body size.

In the settled farming regions of South and Southeast Asia, it is normal to commence the training of working cattle when they are 2 to $2\frac{1}{2}$ years old and such cattle can be fully utilized when they are 3 to $3\frac{1}{2}$ years of age. However, where cattle are raised under harsh conditions as are indigenous Tharparkars, handling may only commence at 4 years of age and the cattle may not be fully worked until they are 5 or 6 years old. In the forest areas of Chile, cattle used for timber hauling are first trained at approximately 3 years old and are fully worked when they are 5 years of age.

Cattle may be trained as workers in a relatively short time. The duration of training will vary from region to region, but it rarely has to be longer than 3 months and is often only a few weeks. The more the animals have been handled since birth the easier they are to control and train.

Training must be directed to removing apprehension and then gradually inducing the cattle to respond to directions of voice and hand. After this first stage too much work effort must not be demanded of them. To do so leads to a loss of self-confidence by the cattle that may be reflected in refusal to work or rebellion. Then, on the slightest pretext, the animal may sink resignedly to the ground and refuse to rise or becoming aggressive. As soon as the animal learns readily to answer control it should be yoked with a well-trained animal, but should not be expected to pull a load immediately. Once the animal has learnt to accept the yoke a light load should be attached to it. The load should be gradually increased. Training should be regular and not sporadic and it is better to train for two or three short periods a day for a few weeks than for one short period a day for a more prolonged period.

In most regions in Asia head control is effected by the use of a rope, approximately 0·8 to 1·3 cm (0·3 to 0·5 in) in diameter, that passes through a hole punched in the middle cartilage of the nose. The rope may have a knot or some other device on one side that prevents it being pulled through the hole in the septum, or the two ends may run either side the face of the animal and be looped around the horns. These ends can then be spliced so that one completes a loop around the horn and the other is elongated into a rein of whatever length may be desired. The age at which this device is fitted varies from region to region, but the hole in the septum is often punched when the animal is quite young and a first rope fitted. Some authorities discourage this practice.

In some regions a rope around the horn may be deemed sufficient to control the animal, and in others a halter like those worn by horses may be used. Well-trained animals will respond to voice control. A verbal order should be expressed at the same time as control is exercised through the rope. Then control through the rope can be gradually relinquished and replaced by control through the voice.

Field cultivation is usually seasonal. This means that for long periods of the year working cattle used for cultivation purposes will be idle. During these periods the cattle should be kept in good condition but not allowed to fatten; if stall fed they should be exercised daily. Occasional grooming is also very desirable. During periods of intense activity they must not be overworked. Under very hot conditions a working day of approximately 5 or 6 hours is probably the maximum that should be considered. For example, Hattersley (1951) stated that a working day of 5 hours is sufficient in the Sudan for a pair of bullocks harnessed to a ridging plough, although he also stated that an occasional extra 2 or 3 hours' work might be demanded of the animals. It is normal in Southeast Asia to commence work at 05.00 to 06.00 hours in the morning and to end work between 10.00 and 12.00 hours. In cooler weather it may be possible to work animals for 7 hours or longer and occasionally for up to 10 hours. If this is contemplated the working day should be divided, the cattle working between 06.00 and 11.00 hours in the morning and between 16.00 and 18.00 hours in the late afternoon. It has been estimated by Nourrissat (1965) that in Senegal male and female cattle are worked for totals of 500 and 350 hours respectively, during the year. In the rice-growing regions of Southeast Asia the authors estimate that the total number of hours worked per year is somewhat less.

If cattle are overworked they will lose weight. Continued overworking will of course lead to the loss of the animal, but the good farmer will quickly appreciate that his animal is overworked and take appropriate measures to correct the situation. The difficulty that is usually experienced by the average farmer is the early detection of loss of body weight. Although a loss of body fat is usually associated with an immediate deterioration in the general appearance of the animal, so many working animals utilized in the tropics are always thin that it may sometimes be difficult to detect that they are getting thinner, particularly as there are normally no weighing facilities.

Each working animal has its own idiosyncrasies and characteristics and paired animals must be matched in temperament as well as in physical characteristics. The good farmer attempts to provide shade and the odd mouthful of feed when his working cattle are resting, sees that they obtain an adequate supply of drinking water, treats them if they are sick and maintains an unhurried and relaxed friendship with them.

Well-managed and fed animals should work satisfactorily on the farm until they are about 17 years of age. In the Chilean forests, when cattle are worked for 250 days of the year, the average working life is said to be 8 years.

Feeding

As the relationship between energy output for work purposes and energy input in the feed is approximately 0·1–0·09 to 1·0 (FAO, 1972) the theoretical requirements of working cattle for energy are approximately ten times the energy requirements for work output. The increase in digestible protein requirements above maintenance are probably negligible (Kehar *et al.*, 1943). In the Punjab, however, Lander (1949) tentatively calculated that a 454 kg (1,000 lb) bullock would require an additional 0·15 kg (0·33 lb) and 0·013 kg (0·028 lb) of total digestible nutrients (TDN) and digestible protein (DP) per working hour, respectively.

In India Lander (1949) suggested that the following rations were suitable for three types of working cattle managed in three different environments.

1. Cattle weighing approximately 363 kg (800 lb) working a 6-hour day in southern India:

Rice straw	4·5 kg (10 lb)
Green sorghum	9·0 kg (20 lb)
Mustard (*Brassica juncea*)	0·9 kg (2 lb)
or	
Sorghum straw	6·8 kg (15 lb)
Rape (*B. napus*)	0·5 kg (1 lb)

2. Cattle weighing approximately 454 kg (1,000 lb) used for ploughing for a 6-hour day during the hot season in northern India:

Wheat *busa* (chopped wheat straw)	2·3 kg (5 lb)
Jowar (*Sorghum bicolor*)	11·3 kg (25 lb)
and *guar* (*Cyamopsis psoralioides*)	
Gram (*Phaseolus* spp.)	1·8 kg (4 lb)

3. Typical village working oxen in the Punjab:

Wheat *busa*	8·2 kg (18 lb)
Rape cake	0·9 kg (2 lb)
or	
Jowar stalks (sorghum)	8·2 kg (18 lb)
Guar grain	0·9 kg (2 lb)

If cattle are worked but not stall fed they will require at least 7 hours grazing on moderately good forage. Fortunately, in South and Southeast Asia grazings are usually at their best during the season when the cattle are worked. During the dry season in the wet and dry tropics or in semi-arid regions it is unlikely that grazed working cattle will be able to maintain their condition unless they are fed a supplement. During the dry season in northern Nigeria Hartley and Ross (1938) considered that cattle that were not working required a supplement of approximately 3·2 kg (7 lb) of forage, of which half should be legume straw. They also suggested that if cattle were expected to work at this time then they needed an additional supplement of 0·5 kg (1 lb) of *dhusa* (sorghum bran), containing about 0·34 kg (0·75 lb) of TDN and 0·026 kg (0·057 lb) of DP, for each hour worked. They also recommended that 3 or 4 weeks before the beginning of the working season cattle should be fed 1·4 kg (3 lb) of *dhusa* or 1·4 kg (3 lb) of forage and 0·5 kg (1 lb) of *dhusa* in addition to their normal maintenance ration in order to ensure that they would be in good condition when work commenced.

Working cattle must always have access to shade when not working and ample supplies of water. During very hot weather they should be watered three times daily, but during cooler weather twice will suffice.

Working cattle like all other classes of cattle should always have access to a mineral ration.

Disease and ill-health

Working cattle must be vaccinated in the same way as other cattle in the region – that is, in accordance with what diseases are prevalent.

In West Africa, where N'dama and Dwarf Shorthorn cattle are tolerant of trypanosomiasis and are used for working purposes in tsetse-fly-infested areas, special care must be taken not to overwork them as their tolerance can break down if they become too fatigued. In areas in East Africa where East Coast fever (ECF) is endemic special attention must be given to tick control. Everywhere farmers should be encouraged to pick ticks off their working cattle by hand, as this excellent method of control is quite practical when animals are handled daily.

When working cattle are stall fed special attention should be given to the control of ringworm and mange.

Working cattle are subject to specific injuries that may occur if they are not properly managed. Yoke galls and harness sores are a major cause of ill-health. These are particularly liable to occur during the first weeks of work before the skin has become accustomed and hardened to the almost inevitable friction which is exaggerated by the unsteady traction exerted by the inexperienced animal. Deeper injuries arise from bruising or from excessive pressure exerted by the weight of the load for prolonged periods when the tissues beneath the skin may be deprived of their normal blood supply. A yoke with a broad, smooth bearing surface allows the weight to be distributed over a larger area of skin and is less likely to cause trouble than one that is narrow based. Yoke galls and injuries can be avoided or their worst effects mitigated by ensuring that: the initial work periods are short; the load is removed from the neck during lengthy rest periods; the load is properly balanced and no unnecessary weight is placed on the neck; the skin and yoke are kept clean; the surface of the yoke is smooth; and the skin is greased while cattle are working in the rain.

Injuries may also be caused by the operator pulling too hard on a nose rope. This type of injury should never occur if the operator is properly trained and cares for the well-being of his animal.

Working cattle occasionally suffer from muscle strains. These are also due to poor management and they may cause the animal intense pain, followed by swelling of the muscular tissue and lameness. Complete rest is indicated. Lameness may also be caused by stones in the hooves. These must be removed. In some regions of the tropics working cattle are shod if they have to work on very stony soils.

Choice of equipment

Yokes

When an animal is worked by itself a single forehead, head, neck or shoulder yoke may be used.

According to the FAO (1972) single forehead and neck yokes (Figs. 5.27 and 5.28) have been successfully used in Zaire.

Simple and effective head yoke equipment, designed by Read (1942) at

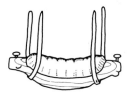

Fig. 5.27   A single forehead yoke.

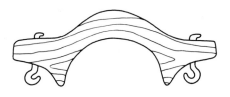

Fig. 5.28   A single neck yoke.

Hissar in India, consists of the head yoke proper, a surcingle, a pair of traces and a drawbar.

Three types of single shoulder yokes described by the FAO (1972) are shown in Fig. 5.29.

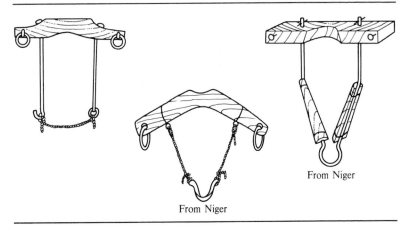

From Niger

From Niger

Fig. 5.29   Three types of single shoulder yoke.

Leather harness, either in the form of a breast strap or a shoulder collar as used with horses, can be employed when cattle are worked by themselves. However, this type of harness is unsatisfactory as it appears to cause discomfort and to discourage traction. This is presumably because the shoulder muscles of cattle are not so well developed as those of the horse and neither protect the joint nor cushion the skin.

Two types of double yoke are normally used, the double neck yoke and the double shoulder yoke. A series of double neck yokes used in Africa are described and illustrated by the FAO (1972). Possibly the most serviceable type of double neck yoke is one from Asia of the type illustrated in Fig. 5.30. It consists of a smooth round pole 142 cm (56 in) in length, with a diameter of at least 9 cm (3·5 in). The pole is fitted

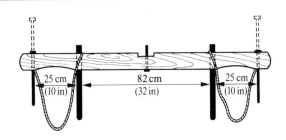

25 cm
(10 in)

82 cm
(32 in)

25 cm
(10 in)

Fig. 5.30   A very serviceable double neck yoke originating from Asia.

at the centre with a bolt or swivel to which the shaft can be attached, or with a projection to which the shaft can be tied. On either side of the bolt, at a distance of 41 cm (16 in), the pole is bored and pegs with a diameter of 2.5 cm (1 in) and made of tough, smooth wood are inserted. These wooden pegs project downwards at right angles to the pole for a distance of 31 cm (12 in). At a distance of 25 cm (10 in) further along the pole from the wooden pegs, flat-headed iron rods 1·5 cm (0·6 in) in diameter – or somewhat thicker, tough wooden pegs – are inserted parallel to the first wooden pegs. These rods or pegs should be capable of moving upwards or downwards. They come down on either side of the neck when the yoke is in position and maintain a proper distance between the cattle. The bearing surface between the neck rods is slightly bevelled so as to form a shallow arch which adapts the yoke more closely to the neck and so increases its area of contact. The edges of these shallow arches must be rounded off.

The shaft of this type of yoke is made of tough, smooth timber. It should be stout enough to bear whatever load it is meant to take and sufficiently smooth to prevent bruising or cutting when bumped against.

Many variations of this simple yoke have been designed with the objective of making it more efficient. These include modifications to make it fit more comfortably over a larger area of the neck when under pressure, lightening the weight and increasing the strength and removing projections which may cause bruising or impede easy handling. None except the last appear to confer any great benefit in practice.

A series of double shoulder yokes used in Africa are described and illustrated by the FAO (1972). One advantage of the double shoulder yoke is that paired working cattle do not have to be of the same size. It can also be fitted to hornless cattle. It does, however, have serious disadvantages (FAO, 1972), and bullocks fitted with this type of yoke are more difficult to handle.

Implements

In Asia the majority of field implements for use with working cattle and/or buffaloes are of ancient origin and design. They are usually of simple but robust construction. Some are efficient while others have outlived their usefulness. In Africa all cultivation in the past was by hand, and all types of animal-drawn implements are exotic and novel.

Since the advent of tractors the world's agricultural machinery industry has virtually ignored the vast market that still exists for animal-drawn implements in Asia and the new, developing market in Africa. At the same time inventiveness has not been a conspicuous cultural trait in the traditional societies of either Asia or Africa.

The consequence is that very little advance has taken place in the design of efficient implements for use with working cattle. The requirements of such implements are that they should be:

1. Lightweight, as there is a very definite limit to animal traction power;
2. Simple to operate and service, as the majority of farmers in Asia and Africa are mechanically illiterate;
3. Robust, as there are usually few after-purchase service organizations in the rural areas of Asia and Africa;
4. Low in cost, as the majority of the potential users will possess little capital and/or purchasing power.

Some of these requirements may appear incompatible, but at least a major effort should be made to satisfy them. First priority should be given to the design of improved implements for soil cultivation, seeding, weeding and harvesting, while attention should also be directed to the need for new implements for forage harvesting, fertilizer spreading and crop protection. Detailed information on implements now available in some regions of Africa are given by the FAO (1972).

Estimation of body and carcase weight

Very experienced cattle dealers and butchers can judge the probable carcase weight of live cattle with astonishing accuracy by sight, but such ability is not at the command of the average stockowner. Unless the latter has some guidance his estimate of liveweight is a guess which may be very wide of the mark.

Certain body measurements when properly applied give an indication of liveweight which is remarkably accurate. One formula that is used is

$$LW = \frac{L \times G^2}{300}$$

where LW is the liveweight in pounds, L the length from the point of the shoulder to the pin bone in inches and G is the chest girth in inches.

We have found that estimates made using this formula for Zebu cattle weighing 136 to 408 kg (300 to 900 lb) have seldom been wrong by more than 10 per cent and have usually been correct to within 5 per cent. Using this formula liveweights are more often under- than overestimated.

It is not always easy to make accurate measurements of either the length or the chest girth of cattle, even if they are quiet. In taking these measurements it is desirable that the animal should not drink or eat for 12 hours, and should stand with all four legs squarely under the body with the head held in the normal position. In chest girth measurements the tape should be passed around the body immediately behind the shoulders, at the smallest circumference, and pulled up so that it fits tightly to the body.

In India it has been recommended that when the above formula is used to estimate the liveweight of steers it should be modified as follows:

$$LW = \frac{L \times G}{Y}$$

where Y is 9·0 if G is less than 65 in, 8·5 if G is between 65 and 80 in and 8·0 if G is greater than 80 in.

Bennett (1951) derived a formula for estimating the liveweight of steers whose chest girth varies from 63 to 80 in. It is as follows:

$$LW = 1.04 \ (27 \cdot 5758 \times G) - 1049 \cdot 67$$

When the liveweight is known, an approximate estimate of the dressed carcase weight can be made according to the 'condition' of the live animal. The dressed carcase weight of very fat animals ranges from 62 to about 65 per cent; that of animals in good condition from the better indigenous breeds from about 54 to 56 per cent; and that of indigenous animals in poor condition from 50 per cent downwards. The *Bos* (*Bibos*) spp. breeds must be exempted from this general statement. Even when they are not fat they possess a high carcase dressing-out percentage.

Using temperate-type *Bos taurus* cattle Bennett (1951) derived the following formula for calculating the dressed carcase weight:

$$DCW = 44 \cdot 08 - (0 \cdot 0029 \times LW) - (0 \cdot 115 \times h) + (0 \cdot 2658 \times g) - (0 \cdot 0801 \times b)$$

where DCW is the dressed carcase weight in pounds, LW the liveweight in pounds, h the height in centimetres, g the chest girth in centimetres and b the belly girth in centimetres.

It is not known whether this formula can be used for estimating dressed carcase weight of the steers from indigenous tropical breeds.

Dentition of cattle as an indication of age

The eruption of each pair of teeth takes place at approximately the same time of life and thus an indication of an animal's age may be obtained by an examination of its teeth. As far as cattle are concerned, the indication is a very approximate one, because differences in age of as much as 16 months may be found in cattle with teeth at the same stage of development. Differences of this degree are unusual, but an allowance must be made for a variation of up to 6 months.

The front teeth of cattle are easily examined and it is therefore to them that attention is generally confined, the stage of development of the molar teeth being noted only when further confirmatory evidence is required. On each side of the lower jaw there are four incisors or front teeth and six molar teeth in the adult bovine. In the upper jaw there are the same number of molars but no incisors.

Many factors influence dentition, the chief of which are breed and the standard of nutrition on which the animal has been reared. There is a very marked difference between the ages at which the teeth are erupted in cattle of the early-maturing breeds of temperate origin and the late-maturing breeds of the tropics. There is also a difference, but a less marked one, between breeds of tropical cattle and groups within the breeds which have been raised on different kinds and amounts of food. In addition there are individual variations at least as great as the average between groups which cannot be specifically accounted for.

Lall (1948) collected information submitted by government-farm staff who examined Indian cattle grouped according to their breed and recorded age. Because of the method used and because on some farms births were recorded only according to the quarter of the year in which they occurred, no exactness can be claimed for the data collected. The information he received referred to most of the important Indian breeds and he considers that the data provided, shown in Table 5.33, approximate to the average closely enough to be of practical use.

Table 5.33   *Average age of cattle at eruption of their permanent teeth*

Type of teeth	Age (months)			
	Indigenous[1] Indian cattle	Indigenous[2] African cattle	Ranched[3] American cattle	Purebred[3] British cattle
Incisors				
First	24–30	28	24	21
Second	36	34	30–36	27
Third	48	41	42	33
Fourth	54–60	49	54–60	39
Molars				
First	24		24	24
Second	24		24	24
Third	36		33	33
Fourth	6		6	6
Fifth	18		12–15	12–15
Sixth	24		21	21

Sources: (1) Lall (1948). (2) Joubert (1956) and Kikule (1953). (3) Miller and Robertson (1943).

In tropical Africa recorded observations are few and refer only to a small number of cattle. The usual individual and breed differences were noted, but the average of the groups recorded by two observers (Joubert, 1956; Kikule, 1953) are very similar. The average ages at eruption of the permanent incisors of cattle of African breeds are also shown in Table 5.33.

Observation of the ages at eruption of the permanent incisors of seventy-eight White Fulani reared on a high plane of nutrition in Nigeria indicated that the average quite closely approximated those of mixed East African Shorthorn Zebu and Ankole at Entebbe, Uganda, but there were several individuals far removed from the average.

The corresponding data for 'highly bred stock' in England and for ranch cattle in the United States (Miller and Robertson, 1943) are also shown in Table 5.33.

When examining the teeth of cattle there may be some difficulty in deciding if the four pairs of front teeth are old temporary or permanent ones, but if there are six molars at each side of the jaw this confirms that the front teeth are permanent.

References

Alim, K. A. (1960) Reproductive rates and milk yield of Kenana cattle in the Sudan. *J. agric. Sci. (Camb.),* **55**, 183–8.
Amble, V. N. and Jain, J. P. (1967) Comparative performance of different grades of crossbred cows on military farms in India. *J. Dairy Sci.,* **50**, 1695–1702.
Bauer, M. (1965) Five years study of ranch breeding stock, 1959–1964. *Rhod. agric. J.,* **62**, 28–33.
Beattie, W. A. (1962) *Beef Cattle Breeding and Management.* Pastoral Review Pty Ltd: Sydney.
Bennett, J. A. (1951) Value of body measurements for estimating weight and condition in steers. *Fm. Home Sci. (Utah agric. Exp. Stn),* **12**, 3.
Bishop, A. H. (1961–62) *Farm Fence Construction.* Department of Agriculture: Victoria, Australia.
Bonscharain, G. P. (1964) *Interim Report to the Government of Kenya on the Mariakani Milk Scheme.* FAO: Rome.
Branton, C., McDowell, R. E. and Brown, M. A. (1966) Zebu-European crossbreds as a basis of dairy cattle improvement in the USA. *South. Coop. Ser. Bull.,* No. 114, Louisiana Agric. Exp. Stn: Baton Rouge.
Chandler, R. L. (1958) Studies on the tolerance of N'dama cattle to trypanosomiasis. *J. Comp. Path.,* **68**, 253–60.
Chester, R. D. (1955) Management problems of the cattle industry of Northern Australia. *FAO Meeting on Livestock Production under Tropical Conditions,* Brisbane. 22–27 Aug. 1955. FAO: Rome.
Commonwealth Scientific and Industrial Research Organisations (CSIRO) (1955) *Round Fence Posts: Preservative Oil Treatment.* CSIRO Leaflet Series No. 12. CSIRO: Melbourne.
Creek, M. J. (1972) The Kenya feedlot project. *World Anim. Rev.* (3), 23–7.
Curson, H. H. and Thornton, R. W. (1936) A contribution to the study of African native cattle. *Onderstepoort J. vet. Sci.,* **7**, 613–739.
de Pinho Morgado, F. (1961) Methods used for the formation of a group of dairy cattle adapted to the conditions in regions at low altitudes in Mozambique (in Portuguese). *Anim. Serv. Vet. Moçambique* (7), 323–30. *Abstracted: Anim. Breed. Abstr.,* **33**, 43 (1965).
Donaldson, L. E. (1962) Some observations on the fertility of beef cattle in North Queensland. *Aust. Vet. J.,* **38**, 447–54.
Doutressoulle, G. (1947) *L'Élevage en Afrique Occidentale Française.* Edn Larousse: Paris.
Dyer, I. A. and O'Mary, C. C. (1972) *The Feedlot.* Lea and Febiger: Philadelphia.
Epstein, H. (1969) Domestic animals of China. *Tech. Comm. Comw. Bur. Anim. Breed. Genet.,* No. 18. Comw. Agric. Bur.: Farnham Royal, UK.
FAO (1967) *Agricultural Commodities – Projections for 1975 and 1985.* FAO: Rome.
FAO (1972) *The Employment of Draught Animals in Agriculture.* Issued by arrangement with Centre D'Études et d'Expérimentation du Machinisme Agricole Tropical. FAO: Rome.
FAO (1974) *Production Yearbook, 1973,* Vol. 27. FAO: Rome.

Faulkner, D. E. and Epstein, H. (1957) The indigenous cattle of the British dependent territories in Africa with material on certain other countries. *Pub. Col. Adv. Comm. Agric. Anim. Hlth. For.*, No. 5. HMSO: London.

Few, F. G. (1946) A water-cooling tower for milk and cream cooling on the dairy farm. *Queensland Agric. J.*, **62**, 279–89.

Fischer, H. (1967) Stierkampf in Thailand (in German). *Tierärztl. Umsch.*, **22**, 368–70. *Abstracted: Anim. Breed. Abstr.*, **36**, 27 (1968).

Francis, J. (1970) Breeding cattle for the tropics. *Nature (Lond.)*, **227**, 557–60.

Hancock, J. and Payne, W. (1955) The Direct Effect of Tropical Climate on the Performance of European-type Cattle. I. Growth. *Emp. J. Exp. Agric.*, **23**, 55–74.

Hardison, W. A. (1967–68) Grass and livestock production in the tropics. *Philipp. J. Anim. Sci.* (4 and 5), 43–65.

Haring, F., Wode, E. and Hesse, H. J. (1956) Pulling capacity of cows with reference to breed differences (in German). *Mitt dtsch. Landw.-Ges.*, **71**, 533–6. *Abstracted: Anim. Breed. Abstr.*, **24**, 335 (1956).

Hartley, K. T. and Ross, S. D. (1938) *Proc. 3rd West Afr. Agric. Conf.* Govt. Printer: Lagos.

Hattersley, M. C. (1951) Kenana cattle at the Gezira Research Farm. *E. Afric. agric. J.*, **17**, 27–31.

Hill, G. D. (1969) Grazing under coconuts in the Morobe District. *Papua New Guinea agric. J.*, **21**, 10–12.

Hirsch, S. and Shindler, H. (1957) The Syrian and Dutch Friesian cattle and their crosses in Israel. *Ktavim*, **7** (2–3). Series No. 185E. Agric. Res. Stn: Rechovat.

Hunting Technical Services (1974a) *Southern Darfur Land-Use Planning Survey. Development Plan.* Annex 3. 'Animal Resources and Range Ecology'. Hunting Technical Services: Boreham Wood, UK.

Hunting Technical Services (1974b) *South Thailand Regional Planning Study. Sector Studies.* 6. 'Livestock'. Hunting Technical Services: Boreham Wood, UK.

Hunting Technical Services (1976) *Savanna Development Project Phase II.* Annex 3. 'Livestock and Range Resources'. Hunting Technical Services: Boreham Wood, UK.

Joblin, A. D. H. (1966) The response of Teso zebu milking stock to moderate levels of supplementary feeding. *E. Afric. agric. For. J.*, **31**, 368–74.

Joshi, R. N. and Phillips, R. W. (1953) *Zebu Cattle of India and Pakistan.* FAO Agric. Study No. 19. FAO: Rome.

Joubert, D. M. (1956) The effect of breed and plane of nutrition on dentition in the cow. *Proc. Brit. Soc. Anim. Prod.* Oliver and Boyd: Edinburgh.

Kehar, N. D., Mukherjee, R., Marty, V. V. S. and Sen, K. C. (1943) Studies on protein Metabolism. 2. The effect of muscular work on endogenous protein catabolism in cattle. *Indian J. vet. Sci.*, **13**, 263–6.

Kikule, S. B. (1953) Age-changes in the teeth of zebu cattle. *E. Afric. agric. J.*, **19**, 86–8.

Kliesch, J. and Neuhaus, U. (1948) The suitability of lowland cattle as draft animals (in German). *Tierzucht.*, **2**, 10–14. *Abstracted: Anim. Breed. Abstr.*, **20**, 216 (1952).

Kumar, S. S. R. (1969) A report on some important economic traits of Red Sindhi and Jersey grades. *Indian vet. J.*, **46**, 679–84.

Lall, H. K. (1948) Dentition in Indian cattle. *Indian J. vet. Sci.*, **18**, 37–9.

Lander, P. E. (1949) *The Feeding of Farm Animals in India.* Macmillan: London.

Ledger, H. P. (1968) Carcass analysis techniques as an aid to planning for improved beef production in Sacker, G. D. and Trail, J. C. M. (eds), *Proc. Beef Cattle Breed. Develp. Conf.*, pp. 51–7. Min. Anim. Ind. Game Fish.: Uganda.

Loosli, J. K. and McDonald, I. W. (1968) *Non-protein Nitrogen in the Nutrition of Ruminants.* FAO Agric. Studies No. 75. FAO: Rome.

McCabe, T. W. (1955) *The Pattern of World Milk Production.* Foreign Agric. Rep. No. 83. Foreign Agricultural Service, US Dept. Agric.: Washington.

McCarthy, W. O. and Hamilton, C. P. (1964) Comparative performance of beef breeds in Central Queensland. 1. Productivity. *Trop. Agric. (Trin.)*, **41**, 293–7.

McDonald, P., Edwards, R. A. and Greenhalgh, J. F. D. (1973) *Animal Nutrition* (2nd edn). Longman: London.

McDowell, R. E. (1966) The role of physiology in animal production for tropical and sub-tropical areas. *World Rev. Anim. Prod.,* **1,** 39.

McDowell, R. E. (1971) Feasibility of commercial dairying with cattle indigenous to the tropics. *Cornell Int. Agric. Dev. Bull.,* No. 21. Cornell Univ.: Ithaca, New York.

McDowell, R. E. (1972) *Improvement of Livestock Production in Warm Climates.* Freeman: San Francisco.

MacFarlane, J. S. (1966) Castration in farm animals. *Vet. Rec.,* **78,** 436.

MacMillan, H. R. (1952) *Tropical Planting and Gardening* (5th edn). Macmillan: London.

Madsen, O. and Vinther, K. (1975) *Performance of Purebred and Crossbred Dairy Cattle in Thailand.* Thai-Danish Dairy Farm and Training Centre. Dairy Farming Promotion Organization of Thailand: Bangkok.

Mahadevan, P. (1955) Population and production characteristics of Red Sindhi cattle in Ceylon. *J. agric. Sci. (Camb.),* **48,** 164–70.

Mahadevan, P. (1966) Breeding for milk production in tropical cattle. *Tech. Comm.* No. 17. *Comw. Bur. Anim. Breed. Genet.* Comw. Agric. Bur.: Farnham Royal, UK.

Mahadevan, P., Galukande, E. B. and Black, J. G. (1962) A genetic study of the Sahiwal grading-up scheme in Kenya. *Anim. Prod.,* **4,** 337–42.

Mason, I. L. (1951) The classification of West African livestock *Tech. Comm.* No. 7. *Comw. Bur. Anim. Breed. Genet.,* Comw. Agric. Bur.: Farnham Royal, UK.

Mason, I. L. and Maule, J. P. (1960) The indigenous livestock of eastern and southern Africa. *Tech. Comm.* No. 14. *Comw. Bur. Anim. Breed. Genet.,* Comw. Agric. Bur.: Farnham Royal, UK.

Miller, W. C. and Robertson, E. D. S. (1943) *Practical Animal Husbandry.* Oliver and Boyd: Edinburgh.

Misra, R. C. and Kushwaha, N. S. (1970) Study of some economic characters of dairy cattle as influenced by age at first and subsequent calvings. *Indian vet. J.,* **47,** 331–6.

Montsama, G. (1967) *Problems of Cattle in Grazing Areas.* Pub. No. S-19. ITC–UNESCO Centre for Integrated Surveys: Delft, Netherlands.

Motta, M. S. (1961) *Ann. Rep. (1960).* Pasture Section, Dept. Anim. Husb., Min. Agric. Lands: Jamaica.

Mukherjee, D. P., Dutta, S. and Bhattacharya, P. (1941) Studies on the draught capacity of Hariana bullocks. *Indian J. vet. Sci.,* **31,** 39–50.

National Academy of Sciences – National Research Council (1966) *Nutrient Requirements of Dairy Cattle* (3rd rev. edn). NAC–NRC, Pub. No. 1349. NAC–NRC: Washington.

Nestel, B. L. (1965) Some aspects of livestock development. *The Veterinarian (Oxford),* **3,** 151–9.

Nourrissat, P. (1965) Draught cattle in Senegal (in French). *Agron. trop. (Paris).,* **20,** 823–53. *Abstracted: Anim. Breed. Abstr.,* **36,** 192 (1968).

Payne, W. J. A. (1964) The origin of domestic cattle in Africa. *Emp. J. exp. Agric.,* **32,** 97–113.

Payne, W. J. A. (1965) Specific problems of semi-arid environments. *Qualitas Plantarum et Materias Vegetabiles,* **12,** 269–94.

Payne, W. J. A. (1968) Problems and advances under humid tropic conditions. *Proc. 2nd World Conf. Anim. Prod.,* Session III, p. 52. Amer. Dairy Sci. Ass.: Urbana, Illinois.

Payne, W. J. A. (1970) *Cattle Production in the Tropics,* Vol. 1. Longman: London.

Payne, W. J. A. (1976) 'Systems of Beef Production in Developing Countries', in Smith, A. J. (ed.), *Beef Production in Developing Countries,* pp. 118–31. Univ. Edinburgh: Edinburgh.

Payne, W. J. A. and Hancock, J. (1957) The direct effect of tropical climate on the performance of European-type cattle. II. Production. *Emp. J. exp. Agric.,* **25,** 321–38.

Payne, W. J. A. and Rollinson, D. H. L. (1973) Bali cattle. *World Anim. Rev.* (7), 13–21.

Payne, W. J. A., van der Does, C., Kronenberg, J. B. M., Aquino, A. R., Salvatierra, S.A. and Dimayuga, E. C. (1967) Dairy Calf Management Studies in a Humid Tropical Environment. 1. The effect of three different methods of management on growth and mortality. *Proc. 4th Ann. Conf. Philipp. Soc. Anim. Sci.,* Manila, 7–8 Sept.

396   *Cattle*

Philipp, P. F. 1961) The economics of ranch fencing in Hawaii. *Univ. Hawaii Agric. Exp. Stn. Agric. Econ. Bull.,* No. 20.

Phillips, D. S. M. (1956) The Ruakura pipe-line milking machine. *Agric. Rev.,* **11,** 28–35.

Phillips, R. W., Johnson, R. G. and Moyer, R. T. (1945) *The Livestock of China.* Dept. State Publ. 2249 (Far Eastern Series 9). US Govt. Print. Office.: Washington.

Pires, F. L., Benintendi, R. P. and Santiago, A. A. (1967) Age at first calving and calving interval in Krankrej dairy cattle (Portuguese with English summary). *Bolm. Ind. anim.,* N.S., **24,** 123–7.

Plasse, D. B. (1973) 'Crossing Zebu, Native and European Breeds in Venezuela and Other Parts of Latin America', in Koger, M., Cunha, T. J. and Warwick, A. C. (eds.), *Crossbreeding Beef Cattle,* Series 2. Univ. Florida Press: Gainesville.

Preston, T. R. and Willis, M. B. (1969) Sugar cane as an energy source for the production of meat. *Outlook in Agriculture,* **6,** 29–35.

Preston, T. R. and Willis, M. B. (1970) *Intensive Beef Production.* Pergamon: Oxford.

Rao, A. R., Sastry, A. P., Reddy, K. K. and Rajulu, P. V. (1969) Studies on Reproductive Characters of Ongole Cattle. 1. Age at first calving, intercalving period and sex ratio. *Indian vet. J.,* **46,** 679–84.

Read, W. S. (1942) The head-yoke for single draught oxen. *Indian Fmg.,* **3,** 81–4.

Reynolds, W. M. (1968) Fencing for the Philippine farm and ranch. *Dairy Train. Res. inst. Univ. Philipp. Farm Bull.,* No. 1. Coll. Agric.: Los Baños, Philippines.

Rodda, T. E. (1956) Erecting a seven-wire fence. *New Zealand Dept. Agric. Bull.,* No. 265. NZ Dept. Agric.: Wellington.

Rogerson, A., Ledger, H. P. and Freeman, G. H. (1968) Food intake and liveweight gain comparisons of *Bos indicus* and *Bos taurus* steers on a high plane of nutrition. *Anim. Prod.,* **10,** 373–80.

Ruthenberg, H. (1971) *Farming Systems in the Tropics.* Clarendon Press: Oxford.

Shu, P. C., Lang, J. K., Hsu, Y. C. and Chen, S. Y. (1964) Studies of the crossbreds of Holstein and Syh-Yang cattle (Chinese). *Acta vet. zootech. sinica,* **7,** 23–32. *Abstracted: Anim. Breed. Abstr.,* **33,** 365 (1965).

Slijper, E. J. (1951) On the hump of the Zebu and Zebu-crosses. *Hemera Zoa (Bogor),* **58,** (1) and (2). *Abstracted: Anim. Breed. Abstr.,* **19,** 309 (1951).

Smith, C. A. and Hodnett, G. E. (1962) Compensatory growth of cattle on the natural grasslands of Northern Rhodesia. *Nature (Lond.),* **195,** 919–20.

Steenkamp, J. D. G. (1963) Climate and agriculture. *Proc. 6th Ann. Conf. Prof. Off. Dept. Res. Specl. Serv. Rhodesia and Nyasaland (Gwebi),* p. 151. *Abstracted: Anim. Breed. Abstr.,* **33,** 373 (1965).

Stewart, J. L. (1937) The cattle of the Gold Coast. *Vet. Rec.,* **49,** 1289–97.

Stobbs, T. H. (1966) The introduction of Boran cattle into an ECF endemic area. *E. Afr. agric. For. J.,* **31,** 298–304.

Stobbs, T. H. (1969) The use of liveweight gain trials for pasture evaluation in the tropics. 5. Type of stock. *J. Brit. Grassland Soc.,* **24,** 345–8.

Strohman, R. E. (1957) Preservative treatments for eucalyptus fence posts. *Univ. Hawaii Agric. Exp. Stn. Bull.,* No. 114.

Sutherland, D. N. (1959) Factors affecting the performance of beef cattle on unimproved pastures in Queensland. *Aust. vet. J.,* **35,** 129–34.

Taylor, J. C. (1959) A relationship between weight of internal fat, fill and the herbage intake of grazing cattle. *Nature (Lond.),* **184,** 2021–2.

Tothill, J. D. (ed.) (1948) *Agriculture in the Sudan.* Oxford Univ. Press: London.

Touchberry, R. W. (1967) A study of the N'dama cattle at the Musaia Animal Husbandry Station in Sierra Leone. *Bull. Univ. Ill. Agric. Exp. Stn–AID–Njala Univ. Coll., Sierra Leone,* No. 724.

Trail, J. C. M. and Sacker, G. D. (1966) Ankole longhorn cattle growth rates, horn dimensions and effect of dehorning on liveweight gain in Uganda. *Trop. Agric. (Trin.),* **43,** 241–5.

Van de Vyer, B. J. (1954) Urea as a source of protein for cattle. *Fmg. S. Africa,* **29,** 286.

Warner, J. N. (1951) *Dairying in India.* Macmillan: Calcutta.

Wellington, K. E., Mahadevan, P. and Roache, K. L. (1970) Production characteristics of the Jamaica Hope breed of cattle. *J. agric. Sci. (Camb.)*, **74**, 463–8.

Wijeratne, W. V. S. (1970) Crossbreeding Sinhala cattle with Jersey and Friesian in Ceylon. *Anim. Prod.*, **12**, 473–83.

Wilson, P. N. (1962) *Report on Cattle and Grassland Demonstration Tour, Jamaica*, p. 19. Govt. Jamaica and Caribbean Commission.

Wilson, P. N. and Osbourn, D. F. (1960) Compensatory growth after undernutrition in mammals and birds. *Biol. Rev.*, **35**, 324–63.

Woytinsky, W. S. and Woytinsky, E. S. (1953) *World Population and Production*. Twentieth Century Fund: New York.

Chapter 6

Buffalo

by **P. Bhattacharya**
*Formerly a member of the National Commission on Agriculture,
New Delhi, India*

Buffaloes belong to the Bovinae sub-family. Their relationship to other Bovinae such as cattle and bison is shown in Fig. 5.1 (Ch. 5, Pt II). Although the American bison (*Bison bison*) is sometimes referred to as a buffalo, this is a misnomer that is apparently due to a past misconception. As can be seen from Fig. 5.1 the bison belongs to a separate sub-genus of the Bovinae.

There are four wild species of buffalo (Fig. 5.1), but all existing types of domestic buffalo appear to have been derived from *Bubalus arnee*, the wild buffalo of mainland Asia.

It is customary to divide all types of domestic buffalo (*Bubalus bubalis*) into two groups – the river and the swamp buffaloes. As the name implies, the water buffalo, whether of the river or the swamp type, has an inherent predilection for water and loves wallowing in water or mudpools. The river buffalo, as a rule, shows preference for clean running water, whereas the swamp buffalo likes to wallow in mudholes, swamps and stagnant pools. Like cattle, buffaloes are good swimmers.

Origin and distribution

As stated above, all domestic buffaloes are presumed to have evolved from the *arni* (*Bubalus arnee*), the wild buffalo of India, representatives of which are still to be found in the jungles of Assam. Phillips (1948), however, has drawn attention to the close similarity of the characteristic forehead of the Jaffarabadi, a high-milk-yielding breed of domestic river buffalo of India, to that of *Syncerus caffer*, the wild buffalo of Africa.

Apart from a report of the crossbreeding of cattle (*Bos taurus*) and buffalo from China (Van fu Czao, 1959) there is no authentic account of a successful hybridization of the buffalo and *B. indicus* or *B. taurus*. It is generally believed that this is impossible. The number of chromosomes in buffalo and cattle differ considerably, there being forty-eight in the buffalo (Dutt and Bhattacharya, 1952) and sixty in cattle. The author conducted a controlled experiment at the Indian Veterinary Research Institute (IVRI) to determine if fertilization of the ova took place in crossing between male cattle (*B. indicus*) and female buffalo. For this purpose the buffaloes were artificially inseminated at oestrus and the ova were recovered and examined at subsequent different intervals by slaughtering the animals. It was observed that even though spermatozoa reached the ovum there were no instances of penetration of the zona. However, no investigation was carried out to examine the result of reciprocal crossings.

It is generally believed that the African buffalo (*Syncerus caffer*) cannot be domesticated. This may not be an inherent characteristic of the animal and the impression might have arisen because few serious attempts have been made at domestication. Rouse (1970) reported an incident at Lilfordia Estates, outside Salisbury in Rhodesia, that demonstrated that African buffaloes can be rather easily tamed. Twelve buffalo calves and one bull were placed with a group of Africander cattle and allowed to run with them in fenced pastures. In 1965, when the buffaloes were 3 years old, they were as docile as the Africander cows. There are also instances that go to show that domestic buffaloes can very easily revert to the wild or semi-wild state. Domesticated swamp buffaloes were introduced into Australia during the first half of the nineteenth century, but due to lack of management, a large number of the imported animals turned wild and today there are perhaps more than 200,000 feral buffaloes roaming in northern Australia. In Borneo also, where swamp buffaloes were possibly introduced some time between the twelfth and the fifteenth centuries, a large number of animals, though claimed by owners, are now in a semi-feral state. Feral buffaloes are also numerous in southeast Sumatra.

Information on the origin and the precise period of the domestication of the buffalo is lost in antiquity. Archaeological findings in India suggest that the buffalo was domesticated during the period of the Indus valley civilization, some 4,500 years ago. There are reasons to believe that domestication of the swamp buffalo took place independently in China about 1,000 years later. There are, however, some conflicting opinions concerning the priority of domestication of the animal in India or in China. However, all are agreed that the movement of the buffalo to other countries, both eastwards and westwards, and to other continents, occurred from these two sources. Buffaloes were unknown in Egypt during the time of the Pharaohs (Cockrill, 1966a). Movement of the buffalo to that country took place some time around AD 800. Importation of buffaloes to other countries in Southeast Asia, western Asia, Europe, Australia and to South America followed, the spread being slow and gradual. However, attempts at the introduction of these animals in some countries did not meet with success. The Earl of Cornwall, a brother of Henry III, brought buffaloes to England, but the animals did not thrive (Cockrill, 1967). Introduction of the buffalo to African countries south of the Sahara has not so far been very successful. The outcome of the venture of establishing the buffalo in Australia has been mentioned

Table 6.1   *World distribution of buffaloes*

Continent	Country	Number in '000		Percentage increase or decrease 1961–65 to 1972	As percentage of world total in 1972
		1961–65	*1972*		
Africa		1,559	2,200	+ 41	1·74
Tropics		–	–	–	
Other		1,559	2,200	+ 41	
	Egypt	1,559	2,200	+ 41	
Americas		72	147	+ 104	0·12
Tropics		72	147	+ 104	
	Brazil	67	140	+ 109	
	Trinidad	5	7	+ 40	
Other		–	–	–	
Asia		113,184	123,382	+ 9	97·55
Tropics		45,386	48,259	+ 6	
	Bangladesh	505	700	+ 39	
	Brunei	14	18	+ 29	
	Burma	1,117	1,620	+ 45	
	Hong Kong	2	1	– 50	
	India (part)	25,936	27,400	+ 6	
	Indonesia	2,961	2,980	1	
	Khmer Republic	596	800	+ 34	
	Laos	527	950	+ 80	
	Malaysia	359	306	– 15	
	Philippines	3,357	4,711	+ 40	
	Singapore	3	3	0	
	Sri Lanka	855	710	– 17	
	Thailand	6,859	5,800	– 15	
	Vietnam	2,295	2,260	– 2	
China		28,318	29,680	+ 5	
Other		39,480	45,443	+ 15	
Europe outside USSR		407	295	– 28	0·23
	USSR	385	460	+ 19	0·36
Oceania		1	–	–	negl.
Tropics		1	–	–	
	Guam	1	–	–	
Other		–	–	–	
World		115,608	126,484	+ 9	
Tropics		45,459	48,406	+ 6	38·27
Other		70,149	78,078	+ 11	61·73

Note: Data for the whole of China is excluded from the tropical area and no account is taken of small numbers of domestic buffalo and feral buffalo which are present in some tropical countries.

Source: FAO (1973).

earlier. At present attempts are being made in Australia to redomesticate the feral buffaloes and the results so far achieved are encouraging.

In contrast to cattle, with their ubiquitous distribution all over the globe where there is human habitation, the water buffalo is to be found only in certain regions (Table 6.1). The distribution of the buffalo is conspicuous by its being confined principally to the areas where animal husbandry is poorly developed and badly organized. By and large, buffaloes are owned only in small numbers by small farmers or poor stockowners. In fairness to buffalo stockowners in these regions, it may be stated that they maintain buffaloes not from ignorance of the potentialities of other large ruminants but because they find that in the prevailing agricultural situation no other domestic animal will thrive like the buffalo and be so useful and economical.

According to the FAO (1973) the total buffalo population in the world during 1972 was a little over 126 million. The total buffalo population of the world is steadily increasing, although a declining trend in population can be noticed in European countries. It should be mentioned that large errors may exist in the population estimates of buffaloes as the census organization in many countries where buffaloes abound is not very well developed.

India possesses the largest number of buffaloes: more than half of the world's buffalo population. India is followed by China, Pakistan, Thailand, the Philippines, Nepal, Indonesia, Vietnam, Egypt, Burma, Turkey, Sri Lanka, Iraq, Iran and other countries. The largest concentration of swamp buffaloes is found in the rice-growing countries of Asia. In India and Pakistan, only buffaloes of the river type exist.

General characteristics

As compared to cattle (*Bos taurus*; *B. indicus*) buffaloes are big-boned, rather massive animals with bodies set low on strong legs with large hooves. Unlike the Zebu (*B. indicus*) buffaloes do not have a dewlap or hump. The body frame of a good milk-type river buffalo conforms to that of dairy-type cattle, and the shape of the body of the swamp buffalo is similar to the body frame of the draft breeds of Zebu. All buffaloes have horns that are generally more massive than those of cattle. Unlike the smooth, round and conical horns found in cattle, the buffalo possesses horns that are broad, flat and almost rectangular in cross-section near the base and with prominent ridges across the long axis. The direction of growth of the horns varies. Swamp and several breeds of river and nondescript buffaloes have backswept horns, whereas two of the milk breeds of river buffaloes have very tightly curled horns. Some buffaloes have fantastically long horns that may measure more than three-quarters of the total length of the body.

At birth and during early calfhood buffaloes have a good coat of soft hair like that of cattle, but hair on the body becomes sparser as the animal grows. The amount of hair coat retained by the adult buffalo varies considerably, depending on the breed, season and housing practices. The body of some adult buffaloes may appear to be practically bare. The hair of the adult buffalo is coarser and much sparser than that of cattle and the colour may be black, dun, creamy yellow, dark or light grey, or white. White markings in the form of stripes below the jaw extending from ear to ear, and/or on the lower side of the neck near the base or around the brisket, are commonly found in the swamp and the Surti breed of river buffalo. Some of the buffaloes owned by the marsh Arabs in Iraq also exhibit such markings and some others are conspicuous in having a piebald coat.

Star, blaze or socks and a white switch at the end of the tail are frequently found in animals of the river buffalo breeds. Among swamp buffaloes white animals are not uncommon. The incidence varies in different areas and appears to be the result of some selection based on local beliefs and superstitions. The incidence is relatively low in Borneo, China and Taiwan where there is a prejudice against these animals, but in Bali and parts of Thailand more than 50 per cent of the buffaloes may be white as these animals are considered auspicious.

Hair whorls of swamp buffaloes are characteristic and distinctive and could be used as an important means for identification of an animal (Cockrill, 1966b). The colour of the skin may vary from jet black to light pink and may be unpigmented in localized areas, black or slate grey being the most common in dark-coloured animals. It is doubtful if true albino buffaloes exist. Cases of leucoderma, however, are known to occur in buffaloes (Datta, 1965). The aetiology of leucoderma is unknown and the disease does not affect production in any manner.

The sheath of the male swamp buffalo adheres close to the body except at the umbilical end, as in European cattle. In the river buffalo the sheath is more pendulous and is somewhat similar to that of Zebu cattle. There is no tuft of hair at the preputial opening in the buffalo. The scrotum of the male buffalo, both of the swamp and the river types, is much smaller than that of male cattle of similar size. In the swamp buffalo there is no constriction near the attachment of the scrotum to the abdominal wall, but a distinct neck can be seen in the river buffalo at that place.

Among the river buffaloes a few well-defined breeds with standard qualities and with specific physical characters that differentiate them unmistakably from other types can be found only in India and Pakistan. These are all milk breeds, but the number of animals in these breeds forms only a very small fraction of the total buffalo population in the two countries. The vast majority of buffaloes belong to a nondescript class and these vary greatly in size, weight and general features. These animals are the product of centuries of indiscriminate breeding without any selection criteria.

In Russia, development of a breed of buffaloes commenced in 1935 in the Caucasus, and the Caucasian buffaloes so developed were given a breed status in November 1970. This is a dual-purpose breed with good meat and fairly satisfactory milk qualities (Agabeili *et al.*, 1971).

Cockrill (1967) prefers to group all the swamp buffalo types together as one breed, as no distinct breed has so far been evolved. Like the river-type nondescript buffaloes there are also many variants to be found in swamp buffaloes. The large swamp buffalo of Thailand may weigh well over 900 kg (1,984 lb) while the carabao of the Philippines or the small water buffalo of Borneo may only weigh 370 kg (816 lb) or even less.

Four milk breeds of India and Pakistan

Of the Indian and Pakistani milk-breed buffaloes, the Murrah, Nili, Surti and Jaffarabadi have good milk qualities. The characteristics of these breeds are described below.

Murrah (Plate 6.1)

Habitat.   The home of the Murrah is in Haryana State and the Union territory of Delhi in India. They are also bred in large numbers in the State of Punjab in India and in the Punjab province of Pakistan and also in the northern part of Uttar Pradesh in India and Sind in

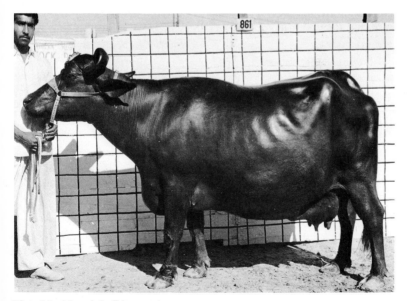

Plate 6.1   Murrah buffalo cow.

Pakistan. The best specimens of the breed are found in the Rohtak, Hissar and Jind districts of Haryana and the riverine tracts of Sind (Pakistan).

General description.   The head of the Murrah buffalo is relatively small in proportion to the body size, shapely and fine in the female, heavier and coarser in the male. The face is clean cut, with prominent, limpid, bright eyes. Ears are small, well shaped and drooping. Horns are short, tightly curled, growing upwards and backwards. The neck is long and thin in females but thick and massive in males. The chest is well developed and wide across the brisket. Legs are straight, short and strong with good-size black hooves.

The body frame is compact, deep and capacious, and in females it is as wedge-shaped as that of dairy cattle. The navel flap is small. The udder is of good size and well shaped, possessing prominent milk veins. The teats are well spaced, of good size and long. The tail is long and thin, reaching the fetlocks, often with white markings towards the end and usually ending with a white switch.

The skin is thin, soft and pliable with very little hair on the body in adult animals. The popular skin colour is jet black, but animals with fawn-grey body hair are not uncommon. White markings on the face or limbs are not liked.

Nili (Plate 6.2)

Habitat.   The home of Nili buffaloes is partly in Pakistan and partly in India; the major part being in Pakistan. The animals are bred in the

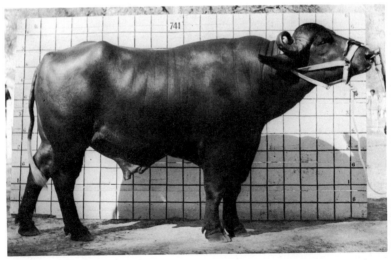

Plate 6.2   Nili buffalo bull (Indian Council of Agricultural Research, New Delhi).

Montgomery, Multan and Lyallpur districts of Punjab province in Pakistan and the Ferozepur district of the State of Punjab in India. The best specimens of the breed are found in the valleys of the Ravi and Sutlej rivers. The name of the breed is supposedly derived from the deep blue colour (Nili) of the water of the Sutlej river.

General description. The Nili buffalo possesses a shapely, long head with a fine muzzle and wide nostrils. The head is rounded and convex at the top, depressed between the eyes and has a prominent nasal bone. The horns are small but broad, thick and tightly curled. Ears are medium-sized and pointed at the apex. The neck is long, thin and fine in the female and thick and massive in the male.

The body frame is deep, of medium size and is set low on short, straight, strong, big-boned legs. The udder is well developed, shapely and well placed. The teats are of good size and are attached well apart. The milk veins are prominent. The tail is long and fine, almost touching the ground, and invariably possesses a white switch.

The skin is smooth and soft and black colour is most common. Animals with brown colour are acceptable. The skin of the udder and brisket frequently shows pink patches. Animals with wall eyes (one or both) and with white markings on the forehead, face, muzzle and limbs are greatly valued.

Surti (Plate 6.3)

Habitat. The home of the Surti breed of buffaloes is in the south-western part of Gujarat State in India. The best animals of the breed are found in the Kaira, Nadiad and Baroda districts.

General description. The Surti buffalo has a fairly broad, rather long head, with a convex shape at the top between the horns. The face and muzzle are clean cut and the nostrils are big. The eyes are bright, clear and prominent. Ears are medium-sized and drooping and the skin on the inner side of the ear is pinkish in colour. Horns are flat, sickle-shaped and of good size with ridges across the long axis as in other buffaloes. They grow in a downward and backward direction and then upwards at the tip, forming a hook.

The neck is well shaped and long in the female and thick and heavy in the male. The chest is broad and the brisket is prominent.

The body is medium-sized, well built and wedge-shaped, and set rather low on straight, strong legs with broad black hooves. No other breed of buffalo has as straight a back as the Surti. The tail is long, thin and flexible, usually with a white switch. The udder is well developed and finely shaped, and well placed between the hind legs. The teats are medium in size and well spaced. The skin is rather thick but soft, smooth and pliable, having a sparse hair coat. The skin colour is black or brown

Plate 6.3   Surti buffalo cow (from Cockrill, 1974).

and the colour of the hair varies from rusty brown to silvery grey. Good specimens have two white chevrons – one around the jaw extending from ear to ear and the other around the brisket.

Jaffarabadi (Plate 6.4)

Habitat.   The home tract of the Jaffarabadi buffalo lies in the Gir forest of Gujarat State in India.

General description.   It possesses a rather heavy head with fairly large, thick, flat horns which tend to droop on each side of the neck and then turn up at the tips in a curl but not so tight as in the Murrah or Nili breeds. A noticeable feature of the breed is the very prominent bulging forehead of the animal. The neck is strong and well built.

The body is massive, relatively long and not very compact, and is set somewhat higher on the legs, which are straight and strong. The udder is well developed and the teats are of good size and well placed. The usual colour is black.

Like cattle, the buffalo renders invaluable service to mankind by way of work and the supply of milk and manure while alive, and meat and other useful materials like hide, horns, hooves, bones, etc., after death. The number of people served by the buffalo is enormous and there are large areas where human survival is dependent on this animal. In spite of these facts the study of these animals has remained neglected until very recently. The benefits of science and technology have hardly impinged

Plate 6.4   Jaffarabadi buffalo bull (P. Battacharya).

on the husbandry of the buffalo population to enable a fuller expression of its production potentialities to be achieved. The greatest handicap to its development lies in very large gaps in our knowledge of the physiology of the animal, disease prevalence in the species and the husbandry practices most suitable for animals located in widely varying environmental conditions. Of late, scientific workers in countries such as India, Egypt, Pakistan, Thailand, etc., have been studying the animal in depth with a view to evolving efficient buffalo husbandry techniques, and as a consequence considerable information is now accumulating. However, available published material is still very scanty and what is published is often fragmentary and incomplete and sometimes contradictory. This should not be unexpected as it is only with the passage of time that sufficient information will accumulate to make the knowledge of the different disciplines concerned with buffalo husbandry clearer and more complete.

Growth and reproduction

Growth

Information available on the birth weight of buffaloes and their growth rate up to the breeding age is very meagre, and for most of the data available desirable collateral information on nutritional status, management, sequence of calving, breeding age and liveweight of the dam, season of birth, etc., is missing. Consequently, it is not possible at present to accurately estimate growth potential.

The average birth weight of the Egyptian buffalo is 40 kg (88 lb) when both sexes are included. The average for male and female calves is 41 kg (90 lb) and 38 kg (84 lb), respectively (Tantawy and Ahmed, 1953). This birth weight is considerably higher than the range of 27 to 37 kg (60 to 82 lb) and the average of 30 to 32 kg (66 to 71 lb) reported for Murrah, Nili and Surti buffaloes in India (Arnuchalam *et al.*, 1952; Agarwala, 1962; Bhalla *et al.*, 1967; Tomar and Desai, 1967; Arya and Desai, 1969; Amble *et al.*, 1970). In Pakistan 32 kg (71 lb) is accepted as the 'standard' birth weight of buffaloes in the military dairy farms (Rife, 1959).

A heritability of 0.733 ± 0.182 for the birth weight of female Murrah buffaloes was estimated by Tomar and Desai (1965).

Variations in daily body gain from 0.58 kg (1.3 lb) in the first week to 0.86 kg (1.9 lb) in the twelfth week after birth and a subsequent decline to 0.49 kg (1.1 lb) at one year of age, and maintenance of this fairly constant rate of growth until attainment of puberty, have been reported in a study on Murrah buffaloes in India (Arora and Gupta, 1962). In another report on the same breed the changes in body weight recorded were as shown in Table 6.2. Unlike the earlier report on Murrah buffaloes,

Table 6.2 *The average liveweight of Murrah buffaloes at different ages*

Age	Liveweight (kg (lb))
Birth	31.1 ± 0.13 (68.5 ± 0.28)
1 week	35.3 ± 0.15 (77.8 ± 0.32)
4 weeks	48.1 ± 0.21 (106.1 ± 0.46)
24 weeks	140.1 ± 0.82 (308.9 ± 1.80)
1 year	236.7 ± 1.09 (521.8 ± 2.44)
2 years	374.8 ± 1.86 (826.3 ± 4.08)

Source: Tomar and Desai (1965).

two growth spurts were observed in this study – one for a short time subsequent to birth and up to the age of about $6\frac{1}{2}$ months, and the other between 20 and 24 months of age. In Egyptian buffaloes liveweight gain was also reported to be rapid from birth to 3 months and again from 16 to 22 months (Ahmed and Tantawy, 1954). Up to the age of first service, Murrah and Nili heifers grow practically at the same rate (Amble *et al.*, 1970). The comparative growth rates of Egyptian and Italian buffaloes from birth to 2 years of age are shown in Fig. 6.1.

It will be seen that the birth weight of the Egyptian buffalo was slightly higher than that of the Italian buffalo and that the rate of growth in the two types was very similar up to the age of 2 months. After this period the Italian buffalo continued to grow at a much faster rate and at 2 years of age weighed considerably more than the Egyptian buffalo.

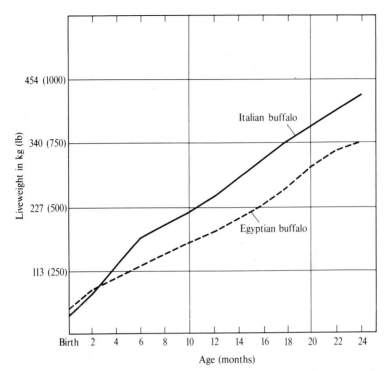

Fig. 6.1 Comparative growth of Egyptian and Italian buffaloes (Maymone, 1942; Knapp, 1957; Ahmed and Tantawy, 1954).

Knapp (1957) attributed the difference in growth rate in favour of the Italian buffalo not to differences between the breeds, but primarily to the difference in nutritional status.

It was reported to the author that in two feeding trials in Iraq, where growth rates to slaughter of buffalo and indigenous cattle were studied, the growth response of the buffalo was in both instances markedly higher than that of the cattle. Daily gains of 0·728 kg (1·61 lb) and 1·163 kg (2·65 lb) in the buffalo and 0·544 kg (1·19 lb) and 0·889 kg (1·96 lb) in the cattle, respectively, were recorded in the first and second trials.

For Caucasian buffaloes daily gains to the extent of 0·8 to 1·2 kg (1·76 to 2·65 lb) on intensive fattening have been reported (Agabeili *et al.*, 1971).

Heat stress during summer may depress the growth rate of young buffalo calves. In a study of Murrah buffalo heifers between 6 and 18 months of age it was observed that calves given relief from heat stress by shelter and water sprinkling exhibited a more rapid gain (15 per cent) in liveweight and body length (30 per cent) in comparison with calves not given these advantages (Tripathi *et al.*, 1972).

Factors that are known to influence the birth weight and growth rate of cattle also appear to influence the buffalo in a similar manner (Tantawy and Ahmed, 1953; Tomar and Desai, 1965).

Reproduction

Male.   Spermatogenesis in the buffalo starts quite early in life and meiotic division of the spermatogonial cells has been observed as early as one year of age in the Indian buffalo (Dutt and Bhattacharya, 1952). It is likely that spermatogenesis may start even earlier. There is a belief that the buffalo grows at a slower rate than cattle, even with good feeding and management, and attains sexual maturity at a later age. There are, however, reports from Italy and Russia of the buffalo bull being put to service at around 2 years of age and this is not much different from the age at which male cattle are used for breeding. The author noted that the age at first service of the buffalo bull is around 3 years in Iraq although some well-fed and well-developed bulls may be put at stud at 2 years. In India, Pakistan and Egypt the buffalo bull is generally not used at stud before 3 to $3\frac{1}{2}$ years of age. The duration over which the buffalo bull may be retained for service is as yet a subject of individual opinion as no systematic study appears to have been made of this aspect of husbandry. MacGregor (1941) stated that in the buffalo 'by six or seven years there is frequently a loss in potency with a rising proportion of unsuccessful services but desire continues until he is 12 years or more, during which time his muscular strength seems to increase. Complete senility, that is, loss of muscular strength as well as desire, does not manifest itself until he is over 15 years of age'. Others have expressed the view that the buffalo bull can be retained for service up to 10 to 15 years of age (Hafez, 1952). Buffalo bulls are used for breeding in Iraq for periods varying between two and 10 years. In Italy, bulls are replaced after only 4 or 5 years of service. Divergent views have been expressed about the number of female buffaloes to be allowed per bull. According to MacGregor (1941) 'a good buffalo bull of the river type can serve 100 cows a year, but it is unusual to allow more than 12 cows to each bull as each of them will be served several times during her heat'. Hafez (1952) stated that a buffalo bull can serve fifty female buffaloes in a year and Lazarus (1946) was of the opinion that the buffalo bull should be used sparingly so that he does not serve more than seventy-five times a year. The author has noted that the number of females allotted to one buffalo bull in Iraq villages varied widely from 12:1 to 600:1, but in the majority of villages it was less than 100:1.

In Egypt, 75 per cent of the services in buffaloes occur during the 4 months of the year that constitute the breeding season and the bull is used at least three times a week during this period. With such heavy service there is deterioration in semen quality and consequent lowering of fertility (Asker and El-Itriby, 1958). It has also been observed in Egypt that with three semen collections per week or with one collection per week from the buffalo bull there was a comparative deterioration in the semen quality in the first instance. With semen collection twice a week for a period extending over 3 years, there was no deterioration in semen quality or sex vigour in Murrah buffalo bulls maintained at the IVRI.

Sex vigour of the buffalo declines during the hot summer and improves with the onset of the colder season (Misra and Sengupta, 1965).

Female. Reports from several countries on the age of puberty of buffalo heifers show a wide variation, but in general it seems that the female buffalo attains puberty at a considerably later age than cattle. However, without more detailed information this should not be accepted as a characteristic species difference. In Egypt, buffalo heifers have not been observed to exhibit first oestrus before they were over 13 months of age (Hafez, 1955). Age of puberty of buffalo heifers in the Philippines varies between 26 and 29 months (Villegas, 1930). Female buffaloes in Cambodia attain puberty at 3 years, whereas cattle heifers in that country achieve this physiological status some 6 months earlier (Baradat, 1949). Buffaloes in Azerbaijan exhibit first oestrus at 2 to 3 years of age, but with good feeding puberty is attained earlier (Gorbelik, 1935). With the wide variation in reported age for puberty in the buffalo heifers from different countries, it is obvious that wide variations will be found on age of conception and the age at first calving. From available reports it appears that, in general, buffalo heifers are not bred before they are $2\frac{1}{2}$ to 3 years of age. More commonly the buffalo heifers are put to the bull at $3\frac{1}{2}$ years or later.

Oestrus, oestrous cycle and ovulation

Reports on oestrus phenomenon in buffaloes also show marked variations which could be due to differences in breed, environmental conditions and management. Reports from India, Pakistan and Egypt indicate that the signs of oestrus in the buffalo of the river type are less intense than in female cattle (Hafez, 1954; Ishaq, 1956; Luktuke and Ahuja, 1961). On the other hand, the symptoms of oestrus in the carabao of the Philippines are said to be more obvious than in female cattle (Ocampo, 1939–1940). In 84 per cent of cases incidence of oestrus in the Egyptian buffalo was observed between 18.00 and 06.00 hours (Hafez, 1954), but it has been reported that in Indian buffaloes oestrus usually commenced during the morning. According to some reports, mating desire in the buffalo ceases during the day and female buffaloes breed only at night (Mac-Gregor, 1941; Cockrill, 1967). This may be true for wild or swamp buffaloes, but it is not true for the river-type buffaloes of India and Pakistan. Incidence of silent heat is high in buffaloes and many oestruses may go unnoticed unless great care is exercised in detection.

In a study on Murrah buffaloes, oestrus during gestation was observed in 6·1 per cent of the animals and on an average the oestrus symptoms were exhibited 108.4 ± 11.8 days post conception (Luktuke and Roy, 1964).

Post-partum heat in the river buffalo when appearing early may be manifest around 40 days following parturition, but in most instances appears after a period exceeding 100 days following the birth of the young (MacGregor, 1941; Shalash, 1958; Luktuke and Roy, 1964). The swamp buffalo in Malaysia exhibits first heat after parturition at about 65 days (MacGregor, 1941).

The length of the oestrous cycle of the buffalo is similar to that of cattle and is on average around 21 days (Shalash, 1958), but considerable variations in the length of the cycle can commonly be observed.

Fern-pattern formation by cervical mucus on drying was detected to be at a maximum during oestrus in the buffalo (Raizada *et al.*, 1968). It was further noticed that a high percentage of pregnancies resulted from insemination at oestrus, natural or induced, which was associated with typical fern-pattern formation in the cervical mucus.

Ovulation in the buffalo occurs subsequent to the cessation of oestrus as in the case of cattle and the time interval in the two species also appears to be similar (Shalash, 1958; Rao *et al.*, 1960; Basirov, 1964).

The 'lutein' tissue that forms in the ovary following ovulation is white in the buffalo as contrasted to the yellow colour observed in cattle.

The gestation period of the buffalo is longer than that of cattle and normally exceeds 300 days. The average for river buffaloes in India and Pakistan is around 307 days and it appears that the buffaloes in Egypt carry their young a week or 10 days longer. The gestation period of the swamp buffalo is considerably longer than that of the river buffalo and lasts for 330 to 340 days (MacGregor, 1941; Hua 1957).

Calving interval

Reports on calving interval in the buffalo present very widely differing data. Except for a report from Italy in which an interval of less than 400 days is indicated most of the other reports give considerably longer intervals. Short calving intervals, as reported from Italy, possibly indicate a better plane of nutrition and management of the herds. There are some reports which indicate that those buffaloes which calve at an early age have a relatively shorter calving interval than those which are late calvers (Alim and Ahmed, 1954; Salerno, 1960). Seasonal difference in calving interval has been reported in Murrah buffaloes, and it has been observed that in the animals which calve between June and November the average interval is 428.7 days, but in buffaloes calving between December and May the interval is 507.1 days (Singh *et al.*, 1958). With good management, it should be possible to produce a calf a year from the buffalo although two in 3 years is the norm (Cockrill, 1967).

Estimates by several workers of repeatability and heritability of calving interval in the buffalo suggest that the genetic component of this attribute is very small and hence selection for a shorter calving interval is not likely to be rewarding.

Twinning

Twin births in the buffalo have been reported from Egypt, Italy and India. It appears that the frequency of twin births in Indian buffaloes is considerably lower (0·06 per cent) than that in Egypt (0·2 to 0·6 per cent) and Italy (0·3 per cent). Cockrill (1970), however, reported a high incidence of about one per cent of twinning in Surti buffaloes at Anand in India. The relatively higher incidence of twinning at Anand is attributed by Cockrill to the practice followed in that area of making two inseminations within the oestral period.

Artificial insemination

Artificial insemination (AI) as a breeding tool has been used on a field scale so far only in a few buffalo-rearing countries. It has been practised on the largest scale in India where it is claimed that the first buffalo calf in the world bred by means of AI was born in the Allahabad Agricultural Institute on 21 August 1943.

The anatomy of the reproductive organs and the physiology of reproduction being similar in many ways in the buffalo and in cattle, as a common-sense approach the introduction of AI in the former species was made following the established methods used in the latter species. However, it soon became obvious that to achieve the best results in the buffalo the techniques used for cattle could not be applied *in toto* and some modifications were required. Only some of the salient points of difference between the two species relating to animal behaviour, seminology and techniques are discussed later.

The male buffalo can be trained more easily than male cattle for donating semen by artificial service. The buffalo is less choosy concerning the teaser and readily mounts an anoestrous female or even a male buffalo in the service crate. Coat colour or the physiological status of the female buffalo in the service crate does not alter the reaction time of the buffalo bull (Prabhu and Bhattacharya, 1954; Prabhu, 1956). The thrust given by the male buffalo during service is less vigorous than that observed in male cattle. As in the case of male cattle, collection in the artificial vagina is also the most convenient method of obtaining semen from the buffalo with slight modification of the temperature of the artificial vagina. With the temperature of the artificial vagina reaching 41°C (105·8°F) there is bursting and breaking of buffalo spermatozoa, but a temperature of 39°C (102·2°F) caused no damage to the cells (Mahmoud, 1952). Although it is possible to collect semen from the buffalo by the massage technique, the animal is less responsive to this method of ejaculation than male cattle and also requires a longer period for training. The semen collected by this method is relatively poorer in quality and there are no records of fertility with use of such ejaculate.

The capillaries of the rectal wall are more fragile in the buffalo than in cattle and hence manipulation through the rectum while massaging must be done with great care as otherwise bleeding may result as a consequence of the breaking of the capillary vessels. Electro-ejaculation from the buffalo is still in the experimental stage, and although successful collections have been made by use of this technique it is not likely to come into general use in the near future.

Morphological characteristics of the spermatozoa of the buffalo and cattle differ. MacGregor (1941) was possibly the first to report that the head of the buffalo spermatozoa is more rectangular than that of male cattle and that the stained portion of the head is also slightly narrower in the former species. According to Rao (1958) spermatozoa of the buffalo possess distinct morphological characteristics by which they can be readily differentiated from spermatozoa of other domestic animals. Comparative morphology of the spermatozoa of Egyptian buffaloes and indigenous cattle can be seen in Table 6.3.

Table 6.3 *Comparative morphology of the spermatozoa of buffaloes and cattle*

Spermatozoa measurements	Buffaloes			Cattle		
	Mean (μ)	SD (μ)	CV (%)	Mean (μ)	SD (μ)	CV (%)
Head length	7·436	0·442	5·9	9·126	1·326	14·5
Head breadth (anterior)	4·264	0·520	12·3	4·732	0·494	10·4
Head breadth (posterior)	3·172	0·442	14·0	2·730	0·520	19·4
Ratio head breadth (anterior) to head breadth (posterior)	1·340	0·330	24·8	1·790	0·320	1·7
Neck	0·442	0·208	47·1	0·650	0·338	51·5
Length of middle-piece	11·648	0·936	7·9	12·558	0·624	4·9
Breadth of middle-piece	1·092	0·286	26·2	1·006	0·286	26·8
Length of tail	42·882	3·042	7·1	46·280	6·084	13·2

Source: Mahmoud (1952).

The morphology of spermatozoa changes with the age of the buffalo (Venkataswami and Vedanayagam, 1962) and with ageing in different diluents.

Unlike cattle semen, which has a yellowish tinge, the semen from healthy buffalo bulls is milky white in colour or milky white with a light tinge of blue (Shukla and Bhattacharya, 1949; Mahmoud, 1952). Cattle semen gives a colour reaction of various shades with DOPA (3–4 dihydroxyphenylalanine) (Mukherjee, 1964), but such a reaction is not detected with buffalo semen.

Volume, sperm concentration, initial motility and speed of travel of spermatozoa are generally lower in buffalo than in cattle semen.

Compared to cattle spermatozoa, the spermatozoa of the buffalo have an inherently poorer metabolic activity as judged by O_2 uptake and fructolysis (Table 6.4). Variation in semen quality due to changes in the climate is also more pronounced in the buffalo than in cattle, as evidenced by changes in the respirometric activity of spermatozoa in different buffers during summer and winter (Table 6.5).

Table 6.4 *Difference in the mean values of various characteristics of cattle and buffalo semen*

Semen characteristic	Cattle	Buffalo	No. of observations	Significance
Sperm density/ml × 10^6	1,389·6 ±48·5	1,234·9 ±43·1	117	*
Live sperm/ml × 10^6	1,036·5 ±46·4	891·7 ±42·5	117	*
O_2 uptake μl in saline/hour	112·2 ± 6·6	81·2 ± 5·8	117	**
O_2 uptake μl in phosphate/hour	85·8 ± 4·6	64·6 ± 6·8	117	**
O_2 uptake μl in Kreb's/hour	116·6 ± 6·2	70·0 ± 5·2	117	**
Fructolysis/10^9 sperm/hour	1·79± 0·08	1·54± 0·08	117	*
Fructolysis/10^9 live sperm/hour	2·45± 0·10	2·15± 0·09	117	*

* Significant at 5 per cent level.
** Significant at 1 per cent level.
Source: Sinha *et al.* (1966).

Table 6.5 *Oxygen uptake by buffalo and cattle spermatozoa in different diluents during summer and winter*

		Summer	Winter	Significance of difference between summer and winter
O_2 uptake (μl O_2)/5·10^9 (sperm diluted with saline)	Buffalo	38·04± 4·9	101·8±17·8	**
	Cattle	105·2 ±13·9	151·2±19·2	Not significant
O_2 uptake (μl O_2)/5·10^9 (sperm diluted with phosphate buffer)	Buffalo	34·9 ± 5·7	64·7±10·3	**
	Cattle	74·4 ±10·7	91·8±11·5	Not significant
O_2 uptake (μl O_2)/5·10^9 (sperm diluted with Kreb's buffer)	Buffalo	32·7 ± 6·3	104·5±15·3	**
	Cattle	90·1 ±13·3	141·9±18·5	*

* Significant at 5 per cent.
** Significant at 1 per cent level.
Source: Personal communication from Dr A. Roy.

The depressing effect of the phosphate ion, and the stimulating effect of the chloride ion on the O_2 uptake pattern, as can be found in cattle spermatozoa, are not observable in buffalo sperm cells. This would suggest that either the influence of certain ions like phosphate and chloride on aerobic metabolism of buffalo sperm cells is intrinsically different from that of their effect on cattle sperm, or that the seminal plasma of the buffalo has properties which in some way obliterate the specific effects of the chloride or phosphate ions on O_2 utilization *in vitro* (Sinha *et al.*, 1966). The work of Roy *et al.* (1960) lends some experimental support to the second hypothesis (Table 6.6).

Table 6.6 *Differences in some chemical attributes of buffalo and cattle semen*

Constituent	Buffalo	Cattle	Statistical
	(mg/100 ml semen or seminal plasma)		significance
Total reducing substances	700 ± 52	769 ± 42	
Fructose	355 ± 17	611 ± 39	**
Calcium	40 ± 2	25 ± 5	**
Chloride	373 ± 55	249 ± 26	*
Inorganic phosphate	6·4 ± 0·6	5·9 ± 0·5	
	(6·3 ± 0·4)	(5·6 ± 0·4)	–
Acid-soluble phosphate	72 ± 3·9	29 ± 3·2	**
	(64 ± 2·2)	(27 ± 2·9)	**
Total phosphorus	103 ± 8·9	74 ± 2·5	**
	(95 ± 7·2)	(42 ± 4·8)	**
Acid phosphatase activity	308 ± 44	145 ± 11	**
(Bodansky unit)	(307 ± 41)	(167 ± 11)	**
Alkaline phosphatase activity	252 ± 37	134 ± 14	*
(Bodansky unit)	(266 ± 42)	(152 ± 18)	*

Note: Figures in parentheses indicate values in seminal plasma.
* Significant at 5 per cent level.
** Significant at 1 per cent level.
Source: Roy *et al.* (1960).

Several of the diluters, which proved very satisfactory for extension and storage of cattle semen, did not give as satisfactory results when used for buffalo semen. Egg-yolk phosphate buffer (EYP) has proved unsuitable for use with buffalo ejaculate. Egg-yolk citrate (EYC) is fairly satisfactory for dilution and storage of buffalo semen but not as good as it is for cattle semen.

For several years now, active research has been carried out in various laboratories in India to evolve diluents for buffalo semen as satisfactory as those used for cattle semen and to determine the cause(s) for the relative poorer keeping quality of the ejaculate from the buffalo. The results of a considerable number of comparative *in vitro* studies using different diluents, including Kampschmidt's glucose sodium bicarbonate egg-yolk extender (with or without addition of sulphamezathene), seem to indicate that the latter diluent may prove satisfactory for AI of the buffalo. Higher fertility results have also been reported with the use of Kampschmidt's diluent (Gokhale, 1958).

Highly encouraging results with the use of citric acid whey (CAW) for dilution and storage of buffalo semen at refrigeration or deep-freezing temperatures have recently been reported from the National Dairy Research Institute (NDRI) in India. Results of limited fertility trials using buffalo semen diluted in CAW are also quite encouraging. The survival of spermatozoa in CAW is extremely sensitive to the pH of the diluent and sperm motility is maximal at pH 6·8.

Very satisfactory results have been reported from Pakistan with the use of homogenized milk as a diluent for buffalo semen.

Deep freezing of buffalo semen is still in the experimental stage. Successful freezing with recovery of about 40 to 80 per cent of the initially motile spermatozoa on thawing has been reported by investigators in India (Roy *et al.*, 1956). In a trial involving twelve inseminations a conception rate of 58·3 per cent was obtained at the NDRI with use of frozen buffalo semen. There is also one report available from Russia in which 77 per cent fertility is claimed with use of buffalo semen deep frozen for 4 months (Basirov, 1964).

Aly-Nour El-Din (1964) reported that the use of diluted semen containing adiurekrin – a preparation of the posterior lobe of the hypophysis having an oxytocic effect – at the rate of 3·5 IU per ml diluent improved the conception rate from 58 per cent in the control group to 74 per cent in the treated group in female buffaloes, especially those with atony of the uterus. The higher rate of fertility is presumably attributable to the improved contractility of the uterine musculature and the arrival of spermatozoa in time for fertilization of the ovum.

In an attempt to determine the chemical basis, if any, of the relative poorer preservability of buffalo semen under conditions identical with those obtainable for conventional, *in vitro* storage of cattle semen, Roy *et al.* (1960) made a comparative study on the semen biochemistry of buffalo and cattle. Their findings are shown in Table 6.6.

The significantly higher concentration of calcium, esterified phosphate and the phosphate-splitting enzymes in buffalo semen might, according to Roy *et al.* (1960), create conditions that adversely influence the viability of spermatozoa in stored semen.

For insemination of the female buffalo the rectovaginal technique is preferable when suitably trained technicians are available, but when insemination is done by lay inseminators the speculum method may be used, with adequate sanitary precautions. It is generally accepted that the site of deposition of semen should be the same as in female cattle to give similar fertility results in the buffalo. It has been found in India that the speed of travel of spermatozoa in the reproductive tract of the female buffalo is about the same as that reported by Van Demark and Hays (1954) for female cattle and that spermatozoa reach the anterior third of the fallopian tubes in 3 minutes and 20 seconds following AI.

The optimum number of actively motile spermatozoa required for insemination of the buffalo is not known and needs to be determined. Also, the comparative value of different semen diluents in relation to fertility has not been studied in detail in the buffalo and is awaiting proper exploration.

Conception rate

Information available on conception rate in buffaloes either by natural service or by AI is very limited. Furthermore, the assessment of conception rate has been made by different workers following different methods under widely differing husbandry practices. Consequently, it is very difficult, if not impossible, to draw any definite, general conclusions. Conception rates varying from 50 to over 90 per cent have been reported for buffaloes in India. In an assessment (1956–59) of conception rate in Murrah buffaloes at the IVRI, following AI, it was found that out of 102 animals that conceived, 66·2, 21·6, 5·4 and 6·3 per cent became pregnant by the first, second, third and fourth or subsequent insemination, respectively. The average number of inseminations required per conception was 1·56. Fertility was ascertained by rectal palpation and by calving results.

Conception rates of 36·2 per cent for Egyptian buffalo and 35·1 per cent for indigenous cattle were reported by Oloufa (1955). Subsequently, El-Itriby and Barrada (1959) estimated conception rates by using data from four AI centres in Egypt and found a variation of from 64 to 82 per cent. Hafez (1953) found the average number of services required per conception in the buffalo to be 1·46. In the study by Hafez it was noticed that 55·6 per cent of the animals conceived following the first service.

A conception rate of 72 per cent was not uncommon in buffaloes bred by AI in Pakistan (Rife, 1959).

Nutrition

In any programme of livestock development an aspect of husbandry that needs to be given close consideration is nutrition. With the present underdeveloped state of buffalo husbandry it is all the more necessary to give greater and more intense attention than has hitherto been given to this very important subject if the production potential of these animals is to be exploited more fully.

As stated earlier, the vast majority of buffaloes are reared in regions of the globe that are poorly developed and are owned by farmers of small means who have hardly any capacity for financial investment. Consequently, most buffaloes are presently being maintained at no or very little cost to their owners and are existing at barely subsistence level with only marginal production. Their output, although small and constituting only a part of the production potential of the animals, is still of some benefit to their owners. There is no doubt, however, that the present low level of economy of buffalo production cannot be accepted and allowed to continue and effective means have to be evolved to improve production. To accomplish this, optimum nutrition of the animals, consistent with economy, becomes a subject of major considera-tion. The problem, however, is very complex and difficult. As a general rule, in the regions where buffaloes abound there is considerable quantita-tive deficiency of feeds and fodders, and available foodstuffs are possibly qualitatively deficient. In this situation it becomes very necessary to search for non-conventional materials that can be utilized as feeds to make good the quantitative deficiency and to evolve processes by which qualitative deficiencies of feeds can be rectified.

One basis for progress in livestock development is research, as this provides the necessary data for the formulation of effective developmental programmes. In order to prepare such a programme concerned with the nutrition of the buffalo and to ensure the supply of the optimal nutri-tional requirements of buffaloes of different ages and levels of production in different regions, two things are absolutely necessary. One relates to the collection of information on the nutritional composition of the locally available feeds and fodders and the other concerns a knowledge of the alimentary physiology of the buffalo. As the nutritional physiology of cattle has been investigated in great detail, and as cattle and buffaloes are similar in many respects, it would be profitable to know if their alimentary physiology differs and, if so, in what details. Unfortunately, in many of the buffalo-rearing countries the organizational base for research in animal nutrition is weak and inadequate. As a result, very large gaps at present exist in knowledge relating to different aspects of the nutrition of the buffalo.

Researches on animal nutrition with special emphasis on cattle have been in progress for quite a long time in India, and information has been gathered on the nutrient composition of most of the common locally available feeds and fodders. As a result of these studies it has been revealed that in India animal feeds are generally poorer in crude protein and ether extract content than they are in temperate-zone countries. In general, the fibre content is also higher. The phosphorus content has been reported to be low. It is likely that investigations on the com-position of locally available feeds and fodders in other buffalo-rearing countries would reveal similar information.

During the last three decades research on alimentary physiology of the buffalo and on the comparative physiology of the buffalo and cattle has been engaging the attention of a number of workers in animal nutri-tion in India and Egypt. However, investigations have only been sporadic and fragmentary in nature and the findings of different workers have not been in agreement. From observations under field conditions that buffaloes thrive better than do cattle on coarse fodders, an impression has grown that buffaloes are more efficient than cattle in digesting and utilizing crude fibre and cellulose. The results of some of the controlled studies on comparative nutritional physiology of cattle and the buffalo lend support to this view (Mudgal and Ray, 1962; Ichhponani *et al.*,

1969), whereas the findings of some other workers, which include some more recent investigations, do not sustain this view (Naga and El-Shazly, 1969; Ludri *et al.*, 1971). The possibility cannot be ruled out that the better performance of buffalo fed coarse roughage is not related to the superior capacity of this species for the digestion of crude fibre and cellulose but is due to the buffalo being less discriminating in foraging and therefore consuming a larger quantity of coarse fodder that is not readily eaten by cattle. In the digestion of crude protein not much difference between the buffalo and cattle was observed by Singh (1933), but Langer *et al.* (1968) reported that when a ration was deficient in carbohydrate the rumen microbes could utilize dietary nitrogen more efficiently in the buffalo. By incubation of rumen liquor of the two species with two different feeds, the TCA-insoluble protein nitrogen concentration was found to be significantly higher in the buffalo (Singh *et al.*, 1968). With urea feeding, the TCA-insoluble protein nitrogen concentration increased in both species, but it was higher in the buffalo. The residual nitrogen (non-protein nitrogen (NPN) other than ammonia) content, as also the ammonia level, were significantly higher in the buffalo than in cattle rumen liquor. The intraruminal environment of the buffalo is believed to be more favourable for propagation and growth of microbial types that utilize NPN and for maintenance of a faster rate of microbial activity. Pant (1966) noticed a consistent and significantly higher number of microidophils in buffalo than in cattle rumen contents, but Naga and El-Shazly (1969) observed that the number of protozoa was greater in the rumen of cattle than in the rumen of the buffalo although Naga *et al.* (1969) stated that active ciliate protozoa were developed earlier in buffalo calves. According to a number of reports volatile fatty acid (VFA) production is higher in the buffalo (Ichhponani *et al.*, 1969; Punj *et al.*, 1968), but these findings have not been corroborated by the work of several other investigators (Ludri *et al.*, 1971; Naga and El-Shazly, 1969). There is also disagreement on the comparative consumption of dry matter per unit body weight by the buffalo and cattle. It is quite obvious that from the present status of knowledge of the comparative alimentary physiology of the buffalo and cattle it is not possible to draw any definite conclusions as to whether one species differs from the other in any material manner in relation to digestion and utilization of nutrients in commonly used feeds and fodders, or if one species is superior to the other in digestive and metabolic functions. Optimal nutritional requirements of the buffalo, therefore, remain unknown at present. It should, however, be realized that even with more intensive investigations knowledge will still be far from complete in these fields. Adoption for the buffalo of the feeding standards as recommended by the National Research Council of the United States or the Agricultural Research Council of the United Kingdom for cattle appears to be the only practical course to follow at present in the absence of more complete knowledge on alimentary physiology and the nutritional requirements of the buffalo.

With accumulation of more data it is likely that in future it should be possible to formulate economic and nutritious rations specifically for the buffalo.

Adaptability

Environmental physiology of the buffalo is a field of study that has so far remained practically unexplored. Consideration of the global distribution of the buffalo and the widely differing geographical conditions under which they are thriving suggests that this species is adaptable to a large range of environmental conditions. This is particularly true of the river buffalo (Plate 6.5).

The buffalo is considered an animal of the plains, but the native buffaloes of Nepal can be found distributed from the plains of the Terai

Plate 6.5   Buffaloes wallowing in a river in India (Indian Council of Agricultural Research, New Delhi).

region up to an elevation of 2,700 m (approx. 8,900 ft). Buffaloes of the Murrah breed from the plains of India have been introduced into the mid-altitude region of Nepal. These animals seem to have easily adapted to this hilly environment and are thriving. The introduction of buffaloes to Ootacamund in the Nilgiri hills in India at an elevation of 2,300 m (approx. 7,500 ft) has been equally successful. In Bulgaria buffaloes are used for drawing snow-ploughs (Cockrill, 1968). The best milk breeds of buffaloes in India and Pakistan are mostly confined to areas where the summer temperature rises above 46°C (115°F) and the winter temperature may fall below 4°C (39·5°F). Nondescript buffaloes are found scattered all over India and Pakistan. The great adaptability of the species is also apparent from the observation made on many occasions that in areas where there is barely enough sustenance to maintain life – such as stubble fields or marshy lands with sedge, reeds, water weeds and grasses, mostly refused by cattle – the buffalo is capable of maintaining itself in good condition, whereas cattle rapidly deteriorate. The buffalo not only maintains itself but can also work and supply milk when fed the poorest of diets.

The swamp buffalo apparently is not as adaptable as the river buffalo. They are to be found only in swampy and marshy areas and in hot climates. Swamp buffaloes must have almost unlimited access to water to keep them cool.

It is generally accepted that buffaloes possess poor heat tolerance. This view stands in need of some modification. There is no doubt that when exposed to direct solar radiation or if made to work in the sun during hot weather, buffaloes exhibit signs of great distress. On account of their dark skin and the sparse coat of hair on their body, there is great absorption of heat from direct solar radiation. Coupled with this, there is also less efficient evaporative cooling from the body surface of the animal due to a rather poor sweating ability. The causes of distress of the buffalo in the sun can therefore be easily understood. However, if kept in the shade, and rested or put to work at a slow pace unexposed to the sun during the hot weather their tolerance to heat is of no mean order. In fact, controlled field studies with river buffaloes have revealed that their thermoregulatory mechanisms function efficiently in the shade and that these are more effective than they are in cattle, when the speed of recovery from the effect of stress is taken as a measure of efficiency (Badreldin and Ghazy, 1952; Mullick, 1960). Results of investigations by Pandey and Roy (1969a) on seasonal changes in body temperature, cardio-respiratory and haematological attributes and body water and electrolytic status of the buffalo under conventional farm management lend further support to their view. Pandey and Roy (1969b) have emphasized that the plethora of changes observed in the buffalo are orderly manifestations of various physiological adjustments necessary for adaptation to higher environmental temperature and that these changes are within physiological limits.

At the IVRI, groups of unbred Murrah buffalo heifers varying in age from 18 to 24 months were subjected to experimental treatment for assessing their adaptability to severe heat stress. For this purpose, the heifers were exposed to either hot-humid (temperature 40·5°C (105°F), vapour pressure 39·5 mm Hg) or hot-arid (temperature 48°C (118·4°F), vapour pressure 10 mm Hg) conditions for 6 hours in a controlled psychrometric chamber and their physiological responses as manifested by changes in rectal temperature, respiration and pulse rate, respiratory volume, etc., recorded at hourly intervals. Previous to exposure to heat stress the animals were maintained for 24 hours under cool comfortable conditions (temperature 18·5°C (65·5°F), vapour pressure 8·5 mm Hg) and the physiological attributes recorded as under hot environments. For comparative evaluation, groups of Zebu heifers were also tested similarly within the span of a few days during the same season. It was observed that under cool, comfortable conditions the average rectal temperature, pulse rate and respiration rate of the buffalo were lower than those of the Zebu, but on exposure to hot-humid conditions the rectal temperature and respiration rate of the buffalo exceeded those of the Zebu towards the end of the exposure period. On exposure to hot-arid conditions the buffalo heifers reacted more strongly than Zebu heifers as evinced by alterations in rectal temperature, respiratory volume and respiration rate. In relation to the physiological reaction of the animals under cool, comfortable conditions, the effect of stress on exposure to a hot-arid environment was rather mild in the case of the Zebu heifers but more severe for the buffalo heifers. The difference in response of the animals to the two types of hot conditions was much less marked in the buffalo than in the Zebu heifers. These investigations have shown that the buffalo has the capacity to withstand very severe heat stress (Guha, 1967). In similar experiments using European-type cattle in the United States, with considerably less severe heat stress, some of the test animals had to be removed from the chamber prematurely as they exhibited a precipitous rise in rectal temperature. In the investigations at the IVRI, on no occasion did it become necessary to remove an animal before the completion of a full 6 hours of exposure to heat stress.

Though the thermoregulatory mechanism of the buffalo is reasonably efficient there are reports of the reproductive system being adversely affected by climatic changes. The semen quality of the buffalo deteriorates like that of cattle, sheep and goats during summer, but unlike other species the Murrah buffalo fails to retain the quality of its semen at a high level during winter (Mukherjee and Bhattacharya, 1953; Kushwaha *et al.*, 1955; Sengupta *et al.*, 1963). The buffalo appears to be sensitive to extremes of cold and heat and less able than cattle to adapt itself to a colder climate (Kaleff, 1942). Failure during the winter to produce the same high quality of semen as is produced in spring may be the result of the sensitivity of the buffalo to a cold environment. Some degree of seasonal variation in breeding efficiency is usual with most domestic livestock, but the variation is more marked in the buffalo. A seasonal trend of reproduction among Philippine buffaloes was first reported by Villegas (1928). Subsequently, this peculiarity of breeding of the buffalo was reported by many workers from India, Pakistan, Egypt, Bulgaria and Italy. Analysing the data from various farms in India and Pakistan, Rife (1959) observed that there was practically no incidence of oestrus during the hot months and that the oestrous symptoms were not pronounced during the adjacent periods. Pattabiraman (1956) noted that there was no particular season of breeding for Murrah buffaloes, although there was a tendency for better performance during the cooler months. The author has noted that buffaloes in the marshes of southern Iraq breed throughout the year, but more so in the spring and a little less so in the autumn.

The depression of the breeding function of buffaloes during hot months led many to suspect that it was in some way related to high environmental temperatures or to the temperature–humidity complex of the tropical summer. Others considered that in addition there might be a photoperiodic effect. In order to investigate this problem Roy *et al.* (1968) conducted a series of systematic investigations. From the results of the earlier experiments it appeared that air temperature and humidity were having a direct effect on breeding efficiency as improvements in breeding performance were obtained by alterations in housing conditions to provide relief from heat stress. Subsequent investigations have suggested that the photoperiod, rather than the heat stress factor, is primarily involved. Further studies and a more critical evaluation of the experimental results have led this team to believe that what in fact happens in the buffalo is a change in the manner of manifestation of oestrous symptoms during the summer months and that with proper husbandry practices it is possible to make the buffalo breed fairly uniformly all through the year. There are many questions relating to the reproduction of the buffalo that still remain to be investigated, and it is very likely that a number of factors singly or in combination are operational in causing the marked seasonal breeding behaviour.

The milk yield of the buffalo is also adversely affected during summer. If those buffaloes in the optimal period of their lactation are splashed on the body with water during the summer season there is an increase in milk production, but in buffaloes not given this treatment the milk yield becomes irregular and declines (Sinha and Minett, 1947).

Production

Work

The buffalo has been used as a work animal for thousands of years. Its body build, enormous strength, docile temperament, amenability for easy training and capacity for long sustained work make it an excellent animal for haulage and many kinds of agricultural work. A survey by Cockrill (1968) has revealed that in more than a score of Asian countries buffalo provide the most efficient and the cheapest source of power. Both the swamp and the river buffalo make good work animals, but for paddy cultivation in the rice-growing areas in eastern Asia the swamp buffalo is unmatched for efficiency. They are used for ploughing the soil, for puddling the earth and harrowing the fields after flooding and for making the bed ready for planting the rice seedlings. The large hooves and great flexibility of the pastern and fetlock joints enable the swamp buffalo to work with ease in thick, muddy, waterlogged paddy fields. Their proclivity for water also makes them very well adapted for this kind of work in slush and mud. It is a common sight to find the buffalo working contentedly and with ease in knee-deep, muddy water in rice fields. Although possessing a massive body frame and large hooves, buffaloes are quite nimble-footed and work with ease in very small plots without damaging the low mud walls, called 'bunds', forming partitions between the plots. Apart from ploughing and harrowing, buffaloes are used for many other types of work such as threshing, drawing water for irrigation, expressing oil from oil seeds or juice from sugar cane in simple mills, puddling clay for preparing bricks, logging and haulage of loads on sledges or carts. In Pakistan and Sabah buffaloes are widely used as pack animals and for riding. Buffaloes play a role even in races and games in Indonesia and Sabah.

Although the majority of working animals are males, female buffaloes, dry or with a poor milk yield, are also sometimes put to work. This practice is not uncommon in Egypt, parts of Indonesia and the Philippines. For drawing heavy loads buffaloes are hitched singly or in pairs to crudely built wooden carts. They are used extensively for this purpose in India, Pakistan, Indonesia and other countries, particularly in and around urban areas. Buffaloes are slow as compared to oxen for traction but can draw much heavier loads and have greater staying power. On good roads, it is not unusual to find a pair of buffaloes drawing a load of about 2 t (2·02 tons) at a slow pace of 3·2 km (2 miles) an hour. As buffaloes are incapable of working for long on hot days when they are exposed to direct sunlight during the hot summer they need be put to work at night or in the early morning. As work animals male buffaloes are used both castrated or uncastrated. The practice varies from country to country, following local beliefs and customs. In India and Pakistan castration is not the usual practice and uncastrated animals seldom, if ever, become intractable. Castration, if carried out, is done at a late age as early castration is believed to produce a poor working animal. Docility and mild manner make the buffalo so easy to manage at work that in many instances no restrictive controls are necessary. Whips or chains are seldom used to drive the animal.

For working on hard ground, hooves of buffaloes need protection against excessive wear by shoeing. Thin iron plates are used in India and in Pakistan. Shoes made of straw and 'trompas' – shoes made from old motor tyres – are used for this purpose in Taiwan and East Java, respectively (Cockrill, 1968).

Milk

As a dairy animal the buffalo is found at its best in India, Pakistan, Egypt and Iraq. Even though milking buffaloes constitute only about 40 per cent of the total milking bovine stock in India, it is the buffalo and not the cow that is the principal dairy animal in that country. The buffalo in India yields on an average 504 kg (1,110 lb) of milk per year as compared with an average yield of only 173 kg (380 lb) by cattle. Milk yield varies widely, depending on the breed and husbandry practices. Daily milk yield of the lactating buffalo in India and Pakistan may be as low as 2 to 2·5 kg (4·5 to 5·5 lb) in a poor village animal and as high as 20 kg (44 lb) or more for a good buffalo on a well-managed farm. The average yield from five selected herds in India was found to be a little over 2,055 kg 4,530 lb) per lactation. In another high-yielding buffalo herd 2·7 per cent of the lactating buffaloes gave a yield exceeding 3,630 kg (8,000 lb) of milk per lactation. According to Rife (1959) four well-managed farms in Pakistan showed an average yield of over 1,860 kg (4,100 lb) per lactation with the range varying approximately from 1,507 to 2,128 kg (3,320 to 4,691 lb). In Egypt the average milk yield is lower. Buffaloes maintained on government farms and research stations show an average milk yield of 1,814 kg (4,000 lb) or less per lactation with a range varying from 226 to 3,856 kg (500 to 8,500 lb) according to Ragab *et al.* (1954). The Marsh Arabs of southern Iraq rear their buffaloes with great care but under conditions unendurable to most livestock breeders. Even under these circumstances, an average yield of 6 kg (13 lb) of milk for more than 200 days is not unusual. In the author's opinion these buffalo are potential high yielders and their performance can match those of the good milk breed buffalo in other countries. Attention has not been given so far to developing milk characteristics in swamp buffalo, which have an incredible capacity for work. Yet in the Philippines, where working swamp buffalo are milked, a yield of 2 to 3 kg (4·5 to 6·5 lb) a day is common. Caucasian buffaloes, a new breed developed in Russia, yield on an average 1,352 kg (2,980 lb) of milk containing 8·1 per cent fat in 300 days (Agabeili *et al.*, 1971).

Buffalo milk is much richer than cow's milk with a butterfat content that may be as high as 15 per cent under good feeding and management. The average fat content is possibly a little over 7 per cent. The solids-not-fat content is around 9 to 10·5 per cent and is generally slightly higher than that of cow's milk. Buffalo milk is used for preparing the same products as those made from cow's milk, such as yogurt, sweets, ice-cream and various types of cheese. Soft cheeses made from buffalo milk in the

Philippines and Iraq are delicacies, and mozzarella – the Italian pizza cheese made from buffalo milk in southern Italy – is a product of world fame and a gourmet's delight. In India, good-quality processed cheese is manufactured from buffalo milk. Ice-cream made from buffalo milk, with its rich cream, tastes better than any other available in the market.

A clarified form of butter called *ghee* in India and Pakistan or *semu* in the Arab countries is prepared from buffalo milk. This is extensively used as a cooking medium by millions of people in the Indo-Pakistan sub-continent and in the Arab world and is greatly relished. Buffalo milk, butter and *ghee* are white in colour due to the absence of carotene, but the products are rich in vitamin A.

Meat

Of the present total meat consumption, buffalo meat constitutes only a small fraction. So far it has remained, by and large, only an incidental although important by-product from the buffalo when this animal ceases to be economic in any other manner. In many of the buffalo-rearing countries millions of people are vegetarian by choice, on account of religious prejudices or through sheer economic compulsion. Slaughter of buffaloes below 12 years of age is prohibited in some countries with the exception of infertile, intractable and incapacitated animals. Modern abattoir facilities are also lacking in most places. Consequently, butchering of the animals and methods of handling the meat are usually crude and clumsy and the meat is generally offered for sale without being properly aged. Therefore, most of the buffalo meat available in the market is anything but a gourmet's delight and to the discriminating taste it is a tough, flavourless product much inferior in quality to the more expensive meats obtained from other sources. Even as such it is considered a delicacy by people used to eating buffalo meat. The market meat of the buffalo is used with advantage for preparation of hamburgers, meat rolls and sausages. It also makes good biltong and tasty soup. Like the milk and butterfat, the body fat of the buffalo is white on account of absence of carotene.

Hafez (1952) reported that in buffalo meat the fibres are not interspersed with fat and hence the tenderness produced by 'marbling' is absent. This, however, does not appear to be a characteristic of meat from this species. It is more likely that the coarseness observed in buffalo meat by Hafez was not due to any intrinsic defect but to the fact that the animals were usually old and in poor condition when slaughtered. The dressed carcase of the buffalo generally weighs 45 to 47 per cent of the liveweight of the animal. In Yugoslavia, Bulgaria and Italy where rearing of buffaloes for meat is common, a dressing percentage of 51 is not unusual (Cockrill, 1967). The Caucasian buffalo yields a carcase with a dressing percentage varying from 48 to 53. The variation in the percentage of the protein content of the meat ranges between 19·2 and 22·4 and that of the fat between 11·4 and 22·2 (Agabeili *et al.*, 1971).

In some markets such as Hong Kong buffalo meat constitutes more than half of all the beef sold.

Very recently, studies on the meat-production characteristics of weaned male Murrah buffalo calves were made at the IRVI in India. Groups of 9-month-old calves weighing 75 kg (165 lb) were divided in two groups, one lot being fed *ad lib.* a high grain ration and the other an *ad lib.* roughage-type, leguminous hay and wheat straw ration. On attainment of 300 kg (661 lb) body weight the animals were slaughtered for evaluation of carcase quality. Animals fed the high-grain ration demonstrated growth rates ranging between 0·555 and 0·625 kg (1·230 and 1·290 lb) per day and attained a slaughter weight of 300 kg (661 lb) at 16 to 18 months of age, whereas those on the roughage-type ration gained at the rate of 0·410 to 0·450 kg (0·900 to 0·990 lb) per day and reached slaughter weight in 20 to 22 months. The dressing percentage of the high-grain-fed animals ranged from 56·8 to 59·6 (mean 57·3), while in the animals fed roughage-type rations it varied from 50·8 to 53·5 (mean 50·9). The lean : fat : bone ratios in the grain-fed and roughage-fed groups were 55 : 26 : 28 and 59 : 19 : 21, respectively. The findings of the investigations at the IVRI compare well with those observed in a similar study in the United States on cattle calves, where with feeding all-grain rations to the animals a dressing percentage of 58·5 was obtained (McElroy, 1968).

This investigation with buffalo calves indicates that if the buffalo is properly managed and fed as a meat-producing animal and slaughtered at around 16 to 20 months of age it can produce meat that would equal choice beef obtained from cattle, both in quality and in quantity.

The buffalo hide makes excellent, thick, tough leather much valued for making shoe soles, belts and many other leather articles requiring this kind of material. Strips of buffalo hide softened with fat are woven to make very strong, attractive reins, lassos or ropes. Very good and durable water buckets are made out of the buffalo hide for lift irrigation purposes. The buffalo hide can be split with modern machinery to make thin strong sheets, which after processing and dyeing make as good a leather as that obtained from other animals.

Tasty 'buffalo chips' are made from buffalo hide in parts of Thailand, Nepal and Indonesia and are eaten with relish. The hide is cut into small strips, boiled in water for a long period and dried in the sun. For eating, the pieces are fried in deep fat to make crisp delicious chips. With adequate publicity it should be possible to create an export market for buffalo chips (Cockrill, 1967).

The massive horns of the buffalo provide the raw material for supporting a cottage industry based on the preparation of a wide range of useful as well as fancy and decorative horn articles. The ingenuity, workmanship and beauty of many of these products are really fascinating. In

Malaysia, the musical instrument known as *tetuang* is made out of buffalo horn (Cockrill, 1966a).

Disease

Commonly occurring viral, bacterial and parasitic diseases of the buffalo are much the same as those of cattle. However, the susceptibility of buffaloes and cattle differ in relation to several of these diseases.

In countries such as the Philippines, Vietnam, Cambodia, Laos, Malaysia, Thailand, Burma and India, buffaloes, as reported by several workers, are highly susceptible to rinderpest and may be even more so than the indigenous cattle managed under comparable conditions, although in southeastern Europe the buffalo is found to be relatively more resistant than the local cattle breeds (Mohan, 1968a). In the broadest sense it seems that, subject to local and regional variations, the susceptibility of the buffalo to this disease increases from western to eastern Asia (Vittoz, 1951). The clinical syndromes and the autopsy findings are more or less similar to those observed in cattle. However, the body-temperature curve in the buffalo is quite often erratic. Clinical symptoms tend to be more acute and as a rule the conjunctivae are more severely congested.

In general, it has been observed that buffaloes are less susceptible than cattle to foot and mouth disease. Nevertheless, severe outbreaks among buffaloes are not uncommon and in countries like Laos and the Philippines more buffaloes were affected than cattle in some of the past epidemics.

Haemorrhagic septicaemia (pasteurellosis) appears to run a more acute course in buffaloes than in cattle and the oedematous form is more common.

Reports on the incidence of anthrax in buffaloes vary from country to country. In Egypt the disease appears to be rare in buffaloes. In India also the disease is less common in buffaloes than in cattle. However, the situation is just the reverse in Burma where buffaloes frequently contract the infection; this poses a serious danger to the elephants working in adjacent forests. On some islands in Indonesia the disease occurs in a severe form and affects more buffaloes than cattle (Mohan, 1968b).

Several workers have reported that the buffalo is relatively resistant to tuberculosis. This is one of the most important diseases affecting buffaloes in Egypt, the incidence being higher in housed buffaloes in the southern regions. Slaughter-house examinations of carcases in a Cairo abbatoir showed that about 7 per cent of the buffaloes slaughtered had tuberculous lesions. Tuberculosis tests carried out in four representative areas in India on 44,519 cattle and 40,201 buffaloes under comparable conditions of management showed 4·7 and 13·8 per cent reactors, respectively, in the two species (Lall *et al.*, 1969). Thus the incidence of tuberculin reactors in India was higher in the buffalo than in cattle. The same conclusion was reached by Lall *et al.* (1969) when comparing the rate of infection among cattle and buffaloes on organized farms. Mammalian tuberculin evokes a stronger reaction in buffaloes on intradermal test as compared to that in cattle (Lall, 1946).

Mastitis is one of the serious diseases of the buffalo, especially in those countries where buffaloes are mainly kept for milk production. A mastitis survey carried out on 690 buffaloes in nine dairy herds in different parts of India showed an incidence of 20·7 per cent of sub-clinical or insidious cases and 2·4 per cent of clinical cases. In another random survey of 1,193 buffaloes in the northern part of India, Katra and Dhanda (1964) found an incidence of infection of 11 per cent in the urban and 9 per cent in the rural areas, the corresponding data for 3,097 cows being 10 and 7·5 per cent, respectively. About 98 per cent of the cases were found to be caused by pathogenic species of staphylococci and streptococci while the remaining 2 per cent of the cases were due to other organisms. In Egypt, incidence of mastitis in the two species was virtually the same (Wahby and Hilmy, 1946). In one survey it was found that 9 per cent of 860 buffaloes brought to the Cairo clinic were affected with mastitis (El-Gindy *et al.*, 1964).

Brucellosis is fairly common in buffaloes. In a survey of 13,565 animals in military dairy farms in India, 10 per cent of the buffaloes and 13 per cent of the cows were found to be positive reactors on serological tests (Mohan, 1968b). In Turkey, 42 per cent of 31 buffaloes and 39 per cent of 285 cattle, and in Brazil 41 per cent of buffalo serum samples, gave a positive reaction on agglutination tests (Golem, 1943; Santa Rosa *et al.*, 1961). In Egypt cultures of *Brucella abortus* were isolated from as many as 15 per cent of 200 buffalo milk samples subjected to bacteriological examination (Zaki, 1948). In Indonesia, however, brucellosis was stated to be sporadic in buffaloes, although it was endemic in cattle.

Among the protozoan parasites, *Trypanosoma evansi* appears to be the most important for the buffalo, especially in Southeast Asia. This micro-organism generally causes a latent or sub-clinical form of trypanosomiasis, but severe outbreaks characterized by high temperature, signs of abdominal pain and mortality 6 to 12 hours after the onset of the symptoms have also been recorded. Heavy mortality in buffalo calves due to coccidiosis has been reported from India and Sri Lanka (Mohan, 1968c).

Neoascaris vitulorum is a commonly occurring helminth parasite of buffalo calves and can cause considerable mortality in young stock. Fascioliasis, or fluke infection, is another important disease of buffaloes. In India *Fasciola gigantica* infestation is predominant in the plains while *F. hepatica* is mostly confined to the hilly tracts. In a survey lasting from 1949 to 1953 in Thailand, 7 per cent of 29,421 buffalo livers were found to be cirrhotic due to fluke infestation. In Singapore a large number of buffaloes imported from Thailand were found to be infected with liver fluke. Fascioliasis is also common in the Ararat valley, in Azerbaijan in the USSR and in the Philippines (Mohan, 1968c).

Buffalo appear to be less affected by ticks than are cattle (Mohan, 1968c) and warble infestation is also less prevalent in buffalo (Sen and Fletcher, 1962).

References

Agabeili, A. A., Guseinov, I. A. and Serdyuk, V. S. (1971) A new buffalo breed – the Caucasian (Russian). *Zhivotnovodstvo Mosk.*, **33**, 61–3. *Abstracted: Anim. Breed. Abstr.*, **40**, 25 (1972).

Agarwala, O. P. (1962) Effect of season of calving on milk production in dairy cattle. *Ind. vet. J.*, **39**, 390–3.

Ahmed, I. A. and Tantawy, A. O. (1954) Growth in Egyptian cattle during the first two years of age. *Alex. J. agric. Res.*, **2**, 1–11.

Alim, K. A. and Ahmed, I. A. (1954) Month of calving, age at first calving and calving intervals of the buffaloes in a dairy herd in Egypt. *Emp. J. exp. Agric.*, **22**, 37–41.

Aly-Nour El-Din, A. (1964) Improvement of artificial insemination in buffaloes. *Proc. 5th Int. Congr. Anim. Reprod. (Trento)*, Vol. 4, pp. 201–5.

Amble, V. N., Gopalan, R., Malhotra, J. C. and Malhotra, P. C. (1970) Some vital statistics and genetic parameters of Indian buffaloes at military dairy farms. *Ind. J. Anim. Sci.*, **40**, 377–88.

Arnuchalam, T. V., Lazarus, A. J. and Anantakrishnan, C. P. (1952) Observations on Some Indian Cattle. Pt III. Factors influencing the gestation period and birthweight of Murrah buffaloes. *Ind. J. Dairy Sci.*, **5**, 117–23.

Arora, S. P. and Gupta, B. S. (1962) Growth rate of Murrah buffalo calves. *J. vet. Anim. Husb. Res.* (Mhow, M. P.), **5** (1960–61), 1–4.

Arya, Y. V. and Desai, R. N. (1969) Growth rate and its relationship with weight and age at first calving in buffaloes maintained on military farms. *Ind. vet. J.*, **46**, 61–68.

Asker, A. A. and El-Itriby, A. A. (1958) Frequency of using bulls for service and the distribution of calving in the Egyptian buffaloes. *Alex. J. agric. Res.*, **6**, 25–38.

Badreldin, A. L. and Ghany, M. A. (1952) Adaptive mechanisms of buffaloes to ambient temperature. *Nature (Lond.)*, **170**, 457–8.

Baradat, R. (1949) The livestock of Cambodia. *Rev. Elév. Méd. Vét. Pays trop.*, N.S., **3**, 29–37. *Abstracted: Anim. Breed. Abstr.*, **18**, 249 (1950).

Basirov, E. B. (1964) The biology of reproduction and artificial insemination of buffaloes (in Russian). *Proc. 5th Int. Congr. Anim. Reprod. AI (Trento)*, Vol. 6, pp. 4–10. *Abstracted: Anim. Breed. Abstr.*, **33**, 60 (1965).

Bhalla, R. C., Sengar, D. P. S. and Soni, B. K. (1967) Study on the birthweight of Murrah buffalo and Sahiwal calves and factors affecting them. *Ind. J. Dairy Sci.*, **20**, 139–41.

Cockrill, W. Ross (ed.) (1954) *The Husbandry and Health of the Domestic Buffalo.* FAO: Rome.

Cockrill, W. Ross (1966a) A key animal for a hungry world. *New Scientist*, **20**, 370–2.

Cockrill, W. Ross. (1966b) A note on the hair whorls of the water buffalo. *Vet. Rec.*, **79**, 535.

Cockrill, W. Ross. (1967) The water buffalo. *Scient. Am.*, **217**, 118–25.

Cockrill, W. Ross (1968) The draught buffalo (*Bubalus bubalis*). *The Veterinarian (Oxford)*, **5**, 265–72.

Cockrill, W. Ross (1970) The water buffalo. *Sci. J. (Lond.)* **6**, 34–40.

Datta, S. (1965) Leucoderma (vitiligo) of man and animals. *Bengal Vet.*, **13**, 1–5.

Dutt, M. K. and Bhattacharya, P. (1952) Chromosomes of the Indian water buffalo. *Nature (Lond.)*, **170**, 1129–30.

El-Gindy, H., Farrag, H. F. and Abou El-Asm, L. (1964) A study of the treatment of mastitis in buffaloes and cows in Egypt. *Vet. Med. small Anim. Clin.*, **59**, 380–2. *Abstracted: Vet. Bull.*, **34**, 451 (1964).

El-Itriby, A. A. and Barrada, S. (1959) Personal communication.

FAO (1973) *Production Yearbook*, Vol. 26. FAO 1972: Rome.

Gokhale, D. R. (1958) Glucose sodium bicarbonate and suphamezathine buffer as a diluent of buffalo semen. *Ind. vet. J.*, **35**, 573–81.

Golem, S. B. (1943) Serological examination for brucellosis of man and domestic animals in Turkey (in Turkish). *Turk. Z. Hyg. Exp. Biol.*, **3**, 115–16. *Abstracted: Vet. Bull.* **16**, No. 1712.

Gorbelik, V. I. (1935) The breeding of buffaloes (in Russian). *Trud. Azerbaidzhan. Stanc. Zhivotn.*, **4**, 5–26. *Abstracted: Anim. Breed. Abstr.*, **4**, 162–3 (1936).

Guha, S. (1967) *Final report 1962–67. United States PL-480 Project on Animal Climatology in India.* Ind. Vet. Res. Inst.: Izatnagar (UP), India.

Hafez, E. S. E. (1952) The buffalo – a review. *Ind. J. vet. Sci. Anim. Husb.*, **22**, 257–63.

Hafez, E. S. E. (1953) Conception rate and periodicity in the buffalo. *Emp. J. exp. Agric.*, **21**, 15–21.

Hafez, E. S. E. (1954) Oestrus and some related phenomena in the buffalo. *J. agric. Sci. (Camb.)*, **44**, 165–72.

Hafez, E. S. E. (1955) Puberty in the buffalo cow. *J. agric. Sci. (Camb.)*, **46**, 137–42.

Hua, L. C. (1957) The use of Malayan swamp buffaloes and Murrah/Malayan cross-breds for milk production in Taiping. *J. Malay vet. med. Ass.*, **1**, 141–43.

Ichhponani, J. S., Makkar, G. S. and Sidhu, G. S. (1969) Studies on the biochemical processes in the rumen. IV. Production of volatile fatty acids (VFA) *in vitro* by rumen micro-organisms obtained from the rumina of the buffalo and cattle. *Ind. J. Anim. Sci.*, **39**, 201–6.

Ishaq, S. M. (1956) Oestrus and allied problems in buffaloes. *Agric. Pakist.*, **7**, 361–5.

Kaleff, B. (1942) The breeding biology of the domestic buffalo compared with that of cattle (in German). *Z. Tierzücht ZüchtBiol.*, **51**, 131–78. *Abstracted: Anim. Breed. Abstr.*, **10**, 148–49 (1942).

Katra, D. S. and Dhanda, M. R. (1964) Incidence of mastitis in cows and buffaloes in North West India. *Vet. Rec.*, **76**, 219–22.

Knapp, Bradford (1957) *A Compilation of Available Data on the Water Buffalo,* 53 pp. Int. Co-operation Admin.: Washington.

Kushwaha, N. S., Mukerjee, D. P. and Bhattacharya, P. (1955) Seasonal variations in reaction time and semen qualities of buffalo bulls. *Ind. J. vet. Sci. Anim. Husb.*, **25**, 317–28.

Lall, H. K. (1946) Tuberculin testing in buffaloes with a description of some differences in the macroscopic lesions of the cow and the buffalo. *Ind. J. vet. Sci. Anim. Husb.*, **16**, 24–6.

Lall, J. M., Singh, G. and Sengupta, B. R. (1969) Incidence of tuberculosis amongst cattle and buffaloes in India. *Ind. J. Anim. Sci.*, **39**, 51–8.

Langer, P. N., Sidhu, G. S. and Bhatia, J. S. (1968) A study of the microbial population in the rumina of buffalo (*Bos bubalis*) and zebu (*Bos indicus*) on a feeding regimen deficient in carbohydrates. *Ind. J. vet. Sci. Anim. Husb.*, **38**, 333–6.

Lazarus, A. J. (1946) Buffalo as a dairy animal. *Ind. Fmg.*, **7**, 247–50.

Ludri, R. S., Pant, H. C. and Roy, A. (1971) *In vitro* evaluation of forage nutritive value using zebu and buffalo-rumen inoculum. *Ind. Vet. J.*, **48**, 24.

Luktuke, S. N. and Ahuja, L. D. (1961) Studies on ovulation in buffaloes. *J. Reprod. Fert.*, **2**, 200–1.

Luktuke, S. N. and Roy, D. J. (1964) Studies on post-partum oestrus in Murrah buffaloes. *Ind. J. vet. Sci. Anim. Husb.*, **34**, 166–70.

Luktuke, S. N., Roy, D. J. and Joshi, S. R. (1964) Studies on gestational oestrus in bovines. *Ind. J. vet. Sci. Anim. Husb.*, **34**, 41–5.

McElroy, W. L. (1968) *Feeder's Day Manual*, **43**, Div. Ext.: Univ. Alberta.

Macgregor, M. R. (1941) The domestic buffalo. *Vet. Rec.*, **53**, 443–50.

Mahmoud, I. N. (1952) Some characteristics of the semen of Egyptian buffaloes. *Bull. Fac. Agric. Fouad I Univ. (Cairo)*, No. 15, 16 pp. *Abstracted: Anim. Breed. Abstr.*, **21**, 260 (1953).

Maymone, B. (1942) Die Buffelzucht in Italien. *Z. Tierzücht ZüchtBiol.*, **52**, 1–44.

Misra, M. S. and Sengupta, B. P. (1965) Climatic Environment and Reproductive Behaviour of Buffaloes. III. Observations on semen quality of buffalo bulls maintained under two different housing conditions. *Ind. J. Dairy Sci.*, **18**, 130–3.

Mohan, R. N. (1968a, b, c) Diseases and Parasites of Buffaloes. I. Viral, mycoplasmal and rickettsial diseases. II. Bacterial and fungal diseases. III. Parasitic and miscellaneous diseases. *Vet. Bull.*, **38**. 567–76, 647–59 and 735–56.

Mudgal, V. D. and Ray, S. N. (1962) Studies on the roughage utilisation by cattle and buffalo. *Ind. J. Dairy Sci.*, **15**, 129.

Mukherjee, D. P. (1964) Melanizing activity of semen and its relation to live spermatozoa of bulls, goats and rams. *J. Reprod. Fertil.*, **7**, 29–36.

Mukherjee, D. P. and Bhattacharya, P. (1953) Seasonal variations in semen quality and haemoglobin and cell volume contents of the blood in bulls. *Ind. J. vet. Sci.*, **22**, 73–91.

Mullick, D. N. (1960) Effect of humidity and exposure to sun on the pulse rate, respiration rate, rectal temperature and haemoglobin level in different sexes of cattle and buffalo. *J. Agric. Sci. (Camb.)*, **54**, 391–4.

Naga, M. A., Abou Akkada, A. R. and El-Shazly, K. (1969) Establishment of rumen ciliate protozoa in cow and water buffalo (*Bos bubalus* L.) under late and early weaning systems. *J. Dairy Sci.*, **52**, 110–12.

Naga, M. A. and El-Shazly, K. (1969) Activities of rumen micro-organisms in water buffalo and in zebu cattle. *J. Dairy Res.*, **36**, 1–10.

Ocampo, A. R. (1939–40) Further studies on the breeding habits of the carabao. *Philipp. Agric.*, **28**, 286–307.

Oloufa, M. M. (1955) Breeding efficiency in Egyptian cattle and buffaloes. *J. Anim. Sci.*, **14**, 1252.

Pandey, M. D. and Roy, A. (1969a) Studies on the Adaptability of Buffaloes to Tropical Climate. I. Seasonal changes in the water and electrolyte status of buffaloes. II. Seasonal changes in the body temperature, cardio-respiratory and haematological attributes in buffalo cows. *Ind. J. Anim. Sci.*, **39**, 367–77, 378–86.

Pandey, M. D. and Roy, A. (1969b) I. Variation in volume and composition of body fluids (intestitial, blood and urine) as a measure of adaptability in buffaloes to a hot environment. II. Variation in cardiorespiratory rates, rectal temperature, blood hematocrit and haemoglobin as measures of adaptability of buffaloes to a hot environment. *Brit. vet. J.*, **125**, 382–402 and 463–71.

Pant, H. C. (1966) A note on concentration of 'Oscillospira guilliermondii-type' organisms in the rumen ingesta of buffalo and zebu cattle. *Ind. vet. J.*, **43**, 111–13.

Pattabiraman, D. (1956) A study of Murrah buffaloes in Madras State. *Ind. vet. J.*, **33**, 188–204.

Phillips, R. W. (1948) *Breeding Livestock Adaptable to Unfavourable Environments*. FAO Agric. Study No. 1. FAO: Rome.

Prabhu, S. S. (1956) Influence of factors affecting sex drive on semen production of buffaloes. II. *Ind. J. vet. Sci.*, **26**, 21–33.

Prabhu, S. S. and Bhattacharya, P. (1954) Influence of factors affecting sex drive on semen production of buffaloes. I. Physiological state of the 'teaser' cow. *Ind. J. vet. Sci.*, **24**, 35–50.

Punj, M. L., Kochar, A. S., Bhatia, I. S. and Sidhu, G. S. (1968) *In vitro* studies on the cellulolytic activity and production of volatile fatty acids by the inocula obtained from the rumen of Zebu cattle and Murrah buffalo on different feeding regimens. *Ind J. vet. Sci. Anim. Husb.*, **38**, 325–32.

Ragab, M. T., Asker, A. A. and Ghazy, M. S. (1954) Effect of season of calving, dry period and calving interval on milk yield and lactation period of Egyptian buffaloes. *Ind. J. Dairy Sci.*, **7**, 8–18.

Raizada, B. C., Yadav, P. C., Tewari, R. B. L. and Roy, A. (1968) Studies on the oestrous behaviour based on the cervical mucus crystallisation pattern in buffalo cows and its relationship to fertility. *Ind. J. vet Sci. Anim. Husb.*, **38**, 546–57.

Rao, A. S. P., Luktuke, S. N. and Bhattacharya, P. (1960) Studies on the viability of spermatozoa in the reproductive tract of the buffalo cow. *Ind. J. vet. Sci. Anim. Husb.*, **30**, 246–64.

Rao, C. K. (1958) Development of motility in the spermatozoa of farm animals. *Ind. vet. J.*, **35**, 97–104.

Rife, C. D. (1959) *The Water Buffalo of India and Pakistan*, 37 pp. Int. Co-operation Admin.: Washington.

Rouse, E. J. (1970) *World Cattle*, Vol. II. Univ. Oklahoma Press: Norman, Oklahoma.

Roy, A., Pandey, M. D. and Rawat, J. S. (1960) Composition of bovine semen. *Ind. J. Dairy Sci.*, **13**, 112–16.

Roy, A., Raizada, B. C., Tewari, R. B. L., Pandey, M. D., Yadav, P. C. and Sengupta, B. P. (1968) Effect of management on the fertility of buffalo cows bred during summer. *Ind. J. vet. Sci. Anim. Husb.*, **38**, 554–60.

Roy, A., Srivastava, R. K. and Pandey, M. D. (1956) Deep freezing of buffalo semen diluted and preserved in glycine-egg yolk medium. *Ind. J. Dairy Sci.*, **9**, 61–2.

Salerno A. (1960) Calving interval in buffaloes. *Annali. Sper. agr.*, **156**, 191–206.

Sánta Rosa, C. A., Pestana de Castro, A. F. and Troise, C. (1961) Brucella agglutinin titres in buffaloes in Brazil (in Portuguese). *Arq. Inst. biol. S. Paulo*, **28**, 35–39. Abstracted: *Vet. Bull.*, **32**, 736 (1962).

Sen, S. K. and Fletcher, T. B. (1962) *Veterinary Entomology and Acarology for India.* Ind. Coun. Agric. Res. (ICAR): New Delhi.

Sengupta, B. P., Misra, M. S. and Roy, A. (1963) Climatic environment and reproductive behaviour of buffaloes. Effect of different seasons on various seminal attributes. *Ind. J. Dairy Sci.*, **16**, 150–65.

Shalash, M. R. (1958) Physiology of reproduction in the buffalo cow. *Int. J. Fertility.* **3**, 425–32.

Shukla, D. D. and Bhattacharya, P. (1949) Studies on the semen characteristics of Indian breeds of livestock. *Ind. J. vet. Sci. Anim. Husb.*, **19**, 161–70.

Singh, B. (1933) Metabolism studies on dry and milking animals. *Agric. Livestock India,* **3**, 411.

Singh, R. B., Sharma, S. C. and Singh, S. (1958) Influence of the season of calving on inter-calving period in Murrah buffaloes and Hariana cows. *Ind. J. Dairy Sci.*, **11**, 154–60.

Singh, S., Langar, P. N., Sidhu, G. S., Kocher, A. S. and Bhatia, I. S. (1968) Study of the rumen biochemical activity in the buffalo and zebu under non-urea and urea feeding regimens. *Ind. J. vet. Sci. Anim. Husb.*, **38**, 674–81.

Sinha, K. C. and Minett, F. C. (1947) Application of water to the body surface of water buffaloes and its effect on milk yield. *J. Anim. Sci.*, **6**, 258–64.

Sinha, R. C., Sengupta, B. P. and Roy, A. (1966) Climatic environment and reproductive behaviour of buffaloes. IV. Comparative study of oxygen uptake and aerobic fructolysis by Murrah (*B. bubalis*) and Hariana (*B. indicus*) spermatozoa during different seasons. *Ind. J. Dairy Sci.*, **19**, 18–24.

Tantawy, A. O. and Ahmed, A. I. (1953) Some factors influencing birth weight in Egyptian cattle. *Alex. J. agric. Res.*, **1** (1) (15 pp.).

Tomar, S. P. S. and Desai, R. N. (1965) A study of growth rate in buffaloes maintained on military farms. *Ind. vet. J.*, **42**, 116–25.

Tomar, S. P. S. and Desai, R. N. (1967) Factors influencing the inheritance of birth weight of buffalo calves on military farms. *Ind. Vet. J.*, **44**, 694–701.

Tripathi, V. N., Thomas, C. K., Sastry, N. S. R., Pal, R. N. and Gupta, L. R. (1972) Effect of shelter and water sprinkling on buffaloes growth rate. *Ind. J. Anim. Sci.*, **42**, 745–9.

Van Demark, N. L. and Hays, R. L. (1954) Rapid sperm transport in the cow. *Fert. Sterility*, **5**, 131–7.

Van fu Czao (1959) Buffalo and cattle hybrids (Romanian). *Zivotnovodstvo.* **21,** 92. *Abstracted: Anim. Breed. Abstr.,* **27,** 298 (1959).

Venkataswami, V. and Vedanayagam, A. R. (1962) Biometrics of spermatazoa of cattle and buffaloes. *Ind. vet. J.,* **39,** 287–91.

Villegas, V. (1928) The trend of sexual reproductive seasons amongst horses, cattle, water buffaloes, sheep and goats under Los Baños conditions: a preliminary report. *Philipp. Agric.,* **17,** 477–85.

Villegas, V. (1930) Observations on the breeding activities of carabao. *Philipp. Agric.,* **19,** 3–9.

Vittoz, R. (1951) La sensibilité du buffle domestique au virus de la peste bovine augmenté du Proche-Orient à L'Extrême-Orient. *Bull. Off. Int. Epizoot,* **36,** 19–72.

Wahby, A. M. and Hilmy, M. (1946) Prevalence of bovine mastitis in Egyptian dairy cattle. *J. comp. Path.,* **56,** 246–53.

Zaki, R. (1948) *Brucella abortus* infection among buffaloes in Egypt. *J. Comp. Path.,* **58,** 73–9.

Further Reading

Comissáo Nacional De Pecuária De Leite. *A Criação De Búfalos Para Fomento Da Produção Leiteira Na Amazonia.* Ministerio Da Agricultura: Rio De Janeiro, 1958.

Moran, J. B. and Ford, B. D. (eds.) *A Collection of Papers Related to the Northern Territory Buffalo Industry.* 9th Biennial Conf., Aust. Soc. Anim. Prod., Canberra, 1972.

Chapter 7

Sheep

Utility

In the past sheep were maintained in the tropical regions of Africa and Asia mainly for the production of meat. Subsidiary functions were the production of wool, hair, skins, milk and manure. Lall (1950) reported that there is even a breed of sheep reared in the foothills of the Himalayas in India, known as the Rampur Bushahr or Bushier, whose wethers are used as pack animals, each carrying a load of 2·3 to 3·2 kg (5 to 7 lb). The order of importance of sheep products varies according to consumer demands within the region. For example, in many districts of southern India and in parts of Indonesia sheep are raised primarily for the manure they produce. Some African peoples consider milk to be the chief product after meat; while for others fat meat is the primary product.

This situation is now changing in some tropical countries. In India, for example, a 'white revolution' is spreading throughout sections of the sheep industry. Fine wool is being produced on an ever-increasing scale. This is a particularly surprising development as in the past there has been little demand for fine wool and indeed a striking characteristic of a large number of indigenous Asian and African breeds is that they possess either a completely hairy coat or one containing a low percentage of wool. Crossbreeding and upgrading using exotic wool breeds has commenced on a large scale, new wool-grading centres have been opened and the sheep industry appears to be progressing on a broad front and at a very rapid pace. Some indication of what is happening can be gleaned from the fact that the number of machine-sheared sheep has risen from 800 in 1965 to 182,000 in 1970 in the State of Rajasthan alone.

In the Americas and Oceania, where there were no indigenous breeds of sheep before the advent of the Europeans, the situation has been quite different. Woolled sheep have been introduced into these continents within historical times and the fine wool now produced by the Merino breed in tropical Australia is of considerable economic importance to that country. Woolled sheep have, however, not established themselves very successfully in tropical America.

However, the successful introduction of woolled sheep into tropical

Australia does suggest that, given suitable economic incentives and the necessary level of technical skill, woolled sheep could also be introduced into the drier areas of the tropics in Africa, the Americas and Asia. In addition, improved exotic breeds of meat and wool sheep could certainly be introduced into many of the montane areas of the tropics.

Origin

Sheep are classified in the sub-family Caprinae and all domestic sheep are included in the genus *Ovis aries*. There are four major species of wild sheep. These are: the Moufflon (*O. musimon*), of which several sub-species exist in Europe and western Asia; the Urial (*O. orientalis*; synonym *O. vignei*), of which there are many sub-species found from Afghanistan to western Asia; the Argali (*O. ammon*), found in central Asia; and the Bighorn (*O. canadensis*), extant in northern Asia and North America. The first three, but not the latter type, have all contributed to the genetic makeup of modern breeds of sheep.

According to Zeuner (1963) sheep were domesticated at about the same time as goats and before crop agriculture had fully developed. He considered that the original centre of domestication was the Aralo-Caspian steppe. From this centre sheep breeding spread into what is now Iran, eastwards into the Indian sub-continent and Southeast Asia, westwards into western Asia and on into Europe and Africa. During historical times sheep have been introduced into the Americas, Australia and some of the small oceanic tropical islands.

No wild sheep were domesticated in Africa. The wild animal known as the Barbary sheep or Arni (*Ammotragus lervia*), though called a sheep and closely related, has never been domesticated and it is not considered that it has contributed in any way to modern African breeds of sheep.

Four different major types of sheep have been introduced by man at different periods into Africa since domestication of the species in Asia. One of these introductions was a primitive type of Moufflon that may have come either from Europe via the North African coast or from Asia via Egypt. These sheep are generally small and thin-legged and possess a hairy coat, and they are now distributed from the Sudan and East Africa to West Africa, typical breeds being the Dinka of the Sudan, the Baluba of Tanzania and the Dwarf Forest sheep of West Africa.

The screw-horned hairy sheep of Urial origin that entered Africa through Egypt may have been the first introduction of sheep into Africa or they may have been preceded by the smaller hairy sheep of Moufflon origin. Modern African breeds that are probably descended from this introduction are the long-legged, thin-tailed hairy sheep of the higher rainfall savanna areas in West Africa, such as the Guinea and Hausa breeds.

A third introduction was the woolled sheep of the 'Ammon' type.

These apparently replaced the hairy sheep in Egypt proper and spread out into the drier areas. They did not, however, penetrate into the higher rainfall areas such as the Congo basin.

The semi-fat-tailed, coarse-woolled, Ammon-type sheep were probably introduced into Africa from two sources. In the north they were introduced via the isthmus of Suez around 2000 BC. These sheep penetrated as far as central Chad, but were separated from another group that entered Africa via the straits of Bab-el-Mandeb by the thin-tailed breeds of the Sudan. The fat-tailed sheep entering East Africa were taken by migratory peoples to the far south of Africa and their descendants are the present fat-tailed breeds of Northeast, East, Central and South Africa.

Later, fat-rumped hairy-type sheep were introduced into Eritrea, Somalia and East Africa from the Arabian peninsula. Today the coarse-woolled, fat-tailed sheep and the hairy, fat-rumped sheep coexist in Northeast and East Africa.

Fat-rumped sheep of Somali–Arabian origin were introduced into the Cape province of South Africa during the nineteenth century and were quickly improved to form the breed known as the Blackhead Persian. This breed spread rapidly throughout South Africa and was taken northwards into Rhodesia, Zambia and East Africa where it has been extensively used for crossbreeding purposes.

In the Himalayan areas of the Indian sub-continent there are sheep breeds that have been derived from both Urial and Argali stock, and in the drier regions in north India fat-tailed breeds thrive. As one proceeds to the south in the sub-continent fat-tailed and thin-tailed, coarse-woolled breeds are gradually replaced by thin-tailed, hairy breeds.

In the humid regions of Southeast Asia there are few sheep breeds and the majority of the sheep are small and of the hairy type, although in Indonesia there is a fat-tailed breed that may have originated from India or western Asia and a poor-woolled breed originating from crosses between the original indigenous hairy sheep and woolled sheep introduced from the Cape and Australia. In the rain-forest areas of south Thailand and Malaysia there are poor, coarse-woolled sheep that appear to have originated from crossbreds between woolled Chinese sheep brought south by the Thai and other peoples and the indigenous hairy sheep of the region.

The long-legged and the smaller hairy sheep from West Africa were taken to Brazil, Guyana and the West Indies in the seventeenth century where they established themselves in humid, tropical regions to which the Iberian sheep breeds that had been introduced rather earlier had never really acclimatized.

There is evidence that sheep – perhaps more than any other species of domestic animal – are particularly sensitive to changes in environmental conditions. They thrive only within homoclimes and even within these they have more difficulty in adjusting themselves to changes in diet and exposure to new diseases than have other breeds of livestock. So marked is this characteristic that in Britain hill sheep are said to be 'hefted' or acclimatized to a specific hill environment and they do not accept changes in location easily. Within the tropics sheep appear to thrive best in semi-arid upland areas where the vegetation is of the short-grass or steppe type.

Numbers and distribution

Some details of the world's sheep population are given in Table 7.1. It has increased by some 6 per cent during the last decade, the major increases being in Asia and Africa.

Table 7.1   *World distribution of sheep*

Continent	Number in '000		Percentage increase or decrease 1961–65 to 1972	As percentage of world total in 1972
	1961–65	1972		
Africa	121,866	143,301	+ 18	13·6
Tropics	58,600	72,901	+ 24	6·9
Other	63,266	70,400	+ 11	6·7
Americas	158,510	144,257	− 9	13·6
Tropics	48,465	56,910	+ 17	5·4
Other	110,045	87,347	− 21	8·2
Asia	232,683	278,832	+ 20	26·4
Tropics	30,804	33,563	+ 9	3·2
China	64,520	71,300	+ 11	6·7
Other	137,359	173,969	+ 27	16·5
Europe				
Outside USSR	133,977	127,533	− 5	12·1
USSR	133,867	139,916	+ 5	13·2
Oceania	211,474	222,845	+ 5	21·1
Tropics	40,244	40,748	+ 1	3·9
Other	171,230	182,097	+ 6	17·2
World	992,377	1,056,684	+ 6	
Tropics	178,113	204,122	+ 15	19·3
Other	814,264	852,562	+ 5	80·7

Source: FAO (1973).

Within Africa the total numbers of sheep have increased in both the tropical and the non-tropical areas. Approximately one-quarter of all African sheep are to be found in South Africa and this country's sheep population has in the immediate past shown some decline. Within tropical Africa sheep are important in Ethiopia, Kenya, Mali, northern Nigeria, Somalia, the Sudan and Tanzania.

In the Americas the sheep population has declined during the decade. The decline has been greatest in non-tropical North America, although there has also been some decline in numbers in non-tropical South America. Within tropical America the largest national flocks are to be found in Mexico, Bolivia, Brazil and Peru. The sheep population has increased appreciably in Brazil and Ecuador.

Although the sheep population has increased markedly in Asia, the increase has been mainly in the non-tropical areas, particularly in China, Afghanistan, Iran and Turkey. Within tropical Asia, with the exception of India, sheep populations are relatively small, but there has been a very marked increase in the sheep population of Burma.

Virtually all the sheep in tropical Oceania are to be found in the drier areas of tropical Australia. Sheep husbandry in tropical Australia is very dependent upon favourable climatic conditions, and as a consequence the sheep population continuously fluctuates in total number, varying with cyclic drought conditions.

Breeds

There is no accepted classification of indigenous tropical sheep breeds, but it is possible to classify them broadly according as to whether they are hairy-coated or woolled, thin-tailed, fat-tailed or fat-rumped, and whether they are horned or polled.

Classification by phenotypic characteristics is by its very nature somewhat arbitrary and it is often difficult to decide whether sheep with mixed hair and wool coats should be classified as being hairy or woolled sheep. As will be seen below, some breeds have been classified as both hairy and woolled as both types coexist in the flocks. Similarly there are no clear anatomical distinctions between fat-rumped and fat-tailed sheep. There are a large number of intergrading types. Some sheep possess two large fatty entities on the rump, in addition to a fairly long twisted tail, in which fat may be deposited as far as the tip.

A classification of breeds of sheep has been made using the criteria outlined above. It is not suggested that this classification is either absolutely correct or that it includes all the breeds of sheep that exist in the tropics. It does, however, include the majority of the major breeds and it is possibly a useful first exercise in the classification of tropical sheep breeds. It also includes a few breeds peripheral to the tropics that are of the same type as neighbouring tropical breeds.

Africa

1. *Hairy sheep*
(a) Thin-tailed. (i) Small type: West African Dwarf. (ii) Larger type: Maure; Guinea; Hausa – synonym Yankasa (Nigeria); Tuareg (Niger); Fulani – synonyms Ouda, Uda; Gezira.
(b) Fat-tailed. Sudanese Desert.

2. *Woolled sheep*
(a) Thin-tailed. Baluba; Congo; Fulani – synonyms Ouda, Udu; Sudanese – synonym Nilotic.
(b) Fat-tailed. Akeli (Eritrea); Arnsi-Bale (Ethiopia); Guzai (Eritrea), Kikuyu (Kenya); Kipsigis (Kenya); Landim (Mozambique); Madagascar (Malagasy Republic); Masai (Kenya and Tanzania); Mashona (Rhodesia); Mens (Ethiopia); Mondombes (Angola); Nandi (Kenya); Northern Angola fat-tailed; Rashaidi (Eritrea); Rwanda and Burundi fat-tailed; Samburu (Kenya); Somali (Somalia); Sukuma (Tanzania); Tucur (Ethiopia); Uganda fat-tailed; Ugogo (Tanzania); Zambia fat-tailed; Zhagawa (western Sudan and Tschad).
(c) Fat-rumped. Somali (Somalia); Blackhead Persian (East and Central Africa).

Americas

1. *Hairy sheep.* Bahaman; Black Bellied Barbados; Morado Nova (Brazil).

2. *Woolled sheep.* Criollo (Venezuela).

Asia

Western

1. *Hairy sheep*
(a) Thin-tailed. Iran thin-tailed – synonym Zel.
(c) Fat-rumped. Hejazi (Arabian peninsula).

2. *Woolled sheep*
(b) Fat-tailed. Arabi (Arabian peninsula to southwest Iran); Awassi (western Asia); Bakhtiari (Iran); Karakul (Iran); Kizil (Iran); Kundi (Iran); Moghani (Iran); Sanjabi (Iran).

Indian sub-continent

1. *Hairy sheep.* Ganjam; Godavari; Jaffna (Sri Lanka); Mandya; Marathwada; Nellore; South Madras; Tenguri.

2. *Woolled sheep*
(a) Thin-tailed. (i) Horned: Bellary; Deccani; Kuka. (ii) Polled: Bikaneri;
    Damani – synonym Lama; Hussan; Jalauni; Kagani; Kathiawar;
    Lohi; Thal – synonyms Buti, Chundi, Lessarkani, Porakani, Tilari.
(b) Fat-tailed. Balkni; Baluchi – synonyms Kachi and Mengali; Bibrik;
    Dumari – synonym Harnai; Hashtnagi; Rakhshani; Waziri.

Southeast Asia

1. *Hairy sheep*
(b) Fat-tailed. Donggala (Indonesia); Javanese.

2. *Woolled sheep.*   Malaysian; Priangan (Indonesia); South Thai.

It is of course impossible in an introductory text to describe all these
breeds, but some characteristics of a limited number of typical breeds are
listed below.

West African Dwarf (Plate 7.1).   This breed is found throughout the more
humid areas of West Africa. The coat is usually white in colour or a
mixture of black and white. The hair is fine and these sheep possess

Plate 7.1   West African Dwarf ram.

a well-developed neck ruff. Their legs are long in proportion to the size of their body and they possess a long thin tail. Average mature weight is approximately 36 kg (80 lb) and well-fed lambs weigh 31 kg (68 lb) at 6 months of age.

Fulani – synonyms Ouda and Uda (Plate 7.2).   This breed represents a type of sheep found throughout the sahel and savanna zones of tropical Africa, from western Ethiopia to northern Nigeria. They are large, mature

Plate 7.2   Fulani or Uda ram.

males measuring up to 84 cm (33 in) at the shoulder, long-legged, thin and long-tailed and possess moderately long, floppy ears. They have been classified as both hairy and woolled sheep, as although they are generally smooth-coated they sometimes possess some kempy wool. Males are horned. The horns may be quite large, emerging sideways and slightly backwards with a twist. Mature males and females weigh on average 68 kg (150 lb) and 36 to 41 kg (80 to 90 lb), respectively.

Sudanese Desert (Plate 7.3).   This is a large, fat-tailed, long-legged, hairy breed. The coat colour is normally brown or pied. These sheep possess long lop ears and a long, tapering tail which, when the animal is in good condition, carries much fat evenly distributed down both sides. Mature rams weigh up to 68 kg (150 lb) and the maximum milk production of the ewes is 2·3 to 2·7 kg (5 to 6 lb) of milk a day (Tothill, 1948).

Plate 7.3   Sudanese Desert sheep.

Nilotic.   This is a small, woolled, short-legged, thin-taiied breed. The fleece is short, fine and usually white in colour, although it may possess black and tan patches. Mature weight is approximately 11 kg (25 lb) and the ewes are poor milkers. These sheep are very well adapted to a swampy environment.

Zhagawa.   This is a small, woolled, fat-tailed breed owned by a transhumant tribe in the Northern Darfur province of the western Sudan. These sheep possess a long black coat.

Masai.   These are large, long-legged, fat-tailed, coarse-woolled sheep owned by the Masai, who live in Kenya and Tanzania. They are representative of a large number of different breeds of fat-tailed sheep found throughout Northeast, East and Central Africa.

Somali.   The fat-rumped Somali breed closely resemble the Blackhead Persian. The limbs and under parts of the body of these sheep are always wholly white. Mature males weigh up to 42 kg (93 lb). This breed produces excellent mutton and a very valuable skin.

Blackhead Persian (Plate 7.4).   This large, fat-rumped breed was developed in South Africa from fat-rumped, Somali-type sheep first im-

Plate 7.4 Blackhead Persian ram.

ported into Port Beaufort, South Africa, in 1870 (Joubert, 1969). Two types are distinguished in South Africa. One possesses a long, coarse, woolly coat and the rams are usually horned. The other has a smooth 'kempy' coat and is polled. The coat colour is black on the head and part of the neck and white elsewhere. The head and the ears are small, the ears short and sharply pointed and there is a well-developed dewlap. The legs are slender. The rudimentary tail is short, approximately 5 cm (2 in) in length and the fat masses on the rump may weigh up to 11 kg (25 lb). A major attribute of sheep of this breed is their ability to live in arid environments where few if any other improved breeds would survive. This sheep has been used more often than any other breed to upgrade indigenous breeds in the semi-arid areas of East and Central Africa. The major disadvantage of these animals is that they are too fat at maturity. In an endeavour to produce sheep possessing the hardiness of the Blackhead Persian but with less propensity to accumulate fat, Blackhead Persians have been crossed with Dorset Horns in South Africa to produce a breed known as the Dorper.

Black Bellied Barbados (Plate 7.5). This is a moderately large, long-legged, hairy breed developed on the island of Barbados by crossing West African Dwarf sheep, originally imported at the same time as the African slaves who worked on the sugar plantations, with temperate-type sheep breeds. The coat is usually smooth, though rams possess a ruff, and is

Plate 7.5   Black Bellied Barbados ram.

brown to brownish black in colour. Males weigh 45 kg (100 lb) at one year of age. This is undoubtedly the most promising breed in the Americas and is said to be more tolerant than most of internal parasites.

Criollo.   This breed, originally developed in the north of South America from the Churro and the Spanish Merino, has been upgraded. For this purpose Corriedale, Romney Marsh and English Down breeds have been used in the montane areas, where the climatic environment is favourable, and Merino and Rambouillet breeds in the drier areas.

Hejazi.   This fat-rumped, hairy breed is important as it typifies a type of sheep common throughout Arabia and around the Horn of Africa that is capable of thriving under arid tropical conditions. They are quite small, measuring no more than 66 cm (26 in) in shoulder height, and their legs are rather long and thin. They possess a clearly defined throat ruff. Mature animals weigh up to 32 kg (70 lb) and they fatten easily although their mutton is of poor quality (Epstein, 1954).

Nellore.   This breed typifies the hairy sheep of south India. They are long-legged, measuring some 76 cm (30 in) in height at the shoulder, but they possess quite deep, broad bodies. The rams are horned and heavily maned. Castrated males fatten easily and produce mutton that is locally reputed to be of good quality. Ewes are late maturing and not very prolific. These sheep are excellent foragers and can withstand hot, semi-arid environments.

Lohi. This polled breed typifies the best mutton and milk breeds of India and is indigenous to the western Punjab. The body is deep and wide. The head is rather heavy, with large lop ears and a short thick neck. Average height at the shoulder is 79 cm (31 in). The hindquarters are broad, the legs thick and muscular and the tail thin. The colour is usually white on the body and reddish brown on the head. Average mature males and females weigh 68 kg (150 lb) and 37 kg (81 lb), respectively. The ewes possess well-developed udders and are said to yield up to 3·6 kg (8 lb) of milk per day at the peak of lactation. Sheep of this breed are prolific breeders, respond to stall feeding and by Asian sheep standards fatten quickly (Kaura, 1941).

In the montane areas of the tropics purebred stock of the productive temperate-type breeds may be raised and temperate-type rams are being increasingly utilized to upgrade tropical breeds for wool production, particularly in India and in western Asia.

Reproductive behaviour

In the middle latitudes temperate-type sheep may attain sexual maturity at 4 to 7 months of age and the first oestrus may occur in ewe lambs of the mutton breeds at 8 to 10 months of age. In many breeds of tropical sheep sexual maturity appears to be achieved at a later age, but this may be due to poorer feeding and management. The length of the oestral cycle appears to be similar in both temperate and tropical sheep. For example, in the Awassi breed Amir and Volcani (1965) reported that average cycle length was 18 (16 to 21) days.

The onset of oestrus of ewes in the temperate zone is initiated by changes in the length of daylight, so that in the northern hemisphere the breeding season usually occurs during the autumn when days are becoming shorter. In the tropics, where there are no major fluctuations in the length of daylight, ewes could theoretically come into heat at any time of the year. In the sub-tropics, indigenous sheep in Iran, for example, do not appear to be seasonal breeders. In Australia, Thwaites (1965) conducted an interesting experiment concerned with the effect of daylight on the breeding season of sheep. He studied oestrus activity in three groups of Southdown ewes. One group was exposed to natural daylight conditions (at latitude $30\frac{1}{2}°$S), in a second group seasonal lighting was reversed and in a third group the ewes were exposed to equatorial lighting conditions (equal day and night). Thwaites found that under natural light conditions the ewes exhibited a restricted breeding season that averaged 102·5 days during the autumn and winter months. Within this season they averaged $7·14\pm0·47$ oestrus periods. In the second group the breeding season was reversed. There were some daylight length–ambient temperature interactions, with low ambient temperatures tending to stimulate and high ambient temperatures tending to inhibit the manifestation of oestrus. Under equatorial lighting conditions the normal pattern of seasonal breeding was lost after one year, so that oestrus occurred in any month, although the intensity of breeding was greatly reduced. These experimental results are of the greatest practical importance when we consider the possibilities for breeding sheep in the tropics. It has been known for a long time that when temperate-type sheep are transferred from the temperate zone to the tropics, they may produce lambs during any month of the year but that their overall lambing percentage is often low. All indigenous tropical sheep breed at any season of the year, although their lambing percentages appear to be influenced by seasonal factors and are often quite low. For example, Saraswat *et al.* (1968) bred Bikaneri ewes in the spring, autumn and rainy seasons in Uttar Pradesh, India, and the lambing percentages were 66·6, 74·4 and 72·7 per cent, respectively, while winter-born lambs were heavier than spring- or rainy-season-born lambs at birth and at all stages up to 9 months of age.

From practical observations and the experimental evidence available we may conclude that it might be possible to obtain two crops of lambs each year, and quite definitely it should be possible to obtain three crops of lambs in 2 years from tropical-type ewes, but that the breeding season must be carefully chosen and will vary from region to region on account of the effect of factors other than daylight length on reproductive behaviour. For example, Wilson (1976) stated that the lambing interval of Baggara sheep in the western savanna of the Sudan was $275·2 \pm 58·6$ days with a range of 159 to 420 days, although there was a peak of conception during the rainy season when nutritional intake was high.

One of these other factors is the climatic environment and this affects the reproductive performance of both rams (Moule, 1970) and ewes.

Observations in Australia, India, the United States and elsewhere have suggested that rams appear to be more fertile in the cooler winter season than during the hotter summer season. In Florida, it has been stated that the management of rams in cooled rooms during hot weather improved the quality of their semen (Loggins *et al.*, 1964). Within- and between-breed differences in the reactions of rams to high environmental temperatures have been recorded. For example, it has been shown in Australia that Merino rams possessing a large number of skin folds are less fertile under hot weather conditions than Merino rams possessing less skin folds. In Florida the fertility of rams of the local breed – the Florida – is not affected to the same extent during the hot summer months as is that of Hampshire and Rambouillet rams. In Australia, Lindsay (1969) has shown that the semen quality of Dorset Horn rams was less affected by high environmental temperatures than that of Merino and Border Leicester rams. On the other hand Merino rams maintained sexual activity at higher environmental temperatures than did Dorset Horn and Border Leicester rams.

The decrease in the quality of semen from rams subjected to high environmental temperatures appears to be related to a rise in temperature of the subcutaneous tissue of the scrotum. This must be related to an increase in body temperature caused by general heat stress on the animal. Thus the efficiency of the heat-dissipating mechanisms of the scrotum will have some effect on determining the quality of the semen when the animal is subject to high environmental temperatures. In semen, sperm motility and the percentage of live sperm appear to be the major characteristics affected and the results of experimental work in Australia suggest that the major effects occur during spermatogenesis and not during the storage of the sperm.

There is a report from the USSR that low atmospheric pressure will also reduce sperm quality (Malikov, 1963) and this observation may have practical importance in the montane areas of the tropics.

Little is known of the reaction of rams of tropical breeds to high environmental temperatures. It may be surmised that one of the reasons why lambing is still seasonal in the tropics, despite the fact that ewes have no specific breeding season, may be due to the fact that rams are less fertile at some seasons than at others. On the other hand Wilson (1976) has stated that the libido of Baggara rams in the western savanna of the Sudan appears to be unaffected by season. There is certainly every reason to suggest that when crossbreeding and/or upgrading are contemplated and exotic rams are imported, then every effort should be made to ameliorate climatic conditions for these animals and to breed in the first place during the cooler season. It is also suggested that in the higher montane areas the affect of altitude on the sperm quality of rams may also have to be taken into account.

Rams imported into the tropics from the temperate zone appear to be less fecund and even sterile for up to one year after importation (Moule, 1970) and this effect is distinct from any effect of climatic stress. It is presumably a photoperiodic phenomenon, initiated by the transfer of the animal from an environment with a changing day-length to one in which there is little change in daylight.

In climatic chambers high ambient temperatures exercise a profound effect on the reproductive behaviour of ewes (Ryle, 1961): slightly reducing the number of ovulations, decreasing the development of potential embryos, increasing embryonic mortality and decreasing the birth weight of surviving foetuses. For example, Dutt (1963) has shown that the effect of an ambient temperature of $32.2°C$ ($90°F$) at the time of breeding and 1, 3 and 5 days later was to increase the percentage of morphologically abnormal ova from 3·7 in the control to 30·8 in the 0- and 1-day treated groups. Embryonic loss was significantly higher in the treated groups and ranged from 61·5 to 100 per cent. The most interesting fact that emerged from this experiment was that embryonic loss was significantly higher at the time of breeding and one day later than it was at 3 and 5 days later, suggesting that the sheep zygote appears to be most sensitive to the effect of high body temperature during the initial stage of cleavage while it is still in the oviduct.

Under field conditions in the tropics it is probable that the same effects occur, but their incidence is mitigated by diurnal and seasonal fluctuations in temperature and complicated by interactions with the photoperiodic effect of length of daylight. This even occurs in the temperate zone. For example, in the United Kingdom higher than normal ambient temperatures delay the onset of the autumn breeding season.

Nevertheless, field data from Australia and elsewhere suggests that high ambient temperatures reduce lambing percentages, decrease the incidence of twinning and decrease the birth weight of lambs carried through hot summers. For example, Ampy and Rottensten (1968) have shown that in the Lebanon the twinning incidence of Awassi sheep was 7·1, 9·5 and 24·5 per cent for spring-, summer- and autumn-mated ewes, respectively.

The gestation period of most indigenous tropical sheep breeds is not known with any accuracy, but the range in gestation length appears to be the same as that in the temperate-zone breeds, i.e. 140 to 160 days.

It is possible for a ram to sire up to 60 ewes in one breeding season and the normal practice in the temperate zone is to mate one ram with up to 40 ewes. In the tropics where all-the-year-round breeding is usually practised, where under extensive husbandry conditions the ewes may be very dispersed and where both rams and ewes are probably undernourished, the number of ewes per ram must be severely curtailed. In India it has often been the practice to use one ram per six ewes, in Africa one ram per ten ewes and in Arabia one ram per twenty ewes.

Placing the ewe lamb or ewe on a high plane of nutrition just before the breeding season commences is considered a desirable practice in the temperate zone as it apparently 'triggers off' the shedding of more eggs by the female and an increase in the probability of multiple births. This practice is known as 'flushing'. There is no reason to believe that tropical breeds would not respond in a similar manner and lambing percentages could be very high in tropical flocks that are well fed and managed. In addition, as ewes come into heat at all seasons it would be theoretically possible for each ewe to lamb twice a year or at least three times in 2 years. In practice, management and feeding are normally rather poor and lambs from multiple births have less chance of survival than single lambs. Under these circumstances in most tropical countries no effort has been made to achieve high lambing percentages. Even in tropical Australia average lamb-marking percentages are very low, varying between 35 and 40. This may be typical of the situation in many regions of the tropics.

Diseases and parasites

Sheep diseases and parasites unquestionably take a heavy toll in the tropics and as with all livestock they can best be combated with the aid of good management, proper feeding and strict sanitation.

It is likely that all the common diseases of sheep such as anthrax, blackleg, navel ill, pulpy kidney disease and leptospirosis are prevalent in most areas of the tropics, although they may not yet have been diagnosed. There are, however, some tropical islands where the sheep populations are free of many of these major diseases.

Some diseases that may be specific to or of special importance in the tropics, particularly in Africa, are as follows.

Blue tongue.   A virus disease of sheep that is occasionally found in cattle and wild fauna and is usually transmitted by sand flies of the genus *Culcoides*. It is known to be present throughout Africa, where there are at least twelve strains, and in western Asia. It is seasonal in incidence and mortality can be as high as 90 per cent. Indigenous breeds are less susceptible than exotics. In known infected areas an annual vaccination should be practised.

Rift Valley fever.   The causative virus is closely related to the yellow fever virus and is only found in Africa. Until recently this disease appeared to be restricted to East and South Africa, but it has now been diagnosed in sheep in Tschad and the Cameroun Republic. The vector is usually a mosquito. An attenuated vaccine is available.

Nairobi sheep disease.   This is a tick-borne virus of sheep and goats found in East and South Africa and characterized by an acute haemorrhagic septicaemia. There is a somewhat similar disease in Zaire known as Kisenyi sheep disease. The most common tick vector is *Rhipecephalus appendiculatus*, but other ticks may also transmit the disease. There is no effective treatment or vaccine.

Sheep pox.   A virus disease that is transmitted by direct contact, probably by droplet inhalation. The malignant form occurs in lambs and mortality can be as high as 50 per cent. An aluminium gel adsorbate vaccine exists that confers one year's immunity on the animal.

Heartwater.   A disease caused by a rickettsia-type organism that is transmitted by the tick *Amblyomma hebraeum*. It is common all over Africa and has recently been reported to exist in western Asia. Control can be exercised through control of the tick vector.

Infectious kerato-conjunctivitis.   This is a disease of the eyes of sheep caused by the organism *Rickettsia conjunctiva* in the presence of the bacterium known as *Neisseria ovia*. It is found in Africa, Asia and Central and South America. Suitable treatments have been evolved.

Photosensitization. This is common in sheep in the tropics where the ingestion of toxic plants may cause photosensitization and a high level of radiation aggravates the problem. The retention of affected sheep in a dark shed and proper feeding alleviates the condition.

Footrot. Although this disease is not usually fatal it is of considerable economic importance and compounds the difficulties of managing sheep in wet regions, particularly in the humid tropics. Footrot may be caused by several organisms and it can only be treated by good management of the flock. This includes periodically trimming the feet of the sheep, walking them through foot-baths containing either a 10 per cent formaldehyde or a 30 per cent copper sulphate solution, isolating clinical cases and proper rotation on clean pastures.

Internal parasites

Sheep are probably more susceptible to the ill-effects of internal parasites than other domestic livestock, although there is evidence that some breeds of tropical-type sheep are more tolerant of internal parasites than are temperate-type breeds introduced into the tropics. For example, Jilek and Bradley (1969) stated that indigenous Florida sheep are somewhat resistant to *Haemonchus contortus* and that this resistance appears to be correlated with the frequency of a specific blood type.

The major internal parasites of sheep are large stomach worms (*Haemonchus* spp.); brown stomach worms (*Ostertagia circumcinta*); black scour worms (*Trichostrongylus* spp.); nodular worms (*Oesophagostomum* spp.); intestinal threadworms or *Strongyloides*; *Trichuris ovis*, the whipworm; and the lung worm, *Dictyocaulus filaria*. All these exhibit a somewhat similar life cycle. The adults live in the gut where they mate, the females laying very large numbers of eggs that pass out with the faeces on to the pasture. If the ground is moist and the temperature suitable the eggs hatch in 1 or 2 days and develop into larvae, some of these being subsequently ingested by grazing animals.

Control of internal parasites can only be effective when sheep are well managed. Well-fed sheep do not suffer in the same way as those that are ill-nourished and strict rotational grazing can effectively reduce the level of infection. Nevertheless, in the humid tropics where environmental conditions are ideal for the perpetuation of the life cycle of the parasites, drenching is usually necessary whatever managerial system is practised.

Whatever the cause lamb mortality can be high in tropical sheep. Wilson (1976) in a study of indigenous Baggara sheep in the western savanna of the Sudan found that average mortality was 30·5 per cent up to the age of 6 months with half of this loss occurring during the first 4 weeks of life. The critical periods appeared to be at under one week of age when many lambs died due to mismothering, and at about 2 to 3 months of age when the lambs died from debility and general weakness, probably as a result of poor lactation performance by the dams and a lack of adequate forage once the dry season had commenced. The death rate of twin lambs was almost twice that of single lambs.

A variety of drenches may be used. The most effective are 'broad spectrum' types such as 'tetramisole'. This specific one must not be used with carbon tetrachloride. Phenothiazine is not effective against the immature stages of the parasites and stains the wool of the animal. Thibenzole is ineffective against lungworms. Copper sulphate–nicotine drenches are effective against some intestinal parasites such as *Haemonchus, Trichostrongylus* and tapeworms.

Two other internal parasites of sheep should also be mentioned. These are tapeworms and liver flukes.

The sheep tapeworm (*Coenurus cerebralis*) is only of importance where stray dogs are numerous, as the dog is the alternative host. If dogs eat infected mutton they will eventually void eggs on to the pastures. These are ingested by grazing sheep and the eggs hatch within the sheep, the embryos first entering the bloodstream and later the central nervous system where they create large cysts or 'bladders'. Infected sheep become defective in vision and gait and are termed 'giddy'. There is no effective treatment of 'giddy' sheep and control must be exercised by proper management.

Sheep, like cattle, are susceptible to attack by the liver fluke (*Fasciola hepatica*). Infected sheep void eggs in their faeces on to the pastures. These hatch into embryos that penetrate specific types of snail. The larvae hatch in the snails, leave them and encyst on vegetation. This vegetation is then eaten by sheep, the larvae from the ingested vegetation then penetrate the intestine and migrate to the liver where they mature within 2 to 3 months. The mature parasite produces eggs that commence the cycle once again. Control may be exercised by drenching the sheep with carbon tetrachloride, hexachlorethane or some similar compound. Dosing should be repeated after 4 to 6 weeks and a high calcium content mineral should be fed if it is suspected that there is any deficiency of calcium in the forage. Alternatively, pastures or open water may be treated with copper sulphate to destroy the snails. On pasture 3·5 to 6·7 kg per ha (3·0 to 6·0 lb per acre) of copper sulphate are used and mixed with 1·8 to 3·6 kg (4·0 to 8·0 lb) of a carrier such as sand. In open water one part of copper sulphate per 500,000 parts of water will kill the snails.

External parasites.

The external parasites of sheep such as blowflies (including the screwworm) sheep keds or ticks, mites, lice and fungi such as ringworm are considered to be less harmful than internal parasites, but they still cause immense losses. The incidence of these external parasites varies from region to region, but some form of control by spraying, dipping or dusting is usually necessary.

Feeding and management

Practically all tropical sheep are maintained on unimproved grazings. In Africa and western Asia they are grazed extensively, often together with cattle and/or goats, and in the more arid areas they are sometimes grazed together with camels. In some parts of Asia they are tethered on the roadsides and occasionally, as in the island of Madura in Indonesia, they are managed indoors and fed cut forage and browse. In tropical Australia they are grazed extensively in managed flocks at stocking rates as low as 1·6 to 4·0 ha (4·0 to 10·0 acres) per sheep.

Sheep are selective grazers, preferring short grasses, legumes and a wide variety of low-growing herbs. When they are transferred to a new locality they appear to possess little instinctual knowledge of what forage is suitable and often they do not thrive particularly well for quite a long period. It has been reported from South Africa that average daily intake of dry matter is 1·14 kg (2·52 lb), 0·93 kg (2·07 lb) and 1.27 kg (2·80 lb) per 100 kg/lb liveweight for sheep of the Merino, Blackhead Persian and Dorper breeds, respectively. It would appear from these data that feed consumption of the tropical breeds is somewhat lower than that of temperate-type sheep.

As sheep tend to thrive best in drier climates where the feed supply fluctuates both in quantity and quality from the wet to the dry season, supplementary feeding is often of importance during the dry season. Sheep can in fact be carried through drought periods on hay if it is available, and if this can be supplemented with approximately 0·11 kg (0·25 lb) of a protein concentrate per head per day, normal growth and development may be maintained. Silage has also been used in drought-feeding programmes in Australia, a satisfactory drought ration being 0·9 to 1·4 kg (2·0 to 3·0 lb) of silage containing 5 to 6 per cent of crude protein together with 57 to 85 g (2 to 3 oz) of meat meal per day.

Where sheep are subject to a long dry season productivity can be greatly increased by supplementing their rations while they are on the grazings and by managing those sheep destined for slaughter in a feedlot. Demiruren *et al.* (1971) have shown, for example, that Iranian sheep respond to better feeding and that it is possible to produce ram and ewe carcases weighing 35 kg (77 lb) and 28 kg (67 lb), respectively, from indigenous sheep managed under improved feeding conditions.

Good feeding is particularly important just before the breeding season begins, if seasonal breeding is practised. This practice, as previously stated, helps to improve prolificacy. Of course, under very poor feeding conditions multiple births are a liability, not an asset to the ewe. Good feeding is also required during the latter half of pregnancy. Well-fed wool sheep will usually produce a heavier but coarser fleece.

Salt in one form or another should always be available for sheep, the requirement being approximately 7 g (1 oz) per day. Other minerals, particularly trace minerals such as copper and cobalt, need to be made available in one form or another if a deficiency is known or suspected.

Sheep do not necessarily drink water daily, particularly if they are grazing on lush, wet-season pastures, but they should be given access to free water at all times. The approximate average daily water intake of sheep managed under semi-arid tropical conditions is 4 to 5 litres (0·9 to 1·1 gal). When sheep are fed dry feed indoors they should be supplied with water *ad lib.*

When sheep are fed indoors the feed may consist entirely of succulent fodders or of a mixture of forage and concentrates. For example, in the island of Madura and in south Sumatra in Indonesia sheep are often housed. They may be tethered outside on roadsides or canal banks for a few hours a day, but they are always fed some freshly cut forage and/or browse indoors. Browse from the legume tree *Sesbania grandiflora* is a favourite feed. Concentrate feeds are hardly ever used. The Kikuyu people in Kenya feed their housed sheep sweet potato vines and groundnut haulm. If suitable forage or browse is not available mature sheep may be fed up to 0·45 kg (1·00 lb) per day of a concentrate mixture. A suitable mixture would consist of 90 per cent of a mixture of cereals and cereal brans, such as maize and wheat, rice or sorghum bran or broken rice and rice bran, together with 10 per cent of an oil cake such as peanut, cottonseed or sesame meal and a suitable mineral mixture. The feeding of small amounts of a good legume hay such as alfalfa (lucerne) or a little fresh green forage or browse with this type of concentrate would improve the ration, and may be essential as insufficient carotene in a sheep's ration can cause vitamin A deficiency with resulting infertility.

Castration, if practised, may be carried out using a knife or the elastrator. Demiruren *et al.* (1971) have stated that in Iranian breeds castration does not affect the rate of gain of lambs from birth to 6 months of age.

Docking of the tail is desirable in woolled breeds as it reduces the incidence of blowfly strike. Qureshi (1968) investigated the influence of docking on a breed of fat-tailed sheep and found that the dressing percentage was higher in both males and females when they were docked, being 49·5 and 39·3 and 46·2 and 43·9 in docked and undocked male and female sheep, respectively. Fat deposition, finish and quality were superior in the docked sheep. Qureshi and Shaw (1968) stated that the birth weight of lambs was significantly higher in those born of docked ewes. Demiruren *et al.* (1971) found in Iranian sheep that docking increased the lean and decreased the fat content of sheep carcases.

On the other hand Joubert and Ueckermann (1971) found slightly heavier live and carcase weights in undocked as compared with docked fat-tailed lambs in South Africa. The differences could be accounted for almost entirely by the heavier weight of caudal fat. There was no evidence to suggest that there was an increase in the deposition of internal or subcutaneous fat following docking.

Weaning is usually accomplished at 4 to 5 months of age. Demiruren *et al.* (1971) have shown that in Iranian breeds the rate of gain of lambs is significantly affected by the length of the suckling period up to 120 days from birth. Their data suggested that lambs should not be weaned too early in the Iranian environment.

Woolled sheep should be sheared once a year and shearing is best performed during a period of least stress. One skilled man can shear up to 120 sheep per day.

Dentition.   It is often assumed that the teeth of early-maturing breeds erupt at an earlier age than that of late-maturing breeds, although there is no evidence to support this contention. Within the same breed, however, the teeth of faster-growing individuals do erupt at an earlier date.

In the absence of accurate records of the age at which sheep of specific tropical breeds cut their teeth, the detailed observations recorded by Starke and Pretorius (1955) with regard to sheep of the Blackhead Persian breed and their crosses may be used as an approximate practical guide. Details of their observations are shown in Table 7.2.

Table 7.2   *Ages of sheep according to permanent incisors*

Incisor stage	Possible age (months)	Most likely age (months)
Temporary	up to 18	up to 14
Two-tooth	12–27	14–20
Four-tooth	18–33	21–25
Six-tooth	24–45	26–32
Eight-tooth	above 28	above 32

Source: Extracts from *Farming in South Africa* Vol. 30 reproduced under Copyright Authority 5860 of 25.2.1977 of the Government Printer of the Republic of South Africa.

The age range of eruption includes the period from the appearance of the first tooth of each pair until the next pair erupt. The authors state that, 'the only reliable evidence that can be deduced from these investigations is that a sheep with two broad incisors is 14 to 20 months old and that a 2- to 3-year-old sheep can have either four- or six-tooth (usually indicating an age between 21 and 32 months); and that a 3-year-old sheep can be expected to have its full complement of eight. After 3 years of age the teeth are gradually worn down.'

Productivity

Meat

Most breeds of tropical sheep owe their existence to their ability to survive periods of drought and semi-starvation. Judged by the standards of the temperate zone they therefore respond poorly to good feeding, and on normal grazing grow comparatively slowly and seldom become very fat. However, the investigations of Demiruren *et al.* (1971) suggest that Iranian sheep will respond quite well to improved nutritional levels. The quoted mature weights of the majority of the breeds are therefore usually somewhat low.

Average mature liveweights of a number of Indian breeds are shown in Table 7.3. Few Indian breeds attain a mature liveweight of more than

Table 7.3 *Average mature liveweights and fleece weights of some breeds of sheep in the Indian sub-continent*

Breed	Av. mature liveweight (kg (lb))	Av. fleece weight (kg (lb))	Reference
Baluchi	33–44 (73–97)	1·8 (4)	Lall (1947)
Bellary	32–54 (70–120)	0·7–1·4 (1·5–3·0)	Kaura (1941)
Bhadarwah	32 (70)	0·9–1·4 (2·0–3·0)	Kaura (1942)
Bibrik	27–36 (60–80)	1·8 (4·0)	Kaura (1942)
Bikaneri	36–64 (80–140)	1·3–2·4 (2·8–6·8)	Kaura (1941)
Damani	23 (50)	1·4 (3·0)	Lall (1947)
Dumari	27–32 (60–70)	1·8–2·7 (4·0–6·0)	Kaura (1942)
Deccani	20–32 (45–70)	0·2–0·3 (0·5–0·8)	Kaura (1941)
Hassan	23 (50)	0·2–0·8 (0·5–1·8)	Kaura (1942)
Kaghani	23 (50)	1·1 (2·5)	Lall (1947)
Kathiawar	27–45 (60–100)	–	Kaura (1942)
Jalauni	24–32 (52–70)	–	Lall (1947)
Lohi	36–69 (81–153)	1·4–2·2 (3·1–4·9)	Kaura (1941)
Mandhya	29 (65)	–	Kaura (1942)
Nellore	38–41 (83–90)	–	Kaura (1941)
Rakhshani	32 (70)	1·8 (4·0)	Lall (1947)
Thal	18–27 (40–60)	1·8–2·3 (4·0–5·0)	Lall (1947)
Waziri	23 (50)	0·5 (1·0)	Lall (1947)

Sources: As references.

50 kg (110 lb). Most other tropical breeds appear to possess similar mature liveweights. For example, that of Landim sheep in Mozambique varies from 23 to 28 kg (49 to 62 lb) (de Pinho Morgado, 1961), while that of Sudan Desert sheep is 25 to 52 kg (55 to 115 lb) (Osman *et al.*, 1970) and mature Awassi and the Arabi weigh 42 kg (92 lb) and 38 kg (84 lb), respectively (Asker and El-Khalisi, 1966). According to Epstein (1954) mature Hejazi sheep weigh 30 to 32 kg (66 to 71 lb) and Jones (1964) stated that mature Bakhtiari sheep in Iran weigh 50 to 59 kg (110 to 130 lb).

The sheep of many tropical breeds appear to dress-out rather poorly. For example, Epstein (1954) stated that Hejazi sheep dress-out at 37 to 40 per cent and Osman and El Shafie (1967) stated that the dressing-out percentage of Sudan Desert sheep varied between 36·4 and 52·1. Average dressing-out percentages of tropical-type sheep are probably within the range of 40 to 48. However, Demiruren *et al.* (1971) stated that the dressing-out percentages of range-fed ewes and rams in Iran were 56·5 and 55·3, respectively.

Interest in improvement in production characteristics by the introduction of exotic sheep and the use of crossbreeding has quickened during the last decade. Earlier investigations suggested that although crossbred progeny might grow more rapidly up to weaning they often failed to maintain their advantage as adults under local environmental conditions. For example, in Rhodesia it was shown that the male and female offspring of half- or three-quarter-bred Blackhead Persian × Dorset Horn ewes mated with German Merino rams weighed on average 33 and 29 kg (74 and 65 lb) and 29 and 28 kg (64 and 62 lb) respectively, but that their growth after weaning was very slow.

Data published by French (1938) on the growth of sheep in East Africa three decades ago give some indication of rates of growth that may be obtained on dry-land pasture (Table 7.4). These are only about one-quarter of that expected from a good mutton breed on pasture in the temperate zone.

Table 7.4   *Growth rate of sheep in Tanzania*

Age	Liveweight (kg (lb))		
	Three-quarter grade Blackhead Persian	*Masai*	*Ugogo*
Birth	2·6 (5·8)	3·0 (6·6)	2·1 (4·7)
1 month	5·8 (12·8)	6·3 (13·9)	4·6 (10·1)
3 months	9·9 (21·9)	11·9 (26·2)	8·1 (17·9)
6 months	14·7 (32·3)	17·4 (38·4)	14·7 (32·4)
9 months	17·9 (39·5)	23·0 (50·7)	16·6 (36·6)
12 months	21·0 (46·3)	26·9 (59·4)	19·1 (42·1)
18 months	25·2 (55·6)	34·7 (76·5)	24·8 (54·7)
Average liveweight gain per day	0·047 (0·103)	0·064 (0·142)	0·045 (0·100)

Source: French (1938).

It has been stated in Israel more recently that Awassi × Dorset Horn crossbreds grow at a 20 to 30 per cent faster rate than purebred Awassi during the first 90 days of life. Ramamurti (1964) showed that both liveweight and wool yield of Romney Marsh × Nilgiri crossbreds were significantly higher than those of the indigenous Nilgiri over a 4-year period. Trail and Sacker (1966), crossbreeding East African Blackhead sheep with Dorset Horn, stated that the crossbreds were heavier at birth and that from weaning to maturity the crossbreds' daily liveweight gain was 0·095 kg (0·210 lb) per day compared with 0·036 kg (0·080 lb) per day for the indigenous animals. The mortality rate of the crossbreds was, however, higher – 26·1 compared with 21·0 per cent for the indigenous. In a subsequent paper Trail and Sacker (1969) reported that the quarter- and half-bred Dorset crossbred ewes possessed superior milking abilities and that five-eighths- and three-quarter-bred Dorset lambs were 26 per cent heavier than the half-breds at 2 months of age, and that although all lambs grow at the same rate from 2 to 11 months of age the five-eighths and three-quarter breds retained their initial advantage until maturity.

Milk

In a few countries milk production is of commercial importance, but in most, milk production is for home consumption. For example, the population in many Indian communities and most nomadic sheep owners throughout western Asia derive an important part of their diet from sheep milk. Different types of cheeses and some form of yogurt are commonly made from sheep milk for local and immediate consumption and in India and in western Asia ghee is sometimes made from sheep milk.

Ewes are usually only milked once a day. They are invariably milked by hand, although machine milking is possible. Ewes respond to good management and feeding in much the same way as milking cows.

In western Asia the Awassi is the most productive milk breed. Finci (1957) reported that in Israel the average production in the eleven best flocks was increased by 266 kg (586 lb) in 18 years, the average annual yield in 1955–56 being 359 kg (791 lb) with the best individual yield being 890 kg (1,962 lb). Yield was maximal at the fourth lactation. The fat content of Awassi milk is 6 to 8 per cent. Finci also concluded that high milk production was not incompatible with high fleece yield.

Indian breeds of sheep have not been subjected to intense selection pressure for milk production, but it is likely that many unimproved breeds do have the capacity to produce relatively large amounts of milk. Ewes of the Lohi breed are said to yield up to 3·6 kg (8 lb) of milk a day (Kaura, 1941) while the Kuka breed is said to produce 1·8 to 3·6 kg (4 to 8 lb) of milk per day (Kaura, 1942) and the Sonedi breed, synonym Chanothar, 0·9 to 1·4 kg (2 to 3 lb) of milk daily (Anon., 1953).

In Africa, Dwarf West African ewes managed under conditions where high yields could not be expected average 40 to 50 kg (88 to 110 lb) of milk in 120- to 135-day lactations and when well fed can apparently produce as much as 75 to 85 kg (165 to 187 lb). Sudan Desert ewes will produce up to 2·3 to 2·7 kg (5 to 6 lb) of milk daily.

Atmadilaga (1958) has reported from Indonesia that Priangan ewes weighing 30 to 40 kg (66 to 88 lb) will produce 21 to 53 kg (46 to 112 lb) of milk with a 5 per cent fat content per lactation.

Wool

As tropical countries industrialize, the indigenous wool production industry increases in importance because of the demand for wool generated by new textile industries. Thus in many tropical countries new efforts are being made to upgrade indigenous hairy or coarse wool sheep breeds to produce more and finer wools. As stated in a previous section, even in western Asia and in the northern part of the Indian sub-continent, centre of the world's most exotic carpet industry, efforts are being made to upgrade some of the sheep breeds that at present produce carpet wools. The Commonwealth Bureau of Animal Breeding and Genetics (1971) has assembled abstracts of papers for the period 1951 to 1970 on wool production in tropical breeds of sheep. Readers who are specifically interested in this subject are advised to consult this publication together with one by Lima Pereira (1969).

In West Africa an effort has been made to cross Uda and Yamkasa hairy sheep with wool sheep. Crosses with Merino still produced sheep with excessively kempy fleeces (Burns, 1967). Wensleydale × Uda and Yamkasa crosses are now being investigated.

In western Asia Awassi sheep produce 1·4 to 1·6 kg (3 to 3·5 lb) of wool per year (Asker and Juma, 1966). The 12-month fleece weights of four Iranian breeds were: Kelakui 1·63 kg (3·59 lb) for females and 2·27 kg (5·00 lb) for males; Kizil 2·15 kg (4·74 lb) for females and 3·21 kg (7·08 lb) for males; Bakhtiari 2·29 kg (5·05 lb) for females and 3·36 kg (7·41 lb) for males; Baluchi 2·49 kg (5·49 lb) for females and 3·31 kg (7·30 lb) for males (Demiruren *et al.*, 1971). The average fleece weights of a number of Indian breeds are given in Table 7.3.

References

Amir, D. and Volcani, R. (1965) The sexual season of the Awassi fat-tailed ewe. *J. agric. Sci. (Camb.),* **64,** 83–5.

Ampy, F. R. and Rottensten, K. V. (1968) Fertility in the Awassi Sheep. 1. Seasonal influence on fertility. *Trop. Agric. (Trin.),* **45,** 191–7.

Anon. (1953) *Indian Fmg.,* N.S., **3,** 10 and 26.

Asker, A. A. and El-Khalisi, I. J. (1966) Some observations on commercial flocks of sheep in Iraq. *Ann. agric. Sci., Univ. A' im Shams,* **10,** No. 2 (1965), 17–28. *Abstracted: Anim. Breed. Abstr.,* **35,** 439 (1967).

Asker, A. A. and Juma, K. H. (1966) Some factors affecting fleece weight of Awassi sheep in Iraq. *Iraq. J. agric. Sci.,* **1,** 33–9.

Atmadilaga, D. (1958) Study on the milk yield of Indonesian sheep with special reference to the Priangan breed. *Hemera Zoa,* **65,** 3–14.

Burns, M. (1967) The Katsina Wool Project. 1. The coat and skin histology of some Northern Nigeria hair sheep and their Merino crosses. 2. Coat and skin data from $\frac{3}{4}$ Merino and Wensleydale crosses. *Trop. Agric. (Trin.),* **44,** 173–92, 253–74.

Commonwealth Bureau of Animal Breeding and Genetics (1971) *Wool Production in Tropical Breeds of Sheep.* Annotated Bibliog. No. 179. CBAB and G: Edinburgh.

Demiruren, A. S., Beheshti, R. D., Salimi, H., Saleh, B. A. and Djaferi, A. (1971) *Comparison of the Reproductive and Productive Capacities of Sheep of the Kellakul, Kizil, Bakhtiari and Baluchi breeds in Iran.* Tech. Rep. No. 1. Anim. Husb. Res. Inst.: Teheran.

de Pinho Morgado, F. (1961) Aids to the recognition of the livestock types of Mozambique. The Landim sheep (in Portuguese). *An. Serv. Vet. Moçambique,* (7), (1955–59), 331–346. *Abstracted: Anim. Breed. Abstr.,* **32,** 40 (1964).

Dutt, R. H. (1963) Critical period for early embryo mortality in ewes exposed to high ambient temperature. *J. Anim. Sci.,* **22,** 713–19.

Epstein, H. (1954) The fat-tailed sheep of Arabia. *Z. Tierzücht Zücht Biol.,* **63,** 381–96. *Abstracted: Anim. Breed. Abstr.,* **23,** 50 (1955).

FAO (1973) *Production Yearbook,* Vol. 26 (1972). FAO: Rome.

Finci, H. (1957) *The Improvement of the Awassi Breed of Sheep in Israel.* Weizmann: Jerusalem.

French, M. H. (1938) The growth rates of local and crossbred sheep. *E. Africa. agric. J.,* **8,** 24–5.

Jilek, A. F. and Bradley, R. E. (1969) Haemoglobin types and resistance to *Haemonchus contortus* in sheep. *Am. J. vet. Res.,* **30,** 1773–8.

Jones, R. G. (1964) *Sheep Industry in Iran.* Comm. Res. Branch USAID, Livestock Extension Adviser, 62 pp. (mimeo).

Joubert, D. M. (1969) Indigenous South African sheep and goats, their origin and development. *Trop. Sci.,* **11,** 185–95.

Joubert, D. M. and Ueckermann, L. (1971) A note on the effect of docking on fat deposition in fat tailed sheep. *Anim. Prod.,* **13,** 191–2.

Kaura, R. L. (1941) Some common breeds of Indian sheep. *Indian Fmg.,* **2,** 175–9.

Kaura, R. L. (1942) Some common breeds of Indian sheep. II. *Indian Fmg.,* **3,** 122–5.

Lall, H. K. (1947) Some common breeds of Indian sheep. *Indian Fmg.,* **8,** 605–9.

Lall, H. K. (1950) Breeds of sheep in the Indian Union. *Misc. Bull. Ind. Counc. Agric. Res.,* No. 75. ICAR: New Delhi.

Lima Pereira, J. (1969) Sheep production for wool in tropical areas (in Portuguese). *Estudos Eusaios Docum. Jta. Invest. Utramar,* No. 123, pp. 489. Lisbon. *Abstracted: Anim. Breed. Abstr.,* **39,** 397 (1971).

Lindsay, D. R. (1969) Sexual activity and semen production of rams at high temperatures. *J. Reprod. Fert.,* **18,** 1–8.

Loggins, P. E., Koger, M., Warnick, A. C. and Cunha, T. J. (1964) Spring lamb production in Florida. *Bull. Fla. agric. Exp. Stn,* No. 669, 20 pp. Univ. Florida: Gainesville.

Malikov, D. I. (1963) The effect of atmospheric pressure on reproduction in rams (in Russian). *Vestn. sel-hoz Nauk. (Mosk.),* **8,** 82–6. *Abstracted: Anim. Breed. Abstr.,* **33,** 95 (1965).

Moule, G. R. (1970) Australian research into reproduction in the ram. *Anim. Breed. Abstr.,* **38,** 185–202.

Osman, A. H. and El Shafie, S. A. (1967) Carcass characteristics of Sudan Desert Sheep. *Sudan J. Vet. Sci.,* **8,** 115–19.

Osman, A. H., El Shafie, S. A. and Khattab, A. G. H. (1970) Carcass composition of fattened rams and wethers of Sudan Desert sheep. *J. agric. Sci. (Camb.),* **75,** 257–63.

Qureshi, M. J. (1968) Influence of docking fat-tailed lambs on fat deposition. *Agriculture Pakist.,* **19,** 97–100.

Qureshi, M. J. and Shaw, A. O. (1968) Influence of docking fat-tailed lambs on breeding performance. *Agric. Pakist.,* **19,** 93–6.

Ramamurti, A. (1964) Performance of crossbred progeny of Nilgiri ewes with exotic rams. *Ind. vet. J.,* **41,** 201–5.

Ryle, M. (1961) Early Reproductive Failure of Ewes in a Hot Environment. I. Ovulation rate and embryonic mortality. *J. agric. Sci. (Camb.),* **57,** 1–9.

Saraswat, K. C., Seth, O. N. and Roy, A. (1968) Effect of season on fertility in an experimental flock of Bikaneri (Magra) sheep and liveweight gain of lambs. *Ind. J. vet. Sci.*, **38**, 778–84.

Starke, J. S. and Pretorius, A. G. (1955) Dentition of sheep as an indication of age. *Fmg. S. Africa*, **30**, 53–8.

Thwaites, C. J. (1965) Photoperiodic control of breeding activity in the Southdown ewe with particular reference to the effects of an equatorial light regime. *J. agric. Sci. (Camb.)*, **65**, 57–64.

Tothill, J. D. (ed.) (1948) *Agriculture in the Sudan*. Oxford Univ. Press: London.

Trail, J. C. M. and Sacker, G. D. (1966) Production records of lambs from East Africa, Blackheaded ewes and Dorset Horn rams. *E. Afr. agric. For. J.*, **32**, 133–6.

Trail, J. C. M. and Sacker, G. D. (1969) Growth of crossbred Dorset Horn lambs from East African Blackheaded sheep. *J. agric. Sci. (Camb.)*. **73**, 229–43.

Wilson, R. T. (1976) Studies on the livestock of Southern Darfur, Sudan. III. Production traits in sheep. *Trop. Anim. Hlth. Prod.*, **8**, 103–14.

Zeuner, F. E. (1963) *A History of Domesticated Animals*. Hutchinson: London.

Further Reading

Ensminger, M. E. *Sheep and Wool Science* (4th edn). Interstate: Danville, Illinois, 1970.

Ferguson, W. *The Development of Sheep and Goat Production in the Northern Region of Nigeria*. FAO: Rome, 1964.

Lydekker, R. *The Sheep and its Cousins*. George Allen: London, 1912.

Owen, J. B. Performance recording in sheep. *Tech. Comm. Comw. Bur. Anim. Breed. Genet.*, No. 20, Comw. Agric. Bur.: Farnham Royal, UK, 1971.

Chapter 8

Goats

by **C. Devendra**
Animal Improvement Research Division, Malaysian Agricultural Research and Development Institute, Serdang, Malaysia

Importance

The goat is a particularly important animal in subsistence agriculture on account of its unique ability to adapt and maintain itself in harsh environments. The domestic goat belongs to the genus *Capra* that includes, according to Ellerman and Morrison-Scott (1951), five species: *Capra. hircus*, the true goat, including the bezoar (*C. hircus, aegagrus*); *C. ibex*, the ibex; *C. caucasica*, the Caucasian tur: *C. pyrenaica*, the Spanish ibex; and *C. falconeri*, the markhor. Although the origin of domestic goats remains to be clearly established, the available evidence indicates that the bezoar of southwest Asia is the main ancestor. It is also likely that the markhor of northwest India, together with the bezoar, has contributed to the genetic background of certain breeds in India and western Asia. The Abyssinian ibex and the bezoar are also probably involved in the ancestry of goats in North and East Africa. It is believed that the goat was probably the second animal to be domesticated after the dog.

At least four methods of classifying domestic goats have been advocated based on origin, utility, body size and ear shape and length. Each of these has its special attributes and limitations. For example, origin and utility are too broad in scope, especially as goats in the tropics are often unspecialized, all-purpose animals and their origin lacks documentation. In a more recent classification (Devendra and Burns, 1970), goats were divided into three categories on the basis of body size. Using height at withers as the criterion, the three groups were: large (over 65 cm (26 in)), small (51 to 65 cm (20 to 26 in)) and dwarf breeds (under 50 cm (20 in)). It was found that the large breeds weighed 20 to 63 kg (44 to 139 lb) and were largely dual-purpose in function, small breeds weighed 19 to 37 kg (42 to 82 lb) and the very small goats 18 to 25 kg (40 to 55 lb). Goats in the last group were kept exclusively for meat production.

Goats are multipurpose animals, producing milk, meat, skins and hair. Although some breeds such as the Jamnapari (Plate 8.1) and the Damascus are capable of producing relatively large amounts of milk, the

Plate 8.1   Etawa (Jamnapari) goats in Indonesia.

majority of goats owe their existence to the fact that they thrive as meat producers under conditions in which it is difficult for other species of domestic livestock to survive. Skins are a valuable by-product, especially in countries with a large goat population.

Goat meat is relished in all countries where the meat of both sheep and goats traditionally forms part of the diet. In a number of countries such as Ghana (Jollans, 1959), India (Bose, 1963) and in parts of western Asia, Southeast Asia and the Caribbean (Devendra, 1971), goat meat is preferred to both mutton and beef. This is probably due to the higher lean content of the meat relative to mutton and beef, but it might also be related to certain special features that make goat meat quite different from mutton. Whereas in sheep the fat is distributed all over the body, in goats visceral concentration is characteristic and the grain of the meat is more compact and the colour slightly darker than mutton.

Liveweight exerts a definite influence on meat production. Of the factors affecting liveweight, that of nutrition is particularly important and studies in Uganda, Tanzania, India, Malaysia and the West Indies confirm this. The total edible and saleable proportions of goats vary from one region to another because of differences in eating habits and the value of the by-products. It may be of interest to note that in Africa these have been estimated to be 48·3 and 55·5 per cent (Wilson, 1958), whereas in Malaysia they were 61·2 and 81·5 per cent, respectively (Devendra, 1966b). The dressing percentages for various breeds of goats (Table 8.1) compare quite well with those of sheep and beef cattle and there is some evidence that there is a better response to castration (Congiu, 1954; Hutchinson, 1964) and to improved feeding (Devendra,

Table 8.1 *Dressing percentage of the carcase in representative breeds*

Breed	Location	Carcase weight (kg (lb))	Dressing (%)	Reference
Anglo-Nubian grade	Los Baños, Philippines	11·4 (25·0)	51·4	Gatan (1941)
Indigenous	Merca, Somalia	14·1–22·1 (31·0–48·7)	50·0–52·3	Congiu (1954)
Indigenous	Kinshasa, Zaire	10·5 (23·1)	50·0	Henrotte (1961)
East African	Serere, Uganda	5·9 (13·0)	43·5	Wilson (1958)
Crossbred Boer females		14·7 (32·4)	44·7–55·4	
Indigenous castrates	Mpwapwa, Tanzania	11·1–16·9 (25·0–37·3)	46·5–55·4	Hutchinson (1964)
Indigenous × Boer		21·3 (47·0)	52·4	
		9·5 (21·0)	44·3	
Kambing Katjang	Serdang, Malaysia	21·1 (26·7)	47·4	Devendra (1966b)
		14·7 (32·4)	51·3	

Sources: As references.

1966b). Of interest in this context are the *thenges*, stall-fed castrated goats raised by the Kikuyu in Kenya. They are prodigious yielders of carcase fat.

Goat's milk is also a very useful product and for subsistence peasant farmers it is a most important source of animal protein (Devendra, 1975a). It is used fresh or in the making of yogurt, butter and cheese. In many parts of the tropics there are definite limitations on the availability of nutrients for feeding dairy cattle. Under these conditions that are likely to be operating for a long time, the milking goat is a most useful animal.

The special attributes of goat's milk are that tubercle bacilli are rare, that there is a high proportion of smaller fat globules facilitating easy digestion and that it possesses anti-allergic properties. Its nutritive value does not differ appreciably from that of cow's milk (Parkash and Jenness, 1968). The average composition of goat's milk compared with the milk of Indian and European cows and Indian buffaloes is shown in Table 8.2.

Table 8.2 *Average composition of goat's milk compared with the milk of Indian and European cows and Indian buffaloes*

Species	Fat	Protein	Lactose	Ash	SNF	Total solids
Indian cows[1]	4·8	2·8	4·6	0·74	8·1	13·5
European cows[1]	3·7	3·4	4·8	0·73	8·9	12·7
Murrah buffaloes[2]	6·8	3·9	5·7*	–	9·6	–
Goats[3]	4·9	4·3	4·1	0·89	9·3	14·2

* Including ash.
Sources: (1) Schneider *et al.* (1948).   (2) Ghosh and Anantakrishnan (1963); Ghosh and Anantakrishnan (1965).   (3) ICAR (1962).

Secondary to their value as meat and milk animals is their value for the production of hair and skins. As a by-product of goat-meat production, skins are very important in India, Pakistan and several African countries. The skin of the Maradi (synonym, Red Sokoto (Plate 8.2)) in Nigeria is well known for its superior quality and the premium it commands in world markets. Equally well known are Mubende skins from Uganda. Particular mention must be made of the value of cashmere (synonym, Pashmina), the very fine undercoat of the Kashmiri type of goats that graze at high altitudes in central Asia. Another important product is mohair, the fleece of the Angora goat (Plate 8.3), which is principally produced in South Africa, Lesotho and the United States. The hair of common goats is used extensively in the carpet trade and also in the making of coarse bags, rope and the tents of many western Asian nomads. Goat skins are also used extensively in making rugs, furniture upholstery and in handicraft.

In addition to their main functions goats are important for a number of miscellaneous reasons. They are considered an investment against the failure of cash crops, their ownership bestows prestige and in many

Plate 8.2   Red Sokoto goats near Maiduguri in northeast Nigeria.

Plate 8.3   Angora goats in Lalahan, Turkey.

communities they have a place in local custom, religion and festive occasions (Devendra, 1966a). They are also used for the production of manure and more recently as convenient experimental animals for metabolic studies.

In the past there has been some disagreement as to the value of goats because of the widely held belief that the damage they do to trees and vegetation – especially in arid regions – outweighs their usefulness as producers of meat, milk and skin. There is, however, a growing school of thought that recognizes that the bad reputation of goats stems more from their mismanagement than from any inherent fault, and that with controlled management they can be a great help in agricultural development and food production.

Distribution

At present the total population of goats in the world is about 391 million, with approximately 210 million or 54 per cent being found in the tropics (Table 8.3). The largest concentrations are in Africa and in the Indian sub-continent.

Table 8.3 *The goat population of the world*

Continent and/or region	1961–65		1973		Percentage increase or decrease
	Number ('000)	As percentage of world population	Number ('000)	As percentage of world population	
Europe	14,459	4	11,666	3	−19
USSR	6,422	2	5,604	2	−13
Africa	102,750	28	114,735	29	+12
Tropics	83,838	23	90,752	23	+8
Other	18,912	5	23,983	6	+27
Americas	42,308	11	41,043	10	−3
Tropics	27,900	7	29,560	7	+6
Other	14,408	4	11,483	3	−20
Asia	206,788	55	218,124	56	+5
Tropics	80,103	21	89,889	23	+13
Other*	72,945	20	69,557	18	−5
China	53,740	14	58,678	15	+10
Oceania	189	negl.	203	negl.	+7
Tropics	97	negl.	100	negl.	+3
Other	92	negl.	103	negl.	+12
World	372,916		391,375		+5
Tropics	191,938	51	210,301	54	+10
Other	180,978	49	181,074	46	–

*Excluding China and the Asiatic regions of the USSR.
Source: FAO (1974).

Goats are possibly the most widely distributed of domestic livestock. They are found in countries representing the climatic extremes of the tropics, from the arid and semi-arid areas of South America to the wet and humid tropics of Southeast Asia. Their wide distribution is partially explained by their ability to survive and thrive in environments where vegetation is extremely sparse. Their rustic and hardy qualities enable them to withstand dry environmental conditions much better than cattle. They perform best, however, in the drier tropics and on light sandy soils. In Africa, for instance, the greatest concentrations of goats are to be found in East Africa, northern Nigeria and Morocco. This pattern of distribution is also true of the Indian sub-continent, western Asia, South and Central America and the Caribbean. Dwarf goats are found throughout the humid tropics and it could be that they are especially adapted to this type of climate.

Breeds

Although goats are numerous, present knowledge about the value of many breeds and types is limited. What information there is relates to the better-known breeds and, by comparison, many indigenous breeds

Table 8.4 *Breeds that might be used for improvement purposes*

Specialty	Breeds	Climate of origin	Country of origin
Milk			
High yields	Saanen*	Temperate; tropical, humid	Switzerland
	Anglo-Nubian*	Temperate; tropical, dry	United Kingdom
Medium yields	Damascus*	Sub-tropical, dry	Lebanon, Syria, Cyprus
	Jamnapari	Tropical/sub-tropical, dry	India
	Barbari	Tropical/sub-tropical, dry	India, Pakistan
	Sudanese Nubian	Tropical, dry	Sudan
Meat	Boer	Sub-tropical, dry	South Africa
	Jamnapari	Tropical, dry	India
	Ma T'ou*	Sub-tropical, humid	China
	Kambing Katjang	Tropical, humid	Malaysia, Indonesia
	Fijian	Tropical, humid	Fiji
Prolificacy	Malabar*	Tropical, humid	India
	Barbari	Tropical, dry	India, Pakistan
	Ma T'ou	Sub-tropical, humid	China
	Damascus*	Sub-tropical, dry	Lebanon, Syria, Cyprus
Mohair	Angora	Sub-tropical, dry	Turkey
Skins	Maradi (Red Sokoto)	Tropical, dry	Niger, Nigeria
	Mubende	Tropical, dry/humid	Uganda

*Indicates that the breed is polled.
Source: Devendra and Burns (1970).

Table 8.5 *Production data of some of the breeds that might be used for improvement purposes*

Speciality	Breed	Location	Performance	Reference
Milk				
High yields	Saanen	United Kingdom	1,227 kg (2,705 lb) up to 365 days	British Goat Society (1968)
	Anglo-Nubian	United Kingdom	989 kg (2,180 lb) up to 365 days	
	Damascus	Cyprus	300–600 litre (66–132 gal) in 240 days	Hirsch (1932)
Medium yields	Jamnapari	India	235 kg (518 lb) in 261 days	Kaura (1952)
	Barbari	India	144 kg (317 lb) in 235 days	
	Sudanese Nubian	Sudan	60–70 kg (132–154 lb) per lactation	Mason and Maule (1960)
Meat	Boer	South Africa	40 kg (88 lb) at 12 months	Devendra and Burns (1970)
	Jamnapari	India	8·3–10·4 kg (18·3–22·9 lb) carcase weight: 44·3–45·5 dressing out percentage	Srivastava *et al.* (1968)
	Ma Tou	China	Castrated males 26–52 kg (57–115 lb) liveweight	Epstein (1969)
	Kambing Katjang	Malaysia	14·7 kg (32·4 lb) carcase weight: 51·3 dressing out percentage	Devendra (1966b)
Prolificacy	Fijian	Fiji	10·5 kg (23·1 lb) carcase weight	Thompson (1965)
	Malabar	India	79% twin and triplet births	Shanmugasundram (1957)
	Ma Tou	China	44·7 kids per 100 births	Epstein (1969)
	Damascus	Cyprus	1·76 kids per birth	Epstein and Hertz (1964)
Mohair	Angora	Turkey	Females 1·7–2·0 kg (3·7–4·4 lb) and males 3·0–3·5 kg (6·0–7·7 lb) yield per annum	Devendra and Burns (1970)

Sources: As references.

have been described only superficially. Recently, however, a comprehensive description of some of the more important unimproved goats offering valuable scope for improvement in various regions of the tropics has been made (Devendra and Burns, 1970). It has been estimated that there are approximately 300 breeds and types of goats (Devendra, 1974).

A list of those breeds which appear to offer valuable genetic material for improvement of productivity, under tropical or sub-tropical conditions, whether in their country of origin or elsewhere, is given in Table 8.4, while some details of what is known of their productivity are shown in Table 8.5.

Of the breeds indigenous to the tropics, a number are very well known and have been imported into other regions. The Nubian (Plate 8.4) from the Sudan and the Jamnapari (Plate 8.1) from India, both of which have been used to produce the Anglo-Nubian (Plate 8.5), are good examples. Nubians have been imported into North and Central America and have also been used extensively to crossbreed with indigenous goats for meat production in Venezuela. The Nubian, together with the Jamnapari, are recognized as the best representatives of tropical milch goats. Jamnapari goats have been imported into many countries in Southeast Asia and also into the West Indies.

Particular attention is drawn to the prolific Black Bengal goat (Plate 8·6) of India and Pakistan. It is a small meat breed with a height at the withers of around 45 cm (18 in) and with adult males and females weighing 13 kg (29 lb) and 9 kg (20 lb), respectively.

Dwarf goats are of two types – achondroplastic and non-achondroplastic. The former, characterized by disproportionately short legs, occur

Plate 8.4 Nubian goats in the Sudan.

Plate 8.5   Anglo-Nubian female goat in Trinidad (C. Devendra).

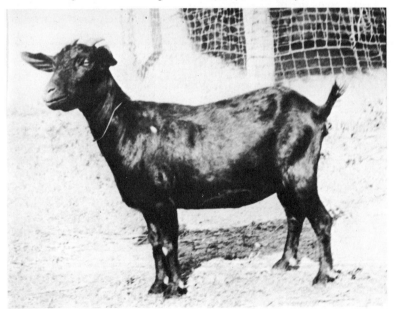

Plate 8.6   Black Bengal female goat in India (Commonwealth Bureau of Animal Breeding and Genetics).

particularly in the humid tropics and it is suggested that this may be due to restricted pituitary function that could be an adaptation to poor nutrition; this probably explains low milk yields and easier disposal of metabolic heat. Non-achondroplastic dwarf goats occur in a few tropical localities, such as the southern Sudan and also parts of China and Taiwan; these are usually good milkers in contrast to the achondroplastic dwarfs.

Special mention must be made of the European breeds in the tropics: Anglo-Nubian, Toggenburg, British Alpine and Saanen. Of these some have done better than others (Maule, 1966). The Saanen and the British Alpine appear to be more promising than the Toggenburg, but both are excelled for tropical use by the Anglo-Nubian. In Malaysia where all four breeds have been introduced, the Anglo-Nubian has been by far the best, producing an average of 1 kg (2·2 lb) of milk per day. In the West Indies 2 to 4 kg (4·4 to 8·8 lb) of milk per day at peak lactation has been obtained. British Alpine goats have also been successful in the West Indies, giving an average of 1·3 kg (2·9 lb) of milk per day, but they have been a failure in Malaysia and Mauritius.

The Toggenburg is probably the least successful of the European breeds that have been introduced in the tropics. Saanens are good milkers and have in most instances performed well following their introduction into Puerto Rico, the West Indies, Fiji, Ghana, Kenya, Malaysia and Australia. Saanens can be acclimatized to sub-tropical environments but are sensitive to strong sunlight. Horned bucks of this breed must be used to avoid hermaphroditism. Some typical milk yields of European breeds in the tropics are reported in Table 8.6.

Angora goats, outstanding for mohair production, originated in central China and have been imported into South Africa, Madagascar, the United States, Pakistan, India and Australia. The hair grows in long white lustrous locks or ringlets, usually 12 to 13 cm (4·1 to 5·1 in) in length but as long as 25 cm (10 in). The average annual yield of mohair per goat in Turkey is 1·5 kg (3·3 lb), whereas in the United States it is 2·9 kg (6·4 lb).

Breeding

Age at first kidding is important because of its effect on the economics of goat production. This means that where goats kid for the first time at an early age, there is a greater population turnover. Sexual maturity in the goat is achieved at 4 to 6 months of age, but management practices are often designed to delay mating until the does are near to mature body weight, so that pregnancy does not coincide with the period when the does are actively growing. The tendency is therefore to mate does at about 12 months so that they kid for the first time at about 18 months of age. Under more extensive and uncontrolled conditions such as in parts of Africa, the Caribbean and Venezuela, the first kidding frequently

Table 8·6 *Some examples of lactation yields of European goats in the tropics and sub-tropics*

Breed	Country or location	Length of lactation (days)	Yield per lactation (kg (lb))	Average yield per day (kg (lb))	Reference
Anglo-Nubian	Mauritius	247	222 (489)	0·75 (1·7)	Delaitre (1965)
	Malaysia	300	250–300 (551–661)	0·8–1·0 (1·8–2·2)	Devendra (1962)
	Philippines	294	167 (368)	0·6 (1·3)	Villegas (1932–33)
	Trinidad	124	143 (315)	1·2 (2·6)	Devendra et al. (1969)
British Alpine	Malaysia	106–253	309 (681)	2·0 (4·4)	Keeping (1951)
	Trinidad	209	274 (604)	1·3 (2·9)	Devendra et al. (1969)
Saanen	Australia	240–270	886 (1,953)	3·5 (7·7)	Pegg (1968)
	Cyprus	240–300	536 (1,182)	2·0–2·25 (4·4–5·0)	Richards (1956)
	Israel	–	approx. 500 (1,102)	2·0–3·4 (4·4–7·5)	Israel: Ministry of Agriculture (1962)
	Puerto Rico	344	704 (1,552)	1·0–2·0 (2·2–4·4)	Sanfiorenzo (1957)

Sources: As references.

occurs at 10 to 12 months. Early physiological maturity is closely related to growth rate and within-breed differences are generally due to variations in feeding, management and disease.

The duration of the oestrous cycle is 18 to 21 days – the same as in sheep – and the duration of oestrus is about 24 to 36 hours, but considerable variation occurs. For several breeds of goats in the tropics the gestation length has been found to be fairly constant at about 146 days, with a range of from 145 to 148 days.

In most tropical goats oestrus occurs all the year round. Such limited evidence as is available suggests that differences between tropical and temperate breeds in oestral activity are due to breed rather than to climate or latitude. Annual kidding appears to be characteristic of temperate breeds in the tropics and some tropical and sub-tropical breeds, which could conceivably mean that genetic factors are very important in these breeds. There is a tendency, however, for the incidence of oestrus to be highest during certain times of the year. In India, for example, it is highest from June to October, and in the Caribbean and Venezuela from August to September.

Since seasons and months have been shown to significantly affect the incidence of oestrus, it is conceivable that climatic factors such as the occurrence of rain, that falls from August to October in northern India, may be associated with other factors such as herbage growth. Environmental factors may well be closely involved; for example, total annual rainfall and the percentage of does kidding or kids born have been shown to be significantly correlated. Meat breeds commonly have a shorter kidding interval than milk breeds presumably because of the influence of length of lactation. For example, for native goats in India and Malaysia the interval between kiddings is 90 to 120 days, but for purebred and crossbred Anglo-Nubian goats it is 327 and 204 days, respectively.

Although two kiddings from a doe per year is possible, in practice this is seldom achieved. More commonly three kiddings are obtained in 2 years and this appears to be the pattern for most indigenous goats in the tropics. Ovulation in the goat occurs towards the end of oestrus, therefore mating is best arranged at that time, which is about 12 hours after oestrus is first observed. Since time of mating can affect the number of kids born, double mating – the second service following 24 hours after the first – is usually advocated.

Twinning is common in goats and there is a good deal of evidence that prolificacy increases with age. For instance, in Malabar goats in India, the proportion of twin and triplet births increased from 19 per cent at the first kidding to 79 per cent in the second and later kiddings (Shanmugasundram, 1957). Also, in Negev and Saanen goats in Israel, the number of kids increased from an average of 1·1 and 1·5, respectively, at first kidding to 1·5 and 2·0 kids per birth at second and subsequent kiddings (Epstein and Hertz, 1964). A similar increase has been shown to occur in Egyptian Baladi goats in which the proportion of multiple births increased up to 4 years of age (Tantawy and Ahmed, 1960). Fertility in goats appears to be maximum at about 5 to 6 years, which agrees with reports on this aspect of reproduction in sheep. It is pertinent to note that milk production in dairy goats also appears to be maximum at about this age. The dam's weight influences litter size and does which are heaviest at kidding tend to produce large litters, the significance of proper nutritional management of goats during pregnancy being obvious.

Systems of management

There are four major systems of goat production in the tropics: subsistence, extensive, intensive and semi-intensive.

In subsistence production a few goats are kept to meet domestic needs for meat and milk. It is essentially a peasant enterprise, but nevertheless a very useful one. These goats may range or be tethered. In Guyana, for example, 48 per cent of the farmers managed goats extensively (Devendra, 1975b).

Extensive systems are generally practised in regions where the land is not immediately suitable for agricultural improvement and/or is too difficult or costly to fence (Plate 8.4). It involves a minimum amount of labour and expense. The main determining features are favourable climatic condition, in particular a short wet season, the availability of grazing and browse, few predators and a low incidence of predial larceny. Under these circumstances goats can also be used to assist in bush

Plate 8.7   Goats fed sago in Brunei.

clearance, and in Nigeria, for example, this has been recognized (FAO, 1966). However, fully extensive systems of management are not so common in the tropics, although in the drier areas of the Caribbean and Venezuela the possibilities for extensive management have been demonstrated and in the Sudanian zone in Africa and in the Arabian peninsula extensive systems are the norm. Some form of housing is sometimes provided for the goats. In this system a carrying capacity of about three to twelve goats per hectare (one to five per acre) is common. In semi-arid areas it is much less. It is possible that in areas where bush clearance has been successful more intensive production could follow.

Intensive production involves continuous housing or 'zero grazing' (Plate 8.7). This provides maximum protection from uncontrollable environmental factors, and gives complete control over the destructive aspects of the goats' feeding habits. Dairy goats in the tropics and small herds of goats in urban-fringe areas are often managed in this way.

Semi-intensive production covers all degrees of compromise between extensive management and 'zero grazing', but usually involves controlled grazing of fenced pastures with some supplementary concentrate feeding. In Jamaica (Devendra, 1971) it has been shown that on improved pangola (*Digitaria decumbens*) pastures, the carrying capacity can be thirty-eight to fifty goats per hectare (fifteen to twenty per acre).

Rearing

It is essential that the kids should consume the colostrum or first milk from their mother, since this stimulates the alimentary canal, provides vitamin A and also contains antibodies that confer immunity against disease. Weaning may be accomplished at any time from birth up to 6 months of age. In meat animals the tendency is to delay weaning to allow the kid to obtain the maximum benefit from the dam's milk, whereas in milk animals it is usual to wean early so that the milk from the dam can be used for domestic or commercial purposes. Early weaning in dairy goats is therefore advantageous. Castration of male kids not required for breeding improves meat quality and should be done soon after birth. Bloodless castration using rubber rings, the Burdizzor castrator, flame-heated sealing irons or the knife method can be used.

No elaborate housing is necessary, but what is provided should be light, well ventilated, well drained and easily cleaned. Two kinds of housing are commonly used. One is the ground-level house common in most parts of the tropics, except in eastern Asia. These are of the lean-to type, 2 to 3 m (6·6 to 9·8 ft) high in front and sloping to 1 to 1·5 m (3·3 to 4·9 ft) at the back, or with the sloping eaves standing out by about 0·5 m (1·6 ft). The floor can be rough concrete or more commonly rammed clay or earth.

The other type of housing is stilted housing where the floor is raised 1 to 1·5 m (3·3 to 21·9 ft) above the ground level facilitating easy cleaning and collection of dung and urine. In India it has been recommended (ICAR, 1962) that up to ten kids can be kept in loose stalls which measure 1·8 × 1·8 m (5·9 × 5·9 ft) and are 1·2 m (3·9 ft) high. For bucks, stalls measuring 2·4 × 1·8 m (7·9 × 5·9 ft) have been suggested. It has also been estimated that an enclosure measuring 12 × 18 m (39 × 59 ft) can accommodate 100 to 125 goats. Under intensive conditions in Malaysia adult Kambing Katjang does weighing about 23 kg (51 lb) and measuring about 0·56 m (22 in) at the withers have been kept in individual pens measuring 0·75 × 4·50 m (2·5 × 14·8 ft) by 4·8 m (15·8 ft).

Feeding

Weaning may be completed at any time after 3 months without using milk substitutes. Until then milk substitutes are necessary. Female kids can be given 1·0 kg (2·2 lb) of milk daily and males 1·5 kg (3·3 lb). These amounts are approximately half those suggested for temperate-type goats, but are adequate even for the larger breeds of tropical-type goats.

Dry matter (DM) intake is an important consideration since it reflects the capacity – in terms of voluntary food intake – to utilize food. With goats there appears to be a distinct difference in intake between meat and dairy types. Meat goats have a DM intake of 3 per cent of their liveweight. Mackenzie (1967) considered that dairy goats have a DM intake of 5 to 7 per cent of their liveweight. There is very little reported information on the DM intake of dairy goats in the tropics; work in Trinidad using imported Anglo-Nubian and British Alpine goats gave mean estimates of 4·1 to 5·4 per cent (Devendra, 1970).

Goats have special feeding habits. On account of their prehensile tongues, they are able to graze very short grass and to browse foliage not normally eaten by other ruminants. Their inquisitive feeding habits enable them to extend their feed preferences and also perform in situations where other ruminants may not be able to survive. It follows that under certain circumstances or with certain foods, in particular those of high fibre content, goats can utilize nutrients much better than many other ruminants.

The energy requirements for maintenance in goats are similar to those of sheep, being 725·8 g starch equivalent (SE) per day per 100 kg liveweight. The energy requirement for liveweight gain is 3·0 g SE per kg liveweight gain. The digestible crude protein (DCP) requirements for maintenance and for milk production are 45 to 64 g per 100 kg liveweight and 70 g per litre of milk, respectively.

While the energy and protein requirements for growth have been fairly well established the nutrient requirements for milk production have not been adequately investigated. Whether one could define the requirements for production in lactating dairy goats by extrapolating data obtained for the dairy cow is doubtful. The requirements for lactation depend upon the composition of the milk and the amount produced per day. Using the Agricultural Research Council (1965) method to derive energy standards factorially, and also using a figure of 70 per cent efficiency of metabolizable energy for milk production established for the dairy cow, a table of requirements (Table 8.7) has been calculated for milk varying in fat content from 3·5 to 5·5 per cent.

The mineral and vitamin needs of goats are equally important. Goats in milk have a very high requirement for sodium chloride, and salt licks and/or mixed mineral licks should be made available. Of no less importance is the provision of adequate water supplies, the demand for water increasing during the dry season.

Table 8.7 *Nutrient requirements for lactation in the goat (per kg of milk)*

Fat content of milk (%)	Starch equivalent (SE) (g)	Digestible crude protein (DCP) (g)	Calcium (g)	Phosphorus (g)
3·5	262	47	0·8	0·7
4·0	280	52	0·9	0·7
4·5	296	59	0·9	0·7
5·0	314	66	1·0	0·7
5·5	331	73	1·1	0·7

Source: Devendra (1970).

The rationing of goats should be realistic and be based on cheap foods such as browse, pasture and agricultural and industrial by-product feeds. The utilization of locally available agricultural by-products and crop residues such as rice straw, sweet potato vines and cassava should be fully exploited. Full advantage must be taken of the ability of goats to digest cellulose particularly well, as they cannot compete with pigs and poultry in efficiency of conversion of concentrates to protein food. These various aspects of the nutrition of goats have recently been discussed (Devendra and Burns, 1970) and Table 8.8 summarizes what is known about the nutritional requirements of the goats.

The type of concentrates that can be fed obviously depends upon what is locally available and in the tropics the variety is very great. Some examples of typical rations are shown in Table 8·9. In Sri Lanka, Wijeratne (1968), using goats for meat production, fed a variety of cultivated grasses, shrubs and tree fodders and concentrate ration (1) at the rate of 0·23 kg (0·50 lb) and 0·45 kg (1·0 lb) per head per day to does and bucks, respectively. In addition bucks were fed 0·11 kg (0·24 lb) of gingelly (*Sesamum orientale*) meal per head per day. Dual-purpose (meat and milk) goats in Malaysia were provided with limited grazing and guinea grass (*Panicum maximum*) *ad lib.*, together with 0·45 kg (1·0 lb) of

Table 8.8 *Summary of the nutritional requirements of the goat*

Nutrient	Requirement
I. Dry matter	2·5–3·0% of liveweight (meat goats): up to 8% of liveweight (milking goats)
II. Energy	
(a) for maintenance	725·8 g SE/100 kg liveweight/day
(b) for liveweight gain	3·0 g SE/g liveweight gain
(c) for milk production	300 g SE/kg milk
III. Protein	
(a) for maintenance	45–64 g DCP/100 kg liveweight
(b) for milk production	70 g DCP/litre milk
IV. Water	450–680 g/day for a goat weighing 18–20 kg
V. Dry matter: total water intake ratio	1:4
VI. Minerals	
Calcium	147 mg/kg liveweight
Phosphorus	72 mg/kg liveweight

Source: Devendra and Burns (1970).

concentrate mixture (2) per head per day. Clamohoy *et al.* (1959) grazed dairy goats mornings and evenings between milkings and fed concentrate mixture (3) at the rate of one per cent of body weight. Common salt was also added to this ration at the rate of one per cent of the total. In the West Indies ration (4) has been found to be useful for intensive and semi-intensive milch goats. The mixture was fed at the rate of 0·9 kg (2 lb) per

Table 8.9 *Typical rations for goats*

Feed	Percentage in mixed ration			
	Sri Lanka (1)	Malaysia (2)	Philippines (3)	West Indies (4)
Corn meal	–	–	55·0	–
Rice bran	20·0	34·0	22·5	–
Wheat flour	8·0	40·0	–	–
Wheat middlings	–	–	–	20·0
Molasses	6·0	2·0	–	20·0
Coconut meal	55·0	10·0	10·0	32·0
Groundnut cake meal	–	12·0	–	–
Soybean meal	–	–	5·0	10·0
Citrus meal	–	–	–	15·0
Sesame meal	6·0	–	–	–.
Fish meal	3·0	–	7·5	–
Mineral mixture	2·0	2·0	–	3·0

Note: References to rations (1), (2), and (3) in the text.

head per day to goats yielding approximately 2 kg (4·4 lb) of milk per day together with Napier grass (*Pennisetum purpureum*) or guinea grass *ad lib*. For meat production under extensive conditions a 1:1:1 mixture of citrus meal, coconut meal and brewer's grains or a 1:1 mixture of citrus and coconut meals is commonly used.

Potential for increased production

With proper management the potential for increased production from goats is considerable. Much will depend on whether their value as small domestic animals is adequately recognized. Small size is significant on account of their economic, managerial and biological advantages. Attendant to these features is their high fertility and short generation interval, which means that milk production begins 5 months after initial mating and that the first carcase may be on sale in less than a year.

Two aspects that merit special mention and may be worthy of exploitation are the higher efficiency for cellulose digestion and food utilization for milk production of goats. Both are important, as they raise questions as to the role of goats in increasing meat and milk production. Evidence from Pakistan (Wahid, 1965) and from Greece and Cyprus (French, 1970) suggests that goats are relatively more efficient and economic than some other ruminants in this role. The prospects for increased productivity, based on exploiting these special features inherent in the goat, should have the objectives of increasing the number and size of kids and frequency of kidding and lengthening the productive life-span.

References

Agricultural Research Council (1965) *The Nutrient Requirements of Farm Livestock. No. 2. Ruminants.* Agricultural Research Council: London.

Bose, A. B. (1963) Place of goat in desert economy. *Agric. Res. (New Delhi),* **3,** 56–7.

British Goat Society (1968) *Herd Book.* British Goat Society: Diss, Norfolk.

Clamohoy, L. L., Arganosa, V. G. and Palad, O. A. (1959) Exploratory goat dairying with native and grade goats. *Philipp. Agric.,* **43,** 243–9.

Congiu, S. (1954) Dressing percentage, liveweight and relative weight of different parts of the body of the goat of Somalia. Correlations between the various parts of the body. *Zootec e Vet.,* **9,** 359–67. Abstracted: *Anim. Breed. Abstr.,* **23,** 165 (1955).

Delaitre, C. (1965) Personal communication.

Devendra, C. (1962) Upgrading of local goats by the Anglo-Nubian at the Federal Experimental Station, Serdang. *Malay. agric. J.,* **43,** 265–80.

Devendra, C. (1966a) The importance of goats in Malaysia. *Z. Tierzücht. ZüchtBiol.,* **83,** 72–9 (in English).

Devendra, C. (1966b) Studies in the nutrition of the indigenous goat of Malaya. 1. The body measurements, composition of sample joints and their relationship to carcase composition. *Malay agric. J.,* **45**, 345–69.

Devendra, C. (1970) The nutrition of the dairy goat. *1st Nat. Seminar Goat Prod., Barquisemeto, Venezuela,* 12–14 Nov. 1970 (mimeo, 11 pp.).

Devendra, C. (1971) Goat production in the Caribbean. *Proc. 2nd Int. Conf. Goat Breed., Tours, France,* p. 47.

Devendra, C. (1974) Goats: their productivity and potential. *Span,* **17**, 130.

Devendra, C. (1975a) Milk production from dairy goats. *Proc. Symp. Bridging the Dairy Gap,* Bull. No. 140. Ministry of Agriculture and Rural Development, Malaysia, p. 98.

Devendra, C. (1975b) Sheep and goat production in Guyana. *Z. Tierzücht. ZüchtBiol,* **92**, 305.

Devendra, C. and Burns, M. (1970). Goat production in the tropics. *Tech. Comm. Comw. Bur. Anim. Breed. Genet.,* No. 19. Comw. Agric. Bur.: Farnham Royal, UK.

Devendra, C., Narinesingh, H. P. and Iton, L. E. (1969) Unpublished data.

Ellerman, J. R. and Morrison-Scott, T. C. S. (1951) *Checklist of Palaeartic and Indian Mammals.* British Museum: London.

Epstein, H. (1969) Domestic animals of China. *Tech. Comm. Comw. Bur. Anim. Breed. Genet.,* No. 18. Comw. Agric. Bur.: Farnham Royal, UK.

Epstein, H. and Hertz, A. (1964) Fertility and birth weights of goats in a sub-tropical environment. *J. agric. Sci. (Camb.),* **62**, 237–44.

FAO (1974) *Production Yearbook: 1973,* Vol. 27. FAO: Rome.

Food and Agricultural Organization of the United Nations (FAO) (1966) *Agricultural Development in Nigeria 1965–1980.* FAO: Rome.

French, M. H. (1970) *Observations on the Goat.* FAO Agric. Studies No. 80. FAO: Rome.

Gatan, A. N. (1941) Edible and inedible portions in the different wholesale cuts of wethers and wether goats at one and a half years of age. *Philipp. Agric.,* **30**, 119–35.

Ghosh, S. N., and Anantakrishnan, C. P. (1963) Composition of Milk. Part IV. Influence of season, breed and species. *Ind. J. Dairy Sci.,* **16**, 190–202.

Ghosh, S. N. and Anantakrishnan, C. P. (1965) Composition of Milk. Part VI. The relationship between milk constituents. *Ind. J. Dairy Sci.,* **18**, 49–53.

Henrotte, A. (1961) A study of the goat population in the lower Congo, *Bull. Agric. Congo,* **52**, 1279–93. *Abstracted: Anim. Breed Abstr.,* **32**, 505 (1964).

Hirsch, S. (1932) Viehzucht und Milch wirtschaft in Syrien. *Z. Zücht.,* Reihe B., **24**, 409–48.

Hutchinson, H. G. (1964) Report of the Livestock Record Division, Ministry of Agriculture: Dar es Salaam.

Indian Council of Agricultural Research (ICAR) (1962) *Research in Animal Husbandry.* ICAR: New Delhi.

Israel: Ministry of Agriculture (1962) *Breeding Dairy Goats in Israel.* Ministry of Agriculture and Israel Goat Breeders Association (ASISA): Jerusalem.

Jollans, J. L. (1959) Meat preferences of people in the central region of Ghana. *J. West Afr. Sci. Ass.,* **5**, 64–78.

Kaura, R. L. (1952) *Indian Breeds of Livestock.* Preon Pub.: Lucknow.

Keeping, G. S. (1951) A review of progress recorded in the upgrading and breeding of pedigree imported and local goats. *Malay agric. J.,* **34**, 32–9.

Mackenzie, D. (1967) *Goat Husbandry* (2nd edn.). Faber and Faber: London.

Mason, I. and Maule, J. P. (1960) The indigenous livestock of eastern and southern Africa. *Tech. Comm. Comw. Bur. Anim. Breed. Genet.,* No. 14. Comw. Agric. Bur.: Farnham Royal, UK.

Maule, J. P. (1966) A note on dairy goats in the tropics. *Anim. Breed. Abstr.,* **34**, 153–8.

Parkash, S. and Jenness, R. (1968) The composition and characteristics of goat's milk: a review. *Dairy Sci. Abstr.,* **30**, 67–87.

Pegg, S. E. (1968) *Goat Production Recording Report, 1967–68.* Queensland Dept. Primary Indust.: Brisbane, Australia.

Richards, K. L. (1956) 'Report of the Agricultural Officer (livestock) for 1955.' *Ann. Rep., 1955,* Ann. 11. Dept. Agric.: Cyprus.

Sanfiorenzo, J. H. (1957) A study of milk production by native Barbados and crossbred goats in Puerto Rico. *Univ. Puerto Rico agric. Exp. Stn Bull.,* No. 139, 37 pp.

Schneider, B. H., Warner, J. N., Dharni, I. D., Agarwal, D. F., Sukhatme, P. V., Pendharker, V. G. and Sankaran, A. N. (1948) *Ind. Counc. Agric. Res., Misc. Bull.,* No. 61. ICAR: New Delhi.

Shanmugasundram, K. S. (1957) Birth rate amongst goats. *Ind. vet. J.,* **34,** 107–17.

Srivastava, V. K., Raizada, B. C. and Kulkarni, V. A. (1968) Carcase quality of Barbari and Jamnapari type goats. *Ind. vet. J.,* **45,** 219–25.

Tantawy, A. O. and Ahmed, I. A. (1960) Studies in Egyptian Baladi Goats. 1. Frequency of multiple births and sex ratios. *Emp. J. exp. Agric.,* **28,** 74–82.

Thompson, P. G. (1965) Goat breeding in Fiji. *South Pacific Bull.,* **15,** 28–30.

Villegas, V. (1932–33) Goat raising. *Philipp. Agric.,* **22,** 36–52.

Wahid, A. (1965) Goat raising in Pakistan. *Agric. Pakist.,* **16,** 509–34.

Wijeratne, W. V. S. (1968) The production traits of a nondescript breed of South Indian meat goats. *Trop. Agric. (Trin.),* **45,** 39–45.

Wilson, P. N. (1958) The effect of plane of nutrition on the growth and development of the East African Dwarf Goat. Part II. Age changes in the carcase composition of the female kids. *J. agric. Sci. (Camb.),* **51,** 4–21.

Chapter 9

Camels

In the past camels were used primarily for the transport of people and merchandise in deserts and semi-arid areas. Milk, meat, wool and hides were by-products of this primary function.

Motorized transport is now rapidly replacing camels in most desert regions so that unless a new role is created for the camel there will be an inevitable decline in their numbers. The camel does, however, possess certain unusual physiological features that enable it to thrive in extremely arid environments, and the necessity for man to exploit these areas may ultimately guarantee the camel's survival as a domestic animal.

Origin

Camels and llamoids belong to the family Camelidae that originated in North America. It is believed (Zeuner, 1963) that the genus *Camelus*, to which both modern species of camel belong, evolved in the Pleistocene period and that the ancestors of modern camels migrated into Asia across the Bering straits in late Pliocene or early Glacial times. The earliest camels were probably closely related to the modern two-humped or Bactrian camel (*C. bactrianus*) that today is found in the cold deserts and semi-arid areas from the Caspian Sea across central Asia to Manchuria. There are still a few wild herds of Bactrian camels in the Gobi desert and it is now believed that these are not feral animals but remnants of the aboriginal wild stock that once ranged across Asia as far as the borders of Eastern Europe. These wild camels have a more slender build and possess smaller humps and feet and shorter hair than domesticated Bactrian camels. Hybrids between the domesticated Bactrian and the wild camels have been reported to exist in Mongolia (Montagu, 1969).

The modern one-humped camel or dromedary (*Camelus dromedarius*) apparently evolved from the Bactrian camel as it possesses a vestigial anterior hump that is present in the embryo as well as in the adult animal (Nawito *et al.*, 1967). It is likely that this evolution took place in one of the hotter and more arid areas of western Asia, possibly central or southern Arabia. No feral or wild types of dromedary are known to exist today, although there is evidence that there were once wild dromedaries in western Asia and parts of Africa (Zeuner, 1963). The present distribution of domesticated dromedaries is in the warmer desert areas from India in the east to Mauritania and Mali in the west of Africa.

Little is known as to the centre of domestication of Bactrian camels. The first records of domesticated dromedaries appear in Arabia around 1800 BC. The centre of domestication may have been central or southern Arabia. After this date there are many records of the use of domesticated dromedaries in western Asia. They were certainly known in what is now Iraq by 800 BC and in India by 500 BC. There are few records of the presence of domesticated dromedaries in Africa before Roman times, but they were common by AD 200. The present distribution probably stabilized after AD 700, with the spread of Islam over the northern part of Africa. Dromedaries were introduced by the Arabs into Spain in AD 1019 and into Sicily in AD 1058. They were familiar further north in Europe, but the only herd known to exist in more recent times is one that developed from dromedaries imported by Ferdinand II of Medici in 1622 and used on the plains of Pisa. This herd is said to have numbered 200 in the nineteenth century (Nawito *et al.*, 1967).

Dromedaries were introduced into the Americas and Australia by settlers, but they have never been utilized in any number in either continent.

Numbers and distribution

It will be seen from Table 9.1 that there are more than 14·5 million camels in the world, that at least 70 per cent of these animals are to be found in Africa, and that the total camel population of the world is not increasing very rapidly, but that this is mainly due to a decrease in camel population in the non-tropical areas.

More than 70 per cent of the total world population of camels are raised in the tropics. Approximately 91 per cent of all the camels in Africa are found in the tropical regions, whereas in Asia the situation is reversed as more than two-thirds of that continent's camel population live outside the tropics. Tropical countries with large camel populations are Sudan, Somalia, Ethiopia, Mauritania, Saudi Arabia and India (part) with 23·4, 20·6, 6·8, 4·8, 4·0 and 3·9 per cent of the total world camel population, respectively (Table 9.2). Outside the tropics the national herds of Mongolia and Pakistan each contain some 5 per cent of the total world population of camels.

The data in Table 9.1 suggest that the camel population is declining in numbers in the non-tropical regions of Africa. On the other hand, camel numbers have been increasing rapidly in some African tropical countries. It seems inevitable that the decline in numbers should continue where the camel is only used for transport purposes. In the countries

Table 9.1   *The camel population of the world*

Continent and/or region	1961–65		1973		Percentage increase or decrease
	No. ('000)	As percentage of world population	No. ('000)	As percentage of world population	
USSR	280	2	230	2	−18
Africa	8,413	67	10,226	70	+22
Tropics	7,401	59	9,316	64	+26
Other	1,012	8	910	6	−11
Americas	6	negl.	8	negl.	+33
Tropics	6	negl.	8	negl.	+33
Other	nil	–	nil	–	–
Asia	3,793	31	4,081	28	+8
Tropics	1,048	9	1,258	9	+20
Other*	2,731	22	2,806	19	+3
China	14	negl.	17	negl.	+21
Oceania	2	negl.	2	negl.	nil
Tropics	2	negl.	2	negl.	nil
Other	nil	–	nil	–	–
World	12,494		14,547		+16
Tropics	8,457	68	10,584	73	+25
Other	4,037	32	3,963	27	−2

*Excluding China and the Asiatic regions of the USSR.
Source: FAO (1974).

Table 9.2   *Distribution of camels in tropical countries*

Continent	Country	No. in 1973 ('000)	As percentage of world total
Africa	Chad	330	2·3
	Ethiopia	995	6·8
	Kenya	325	2·2
	Mali	150	1·0
	Mauritania	700	4·8
	Niger	350	2·4
	Nigeria	18	0·1
	Senegal	20	0·1
	Somalia	3,000	20·6
	Sudan	3,400	23·4
	Upper Volta	5	negl.
Asia	India (part)	563	3·9
	Saudi Arabia	580	4·0
	Yemen Arab Rep.	62	0·4
	Yemen Dem. Rep.	40	0·3

Source: FAO (1974).

around the Mediterranean machines have already virtually displaced camels in the transport industry, and although small numbers of camels are still used for ploughing and other field work they must ultimately almost disappear from the fields.

Under these circumstances, if the camel is to survive as an important domestic animal, as stated in the introductory paragraph, it will need a new role. This can only be that of a milk and meat producer in the semi-arid and arid tropical regions where the environment is too harsh for the survival of other domestic livestock.

Breeds

Bactrian camels are distinguished by two humps of fatty tissue while dromedaries only possess one, by a thick woolly coat that is usually reddish brown in colour, by a deep fringe of hair under the neck and by the possession of shorter limb bones than dromedaries. The dromedary is slightly larger than the Bactrian camel. Its coat is also woolly but shorter than that of the Bactrian and the coat colour is usually fawn or beige. It possesses very broad feet, long eyelashes that help to protect its eyes during dust storms, trapdoor nostrils that can be closed and extremely thick lips (Plate 9.1).

According to Curasson (1947) Bactrian camels and dromedaries have been hybridized in Turkey. The crossbreds possess one hump, are larger than either parent and express considerable hybrid vigour. Hybridization has also been reported at centres in the USSR (Aueljbekov, 1967).

As it is the dromedary that is used in tropical areas it is proposed to confine discussion in this section to these camels. There are a large number of different types of dromedary, many of which are spoken of as 'breeds'. For example, Yasin and Wahid (1957) differentiated fifteen breeds in Pakistan and there are usually several or more 'breeds' in every country or region possessing a dromedary population. These 'breeds' may be classified into two general types, the riding camel and the baggager, but the breeds within these types are not marked by so many pronounced functional or conformational characteristics as distinguish many cattle breeds. Nevertheless, the camels of each country or locality carry hereditary traits which designate one from the other in no uncertain manner, and similarly, family 'lines' within each breed are recognized and critically appraised by traditional camel-owning communities. Environmental influences, however, give rise to types which are more easily distinguished by the inexperienced than the various breeds within the type. There is, for instance, far more in common between the *Egyptian Delta* camel and the riverine *Sindhi* of Pakistan than there is between the *Sindhi* and his immediate neighbour the *Kuchi* which originates from the hills. The small, compact, muscular, heavy-boned hill type, bred in rough upland regions, is very different from the more rangy, long-legged, more

Plate 9.1   Camel (*Camelus dromedarius*) in a market in Northern Darfur, Sudan.

loosely coupled plains camel. The former is only some 1·8 to 2·0 m (6 to 6·5 ft) high, while the latter may be up to 2·14 m (7 ft) high at the withers. The conformation and performance of the plains camel vary in all degrees between the light, fine-boned, thin-skinned, alert, desert-riding type, and the massive, but rather mean-looking phlegmatic baggage type from the riverine areas, accustomed to good living and regulated activities.

There are many niceties of conformation and temperament which enhance or depreciate the utility of a work camel but, provided the animal is healthy and free from injury, the only points of conformation of real importance are that the limbs should be set on straight, the feet do not point outwards, the elbows are not cramped inwards, and the hocks show no tendency to touch either when at rest or on the move. Such conformation should ensure a free, easy, straight gait which is the first essential in a work animal.

A camel selected for immediate work should be in good condition as indicated by a plump, rounded hump, well-covered ribs and muscled loins. It should be able to sit and rise with ease when under load. The subcutaneous oedematous condition which normally arises after a very thirsty camel has been given a large dose of salt and then has been allowed to drink its fill may temporarily make a thin camel look well covered.

No classification of the different breeds of camel is known and there has been no conscious selection for meat- or milk-type camels. Selection for meat and milk production is now required in those areas where other domestic livestock do not flourish.

Productivity

Although the use of the camel for riding and the transport of baggage is probably declining, it is of interest to understand something of this animal's capabilities.

Gillespie (1962) stated that in the Sudan riding camels could attain speeds of 8 km (5 miles) and 16 to 32 km (10 to 20 miles) per hour when trotting and running, respectively. A riding camel can carry two men, but it is generally ridden by one man who may take with him up to 54 kg (120 lb) of baggage. With this burden a pace of 10 km (6 miles) per hour can be maintained on level ground and a distance of 48 km (30 miles) covered each day for prolonged periods. With a single rider, but otherwise unburdened, a good riding camel can move at the rate of 15 to 19 km (9 to 12 miles) for an hour or so and can travel 80 km (50 miles) a day for 2 weeks (Leese, 1927).

The baggage camel travels at a walking pace at just over 4 km (2·5 miles) an hour and can carry a full load for 24 km (15 miles) a day for an indefinite period. What comprises a full load depends upon the strength of the individual camel and may vary from 159 to 295 kg (350 to 650 lb). As much as 544 kg (1,200 lb) may be carried for short distances. When camels were used in the British army, the maximum load normally permitted was 204 kg (450 lb) for 32 km (20 miles) a day over prolonged periods, with one day's rest each week. Podberezkin (1951) has stated that Bactrian camels used for transport can pull loads of up to 1,500 kg (3,307 lb).

There is little detailed information on the milk production of camels and yields vary according to whether the camels are managed under desert or improved conditions. Bactrian camels appear to be capable of producing up to 5,000 kg (11,000 lb) of milk per lactation and this may vary in length from 6 to 18 months. However, the average production is probably only 800 to 1,200 kg (1,780 to 2,070 lb). The percentage butterfat in the milk of Bactrian camels varies from 5·8 to 6·6 (Kulaeva, 1964). Well-fed and managed dromedaries will produce from 2,722 to 3,629 kg (6,000 to 8,000 lb) of milk in a 16- to 18-month lactation, while under desert conditions average lactations yield 1,134 to 1,588 kg (2,500 to 3,500 lb) of milk in 9 months (Yasin and Wahid, 1957; Iwema, 1960). A good dam can yield 9 kg (20 lb) of milk daily at the peak of her lactation. According to Nawito *et al.* (1967) the percentages of fat, protein and lactose in dromedary milk are 3·8, 3·5 and 3·9, respectively.

In Kenya, Ethiopia, Sudan and Somalia – and to a lesser extent in some neighbouring countries – a considerable number of camels are managed and fed specifically for slaughter. Elsewhere camels butchered for meat are the worn out, the incurably injured and the barren. There are no breeds specially developed for meat production. Average dromedaries weigh from 454 to 590 kg (1,000 to 1,300 lb) while average Bactrian camels may weigh somewhat heavier. According to Kulaeva (1964) the dressing-out percentage of Bactrian camels varies from 56 to 70 and the fat in the humps represents 2 to 5 per cent of the total dressed carcase.

Hair is an important by-product of the Bactrian camel. Young camels have a fine hair of good quality, but the hair of older animals is of a poor quality. Podberezkin (1951) and Kulaeva (1964) have stated that the average yield of hair of the Bactrian camel is 4·5 kg (10 lb), with the quality of the hair depending upon age, sex and breed.

Special physiological characteristics of the camel

Schmidt-Nielsen (1964) has described the camel's exceptional tolerance to heat and water deprivation and has stated that this characteristic does not depend on the storage of water in the body. Although the camel is a homeotherm, it is a special type of homeotherm that can vary its normal body temperature over a considerable range. When it is deprived of water, daily fluctuations in body temperature may exceed 6°C (12°F). This physiological characteristic assists the camel in the conservation of water and disposal of heat. As air temperature rises during the day the camel does not attempt to maintain its body temperature constant but allows it to rise. Under these conditions water that would normally be used by the body for evaporative cooling purposes in order to keep body temperature down is unexpended. In this manner excess heat is stored in the body and dissipated during the cooler night. At the same time the elevated body temperature during the daytime reduces the heat flow from the hot environment to the animal's body, thus further reducing water expenditure. This is a specially valuable characteristic for an animal to possess in a desert environment where day temperatures may be very high and the night temperatures quite cool.

The fine hair of the camel is also an important barrier against heat gain from the environment. Furthermore, although camels sweat, water evaporates from the skin and not from the surface of the hair, and this characteristic also assists water conservation.

Camels can concentrate their urine to a marked degree and Schmidt-Nielsen (1964) has stated that they can recirculate and reutilize urinary nitrogen when they are deprived of water. This is obviously a further physiological characteristic that aids camels in unfavourable environments.

As a consequence of possessing special physiological characteristics the camel can withstand a very considerable degree of dehydration and in a hot dry environment it can tolerate the loss of at least 27 per cent of its body weight. In addition it possesses an enormous drinking capacity and is capable of drinking at any one time a volume of water equivalent to as much as 30 per cent of its body weight. This is a very valuable characteristic indeed in an environment where there may be many days' trek from one water hole to the next.

Reproductive behaviour

In the past it has always been considered that the female camel was a seasonal breeder (Poderezkin, 1951; Yasin and Wahid, 1957; Charnot, 1964; Matharu, 1966), but recent investigations in Egypt by Nawito *et al.* (1967) suggest that pregnancy can occur at any time and that the female dromedary is polyoestrous. There could, of course, be as yet undiscovered differences due to the effect of breed or the environment. According to Nawito *et al.* (1967) there is still a considerable seasonal fluctuation in reproductive activity, being greater in winter and spring and less in summer and autumn.

The male camel is somewhat peculiar in that generally he exhibits little sexual activity outside a specific 'rutting' season, when his testes increase in size, his soft palate increases in length and is 'blown up' at irregular intervals and he emits an offensive odour. When not in 'rut' spermatogenesis slows down. The rutting period appears to be associated with the lengthening day – January to March in the northern hemisphere and June to September in the southern. At the equator camels apparently have no definite rutting season. Although the average duration of rut is about 3 months it is affected both by age and nutrition. Old males may continue in rut throughout the year and in the case of well-fed younger males rut may last for up to 5 months. When driven to hard work the male camel's sexual inclinations may diminish or disappear.

Males can be used for service when they are 3 years of age, but their full reproductive powers are not usually developed nor are they normally used until they are 6 years old. When sexually mature the male can serve up to fifty females, and if he is very well fed and cared for he can cover up to seventy in one season (Leese, 1927).

Females are normally sexually mature at 3 years of age, but they are not generally bred until they are 4 years old. They may continue to breed until they are over 20 years old.

In the past there have been varied estimates as to the duration of oestrus and the length of the oestrous cycle. In Bactrian camels oestrus has been stated to last 6 to 8 days while in dromedaries the period is shorter and mean cycle length has been stated to be 14 days (Nawito *et al.*, 1967). It is doubtful, however, whether camels exhibit a normal oestral cycle as Nawito *et al.* (1967) have shown that in the dromedary ovulation is not spontaneous but is induced by copulation. In this respect the sexual behaviour of the camel appears to be similar to that of the llamoids (see Ch. 10, Pt II). Nawito *et al.* (1967) suggest that a more acceptable term to use would be 'follicular wave' and that this could be defined as the time elapsing between one period of acceptance of the male and the next. They further state that in the female dromedaries that were examined in Egypt the length of the 'follicular wave' varied between 11 and 35 days with a mean of 24 days. Within the follicular wave the oestral stage lasts up to 15 days, and at the end of this stage when mature follicles are present in the ovary the female is ready to accept the male. If the female is not mated, ovulation does not take place and the follicle is reabsorbed. This may take from 2 to 13 days.

The copulatory stimulus apparently triggers the release of the gonadotrophin(s) required for ovulation that occurs approximately 36 hours after copulation. Multiple ovulation may occur, but the incidence is low.

Apparently, when mature follicles are available in the ovary the female becomes willing to accept the male. The external symptoms of this condition are the female seeks out a male and stands beside him; she becomes restless, wags her tail and is very ready to be mounted; her vulva becomes slightly swollen and there is some discharge of mucus. Females that are not in heat do not mount others in heat, but they will run after them in a playful manner and attempt to bite their vulva. Males seek out females by smell, usually sniffing along the neck and not at the vulva.

The uterus of the female camel is T- rather than Y-shaped and the left horn is usually larger than the right. According to Nawito *et al.* (1967) in more than 99 per cent of the females implantation takes place in the left horn of the uterus.

The length of gestation has been stated to be 360 to 390 days in dromedaries (Yasin and Wahid, 1957; Matharu, 1966) and 390 to 420 days in Bactrian camels (Podberezkin, 1951). The calving percentage is said to be 35 to 45. Normally only one calf is born every 2 years. Occasionally a female may breed twice in $2\frac{1}{2}$ years.

Oestrus or a follicular wave may occur in well-fed females as early as one month after parturition, though it is more often delayed, sometimes for as long as one year.

Feeds and feeding

Camels prefer to browse (Plate 9.2) rather than graze and need time not only to consume their food but also to ruminate. Their mobility and lesser dependence on drinking water allow them to range over a far greater area than any other domestic animal. As a general rule, when feed

Plate 9.2   Camel browsing on tree forage in Darfur, Sudan.

is fairly easily obtainable, 6 hours is the minimum time that should be allowed for foraging. At least a further 6 hours are needed for rumination. Camels will not usually forage during the heat of the day.

In many territories camels live entirely by browsing, sometimes mostly on low bush plants such as camel-thorn (*Alhagi maurorum*) and salt worts such as *Haloxylon recurvum*. Such camels do not normally relish grass even when it is young and fresh. In other countries, for instance in Somalia, grass forms a principal part of the diet.

If necessary, all camels can be maintained in good condition by hand-feeding them grain and fodder. This practice is of course only utilized under exceptional circumstances, but a certain amount of hand-feeding is often necessary to supplement grazing and browsing in seasons of scarcity or during travel when there is insufficient time for the animals to graze or browse. Some suitable supplementary rations that have been used in the past are shown in Table 9.3.

Peck (1939) considered that camels working under conditions that did not cause them to sweat unduly required 142 g (5 oz) of salt daily. He

Table 9.3 Suitable supplementary rations for camels

	Working Indian or Egyptian baggagers			Somali or Aden camels[1]	Somali Camel Corps[2]
	No grazing (kg (lb))	Poor grazing (kg (lb))	Fair grazing (kg (lb))	Grazing plus (kg (lb))	Grazing plus (kg (lb))
Gram (*Phaseolus* spp.)	2·7 (6)	1·8 (4)		1·8 (4)	1·8 (4)
Split pea (*Cicer arietinum*)					
Jowar (*Sorghum bicolor*)					
Millet			3·6 (8)		
Wheat bran					0·9 (2)
Hay				9·1 (20)	4·5 (10)
Missa bhussa (legume straw)	13·6 (30)	9·1 (20)			
Tibben (chopped wheat straw)			3·6–5·4 (8–12)		
Salt	42 g (1·4 oz)	42 g (1·5 oz)		42 g (1·5 oz)	28 g (1 oz)

Sources (1) Leese (1927). (2) Peek (1939).

found that the improvement in condition in camels fed this quantity of salt was spectacular. There is considerable evidence to show that the amount of salt usually fed to camels is too little unless they spend at least one-third of their time browsing on salt bush species such as *Atriplex*, *Salsola* and *Suaeda* spp. A daily ration of 142 g (5 oz) may be considered the minimum quantity of salt required to keep a full-grown working or milking camel in prime condition.

Although camels can be water-deprived for long periods, where practicable they should be watered as often as is necessary. There are some differences between types of camel in requirements. Riverine camels must be watered daily if they are fully to maintain their condition. Indian desert camels can be maintained in good condition if they are watered every other day and Somali camels will maintain their condition even when watering is infrequent. If there are long intervals between watering camels may drink as much as 91 litres (20 gal) at one time (Leese, 1927).

Management

Females are often worked right up to the time of giving birth and continued in work soon after. This is not a practice to be encouraged, nor is it one that is followed by the professional camel-breeding peoples as it affects the health of both dam and calf and is inhumane. Females should be at liberty on good grazing for at least the last 2 months of pregnancy and for a minimum of 3 weeks after parturition. The newborn camel is a rather delicate creature and a considerable number of them die before they are 3 weeks old. Colostrum or first milk, essential for the health of the very young calf, is considered by the majority of camel breeders to be a rather dangerous substance that should be consumed in minimum amounts. This may be the reason why so many newborn camels are weak. It is usually at least a week before they are able to follow their dam while she grazes. On the other hand, experience has shown that if the young camel habitually drinks to repletion, indigestion, diarrhoea and death often result. It is customary, if the dam is a heavy milker, to remove three-quarters of the available milk and only leave one-quarter for the suckling calf during the first 3 weeks of the lactation and then gradually increase the amount of milk left for the calf.

Calves are usually weaned naturally, the dam drying off after about 9 months if desert fed and approximately 18 months when on a higher plane of nutrition (Leese, 1927). The calf begins to graze when only a few weeks old, the change from milk to solid food occurring gradually and usually without a check to growth. After weaning the young stock graze and browse at liberty until they are about 4 years old. During this period they are gradually trained for work.

For information on the diseases of the camel the reader should consult Curasson (1947).

Working camels

The camel is an amenable, patient animal and is easily trained for work. Females and entire males are used, but castrated males make the best workers, provided that they have not been castrated before they have matured, that is at 4 to 6 years of age. Castrates are seldom able to carry such heavy loads as the entire males, but their work is never interrupted by the rutting period nor are they distracted by females.

Calves are accustomed to handling from the earliest age. At 2 years old they are introduced to the discipline of control by head rope or by a nose peg made of wood, bone or, very occasionally, metal. This is passed through the nose below and towards the extremity of the nasal bones. At first calves merely carry the attachments, but later they are increasingly handled and trained.

As soon as head control has been established the young camel is induced to sit and rise at command. This he is taught by having his head pulled towards the ground while being tapped behind the knee with a stick. The word of command is continually repeated until the young camel kneels in the natural position preliminary to subsiding on its hocks and finally to its breast-pad.

Young camels are then loaded with an empty saddle and later ever-increasing loads are mounted on the saddle. Judgement in this respect too often tends to credit the young animal with more strength than he has, to the detriment of his further growth and development.

Camels are not usually brought into full work until they are 6 years of age and they may continue to work until they are 20 years old. All camels under good management should be retired from work for a definite period each year. This is usually during the rains when the conditions for work are hardest and there are the best opportunities for browsing and grazing.

When the male camel is in rut his usefulness as a working animal is greatly diminished. He loses his appetite, often suffers from diarrhoea, lacks bodily vigour, is exhibitionist, irritable, intolerant of rivals and rebellious of discipline.

For each form of work, even for draught work, a saddle of some sort is required. Fundamentally, all satisfactory saddles are made on the same principle and consist of a rigid frame to lie along the muscular mass on each side of the animal's spine, connected by arches passing over and clear of the spine and strong enough to support the burden to be carried and to protect the spine from it. The hump lies clear between the arches. A pad of some sort generally cushions the skin from the pressure of the frame and a restricted superstructure of padded leather makes the seat of the riding saddle, or an expanded rack-like structure gives space for baggage, or the frame itself supports the shafts of a cart. The saddle is held in position, generally by a single girth, and in hilly country by a breast-rope and crupper or a neck and a tail rope. Even the Somali *herio* is roughly built to this pattern although it consists only of a series of mats looped together and to the camel by one long rope.

Dentition

As so much concerning the management of a camel depends upon its age, the ability to estimate this with a fair degree of accuracy is important. The estimate is made in the usual way from an examination of the incisor and canine teeth of the lower jaw.

At birth the central pair of teeth are already erupted, at 1 month the laterals appear and by 2 months the third pair is through the gum. They are crowded and overlap. By 1 year they have grown up and are in wear. At 2 years they are worn and no longer touch the neighbouring teeth. At 3, they are well worn, and at 4 years they are quite worn down, have a square or irregular table and are loose. By 5 years the central permanent teeth have erupted, followed a year later by the next pair, and all three pairs are visible at 7 years old.

In the upper jaw there are two canine-like temporary teeth on either side, and three such permanent teeth are visible at about $7\frac{1}{2}$ years old. There are two permanent canine-like teeth on both sides of the lower jaw to be seen at the same age. These canines reach their full size at 7 years, when they are long and still sharp-pointed. As the camel ages all the teeth become worn and blunt, and by 12 years the canines are stumps and the incisors upright stubs with square or circular tables (Rabagliati, 1924).

References

Aueljbekov, K. (1967) Camel breeding – a profitable field (in Russian). *Kohevod. konnÿi. Sport* (5), 6–8. *Abstracted: Anim. Breed. Abstr.*, **35**, 670 (1967).

Charnot, Y. (1964) The testicular cycle of the dromedary (in French). *Bull. Soc. Sci. nat. phys. Maroc.*, **44**, 37–45. *Abstracted: Anim. Breed. Abstr.*, **37**, 305 (1969).

Curasson, G. (1947) *Le Chameau et ses Maladies.* Vigot Frères: Paris.

FAO (1974) *Production Yearbook: 1973*, Vol. 27. FAO: Rome.

Gillespie, I. A. (1962) Riding camels of the Sudan. *Sudan J. Vet. Sci. Anim. Husb.*, **3**, 37–42.

Iwema, S. (1960) The ship of the desert (in Dutch). *Veeteelt-en Zuivelberichten.* **3**, 390–394. *Abstracted: Anim. Breed. Abstr.*, **30**, 98 (1962).

Kulaeva, V. (1964) The production of the bactrian camel (in Russian). *Konevod. konnÿi Sport*, **34**, 9–10. *Abstracted: Anim. Breed. Abstr.*, **32**, 535 (1964).

Leese, A. S. (1927) *A Treatise on the One-humped Camel.* Haynes: Stamford, England.

Matharu, B. S. (1966) Camel care. *Indian Fmg.*, **16**, 19–22.

Montagu, I. (1965) Communication on the current survival in Mongolia of the wild horse (*Equus przewalskii*), wild camel (*Camelus bactrianus ferus*) and the wild ass (*Equus hemionus*). *Proc. Zool. Soc. (Lond.)*, **144**, 425–8.

Nawito, M. F., Shalash, M. R., Hoppe, R. and Rakha, A. M. (1967) Reproduction in the female camel. *Bull. Anim. Sci. Res. Inst. (Cairo)*, (2).
Peck, E. F. (1939) Salt intake in relation to cutaneous necrosis and arthritis of one-humped camels (*Camelus dromedarius*, L) in British Somaliland. *Vet. Rec.*, **51**, 1355–1360.
Podberezkin, Ja. (1951) Experience of the work of a better camel-breeding farm. *Konevodstvo* (10), 42–3. *Abstracted: Anim. Breed. Abstr.*, **20**, 75 (1952).
Rabagliati, D. S. (1924) *The Dentition of the Camel.* Govt. Press: Cairo.
Schmidt-Nielsen, K. (1964) *Desert Animals. Physiological Problems of Heat and Water.* Clarendon Press: Oxford.
Yasin, S. A. and Wahid, A. (1957) Pakistan camels – a preliminary survey. *Agric. Pakist.*, **8**, 289–97.
Zeuner, F. E. (1963) *A History of Domesticated Animals.* Hutchison: London.

Further Reading

Bulliet, R. W. *The Camel and the Wheel.* Harvard Univ. Press: Cambridge, Massachusetts, 1975.
McKnight, T. L. *The Camel in Australia.* Melbourne Univ. Press: Melbourne, Australia, 1969.
Maloiy, G. M. O. (ed.). *Comparative Physiology of Desert Animals.* Academic Press: London.

Chapter 10

Llamoids or New World Camelidae

by **Saúl Fernández-Baca**
Formerly Departamento de Produccion Animal e Inspeccion de Alimento, Instituto de Zootecnia, Universidad Nacional Mayor de San Marcos, Lima, Perú

Importance

The llamoids play an important role in the economy of some South American countries, especially Peru and Bolivia, and to a lesser degree Chile and Argentina. They are particularly important on account of their ability to utilize the high-altitude pastures situated at over 4,000 m (13,000 ft) above sea-level that would otherwise be ungrazed, thus providing valuable fibre, nutritious meat and transportation. There is also some evidence that before the Spanish conquest the llama and alpaca were more widely distributed than they are at present.

Despite their usefulness to man, the management of the domestic species has been extremely poor and very little attention has been paid to their breeding and improvement, while the wild species have been excessively slaughtered in order to facilitate the harvesting of their valuable pelts. As a result they are now threatened with extinction. Fortunately, considerable interest has been taken in these animals during the last 15 years and research work undertaken during this period has already provided valuable though not complete information concerning some aspects of their reproductive physiology, anatomy and disease control. The species most studied has been the alpaca and to a lesser degree the llama. Apart from behaviour studies (Koford, 1957) very little research has been undertaken on the vicuña and even less on the guanaco. Under these circumstances the alpaca will be the principal species discussed in this chapter, although where information is available on the other species it will also be presented.

Origin

Four species in two genera constitute the group of llamoids or New World camelids (Fig. 10.1). These are: the llama, *Lama glama* (Linné) (Plate 10.1); the alpaca, *L. pacos* (Linné) (Plate 10.2); the guanaco, *L. guanicoe* (Müller) (Plate 10.3), and the vicuña *Vicugna vicugna* (Molina)

Family: Camelidae
Ancestral llamoid stock separated from ancestral old world camel stock approximately one million years ago

Genus: Lama

Species: *L. guanicoe* (guanaco): wild
L. glama (llama); domesticated
L. pacos (alpaca); domesticated

> *Type:* 'suri'; long straight wool
> 'huacaya'; crimped wool

Genus: *Vicugna*

Species: *V. vicugna* (vicuña): wild

Figure 10.1 Llamoids or New World Camelids.

(Plate 10.4). They are quite often erroneously referred to by the name of Auchenidae or *Auquénidos* – a designation that originated with Illiger in 1811, who gave the name of *Auchenia* to the genus without realizing that it had been previously named as *Lama* by Frish in 1775 (Simpson, 1945). These four species, together with the two species of the genus *Camelus*, belong to the Camelidae family which is, among the living artiodactyls, the only family in the sub-order Tylopoda.

The four species of llamoids are sometimes grouped within a single genus, *Lama* (Simpson, 1945). However, there appears to be sufficient evidence to consider the vicuña generically separate from the other three. The peculiarity of the rodent-like lower incisors of the vicuña – long with parallel sides, and enamel only on one face and an open root – is considered by Koford (1957) as one of the major arguments for a separate generic classification.

Plate 10.1 Llamas (R. Valdiosa).

Plate 10.2   Alpacas at an altitude of 4,500 m (14,800 ft) in Peru (S. Fernández-Baca).

Fossil discoveries indicate that most of the evolution of the Camelidae occurred in western North America. In late Pliocene and Pleistocene eras the llama-like camels extended their range into South America, and the Old World forms spread across the Bering straits into Asia (Romer, 1966). As the separation of these two groups occurred more than one million years ago, it is surprising that their karyotypes did not undergo considerable changes. Taylor *et al.* (1968) found no differences in the karyotypes of the guanaco, the Bactrian camel and the dromedary, except for sex differences. They found a modal chromosome number of 74 for the three species, a similar number to that found in the llama, alpaca, guanaco and vicuña by Benirschke (1967). The similarity of karotypes in the two groups of camelids would indicate, according to Taylor *et al.* (1968), that the morphological and physiological changes that have taken place in response to environmental factors have been accomplished using only single gene mutations, or minor chromosome rearrangements.

Types and distribution

Even though the four species of South American llamoids possess some common characteristics such as body shape, they differ markedly in other ways such as colour pattern and body size.

The llama and the alpaca exist only under domestication and are economically the most important. The llama (Plate 10.1) is the largest,

Plate 10.3   A guanaco (Bruce Coleman Ltd. F. Erize).

Plate 10.4   Vicuñas grazing natural pasture (S. Fernández-Baca).

adults weighing approximately 120 kg (265 lb). It produces a coarse fibre varying in colour from white to black and is often used as a beast of burden by highland farmers from northern Peru to northern Chile and Argentina. The alpaca (Plate 10.2) is smaller than the llama as average adults weigh around 75 kg (165 lb), and it demonstrates the same variation in coat colour as the llama, but produces a finer fibre that grades 80′ on the Bradford scale as compared to 60′ for Merino wool (Hugh-Jones and Bacon, 1964). Alpacas are kept primarily as producers of wool (usually called 'fibre' to differentiate it from sheep wool), although they are also of importance as meat producers. There are two types: the *Suri*, characterized by long, straight hair and somewhat resembling Lincoln sheep; and the *Huacaya*, which possesses shorter, curly hair resembling Corriedale-type wool. *Huacaya* fibre is more desirable from a manufacturer's point of view. Crosses between *Suri* produce approximately 17 per cent *Huacaya*-type offspring, while crosses between *Huacaya* produce only about 2 per cent *Suri*-type offspring. The mechanism of inheritance of colour pattern in the alpaca is unknown, although it is known that crosses between white individuals and white crossbreds produce 50 to 60 per cent offspring with a white coat.

The guanaco and vicuña exist only in the wild state. Guanacos (Plate 10.3) look much like llamas, but the colour of their coat is a fairly uniform reddish brown. They are considered to be the progenitor of the llama and alpaca. Guanacos are rather scarce in the alpaca-breeding areas and most abundant in the southern tip of South America. Their fibre is of little commercial value. The vicuña (Plate 10.4) is the smallest of the group and produces an extremely fine-quality fibre grading 120′ on the Bradford scale. An adult vicuña weighs 35 to 45 kg (77 to 99 lb), has thin legs, a well-developed cranial region and large eyes. The vicuña is also characterized by a bib of long hair that hangs from its brisket. This hair is white, like the rest of the underparts, and contrasts strongly with the dark buffy-brown hue of the remainder of the body.

Vicuñas possess a unique herd structure, the females being divided into groups, each permanently headed by one adult male. Some females will have young running with them. This 'family group' occupies a specific feeding territory that is defended by the male from intruders. It is believed that this peculiar social organization has favoured the survival of the vicuña.

Efforts are being made by the governments of some countries to protect and domesticate vicuñas in order to prevent their extinction. In Peru the National Vicuña Reserve of Pampa Galeras was created in 1966 where studies on behaviour and other aspects of vicuña biology are conducted. The few vicuña in captivity are sheared every 2 to 3 years and yield approximately 0·3 kg (0·7 lb) of wool.

The llamoids share common behavioural characteristics, some of which are quite different from those of most other livestock. They defecate and urinate in relatively confined areas forming 'latrines' even if they have freedom of access to the whole of the pasture. This peculiarity appears to have considerable significance as far as the control of infestations with parasitic nematodes is concerned. Alpacas and probably other llamoids also make communal use of some areas in the pasture for rolling; they form pits that become bare on account of continuous use and these appear to have importance as a medium for the transmission of external parasites, particularly those of sarcoptic mange. When frightened, alpacas are apt to spit and kick and their mating behaviour is remarkable.

Crosses between the various species of llamoids occur and the resulting hybrids are usually fertile (Gray, 1954). The similarity of karyotypes probably explains the reproductive ability of the hybrids. The most common crosses are those between the llama and alpaca, known as the *huarizo*, and between the male alpaca and the female vicuña, known as the *paco-vicuña*. The crossbreds between alpaca and vicuña are very desirable on account of the fine-quality fibre that they produce, the total yield being higher than that of the vicuña.

The present distribution and approximate numbers of the four species are shown in Table 10.1.

Table 10.1   *Approximate numbers and distribution of the llamoids*

Species	Peru	Bolivia	Chile	Argentina
Alpaca	3,290,000	300,000	20–30,000	Few
Llama	954,000	2,500,000	70,000	50,000
Vicuña	10,000	2,000 (?)	Very few	Very few
Guanaco	Very few	Very few	(?)	100,000

Sources: Ministerio de Agricultura y Pesqueria (1966); Moro (1968).

Reproductive behaviour

Reviews of the literature on the reproduction of the Camelidae have been made by Novoa (1970) and England *et al.* (1969) while Fernández-Baca (1970) has reviewed information on the alpaca.

Puberty

Ovarian activity in the alpaca is initiated as early as 10 months of age. There appear, however, to be individual differences and as in other species the plane of nutrition exerts considerable influence on the time of onset of puberty. Yearling females 12 to 14 months of age demonstrate oestral and sexual behaviour similar to that of adult multiparous females, the incidence of ovulations, fertilization and embryonic survival rates in yearlings mated to intact males being similar to those observed in adult

females (Fernández-Baca *et al.*, 1971). However, the general farming
practice is to delay breeding until 2 years of age. Poor growth of the
animals associated with an inadequate food supply contribute to this
practice. Females llamas are also bred beginning at 2 years old. Even
though it has been reported that captive vicuñas are capable of reproduction at one year old (Romero, 1927), the fertility of yearlings in the wild
state is believed to be very low (Koford, 1957). Male alpacas start showing sexual desires and are apt to mount females in heat at about one year
of age. However, the majority of yearling males possess penile adhesions
to the prepuce – a condition characteristic of immaturity that prevents
normal copulation. The general practice is to delay the use of males for
breeding purposes until they are 3 years old.

Breeding season

Llamoids are usually considered to be seasonal breeders. In their natural
habitat their normal breeding season is during the wet, warmer months
of December to March when feed is most abundant. When the males and
females are run together all the year round, as is the practice on many
alpaca and llama farms, births occur only within the period December
to March. This is also true of the wild species, such as the vicuña. When
unmated females are maintained separate from males and service is
allowed only once a month, males and females show normal sexual

Table 10.2 *Seasonal ovulation and fertilization rates of alpacas*

Month	No. served	Ovulated		Percentage fertilized*	No. multiple ovulations
		No.	%		
May	10	8	80	83	1
June	12	8	67	88	1
July	9	8	89	67	1
August	15	9	60	89	1
September	15	10	67	83	1
October	13	9	69	88	1
November	10	9	90	100	0
December	10	9	90	67	0

* Computed from the number of females with at least one dividing ovum compared with
the total number of females that ovulated.
Source: Fernández-Baca *et al.* (1971).

activity throughout the year. As will be seen from the data in Table 10.2
ovulation and fertilization rates, as well as embryonic survival rates, were
not significantly influenced by season (Fernández-Baca *et al.*, 1971) as
the values shown are similar to those observed during the normal breeding season (December to March).

These observations indicate that the continuous association of males and females somehow inhibits the breeding activity of the males to the point where sexual activity ends. This phenomenon has, in fact, been reproduced experimentally, although it is not known what factors are responsible for this inhibitory effect and what, under natural conditions, restarts breeding activity. Environmental factors such as changes in temperature, humidity, light, food supply and probably other visual or olfactory stimuli are likely to influence this 'off and on' mechanism through the central nervous system.

Oestrus and ovulation

Female alpacas do not exhibit a definite pattern of oestrous cycles. They rather show a continuous oestrus and in the absence of the male they will remain in this state for as long as 30 to 40 days, with occasional periods of non-acceptance of no longer than 48 hours (San Martin *et al.*, 1968). Ovulation depends upon coital stimulus and takes place 26 hours post-coitus. Ovulation can also be induced by human chorionic gonado-trophin (HCG) injections and in this case it occurs about 24 hours after injection. It has been reported that doses as low as 25 IU of chorionic gonadotrophin given intramuscularly are sufficient to cause ovulation (San Martin *et al.*, 1968). Similar ovulation patterns have been described in the llama (England *et al.*, 1969), and in the Arabian camel (Nawito *et al.*, 1967).

Penile intromission appears to be necessary to provide an adequate stimulus for the release of gonadotrophin and subsequent ovulation in the alpaca. Mounting stimulus alone, with no penile intromission, results in very low ovulation rates (Fernández-Baca *et al.*, 1970a). The latter also observed that about 20 per cent of the females fail to ovulate in response to single or multiple services by intact or vasectomized males. This phenomenon appears to be related to failure in the release of luteinizing hormone, since single intra-muscular injections of 750 IU of HCG into females in oestrus induced ovulation in all cases (Table 10.3).

Failure to ovulate may be an important contributing factor to lowered reproductive efficiency under practical farming conditions. Nevertheless, as the non-ovulating female remains in oestrus she may have other opportunities to be served and therefore to ovulate provided that her failure to ovulate is not related to any serious endocrine impairment.

Multiple ovulations occur in about 10 per cent of the cases following natural service and in 20 per cent of the cases following gonadotrophin injections. In spite of this relatively high multiple-ovulation rate, multiple births have never been reported in the alpaca or in other llamoids, although double pregnancies are not uncommon during the first month of gestation. Whether the death of one foetus is due to lowered atmospheric pressure, malnutrition or is a species characteristic, is not known.

Ovulation is followed by formation of the corpus luteum, which attains

Table 10·3   *The number of females in oestrus responding to various types of mating stimuli*

Nature of stimulus	Total no. females	No. ovulating	Percentage ovulating	No. with dividing ova	No. with multiple ovulations
Unmated	20	1	5	0	0
Mounted only	13	2	15	0	0
Mounted only + AI	9	3	33	2	0
Interrupted service*	10	6	60	4	1
Sterile service	22	17	77	0	2
Sterile service + AI	21	18	86	3†	1
Single service	44	36	82	30	3
Multiple services	10	7	70	6‡	0
750 IU HCG	10	10	100	0	1
750 IU HCG + AI	18	18	100	4	4

* Service interrupted approximately 5 minutes after onset.
† Ova from three animals not recovered.
‡ Ovum from one animal not recovered.
Source: Fernández-Baca *et al.* (1970a).

its full size of about 16 mm (0·5 in) diameter and secretory activity, some 8 days after ovulation. In the absence of pregnancy the activity of the corpus luteum, as measured by changes in size and steroid output, starts to decline by day 13. The ovaries then show development of new follicles and the female soon returns to oestrus. The regression of the corpus luteum is complete 18 days after sterile copulation (Fernández-Baca *et al.*, 1970b). In the past it was believed that sterile copulation in the alpaca was followed by a long period of pseudopregnancy. It was also believed that the high incidence of pseudopregnancy, due to the high percentage (>21) of azoospermic males, was responsible for the low reproductive rate in the alpaca. Recent research, however, has shown that no such pseudopregnancy occurs. As stated above, after regression of the corpus luteum the females show normal oestral behaviour and when mated are apt to ovulate and become pregnant.

Oestrus and mating behaviour

Alpacas in oestrus show a peculiar behaviour pattern in the presence of the male. They either readily assume the prone position when approached by the male, or get close to copulating males and assume a prone position. Occasionally some females in heat may mount other females. Since unmated females show continuous follicular development and therefore continuous oestrus, one would expect that all females in a herd should be in oestrus at any given time provided that they have not been exposed to males or to other stimuli capable of inducing ovulation. This is so. Observations of mating behaviour, both in corralled females and in the open field (Fernández-Baca and Novoa, 1968a), indicate that males

508   *Llamoids or New World Camelidae*

usually choose the first female they find and almost invariably she will be receptive. Sexual activity was found to be particularly intense during the first week after the males were introduced in two herds of female alpacas, 70 to 72 per cent of the females being recorded as having been served at least once during this period (Fig. 10.2). The percentage served might have been still higher as observations were limited to daylight hours.

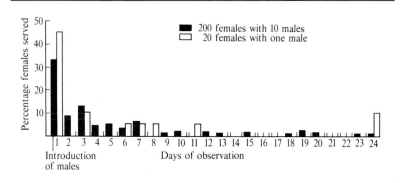

Fig. 10.2   The daily incidence of new services in two herds of alpacas (Fernández-Baca and Novoa (1968), ALPA, Vol 3.

Notes: (1) In one herd there were 10 males and 200 females and in the other herd one male with 20 females.

(2) Each histogram represents the percentages of females served at least once and for the first time on the day of observation.

Copulation takes place with the female in the prone position and may last for 5 to 50 minutes. Apparently there is no relationship between duration of copulation and ovulation induction or fertilization rate. In some cases copulation for 20 minutes failed to induce ovulation, whereas others' services lasting less than 10 minutes resulted in ovulation and fertilization. The male is vociferous during copulation and may, after a period of abstinence, serve up to 18 females during the first day of breeding, but in the following days the number of services declines considerably. Evidence obtained by the use of an urethral fistula suggested that ejaculation is a continuous process during copulation.

Fertilization rates and embryonic mortality

Provided ovulation has occurred, fertilization of the ovum appears to be the usual outcome. In one experiment according to Fernández-Baca *et al.* (1970a) more than 80 per cent of the ova recovered 3 days after service were dividing. However, embryonic mortality within the first month of gestation is much higher in the alpaca than in any other domesticated species. Only some 50 per cent of the fertilized eggs survive beyond 30 days of gestation (Table 10.4). This appears to be a serious reproductive problem in the alpaca. The determining factors are still unknown.

Table 10.4 *Pregnancy rates at different stages after mating and location of embryos*

Group	Days after mating	Animals per group	Number ovulated	Number pregnant	Percentage pregnant	Percentage embryos in left horn
1	3	20	16	14*	70	56
2	28–31	20	–	7†	35‡	87
3	40–45	20	–	7	35‡	71
4	87–95	20	–	8	40‡	100‡

* A total of 16 divided ova recovered from 14 females.
† A total of 8 embryos recovered. Two 31-day-old live embryos were found in one animal, both in the left horn. Two corpora lutea were present on the right ovary.
‡ Significantly different ($p < 0.05$) from values for the third day.
Source: Fernández-Baca *et al.* (1970c).

Pregnancy diagnosis

The behavioural response of the females in the presence of males is an excellent means of pregnancy diagnosis in the alpaca. It has been noted that, without exception, females that showed oestral behaviour 20 or more days after a previous service were non-pregnant and that all females that were pregnant rejected the male, although not all females that rejected the male were found to be pregnant. The latter probably represent cases in which recent embryonic deaths have occurred and in which the corpora lutea have not yet completely regressed. Thus the sexual behaviour of the alpaca is a reliable means of pregnancy diagnosis, provided due consideration is given to cases of recent embryonic losses in which a functional corpus luteum may still be present. Palpation per rectum can be easily performed in the alpaca to confirm a pregnancy diagnosis.

Gestation and parturition

San Martin *et al.* (1968) found mean gestation lengths of 342 and 345 days for *Huacaya*- and *Suri*-type alpacas, respectively, the corresponding modal values being 343 and 346 days. Figure 10.3 shows the growth curve of alpaca embryos measured by changes in body weight and crown–rump length during the first 100 days of gestation. The placenta of the alpaca and the llama is of the simple diffuse type and microscopically it corresponds to the epitheliochorial type with six tissue layers being

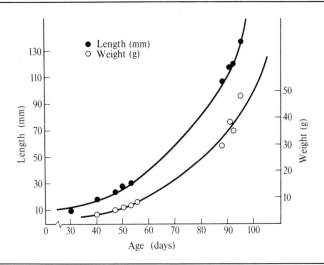

Fig. 10.3   The growth of alpaca embryos (Fernández-Baca *et al.*, 1970c).

present between foetal and maternal circulations (Bustinza, 1961; Morton, 1961). Even though both ovaries are equally active most pregnancies, if not all, are carried in the left uterine horn (Table 10.4). A higher frequency of pregnancies in the left uterine horn has also been reported in the camel. Migrations of embryos from the right to the left uterine horn are not uncommon as evidenced by the presence of the corpus luteum in the right ovary and the embryo in the left uterine horn. Whether this is due to an inadequate environment in the right uterine horn for the development of the embryo, or to some anatomical feature, is not known.

Parturition usually occurs during the morning, thus allowing time for the newborn to dry in the hot sun before the afternoon storms. The female alpaca, unlike other ruminants, never licks her young after birth.

Females usually come into oestrus within 48 hours after parturition. However, regression of the corpus luteum and development of the follicles do not occur until about 6 days post-partum. Uterine involution takes about 15 days in the alpaca. This means that for optimum breeding efficiency females should not be bred until at least 15 days post-partum.

Nutritional characteristics

The alpaca possesses a rumen, although the anatomy of its digestive system is different from other ruminants. Although the third stomach is not sufficiently differentiated anatomically, the existence of four stomachs in llamoids is generally accepted (Vallenas, 1965). One interesting feature is the existence of oblique grooves with glandular pouches in the dorsal sac of the rumen. The role that these glandular structures may play in the process of digestion is unknown. The total capacity of the four compartments has been estimated to be 11·5 litres (2·5 gal), of which the first constitutes 85, the second 4, the third 8 and the fourth 3 per cent of the total, respectively. Calculi are common in the stomachs and intestines of these species and some medicinal properties are attributed to the calculi by the indigenous peoples. Alpacas do not possess a gall bladder. Blood glucose levels in llamoids are much higher than in other ruminants, usually above 90 mg of glucose per 100 ml of blood.

Digestibility trials suggest (Fernández-Baca, 1966) that alpacas can utilize 10 to 50 per cent more of the feed energy available than can sheep (Table 10.5). Similar results have been reported for llamas by Camargo

Table 10.5   *Differences in the digestibility coefficients of forages consumed by sheep and alpacas*

Forage	Digestibility coefficient (%)	
	Sheep	Alpaca
Oat hay	49·7	77·5
Totora (*Scirpus* spp.)	66·4	79·1
Oat silage	54·6	71·2

Source: Fernández-Baca (1966).

and Cardozo (1971). These results suggest that there may be a higher efficiency of feed conversion in the alpaca and the llama than in most other ruminants. The ability of llamoids to utilize crude fibre so efficiently may explain their ability to utilize the poor-quality, highly lignified pastures found at high altitudes.

Management

The number of alpacas and llamas per farm may vary from a few hundreds in small community farms to several thousands in the large haciendas. On most organized farms alpacas are classified according to type (*Suri* or *Huacaya*), hair colour, age and sex, and maintained in herds of 200 to 1,000 head. The proportion of females of breeding age usually varies from 30 to 40 per cent, while the proportion of castrated males kept as fibre producers may be 30 to 35 per cent of the total population. Alpacas depend entirely on natural pastures and the usual stocking rate is about 1·5 to 2·0 ha (3·7 to 5·0 acre) per animal according to circumstances.

The usual breeding season is from January to March on those farms where seasonal breeding is practised. Parturition then occurs at the time when ample feed is available. During the breeding season males are allowed to run freely with the females. The usual ratio is one male to twenty to twenty-five females. Recent research suggests that higher conception rates (70 as compared to the usual 50 per cent) can be obtained when two groups of males are used alternately in a herd of females, thus allowing each group of males a 4- to 5-day resting period. This practice is based on the observation that males display a tremendous copulatory activity during the first 4 to 5 days, but that their activity considerably declines thereafter in spite of the presence of receptive females in the herd. In those herds where males and females are allowed to run together all the year round, parturition occurs only from December to March, indicating that under natural conditions breeding activity is confined to a specific season. Llamas probably behave similarly to alpacas, but so far no experimental evidence is available on their behaviour. The vicuña is much more difficult to breed in confinement, although they have been so bred. Female vicuñas in confinement show apparently normal sexual activity and readily accept service by male alpacas. In contrast, the male vicuña under confinement lacks sexual desire, although its semen production potential appears to be unaltered. Semen from vicuñas has been obtained by electroejaculation and successful inseminations of alpacas have been achieved using vicuña semen.

In most cases parturition occurs without difficulty, dystocia is rather uncommon and foetal membranes are readily eliminated after birth. The young are born in a very advanced state of development and may be able to run a few minutes after birth. They are weaned when they are 6 to 7 months of age. Even though the females may be sexually receptive 48 hours after parturition, breeding should be delayed until involution of the uterus has been completed. This occurs in approximately 15 days.

Males not selected for breeding purposes are castrated at about one year old and kept for fibre production until they are 10 to 12 years old. Alpacas are sheared every year on some farms and every other year on others. Shearing annually is advantageous as:

1. Less damage is done to the fibre by solar radiation and other environmental factors in one year than in two;
2. About 60 per cent of the growth of the fibre occurs during the first year;
3. Low producers can be detected earlier and culled if necessary; and
4. External parasites, especially sarcoptic mange, can be controlled more effectively.

Classification of fibre is not yet a common practice, but it is encouraged. Villarroel (1964) has published a classification scheme for alpaca fibre.

Artificial insemination (AI)

Semen collection is a difficult task in the alpaca due to the peculiar posture adopted and the time involved in copulation. Several methods such as the artificial vagina, intravaginal sacs, etc., have been tried without much success. Currently, the only practical method available is electro-ejaculation. Slightly higher intensity current than that required for semen collection from rams is required for collection of semen from the alpaca. Semen collected by electroejaculation is of low density (around 100,000 sperms per ml). New techniques for semen collection are being tried, one of the most promising being the use of a urethral fistula. Semen of a higher density and larger volume than normal has been collected using this method.

Artificial insemination has been practised in alpacas using freshly collected undiluted alpaca and vicuña semen. Semen collected by flushing the epididymis after castration with heat-treated milk has also been used. Ovulation was induced by service with vasectomized males or by intramuscular injection of 750 IU of HCG. Semen was deposited through the cervix by means of a plastic pipette such as is used for AI in bovines (Fernández-Baca and Novoa, 1968b). Fertility levels with AI have been rather low, being less than 25 per cent. These results are attributed mainly to the poor quality of the semen, but it has been very valuable to be able to demonstrate that crosses of male vicuñas with female alpacas are possible using AI techniques. Male vicuñas kept in captivity usually demonstrate a lack of libido so that crosses of female alpacas with male vicuñas are not possible using natural mating.

It should be noted that alpacas and llamas offer more advantages than some other livestock for the use of AI techniques. Since females demonstrate continuous oestrus they are ready for insemination at any time, provided ovulation is properly induced.

Dentition

The alpaca possesses a total of 30 permanent teeth distributed as follows: one upper and three lower incisors, one upper and one lower canine, and five upper and four lower molars on each side. Some females lack the upper canine tooth. The eruption of temporary incisors takes place approximately as follows: central 0 to 20 days, intermediates 14 to 84 days and laterals 15 to 107 days. The first pair of permanent incisors erupts at about 2 years, the second pair at 3 years and the third at about 4 years of age. The upper permanent incisors and canines erupt at about 3 years in males and after 5 years in females and the lower canines after $2\frac{1}{2}$ years in both males and females (Fernández-Baca, 1961–62).

There is a tendency for the incisors of the alpaca and the vicuña to grow so long that they may hinder eating. Since not all individuals suffer from this condition, even when they are subjected to the same feeding and management practices, this would appear to be a genetically controlled characteristic.

The life-span of the alpaca is about 15 years, but soon after 10 years they usually show a marked wearing of their teeth and are culled from the herd.

Disease

Llamoids suffer from most diseases common to other ruminants, although they appear to be particularly resistant to foot and mouth disease.

New-born alpacas suffer severely from enterotoxaemia produced by types A and C of *Clostridium welchii* (Moro, 1968). In some years the mortality rate due to this disease may be as high as 80 per cent, depending on the availability of pasture and the local management practices. The disease can be controlled at an early stage using antibiotics such as chlortetracycline. The alpacas should be dosed orally with 4 to 5 g a day for 3 to 4 days. Clostridiosis, usually due to *C. septicum*, causes sudden death in adult alpacas. Also of common occurrence in adult alpacas is the so-called alpaca fever or streptococcosis (*Streptococcus pyogenes*). Other diseases that have been recorded include stomatitis in young animals due to *Spherophorus necrophorus*, osteomyelitis of the mandible caused by *Actinomyces* spp., listeriosis, keratitis, mastitis caused by *Escherichia coli*, otitis and rabies.

The three most common internal parasites of llamoids are *Graphinema aucheniae*, *Nematodirus lamae* and *Lamanema chavezi* (Chávez and Guerrero, 1965). The first produces small nodules and congestion of the abomasal mucosa and the latter is a blood-sucking trichostrongyle occurring most frequently in young animals. The same anthelmintics that are used for sheep are effective for alpacas. Sarcocysts occur frequently in the heart, oesophagus, neck and leg muscles of alpaca, seriously decreasing the commercial value of the meat.

External parasites cause considerable economic losses due to damage to the fibre. The most common is *Sarcoptes scabiei* var. *aucheniae* which causes loss of hair and the formation of scaly encrusted sores on the legs, axilla and inguinal regions. It may occasionally prove fatal. *Psoroptes communis* var. *aucheniae* is responsible for ear mange and subsequent otitis.

Productivity

Alpacas are mainly bred for fibre production, although their contribution to meat production is considerable and could be improved. Llamas are kept for fibre and meat production and work purposes.

Fibre production

There is a considerable variation in the quantity of fibre produced by the alpaca from as low as 0·9 kg (2 lb) to as high as 4 kg (9 lb) per animal per year with an average of about 1·8 kg (4 lb). Heritability of fleece weight has not been estimated, but the considerable variability between individuals that are similarly managed and fed suggests a high heritability value. There is a highly significant correlation between body and fleece weights in the alpaca. As a white fleece commands a better price in the market commercial farmers give more attention to selection for colour than to other traits. However, the expansion of the pelt industry is creating more demand for skins of other colours.

The llama produces a coarser and stronger fibre than the alpaca, and this is mainly used in the country of origin. Fleece weight may average approximately 1·8 kg (4 lb) per year, although llamas are not sheared as regularly as alpacas.

Hybrids resulting from crosses between alpaca and vicuña (*paco-vicuña*), and llama and vicuna (*llama-vicuña*) constitute a considerable potential for the production of high-quality fibre. It is in the production of these crossbreds where AI can be applied most profitably.

Meat production

Alpaca meat is similar to mutton in taste and nutritive composition. Meat from young alpacas is said to be even superior in taste to lamb. However, under practical farming conditions only adult animals are slaughtered. Alpacas weigh about 8 kg (17 lb) at birth, double their weight during the first 2 months of life and thereafter increase in weight very slowly, weighing 25 to 30 kg (55 to 66 lb) at weaning, which takes place at 7 months of age. The slower rate of growth coincides with a shortage of feed associated with the dry season, which in the natural habitat of the llamoids extends from May to October or November. A mature 3-year-old male weighs about 75 kg (165 lb) and a female about 65 kg (143 lb). The carcase dressing percentage may be as high as 60, the neck constituting about 10 per cent of this total.

At the present time culling of the animals is based mainly on age so that mostly old animals are slaughtered. The off-take on most alpaca farms is only about 8 per cent, due to the low fertility rates and high mortality of the newborn.

Milk production

Alpacas can be milked, but it is not a common practice. The mammary system is composed of four glands each ending in a nipple. The fat content of the milk varies from 2 to 7 per cent and the protein content from 4 to 8 per cent (Jimenez, 1970). Some females may produce up to 2 litres (0·4 gal) of milk in 24 hours. No data are available on the milk production of the alpaca from parturition to weaning.

Work

The only llamoid used as a beast of burden is the llama. Llamas can carry a load of 25 to 35 kg (55 to 77 lb), depending on the distance they travel and the configuration of the land. Normally only males are used for transport.

The question may be asked, which species is most economic as a meat and wool producer, sheep or alpacas? At present the alpaca is the only animal that can efficiently utilize the high-altitude pastures. At lower altitudes there is no evidence as to the comparative efficiency of sheep and alpacas. It has been observed, however, that when alpacas are managed at low altitudes and feeding and management practices are improved, then there is a marked improvement in the production of fibre and meat.

Factors resulting in low productivity

The major factors affecting the productivity of llamoids are nutrition, low fertility and disease.

Nutritional problems

Alpacas depend entirely on natural pastures. Thus their productivity is markedly influenced by seasonal variation in the quantity of the feed supplied by these pastures. Total rainfall in the alpaca-raising areas varies from 900 to 1,200 mm (35 to 47 in), but more than 90 per cent of it occurs during 4 months of the year (December to March). The remaining months are almost completely dry with considerable solar radiation during the day and a marked drop in temperature ($-10°$ to $-20°C$ ($14°$ to $-4°F$)) during the night. Feed supply is generally adequate during the rainy season but very poor both in quantity and quality during the dry period. There are indications that some reproductive problems, such as ovulation failure and early embryonic mortality, are associated with these inadequate nutritional levels.

No specific nutritional deficiencies such as those caused by a lack of trace minerals or vitamins have been reported in the alpaca, but they are likely to occur. It is worth mentioning that alpacas never receive any mineral supplementation. In fact alpacas are unable to lick, although small rocks are frequently found in their stomachs. These are probably ingested when the animals graze short pastures.

Low fertility

A low reproductive rate is a serious problem on most alpaca farms. It has been estimated that on average about 50 per cent of the females of breeding age fail to produce young each year. This, apart from the economic loss, constitutes a limiting factor in any selection programme planned to lead to genetic improvement of traits of economic importance.

The percentage of early embryonic mortality is much higher in the alpaca than in any other domestic species that has been studied, 50 per cent of the embryos dying during the first month of gestation. There are indications that some endogenous factors, such as left and right uterine horn differences, may play an important role in embryo survival. This view is supported by the fact that as gestation progresses there is a marked increase in the incidence of pregnancies located in the left uterine horn (Table 10.4) and by the evidence of Fernández-Baca (1971) who stated that after 90 days all pregnancies were located in the left uterine horn. The mechanisms involved are still unknown, but they are under investigation. Apart from the possible contribution of endogenous factors to embryo mortality the role of other factors, including nutrition, the genetic make-up and disease, may be equally important. Embryonic mortality is certainly a major cause of low fertility in the alpaca.

Other causes of lowered reproduction are probably ovulation failures and inadequate management during the breeding season. Ovulation failures are not uncommon in the alpaca, the role of the male being very important since ovulation depends on coital stimulus.

Existing managerial systems have not been organized to integrate and utilize the reproductive peculiarities of the alpaca. The fact that most females are sexually receptive at a given time, and that males display a particularly intense sexual activity at the beginning of the breeding period, are some of the factors that must be taken into consideration when designing managerial systems that will achieve higher reproductive rates and result in a higher efficiency of production.

References

Benirschke, K. (ed.) (1967) *Sterility and Fertility of Interspecific Mammalian Hybrids. Comparative Aspects of Reproductive Failures.* Springer Verlag: New York.

Bustinza, M. J. (1961) Estudio macro y microscópico de la placentación en *Lama pacos* (alpaca). B.S. Thesis. Univ. San Marcos: Lima, Perú.

Camargo, R. and Cardozo, A. G. (1971) Ensayo comparativo de la capacidad de digestión en la llama y la oveja. *III Reun. lat. am. Prod. anim. Bogotá*, 1971, p. 46.

Chávez, C. and Guerrero, C. (1965) Parasites and parasitic diseases of *Lama pacos* (alpaca) in Peru. *School Vet. Med., Univ. San Marcos, Lima, Perú.*

England, N. G., Cardozo, A. G. and Foote, W. C. (1969) A review of the physiology of reproduction in the New World Camelidae. *Int. Zoo. Yearbook*, **9**, 104–110.

Fernández-Baca, S. (1961–62) *Rev. Fac. Med. Vet., Univ. San Marcos. Lima, Perú.* **16–17**, 88.

Fernández-Baca, S. (1966) Utilización comparativa de los forrajes por la alpaca y el ovino. *Memorias V Congreso Panam. de Med. Vet. y. Zootecnia*, **1**, 352–5.

Fernández-Baca, S. (1970) Luteal function and the nature of reproductive failures in the alpaca. Ph.D Thesis. Cornell Univ.: Ithaca, NY.

Fernández-Baca, S. (1971) The alpaca: reproduction and breeding (in Spanish). *Boln.*

Divulg. Cent. Invest. Inst. vet. Invest. trop. Altura, Lima (7). *Abstracted: Anim. Breed. Abstr.,* **40,** 366 (1972).

Fernández-Baca, S. and Novoa, C. (1968a) Sexual behaviour of the alpaca (*Lama paco*) in the field at the beginning of the breeding season (in Spanish). *Mems. A. soc. lat-am. Prod. anim.,* **3,** 7–20. *Abstracted: Anim. Breed. Abstr.,* **38,** 319 (1970).

Fernández-Baca, S. and Novoa, C. (1968b) *Rev. Fac. Med. Vet., Univ. San Marcos, Lima, Perú,* **22,** 9.

Fernández-Baca, S., Madden, D. H. L. and Novoa, C. (1970a) Effect of different mating stimuli on induction of ovulation in the alpaca. *J. Reprod. Fert.,* **22,** 261–7.

Fernández-Baca, S., Hansel, W. and Novoa, C. (1970b) Corpus luteum function in the alpaca. *Biol. Reprod.,* **3,** 252–61.

Fernández-Baca, S., Hansel, W. and Novoa, C. (1970c) Embryonic mortality in the alpaca. *Biol. Reprod.,* **3,** 243–51.

Fernández-Baca, S., Novoa, C. and Sumar, J. (1971) Seasonal variations in the reproduction of the alpaca (in Spanish). *III Reun. lat-am. Prod. anim. Bogotá,* 1971, 110. *Abstracted: Anim. Breed. Abstr.,* **40,** 366 (1972).

Gray, A. P. (1954) *Mammalian Hybrids. Tech. Comm. Comw. Bur. Anim. Breed. Genet.,* No. 18. Comw. Agric. Bur.: Farnham Royal, UK.

Hugh-Jones, M. E. and Bacon, A. J. (1964) The 'Augenidos' of South America. *The Veterinarian (Oxford),* **2,** 251–5.

Jimenez, O. R. (1970) Estudio de algunos aspectos sobre le leche de alpaca. *Boln. Extraordinario. Cent. Invest. Inst. vet. Invest. trop. Altura, Lima* (4), 60.

Koford, C. B. (1957) The vicuña and the puna. *Ecol. Monogr.,* **27,** 153–219.

Ministerio de Agricultura y Pesqueria (1966) *Estadistica Agraria, Per.*

Moro, M. (1968) Importancia de las alpacas para el Peru. *Boln. Extraordinario. Cent. Invest. Inst. vet. Invest. trop. Altura, Lima* (3), 61, 313.

Morton, W. R. M. (1961) Observations on the full-term foetal membranes of the Camelidae (*C. dromedarius, C. bactrianus* and *Lama glama*). *J. Anat.,* **95,** 200–9.

Nawito, M. F., Shalash, M. R., Hoppe, R. and Rakha, A. M. (1967) Reproduction in the *female camel. Bull. Anim. Sci. Res. Inst. (Cairo)* (2).

Novoa, C. (1970) Reproduction in Camelidae. *J. Reprod. Fert.,* **22,** 3–20.

Romer, A. S. (1966) *Vertebrate Paleontology* (3rd edn). Univ. Chicago Press: Chicago.

Romero, E. C. (1927) *Llamas y Alpacas, Vicuñas y Guanacos.* Buenos Aires.

San Martin, M., Copaira, M., Zuñiga, J., Rodriguez, R., Bastinza, G. and Acosta, L. (1968) Aspects of reproduction in the alpaca. *J. Reprod. Fert.,* **16,** 395–9.

Simpson, G. G. (1945) The principles of classification and a classification of mammals. *Bull. Amer. Museum Natural History,* No. 85, pp. 1–350.

Taylor, K. M., Hungerford, D. A., Snyder, R. L. and Ulmer, F. A. (Jr.) (1968) Uniformity of karyotypes in the Camelidae. *Cytogenics,* **7,** 7–15.

Vallenas, P. A. (1955) 'Some Physiological Aspects of Digestion in the Alpaca (*Lama pacos*)', in Dougherty, R. W. (ed.), *Physiology of Digestion in the Ruminant,* p. 147. Butterworths: London.

Villarroel, J. (1964) Primera norma técnica para la fibra de alpaca. *Perú Textil.* **20.**

Chapter 11

Game as a Source of Meat

There is, of course, nothing new in the concept of utilizing wild game as a source of meat. Game was the main source of meat before man domesticated a limited number of species, and hunting has continued to be a major occupation of some peoples until very recent times. Even today, game meat contributes substantially to the diet of some indigenous people in a limited number of tropical countries.

What is new is the idea of controlled cropping producing a sustained yield of game animals. Until very recently, game animals were killed for sport or by farmers and/or hunters for food, but game was not considered as a replaceable resource. Consequently, game populations have been almost completely destroyed over vast tracts of the tropical world.

In some countries, a form of controlled cropping has been introduced by banning hunting during the breeding season of specific species or by barring the killing of all females. At the same time, game reserves have been created in both developed and developing countries. It was not, however, until some 25 years ago that conservationists in Africa realized that the creation of game reserves would not necessarily ensure that large numbers of game would survive in that continent. The pressures from the indigenous human populations are too great.

As man increases in number, he is bound to compete with other species and, in particular, with the wild species for land and water. Under these circumstances, unless substantial economic reasons can be advanced for the preservation of wild game, there will be no doubt as to the issue. They will become extinct or, at best, survive in small numbers in national parks and zoos.

In Tanzania, for example, a country where the average annual income per person is very low, the government has to decide whether game reserves should be used for alternative purposes, such as wheat farming or domestic livestock raising. Under these circumstances, it is little use for the outside world to talk of aesthetic and scientific values and of conservation for the sake of preservation. Tanzania must be assured that there are realistic economic motives for the retention of game in the Serengeti. Fortunately, the Serengeti is also an area of scenic value and tourist potential.

Reasons for the preservation of wild game

At least four reasons may be advanced for the preservation of wild game: aesthetic, cultural, biological and economic. In the under-developed world, the most important reason is the latter.

Wilderness areas stocked with wild game have an aesthetic value recognized by some men, but not by all. Once the wilderness and the wild game have gone, they can never be exactly replaced.

Hunting is a comparatively harmless outlet for one of man's most powerful emotions – aggression. Without this outlet, man could be emotionally and culturally poorer and, as increasing numbers of people live in the vast cities created by the new technology and economy, the need for some relatively harmless release for aggressive emotions will probably increase. Hunting can also provide a useful economic return in the form of licences and trophies.

Wild game are of intrinsic scientific interest and utility. They provide a gene pool which may yet be needed and some present wild species may yet be domesticated.

The economic value of wild game has hardly been assessed as yet. They can be used to exploit those areas of the earth's surface which cannot be adequately exploited by existing domestic livestock. As it would appear that many game animals are physiologically geared to a near-maintenance level of production, they can also survive in large numbers in sub-marginal areas without destroying their habitat. They could not only be an additional source of meat but also of economically valuable skins, hair, bones and ivory.

In addition, associations of large numbers of wild animals can become a major tourist attraction with consequent economic benefit. For example, in Kenya in 1969, 'game tourism' yielded an estimated revenue of US$45 million, of which approximately US$34 million remained in Kenya.

Without in any way denigrating the aesthetic, cultural and biological value of wild animals or their use as an outlet for some of man's deep-seated atavistic tendencies, this chapter will focus attention on the utilization of wild animals as an economic asset and, in particular, on their utilization for meat production.

Tropical regions where game could be used for large-scale meat production

There are areas in many tropical countries where game animals could be cropped on a small scale. Even small schemes can be a valuable economic asset. For example, although New Zealand is a major beef and mutton exporter, in 1968 that country was able to export 3,000 tons of venison. Many tropical countries could emulate New Zealand in this respect.

More important, there are some major regions in the tropics where game cropping could, if properly organized, become an industry which would produce considerable supplies of meat.

Semi-arid regions

Bonsma (1951) estimated that 22·5 per cent of the total area of Africa or 6·8 million km^2 (2·6 million miles^2) could be classified as semi-arid. It is likely that the total area is now somewhat larger. In addition, there are large areas of semi-arid land in western Asia, the Americas and Australia.

Of the domesticated livestock, only camels and asses can normally thrive in arid lands. Cattle, sheep and goats do, of course, utilize the ephemeral forage plants which appear after rain, but cannot be managed year-round on desert range. There are, however, a number of antelopes which are indigenous in the arid regions of Africa and western Asia. The three major types are *Oryx* spp., such as the gemsbok and beisa oryx in Africa and the Arabian and scimitar oryxes in western Asia; the addax (*Addax nasomaculatus*), which once ranged throughout North and Northeastern Africa; and *Gazella* spp., such as Loder's gazelle found in the dune areas of the Sahara, Speke's gazelle found in Somalia and the goitred gazelle of Arabia. In addition, gazelle such as Thomson's (*G. thomsoni*) and Grant's (*G. granti*) inhabit the fringe of the semi-arid regions of Africa.

The antelope population of the semi-arid and arid areas of Africa and western Asia has been radically reduced of recent times, but it can be envisaged that proper management of the semi-arid and arid zones could include sustained cropping of antelopes. These animals would have to be reintroduced in many areas and the production of meat per unit area of land would always, of course, be low.

In the semi-arid and some other areas of Australia, it may be economic to crop kangaroos, especially where the climatic environment is unsuitable for domestic livestock. Sharman (1967) has reported that kangaroos survive drought very well and make use of very poor roughage. They are better adapted to marginal land than sheep or cattle and apparently are equally efficient converters of feed into liveweight. The total number of kangaroos which could be involved in cropping schemes would not be inconsiderable as a survey in New South Wales showed that, in that state alone, in 1960 there were at least 10 million. Indeed, it has been stated by the Australian Conservation Foundation (1967) that the red kangaroo (*Megaleia rufa*) is already over-hunted. Certainly large numbers of kangaroos are killed annually, as in 1970 Australia exported kangaroo meat to the United States valued at US$1 million and approximately 400,000 kangaroo hides, also worth US$1 million.

Savanna and steppe regions

Harthoorn (1961) estimated that 10·4 million km² (4 million miles²) of savanna and tropical steppe in Africa were infested with tsetse fly. The majority of existing domestic livestock cannot be utilized in this vast area on account of the danger of contracting trypanosomiasis. Only two major African breeds of cattle, the N'dama and the West African Shorthorn and some remnant breeds, are tolerant of trypanosomiasis. Most game animals are, however, tolerant. Until tsetse-infested land is closely settled, the cropping of game could be an important economic activity on such land. There is usually a multiplicity of game species in such areas, similar to those listed in Table 11.1, so that the opportunities for sustained cropping are particularly favourable.

Table 11.1   *Recommended game crop from 130 km² (50 miles²) of the Henderson ranch, Rhodesia*

Species	Estimated no.	Percentage to be cropped	Carcase weight (kg (lb))	Total carcase weight (kg (lb))
Impala	2,100	25	29 (65)	15,479 (34,125)
Zebra	730	20	116 (255)	16,887 (27,230)
Steenbuck	200	20	5 (12)	218 (480)
Warthog	170	50	32 (70)	2,699 (5,950)
Kudu	160	30	102 (225)	4,899 (10,800)
Wildebeest	160	20	118 (260)	3,774 (8,320)
Giraffe	90	16·6	454 (1,000)	6,804 (15,000)
Duiker	80	35	9 (20)	254 (560)
Waterbuck	35	20	91 (200)	635 (1,400)
Buffalo	30	16·6	259 (570)	1,293 (2,850)
Eland	10	20	272 (600)	· 544 (1,200)
Klipspringer	10	30	6 (14)	19 (42)
Bush pig	10	50	32 (70)	159 (350)
Total				53,664 (118,300)

kg per ha (lb per acre) of game meat: 4·1 (3·7)
kg per ha (lb per acre) of beef after development: 3·4 (3·0)

Source: Dasmann and Mossman (1961).

The *llanos* of Colombia and Venezuela in South America may also be a very suitable region for mixed game and domestic livestock production. For example, the capybara (*Hydrochoerus hydrochoeis*), a rodent known as *el chiguire* in Venezuela, is very well adapted to the seasonally flooded *llanos* environment and is an animal which produces an acceptable meat. It is a herbivore which lives in shallow, but not rapidly flowing, water. Mature animals weigh 40 to 60 kg (88 to 132 lb) and yield a 52 per cent dressing-out carcase. Females, with a gestation period of 104 to 120 days, reproduce twice yearly, giving birth to two to five young at one time.

There is already a considerable Easter-time trade in the meat of the *chiguire* and, with semi-domestication and a sustained cropping programme, productivity could probably be rapidly improved.

Humid forest regions

It is likely that, despite intensive exploitation, at least 25 per cent of the total land area of Southeast Asia, or 1·25 million km² (0·48 million miles²), will remain for the foreseeable future as forest. This vast area could be used for sustained timber production and be restocked with wild game. At present, there are few game in the Southeast Asian forests, as they have been over-hunted, but these forests are the ancestral home of the *Bos* (*bibos*) spp. types of wild cattle and several species of deer. If immediate action was taken to conserve the existing herds of gaur (*B.* (*bibos*) *gaurus*) and banteng (*B.* (*bibos*) *banteng*), their number would eventually increase until, ultimately, a cropping programme could be justified (Payne, 1968). Restocking could be hastened by the introduction of Bali cattle, a domesticated type of banteng, and by allowing introduced cattle to go feral in the forests.

It has also been suggested (Vu Ngoc Tan, 1968) that the raising of indigenous deer such as the sambar (*Cervus unicolour*) and the hog deer (*Axis porcinus*) could be economically attractive. There is no reason why the forests should not ultimately be also restocked with these and other indigenous deer species.

A considerable part of the total area of forest land in Southeast Asia is swamp forest. Consideration should also be given to the possibilities of stocking suitable swamp forests with domesticated swamp buffalo and allowing the latter to go feral. This has occurred fortuitously in south Sumatra, Indonesia, with desirable results. During the Second World War, buffalo were driven into the swamp forest to escape confiscation by the invading armed forces. Today, the descendants of the original buffalo are feral, thriving and increasing in number. They now provide a sustained off-take of animals from an area which would otherwise produce little of economic value.

In West Africa there is a rodent known as the grasscutter (*Thryonomis swinderianus*) whose meat is appreciated by many of the indigenous people. A study of the ecology and reproductive biology of this species is now being made in the Ivory Coast, together with an attempt to breed the animal in captivity.

The largest area of humid forest in the world is to be found in the Amazon basin of South America. The wild game population of this region has never been as varied as that of the Southeast Asian forests and, as elsewhere, it has been considerably reduced in total number by the clearing of the forest and over-hunting. It is suggested that the possibility of introducing exotic game into this forest should be studied. The domesticated water buffalo has already been introduced into agricultural areas of the region and is apparently thriving.

The possibility of conserving and utilizing the manatee (Trichechidae) of the Atlantic and Caribbean and the dugong (Dugongidae) of the Indian Ocean for feeding on aquatic plants in tropical and sub-tropical estuarine areas should also be considered. These water mammals were in the past highly prized for their meat, but they have been over-hunted and are now extinct in many countries.

Montane regions

The high mountain and altiplano areas of Venezuela, Colombia, Ecuador, Bolivia and Peru comprise a major region where the possibilities of sustained game cropping should be considered: not only the possibility of restocking with indigenous wild llamoids, such as the guanaco (*Lama guanicoe*) and the vicuña (*Vicugna vicugna*), but also the possibility of introducing exotic game animals from the montane regions of Asia and elsewhere.

During historically recent voyages of discovery and through migration, man has introduced exotic domesticated and wild plant species from one continent to another, and domestic species together with some wild animals from Europe to the remainder of the world, but he has not generally introduced exotic mammalian species from one region of the tropics to another. It is suggested that the problems of restocking regions denuded of game, particularly by the transfer of game animals from one region to another, should now be studied on a global basis. There are obviously major difficulties to be overcome, such as the possibility of transmission of exotic disease and parasites and the unknown competitive effects of the introduction of a new species on all other species in the environment. However, with time and adequate research these problems could be solved.

An example of what can be achieved by the introduction of exotic species may be studied in the State of New Mexico in the United States. In the 1950s Barbary sheep (*Ammotragus lervia*) were released at several centres in the state and, in addition, there may have been a few of these sheep already present which had been introduced at some previous date. This species has acclimatized and reproduced so well that it may now be hunted for 9 days in each year. More recently, the possibilities of acclimatizing the gemsbok (*Oryx gazella*), the greater kudu (*Tragelaphus capensis*), the Siberian ibex (*Capra siberica*) and the Iranian ibex (*C. aegugrus*) have been studied. The present indications are that the gemsbok and the Iranian ibex will acclimatize and be very suitable species. In November 1970, Iranian ibex were released on a 2,225 m (7,300 ft) peak of the rugged Florida mountain range, some 24 km (15 miles) south of the small town of Deming, New Mexico.

Methods of using wild game for meat production

The possibilities of using wild game for meat production, particularly in Africa, have been widely canvassed and discussed during the last decade. Major sources of information on this subject are publications by Dassman (1964), Ledger (1964a), Talbot *et al.* (1965), Talbot (1966), Ledger *et al.* (1967), Joubert (1968), Crawford (1968) and Skinner (1973).

There are three major methods by which wild game could be utilized for meat production purposes. These are as follows:

- The sustained cropping of indigenous wild or introduced exotic game populations in environments generally considered unsuitable for the economic management of domestic livestock;
- The management of wild or semi-domesticated game with or without domestic livestock on ranches or farms;
- The domestication of some existing wild species and their management – either alone or together with traditional domesticated species.

The sustained cropping of game populations

Wild game must be present in sufficiently large numbers and be able to range over a sufficiently large area before game cropping should be considered as an economic activity. Ledger (1964a) estimated that an area of no less than 20,235 ha (50,000 acres) is required in one block to allow for the migratory habits of the game. Even this area is too small for some antelopes and for the larger game animals. Small gazelles could, however, be cropped from smaller areas.

1. *Advantages*

(a) Wild game can be cropped in regions where domestic livestock cannot be utilized or are marginally economic.

For example, it can be envisaged that in many African countries game-cropping schemes could act as buffer zones between very dry or tsetse-infested regions and ranching areas.

Game animals exhibit numerous adaptive features which make them very suitable for use in the ecosystems in which they are found. This is particularly noticeable in semi-arid and arid areas where some game animals can thrive without continuous access to free water. There is, however, little evidence to suggest that they are able to make better use of the food that they consume than do domestic livestock. For example, Taylor and Lyman (1967) have shown that the productivity of eland is inferior to that of Hereford cattle, a higher food consumption and more protein being required for each unit of meat produced.

(b) The high game biomass available for cropping where there are a multiplicity of animal and plant species.

Lamprey (1964) reviewed the available data on biomass and concluded that in East Africa it could vary from 219 to 20,484 kg per km^2 (1,250 to 116,967 lb per mile^2), depending on environmental and other conditions. The upper limit was exceptional and was calculated in an area where there were numbers of the largest game, such as elephants, hippopotami and buffaloes. Dassman (1963) stated that in Rhodesia game cropping was more profitable than domestic livestock production in those areas where the stocking rate for cattle is less than one livestock unit per 12 ha (30 acres), i.e. the domestic livestock biomass is less than 3,333 kg per km^2 (18,812 lb per mile^2).

The possible high biomass of game animals available for cropping in some environments can be attributed to the fact that the available forage can be most efficiently utilized by many different animal species, each with slightly different food preferences and feeding habits. This situation is well illustrated by the data given in Table 11.1, showing the recommended annual game crop for a ranch in Rhodesia.

Estimates of the biomass of game animals should be accepted with caution as there are so many variable assumptions in the calculations. Nevertheless, the general thesis that in some ecosystems game can provide a very substantial biomass per unit area of land is generally acceptable.

The fact that a specific environment supports a high biomass of game animals does not necessarily mean that productivity per unit area of land will be high. If all the animals grow very slowly, then most of the available feed would have to be used for maintenance purposes and annual off-take could be low. High productivity per unit area of land depends on both a high biomass or stocking density and a high off-take. High biomass and off-take depend upon large quantities of feed being available for the animals on a year-round basis, on high reproductive and growth rates within the species involved and on low mortality rates. For example, if the off-take is 3 per cent in a game-cropping area where the biomass is 20,484 kg per km^2 (Lamprey, 1964), whereas in a ranching area where the biomass is only 10,000 kg per km^2 the off-take is 15 per cent, then total productivity in the ranching area at 1,500 kg of liveweight per km^2 per annum would be more than twice that in the game-cropping area where productivity would be 615 kg of liveweight per km^2 per annum.

The reproductive rates of some game animals (Table 11.2) are quite high, while liveweights (Table 11.3) are of the same order as those for indigenously managed domestic livestock in many tropical countries. Under these circumstances, the off-take from a game population could compare quite favourably with the off-take from an indigenously managed domestic livestock population. Watson *et al.* (1969) have estimated that the off-take of game animals under favourable conditions

Table 11.2 *Reproductive behaviour of some game animals*

Species	Sex	Type of breeding season	Age at first breeding (months)	Gestation length (days)	Birth interval (days)	Births as percentage of breeding females	Reference
Buffalo (*Syncerus caffer*)	Female	All year	57	–	540–730	50–66	Grimsdell (1973)
Eland (*Taurotragus oryx*)	Female	All year (with seasonal peaks)	26–31	268–276	334–74	83	Skinner (1973)
Wildebeest (*Connochaetes taurinus albojubatus*)	Male	Seasonal	40	–	–	–	Estes (1966)
	Female	Seasonal	15–27	240–255	–	96	Watson (1969)
Springbok (*Antidorcas marsupialis marsupialis*)	Male	All year	13	–	–	–	Skinner (1973)
	Female	All year	7	168	–	46–100	Skinner (1973)
Blesbok (*Damaliscus dorcas phillipsi*)	Male	Seasonal	18	–	–	–	Skinner (1973)
	Female	Seasonal	18	225	365	85	Skinner (1973)
Impala (*Aepyceros melampus*)	Male	Seasonal	18	–	–	–	Skinner (1973)
	Female	Seasonal	18	196	365	90	Skinner (1973)
Kudu (*Tragelaphus strepsiceros*)	Female	Seasonal	17	210–214	365	100	Skinner (1973)
Thomson's gazelle (*Gazella thomsoni*)	Female	All year	10	165–195	–	–	Leuthold (1972); Robinette and Archer (1971)

Sources: As references.

Table 11.3 Liveweight of some game animals

Name of animal	Sex	Liveweight (kg (lb))					Reference
		Six months	One year	Two years	Three years	Maturity	
Buffalo (Syncerus caffer)	Male					548 (1208)	Young and Van Den Heever (1969)
Eland (Taurotragus oryx)	Male (Russia)		225 (496)	310 (683)	450 (992)	600 (1323) (at 5 years)	Skinner (1967)
	Male (Rhodesia)		160 (353)	260 (573)	360 (794)	500 (1102)	Skinner (1967)
	Female (Rhodesia)		145 (320)	250 (551)	350 (772)	410 (904)	Skinner (1967)
Wildebeest (Connochaetes taurinus albojubatus)	Male					204 (450) [186 (405)–228 (503)]	Ledger (1964b)
	Female					162 (357) [150 (331)–175 (386)]	Ledger (1964b)
Springbok (Antidorcas marsupialis marsupialis)	Male	20 (44)	25 (55)			37 (82) (at 2 years)	Skinner et al. (1971)
	Female	18 (40)	20 (44)			25 (55)	Skinner et al. (1971)

Blesbok (*Damaliscus dorcas phillipsi*)	Male	30 (66)	52 (115)	70 (154)–73 (161) (at 3 years)	Du Plessis (1972) Kettlitz (1967)
	Female	29 (64)	43 (95)	62 (137)–64 (141)	Du Plessis (1972) Kettlitz (1967)
Impala (*Aepyceros melampus*)	Male	20 (44)	35 (72)	50 (110) (at 3 years)	Child (1964)
	Female	19 (42)	28 (62)	40 (88)	Child (1964)
Oryx (*Oryx beisa*)	Male			173 (381) [133 (293)–189 (417)]	Ledger (1963b)
	Female			149 (328) [130 (287)–163 (359)]	Ledger (1963b)
Uganda kob (*Adenota kob*)	Male			97 (214) [88 (194)–108 (238)]	Ledger (1963b)
	Female			62 (137)	Ledger (1963b)
Thomson's gazelle (*Gazella thomsoni*)	Male			25 (55)	Ledger (1963b)
	Female			20 (44)	Ledger (1963b)
Kudu (*Tragelaphus strepsiceros*)	Male			236 (520)	Huntley (1971)

Sources: As references.

could be of the order of 10 per cent per annum on a sustained yield basis. This is approximately the same off-take as would be achieved by a well-managed indigenous herd, but much lower than the rate which would be achieved by a well-managed modern integrated livestock unit.

(c) The relatively high fertility of many game species.

As will be seen from Table 11.2, the calving percentages of the buffalo, eland and wildebeest compare very favourably with those of indigenous cattle in similar environments, and the age at first breeding of both the eland and wildebeest is lower than is normal in indigenous cattle. It may be concluded that the reproductive efficiency of both the eland and the wildebeest is higher than that of most indigenous cattle.

The lambing percentages of smaller game animals such as the springbok, impala, blesbok and Thomson's gazelle are of the same order as those of indigenous sheep, although they may be somewhat lower than those of indigenous goats. In the case of the springbok, there is some evidence that cropping increases the lambing percentage (Van Zyl and Skinner, 1970). Removal of the lambs at a relatively early age apparently reduces the stress on the ewes due to lactation, and they come into oestrus sooner.

(d) The relative tolerance of many game species to endemic disease and parasites.

There is a tacit assumption in the major part of the game-cropping literature that the disease factor can largely be ignored in wild game. This is definitely not the case. Hammond and Branagan (1973) have reviewed present knowledge of the disease spectrum in wild ruminant game in Africa and have concluded that little is known as yet of the natural incidence of disease among these animals and even less of the epidemiology under ranching conditions. Nevertheless, there is no doubt that whatever the degree of tolerance of trypanosomiasis which African wild ruminants possess, they do in practice continue to thrive in large numbers in tsetse-infested regions where most domestic livestock cannot be managed. There appear to be no specific animal health reasons why advantage should not be taken of this situation by the introduction of sustained yield game cropping.

(e) The high killing-out percentage and lean content of many game carcases.

The killing-out percentage of most game species is relatively high (Table 11.4) and the carcases of African ungulates are characteristically very lean, containing only a fraction of the fat contained by the carcases of domestic ruminants. When game animals are properly slaughtered and their carcases are properly prepared, their meat is perfectly acceptable (Talbot *et al.*, 1965) and the meat of some species is of very high quality. In a study of the quality of the meat of seven wild game species in South Africa, Von la Chevallerie (1972) reported that springbok venison rated higher in quality than that of blesbok, eland, gemsbok, red hartebeest, impala or black wildebeest.

Table 11.4 *Carcase dressing percentage of some game animals*

Name of animal	Sex	No. in sample	Carcase dressing percentage	Reference
Blesbok (*Damaliscus dorcas phillipsi*)	Male	–	52·9	Huntley (1971)
Buffalo (*Syncerus caffer*)	–	–	49·4	Young and Van Den Heever (1969)
	–	–	42·0	Roth (1966)
	Male	8	50·5 ± 2·3	Ledger *et al.* (1967)
Capybara (*Hydrochoerus hydrochoeis*)	–	–	52·0	González Jiménez and Parra (1973)
Eland (*Taurotragus oryx*)	Male (castrated)		63·2	Von La Chevallerie *et al.* (1971)
	Male	–	51·3	Von La Chevallerie *et al.* (1971)
	Male	–	57·4	Keep (1972)
	–	–	58·0	Roth (1966)
	Male	5	59·1 ± 3·6	Ledger *et al.* (1967)
Gerenuk (*Litocranius walleri*)	Male	5	65·0 ± 2·1	Ledger *et al.* (1967)
Grant's gazelle (*Gazella granti*)	Male	6	60·5 ± 2·2	Ledger *et al.* (1967)
	Female	5	59·0 ± 3·3	Ledger *et al.* (1967)
Hartebeeste (Kongoni) (*Alcelaphus caama*)	Male	5	57·2 ± 1·4	Ledger *et al.* (1967)
	Female	5	58·1 ± 2·0	Ledger *et al.* (1967)
Hippopotamus (*Hippopotamus amphibius*)	Male	4	43·0 ± 2·4	Ledger *et al.* (1967)
	Female	4	41·9 ± 2·3	Ledger *et al.* (1967)
Impala	–	41	57·4	Young and Van Den Heever (1969)
(*Aepyceros melampus*)	–	–	61·0	Roth (1966)
	Male	10	58·1 ± 0·9	Ledger *et al.* (1967)
	Female	10	58·3 ± 3·0	Ledger *et al.* (1967)
Kob (*Adenota kob*)	Male	10	57·7 ± 1·9	Ledger *et al.* (1967)
	Female	10	58·3 ± 2·9	Ledger *et al.* (1967)
Kudu (*Tragelaphus strepsiceros*)	–	18	56·6	Huntley (1971)
	–	–	56·0	Roth (1966)
Lesser Kudu (*Strepsiceros imberbis*)	Male	10	62·1 ± 1·5	Ledger *et al.* (1967)
Oryx (*Oryx beisa*)	Male	10	57·0 ± 1·7	Ledger *et al.* (1967)
	Female	10	58·9 ± 2·5	Ledger *et al.* (1967)
Springbok (*Antidorcus marsupialis marsupialis*)	–	–	57·9	Van Zyl *et al.* (1969)
Thomson's gazelle (*Gazella thomsoni*)	–	–	52·6	Hvidberg-Hansen (1971)
	–	–	60·0	Robinette and Archer (1971)
	Male	10	58·6 ± 2·1	Ledger *et al.* (1967)
	Female	10	57·1 ± 2·1	Ledger *et al.* (1967)
	Male	10	54·2 ± 1·7	Ledger *et al.* (1967)
	Female	10	53·6 ± 3·7	Ledger *et al.* (1967)

Table 11.4 (*continued*)

Name of animal	Sex	No. in sample	Carcase dressing percentage	Reference
Topi (*Damaliscus korrigum*)	Male	10	$54·2 \pm 1·9$	Ledger *et al.* (1967)
	Female	10	$54·0 \pm 2·1$	Ledger *et al.* (1967)
Warthog (*Phecochoerus aethiopicus*)	Male	10	$54·7 \pm 2·5$	Ledger *et al.* (1967)
	Female	10	$55·7 \pm 1·9$	Ledger *et al.* (1967)
Waterbuck (*Kobus ellipsiprymnus*)	Male	10	$58·6 \pm 1·4$	Ledger *et al.* (1967)
	Female	10	$58·9 \pm 1·8$	Ledger *et al.* (1967)
Wildebeeste (*Connochaetes taurinus albojubatus*)	Male	10	$55·7 \pm 1·4$	Ledger *et al.* (1967)
	Female	10	$53·2 \pm 1·6$	Ledger *et al.* (1967)
	Male	10	$50·0 \pm 3·2$	Ledger *et al.* (1967)
	Female	10	$51·4 \pm 2·2$	Ledger *et al.* (1967)
	–	–	57·7	Young *et al.* (1969)
Zebra (*Equus burchelli*)	Male	5	55·0	Ledger *et al.* (1967)
	Female	5	53·6	Ledger *et al.* (1967)
Zebu cattle (*Bos indicus*)	Male	10	$58·0 \pm 3·0$	Ledger *et al.* (1967)
	Female (thin cows)	9	$46·8 \pm 1·4$	Ledger *et al.* (1967)

Sources: As references.

(f) The high unit value of some of the by-products of game cropping, particularly in countries where there is a developed tourist industry.

Major by-products are hides and skins, horns, teeth, hair and ivory. Not all the hides and skins from game animals have a curio value, those of the kudu, wildebeest, eland and buffalo being used almost exclusively for leather production. The hides and skins of such animals as zebra, impala and many of the small gazelles and buck do, however, have an enhanced curio value. For example, in East Africa, the hide of the zebra is far more valuable than the meat. The overall economic value of these by-products may be very considerable. It has been estimated, for example, that sustained cropping of elephants in East Africa could yield ivory worth more than US$1 million per year.

(g) A tourist industry could also flourish in areas established for game-cropping purposes.

2. Disadvantages

(a) Slaughtering and processing can be both difficult to organize and expensive to operate.

There are two major possibilities. Either game can be shot on the range and processed in a mobile abattoir or they can be captured and transported to an abattoir located at a permanent site.

Von la Chevallerie and Van Zyl (1971) studied the effect of shooting on the quality of seventy-four springbok and impala carcases. They found that 14 per cent of the total weight of carcase was unfit for human consumption on account of bullet damage. They also noted that the stress of the chase and the death struggle had a detrimental effect on meat quality. Possibly the most efficient ways of shooting game on the range are either from a 'hide' or at night with the aid of a spotlight. It is certainly easier to organize the slaughter and processing of large animals, such as elephants, than it is of gazelles.

It is considered that, in general, the capture of game before slaughter would be a difficult and expensive operation (Plate 11.1). Apparently

Plate 11.1 Netting deer in Mauritius.

blesbok and springbok are amenable to being driven, but most attempts to drive game into funnel-type stockades have ended in failure. The possibility of using light aircraft to drive game towards selected slaughter points is at present under investigation.

If game meat is dried in the field to produce 'biltong', some of the major problems of field slaughter and processing can be overcome. This is, of course, one of the methods employed by poachers. Biltong is, however, no substitute for fresh meat, and the total value of carcases used for biltong production is lower than that of carcases used for fresh meat production.

(b) Marketing difficulties.

On account of the difficulties encountered in slaughtering and processing, most fresh game meat will inevitably be expensive. Under these circumstances, as the purchasing power of the indigenous people may not match their desire for game meat, poaching may become more popular than purchase. The possible exception to this situation is where large game animals producing relatively coarse meat, such as elephant, buffalo and hippopotami, are cropped.

Export possibilities are usually restricted, not by the high price of game meat but by the incidence of epizootic disease in game-cropping regions, in particular foot and mouth disease and rinderpest.

Even where there is a local demand for game meat, marketing difficulties may be serious. Local vested marketing interests may refuse to handle game meat so that a new and possibly expensive marketing organization has to be established.

(c) Game ownership.

In most countries in Africa, and perhaps elsewhere, there are serious legal problems with regard to the ownership of game. Who is to benefit when hunting is superseded by game cropping in those countries where land is owned communally? The indigenous people, the organizers of game cropping or the government? Unfortunately, most indigenous people do not usually possess either the capital or the technical knowledge to organize their own game-cropping schemes.

The situation in the Amboseli Game Reserve in Kenya, although not concerned with game cropping, well illustrates this problem. This reserve includes some 2,072 km^2 (800 miles^2) of Masai grazings, the most important section being 78 km^2 (30 miles^2) known as the Ol-Tukai swamp, where there is always dry-season grazing. This swamp area has to support 25,000 head of Masai-owned domestic livestock and at least 8,000 head of game for several months of the year. The Masai livestock owners question whether they can continue to support such a large game population at the expense of their own herds. At the present time, however, the local Kajiado District Council, in whose area the game reserve is located, derives half of its total revenue from tourist fees. It has been estimated that by the end of the century, the maximum return from the Masai domestic livestock would not exceed US$0·4 million, but that tourist fees could amount to US$1.25 million per annum. Thus, the economic balance is clearly in favour of retention of the game, even at the expense of the domestic livestock. Unfortunately, however, the individual Masai livestock owner does not receive any income from tourist fees and his district council is a rather remote bureaucratic organization.

There is no doubt that if game-cropping schemes are to be successful in areas where land is held communally, then they must be organized in such a way that the indigenous people understand and see that they will benefit economically.

(d) The cost of the required infrastructure.

Game cropping for sustained yield requires an extensive and expensive organization to establish the biological parameters of local game species and to conduct annual population surveys, etc. Policing costs must also increase if poaching is to be contained.

Despite the apparent advantages of game cropping, the industry has not progressed at the speed which was expected by enthusiasts a decade ago. This is presumably because the disadvantages often outweigh the advantages.

Progress has been most rapid in South Africa, where there are many private farm schemes. There is a major government game-cropping scheme in the Luanga Game Reserve in Zambia. Elephant have been cropped in Kenya and hippopotami in Uganda. The Food and Agriculture Organization and the United Nations Development Programme are at present developing a cropping scheme in Kenya, and it is estimated that this scheme will produce 5 million kg (11 million lb) of meat per year and could increase Kenya's total meat supply by 4 to 5 per cent.

The management of game on ranches and farms

Domestic livestock and game have coexisted in some areas for very long periods, particularly in East Africa. However, the game in these areas has never been managed in any way and is likely to eventually disappear unless positive plans are made for its conservation and for sustained cropping.

In addition, there are some ranches and farms in South, Central and East Africa where game animals graze within fenced areas, with or without domestic livestock, and where some degree of management is exercised.

Pioneer work on game ranching was conducted in Rhodesia in the early 1950s, the results being published by Dassman (1964). In South Africa, according to Skinner (1973), farmers can exercise lawful ownership of wild springbok and blesbok by enclosing them in ordinary paddocks. Progress has apparently been rapid in the Transvaal region of South Africa as Riney and Kettlitz (1964) reported that game were being used on over 3,000 farms and that these farms produced annually 3·2 million kg (7 million lb) of game meat. Currently, investigations are in progress in East Africa. Parker and Graham (1973), reporting on the commercial use of Thomson's gazelle and impala on a Kenya beef ranch, stated that the carcases could be processed according to the standards of hygiene applied to domestic livestock and that only 3·3 per cent of them were condemned as unfit for human consumption.

1. *Advantages*

(a) The maximization of biomass.

It is possible, but not yet proven, that wild game and domestic livestock managed on the same area will provide the highest biomass per unit area which can be achieved, particularly if the game animals possess different eating habits and food preferences to the domestic livestock. Watson *et al.* (1969) have stated that in East

Africa the presence of domestic livestock does not necessarily reduce the productivity of wild game.

(b) Economy in infrastructure.

The cropping, processing of carcases and marketing of game produce should be easier and more economical than in schemes for the sustained cropping of wild game as some facilities and infrastructure will already exist on the ranch or farm for the handling of domestic livestock.

2. *Disadvantages*

(a) Animal health.

The game animals may act as a reservoir for epizootic disease and parasites. These may then spread to the domestic animals. This problem is discussed by Hammond and Brannagan (1973).

(b) Absence of a tourist industry.

It is unlikely that a tourist industry could be developed in farming areas, whereas such an industry could provide a major source of income in areas where wild game are cropped.

Domestication of wild game

It is an astonishing fact that only a very few of the total number of available species have ever been domesticated and that almost all present domestic species were domesticated during the Neolithic revolution. There is some evidence that man did attempt to domesticate some additional species (Zeuner, 1963), but that he failed or at least lost interest. For example, the Egyptians semi-domesticated the addax. There are pictures in an Egyptian tomb dated 2500 BC showing addax wearing collars and tethered to stakes. It must be assumed that the few species which were domesticated satisfied man's need for domestic livestock until recent times.

With the present need to exploit all ecosystems to the maximum, it is perhaps a suitable time to consider further attempts at domestication.

The only major attempt being made at the present time is the domestication of the eland (*Taurotragus oryx*). Work has been conducted both in Africa and the USSR. Posselt (1963) reported that a herd of approximately twenty eland have been domesticated in Rhodesia. He stated that adult males and females weigh 730 kg (1,600 lb) and 540 kg (1,200 lb), respectively. Heifers calve at 2 years of age and the gestation period is approximately 34 weeks. The dressing-out percentage of the carcases of mature stock is 58 to 60. Lombard (1966) reported that, in South Africa where eland were fed indoors, the average liveweight gain was 0·5 kg (1·13 lb) per day, and calves attained a liveweight of 136 kg (300 lb) at 5 months of age.

Treus and Lobanov (1971) reviewed details of the acclimatization and domestication of eland at Askaniya-Nova in the southern Ukraine. The attempt at domestication began in 1890, was accomplished by hand-feeding of the young and proceeded to the point when experimental milking could begin in 1947. The eland were allowed to graze freely during the summer months and were penned indoors during the winter months. A total of forty-four females were milked between 1947 and 1971. The average lactation yield was 200 kg (441 lb), the lactation period varying from 100 to 390 days. The peak milk yield of the best milker was 6·9 kg (15·2 lb) per day. The average fat and protein percentages of the milk were 11 and 8, respectively. Mature males and females weighed up to 800 kg (1,764 lb) and 500 kg (1,102 lb), respectively. They stated that the meat was of excellent quality and that the hide was valuable.

Skinner *et al.* (1971) have suggested that there is evidence that two sub-species of the springbok, *Antidorcus marsupialis marsupialis* and *A. marsupialis angolensis*, could be at least semi-domesticated as they are more tractable than most antelopes and can be herded in paddocks.

Attempts are also being made in Africa to domesticate Thomson's gazelle, the red letchwe and the buffalo.

Some consideration should also be given to the domestication of species other than ungulates, such as the turtle in the Caribbean, the grasscutter in West Africa and the capybara in the *llanos* of Colombia and Venezuela.

The advantage of using domesticated or semi-domesticated wild game species is that animal health, slaughter, processing and marketing problems are minimized. The immediate disadvantage is that domestication is a slow and tenuous process and that, even when a wild species has been domesticated, it will be many years before a sufficient number of animals are available for economic exploitation.

Game carcases and meat

Game carcases in the tropics differ quite markedly from the carcases of domestic livestock. The major difference is that the fat content of the carcase is much lower and the lean meat content correspondingly higher. For example, in the Uganda kob (*Adenota kob*), the carcase fat per centage is 6·2 (Ledger and Smith, 1964).

The lean constant, obtained by expressing the weight of lean meat in a carcase as a percentage of the total carcase weight, differs markedly as between game and domesticated livestock (Table 11.5). This constant appears to be unvarying irrespective of age, liveweight and killing-out percentage.

The killing-out percentage of some game animals is also comparable with those of domestic livestock (Table 11.4).

Surprisingly, the percentage hindquarters in game animals is as good, if not better, than in indigenous cattle. Ledger (1963a) reported that it was 58 per cent in Thomson's gazelle compared with 53 per cent in Boran

Table 11.5   *A comparison of the lean constants of game animals and domestic livestock*

Species	Lean constant
Goats	31
Bos taurus-type cattle	32
Bos indicus-type cattle	33
Wildebeest	42
Oryx	45
Thomson's gazelle	46

Sources: Ledger (1963a) and Ledger (1964a).

cattle, while Ledger and Smith (1964) reported that all except the most mature Uganda kob possessed a better hindquarter than Boran cattle.

Ledger (1963a) stated the weight of the fat-free empty digestive tract expressed as a percentage of the total liveweight is approximately the same in ruminant game animals and Boran steers.

It may be concluded that game animals kill-out at almost as high a per centage as well-managed cattle and that their carcases possess a high proportion of hindquarters. The meat is leaner than that of cattle and is, therefore, not so succulent but, according to Ledger (1963a), it is usually tender and possesses a good flavour. These observations from East Africa have been confirmed in South Africa by Von la Chevallerie (1972).

References

Australian Conservation Foundation (1967) Conservation of kangaroos. Viewpoint Series. *Aust. Conserv. Fdn.* (1), 6 pp.
Bonsma, F. N. (1951) In A. Welsh (ed.), *Livestock Production. Africa, South of the Sahara*, p. 125. Oxford Univ. Press: London.
Child, G. (1964) Growth and ageing criteria of impala (*Aepyceros melampus*). *Occ. Pap. Nat. Mus. Rhod.*, **27**, 128–35.
Crawford, M. A. (1968) Possible use of wild animals as future sources of food in Africa. *Vet. Rec.*, **82**, 305–315.
Dassman, R. F. (1963) In Watterson, G. G. (ed.), *Game Ranching in Africa: Land-use Planning. Conservation of Nature and Natural Resources in Modern African States*, p. 133. IUCN: Morges, Switzerland.
Dassman, R. F. (1964) *African Game Ranching.* Pergamon Press: London.
Dassman, R. F. and Mossman, A. S. (1961) The Wildlife Society: Davis, California.
Du Plessis, S. S. (1972) Ecology of blesbok with special reference to productivity. *Wildlife Monographs*, 30. The Wildlife Society: USA.
Estes, R. D. (1966) Behaviour and life history of the wildebeest (*Connochaetes taurinus* Burchell). *Nature (Lond.)*, **212**, 999–1000.
González Jiménez, E. and Parra, R. (1973) The capybara, a meat-producing animal for

the flooded areas of the tropics. *IIIrd World Conference on Animal Production*, Pre-Conference Volume, No. 2, Presented Papers – Tomes 1 and 3. Melbourne, Australia, 1 (b), 1–8.

Grimsdell, J. J. R. (1973) Reproduction in the African buffalo (*Syncerus caffer*) in Western Uganda. *J. Reprod. Fert.*, Suppl. 19, 303–18.

Hammond, J. A. and Branagan, D. (1973) The disease factor in plans for the domestication of wild ruminants in Africa. *Vet. Rec.*, **92**, 367–9.

Harthoorn, A. H. (1961) *Some Aspects of Game Cropping*. Conference on land management problems in areas containing game. Lake Manyara, Tanganyika, 20–22 Feb. 1961.

Huntley, B. J. (1971) Carcase composition of the mature male blesbok and kudu. *S. Afr. J. Anim. Sci.*, **1**, 125–8.

Hvidberg-Hansen, H. (1971) Management and utilisation of Thompson's gazelles on a cattle and sheep ranch in the Kenya highlands. *E. Afr. Agric. For. J.*, **36**, 322–33.

Joubert, D. M. (1968) An appraisal of game production in South Africa. *Trop. Sci.*, **10**, 200–11.

Keep, M. E. (1972) The meat yield, parasites and pathology of eland in Natal. *The Lammergeyer*, **17**, 1–19.

Kettlitz, W. K. (1967) The blesbok (*Damaliscus dorcas phillipsi*) with special reference to the herd in the Percy Fyfe Nature Reserve. *Fauna and Flora (Pretoria)*, **18**, 36–46.

Lamprey, H. F. (1964) Estimation of the large mammal densities, biomass and energy exchange in the Tarangire Game Reserve and the Masai Steppe in Tanganyika. *E. Afr. Wildl. J.*, **2**, 1–46.

Ledger, H. P. (1963a) A note on the relative body composition of wild and domesticated ruminants. *Bull. epiz. Dis. Afr.*, **11**, 163–5.

Ledger, H. P. (1963b) Weights of some East African mammals. *E. Afr. Wildl. J.*, **1**, 123.

Ledger, H. P. (1964a) The role of wildlife in African Agriculture. *E. Afr. agric. For. J.*, **30**, 137–41.

Ledger, H. P. (1964b) Weights of some East African mammals, II. *E. Afr. Wildl. J.*, **2**, 159.

Ledger, H. P. and Smith, N. S. (1964) The carcass and body composition of the Uganda Kob. *J. Wildlife Mgmt.*, **28**, 827–39.

Ledger, H. P., Sacks, R. and Smith, N. S. (1967) Wildlife and food production. *World Rev. Anim. Prod.*, **3**, (11) 13–37.

Leuthold, W. (1972) Gestation period in Thomson's gazelle. *E. Afr. Wildl. J.*, **10** (4), 309–10.

Lombard, J. (1966) *The Meat Industry (South Africa)*, p. 21, March.

Parker, I. S. C. and Graham, A. D. (1973) Commercial use of Thomson's gazelle (*Gazella thomsoni* Gunther) and impala (*Aepycerus melampus* Lichtenstein) on a Kenya beef ranch. *III World Conference on Animal Production*, Pre-Conference Volume No. 2, Presented Papers – Tomes 1 and 3, Melbourne, Australia, 1 (c), 1–13.

Payne, W. J. A. (1968) Development of animal husbandry resources in Southeast Asia. *Proc. Conf. Conservation in Tropical Southeast Asia, Bangkok, Thailand*, 29 Nov.–4 Dec. 1965, (4), pp. 125–31.

Posselt, J. (1963) The domestication of the eland. *Rhod. J. agric. Res.*, **1**, 81–7.

Riney, T. and Kettlitz, W. K. (1964) Management of large mammals in the Transvaal. *Mammalia*, **28**, 189–248.

Robinette, W. L. and Archer, A. L. (1971) Notes on ageing criteria and reproduction of Thomson's gazelle. *E. Afr. Wildl. J.*, **9**, 83–98.

Roth, H. H. (1966) Game utilisation in Rhodesia in 1964. *Mammalia*, **30** (3), 397.

Sharman, G. B. (1967) The red kangaroo. *Sci. J. (Lond.)*, **3** (3), 52–60.

Skinner, J. D. (1967) An appraisal of the eland as a farm animal in Africa. *Anim. Breed. Abstr.*, **35**, 177–86.

Skinner, J. D. (1973) An appraisal of the status of certain antelope for game farming in South Africa. *Z. Tierzüch. ZüchtBiol.* (90), 263–77.

Skinner, J. D., Von la Chevallerie, M. and van Zyl, J. H. M. (1971) An appraisal of the springbok for diversifying animal production in Africa. *Anim. Breed. Abstr.*, **39**, 215–24.

Talbot, L. M. (1966) Wild animals as a source of food. *Bureau of Sport, Fisheries and Wildl. Special Sci. Rep. – Wildlife*, No. 98. Washington.

Talbot, L. M., Payne, W. J. A., Ledger, H. P., Verdcourt, D. L. and Talbot, M. H. (1965) The meat production potential of wild animals in Africa. *Tech. Comm. Comw. Bur. Anim. Breed. Genet.*, No. 16. Comw. Agric. Bur.: Farnham Royal, UK.

Taylor, C. R. and Lyman, C. P. (1967) A comparative study of the environmental physiology of an East African antelope, the eland, and the Hereford steer. *Physiol. Zool.*, **40**, 280–95.

Treus, V. D. and Lobanov, N. V. (1971) Acclimatization and domestication of the eland (*Taurotragus oryx*) at Askaniya-Nova Zoological Gardens. *Int. Zoo Yb.*, **11**, 147–56. *Abstracted: Anim. Breed. Abstr.*, **39**, 581 (1971).

Van Zyl, J. H. M. and Skinner, J. D. (1970) Growth and development of the springbok foetus. *Afr. Wildlife*, **24**.

Von la Chevallerie, M. (1972) Meat quality of seven wild ungulate species. *S. Afr. J. Anim. Sci.*, **2**, 101–3.

Von la Chevallerie, M. and Van Zyl, J. H. M. (1971) Growth and carcass development of the springbok (*Antidorcas marsupialis marsupialis Zimmerman*). *Agro-animalia*, **3**, 115–23.

Von la Chevallerie, M., Erasmus, J. M., Skinner, J. D. and Van Zyl, J. H. M. (1971) A note on the carcass composition of the common eland (*Taurotragus oryx*). *S. Afr. J. Anim. Sci.*, 1, 129–31.

Van Zyl, J. H. M., Von la Chevallerie, M. and Skinner, J. D. (1969) A note on the dressing percentage in the springbok (*Antidorcas marsupialis Zimmerman*) and impala (*Aepyceros melampus*). *Proc. S. Afr. Soc. Anim. Prod.*, **8**, 199–200.

Vu Ngoc Tan (1968) The raising of deer, an attractive resource for developing countries in Southeast Asia. *Proc. Conf. Conservation in Tropical Southeast Asia, Bangkola, Thailand. Nov. 29th–Dec. 4th 1965*, **4**, 132–4.

Watson, R. M. (1969) Reproduction of wildebeest (*Connochaetes taurinus albojubatus* Thomas) in the Serengeti region and its significance to conservation. *J. Reprod. Fert.*, Suppl. **6**, 287.

Watson, R. M., Graham, A. D. and Parker, I. S. C. (1969) A census of the large mammals of Loliondo Controlled Area, Northern Tanzania. *E. Afr. Wildl. J.*, **7**, 43–59.

Young, E. and Van Den Heever, L. W. (1969) The African buffalo as a source of food and by-products. *J. S. Afr. Vet. Med. Ass.*, **40**, 83–8.

Young, E., Wagner, L. J. J. and Bronkhorst, P. J. L. (1969) The blue wildebeest as a source of feed and by-products. The production potential, parasites and pathology of free-living wildebeest of the Kruger National Park. *J. S. Afr. Vet. Med. Ass.*, **40**, 315–18.

Zeuner, F. E. (1963) *A History of Domesticated Animals*. Hutchinson: London.

Chapter 12

Pigs

The primary purpose of pig farming all over the world is the production of meat, including pork, bacon or fat. Secondary considerations are the production of pigskin, bristles and manure.

In the tropics fresh pork has always been and continues to be the most important type of pig meat, but elsewhere processed meat is produced in large quantities, probably because pig flesh can be more effectively preserved with salt than can other types of meat. Processed pork is now finding a ready acceptance among many consumers in tropical countries and consumer preferences are slowly changing everywhere as industrialization advances.

Pigskin has generally been used only for the manufacture of light leather goods and its production has been localized, as has the production of pig bristles. However, the introduction of synthetic leather fabric and bristles may ultimately reduce demand for these natural products.

Pig manure is useful everywhere: as a fertilizer, either for the soil or for fish ponds; for the production of methane gas; and for the culture of algae such as chlorella that can be used as an animal feed. Pig manure contains on average 0·70, 0·68 and 0·70 per cent of nitrogen, phosphorus and potassium, respectively.

Another advantage of pig farming that is now becoming apparent in some tropical countries is that on account of the pig's high fecundity and growth rate, pig production can yield a relatively rapid rate of return on the capital employed.

The worldwide distribution of pigs

The pig is omnivorous and in some respects competitive with man for food, but is also a very useful utilizer of the by-products and wastes from human feeding. Thus pigs are usually most numerous where human food is cheap and plentiful and where there are large quantities of by-products or offals available. The size of the pig population of any given region also, of course, depends upon other factors, for example the climate – only a small number of pigs being found in the arid areas of the world –

542   *Pigs*

and the social and religious beliefs of the indigenous people, there being
few pigs in countries with a predominantly Mohammedan population.
   The distribution on a continental basis of the world's pig population
is shown in Table 12.1. It will be seen that approximately one-fifth of

Table 12.1   *The world's pig population*

Continent and/or region	Pig population ('000)			1972 population as percentage of world total
	1961–65	*1972*	*1972 as percentage of 1961–65*	
Europe	113,830	144,163	127	21·2
USSR	57,809	71,434	124	10·5
Africa	5,406	7,115	132	1·0
Tropics	3,770	5,571	148	0·8
Other	1,636	1,544	94	0·2
Americas	142,172	171,395	121	25·2
Tropics	71,933	89,394	124	13·1
Other	70,239	82,001	117	12·1
Asia	234,367	281,857	120	41·5
Tropics	28,158	37,650	134	5·6
China	196,917	231,079	117	34·0
Other*	9,292	13,128	141	1·9
Oceania	2,513	4,102	163	0·6
Tropics	622	1,102	177	0·2
Other	1,891	3,000	159	0·4
World	556,097	680,066	122	
Tropics	104,483	133,717	128	19·7
Other	451,614	546,349	121	80·3

* Excludes the Asiatic regions of the USSR.
Source: FAO (1973).

the world's pigs are to be found in the tropics and that the pig population
in the tropics is increasing more rapidly than that in the mid-latitude
regions.
   One-third of the total world population of pigs is to be found in China.
It is not known what proportion of these are reared in the sub-tropical
and tropical areas of that country. Of the remainder of the world's pig
population approximately 1, 6 and 13 per cent are to be found in tropical
Africa, tropical Asia outside China and the tropical Americas,
respectively.
   The major centres of pig farming in the tropics are in the non-
Mohammedan areas of Southeast Asia where fresh pork is the major
product, in Brazil where the lard-producing pig was very important in

the past, and in other regions of South and Central America and in some island communities in the Pacific Ocean and the Caribbean. Pig farming is relatively unimportant in almost all regions of Africa, in western Asia and in the Indian sub-continent.

Tropical countries with a total of more than one million pigs in 1972 are shown in Table 12.2.

Table 12.2　*Countries in the tropics with more than one million pigs in 1972*

Continent	Country	Number of pigs (million)
Americas	Bolivia	1·000
	Brazil*	67·000*
	Colombia	1·540
	Cuba	1·450
	Dominican Republic	1·100
	Ecuador	1·390
	Haiti	1·602
	Mexico (part)†	6·154†
	Peru	2·071
	Venezuela	1·691
Asia	Burma	1·600
	India (part)†	2·390†
	Indonesia	4·225
	Khmer Republic	1·100
	Laos	1·200
	Philippines	7·742
	Singapore	1·140
	Thailand	5·200
	Vietnam	10·982

* A large proportion of the pigs in Brazil are raised in the south where the climate is sub-tropical rather than tropical. This is therefore an overestimate of the number within tropical Brazil.
† An estimate has been made of what proportion of Mexico and India are within the tropics.
Source: FAO (1973).

Origin of domestic pigs

There are two conflicting theories as to the origin of domestic pigs. One is that they were independently domesticated at centres in several different regions. The other is that they were domesticated at one centre – in western Asia – and that domestic pigs were gradually diffused from this centre into Southeast Asia, Europe and Africa. Epstein (1971) has, for example, stated that the presence of the domestic pig at Cayöny in southeast Anatolia, Turkey (*c.* 7000 BC), antedates its appearance in all other centres by several centuries. It was apparently domesticated in China in Neolithic times, possibly around 3000 BC (Epstein, 1969).

Today there is a very wide distribution of wild and feral pigs and it is generally believed that all present domesticated breeds have been derived in one way or another from two wild types: *Sus vittatus*, synonym *S. scrofa cristatus*, the wild pig of east and southeast Asia, and *S. scrofa*, the present European wild pig, which may also have existed during the past in western Asia.

Some pigs of the *Sus vittatus* type may have been introduced into Europe in very early times as the Neolithic settlers brought domestic livestock with them from the east (Zeuner, 1963). What is certain is that the Siamese pig, sometimes identified by the separate specific name *S. indicus*, was introduced into the Mediterranean region of Europe in Roman times and was crossbred with local pigs to produce what came to be known later as the Neopolitan pig.

Towards the end of the eighteenth century the typical Old English pig was large and heavy-boned, standing on long legs, possessing narrow and light hams and a highly arched and narrow back. It was usually sandy or reddish brown in colour and its hair was coarse. Its ears were large and floppy. It was very active in foraging but slow maturing. Sows were prolific and good milkers.

From 1770 to 1870 Chinese pigs were introduced into Britain and crossbred with the Old English pigs. It is believed that these imported pigs originated mainly from the Canton area. They were mostly white in colour, but a few were pied or black; possessing a wide head and a dished face, short erect ears, short legs with light hams and a drooping back. They were introduced principally because of their prolificacy and their characteristic of early maturity associated with a capacity to fatten. Some Siamese pigs were also imported into Britain at about the same time. These were of the same general type as the Cantonese pigs, but they possessed black hair and a rich, copper-coloured skin. Later, in 1830, pigs of the Neopolitan breed, black with no bristles, were also introduced into Britain and crossbred with local types. It was the crossbreeding of Chinese, Siamese and Neapolitan pigs with the Old English pig that produced the ancestors of the modern British breeds.

In early colonial days in America pigs of the Old English type were imported, as were pigs from continental Europe. Later these pigs were crossed with improved British breeds and with pigs from Southeast Asia and other parts of the world. Thus modern British and American breeds have been derived from crosses that included Southeast Asian, Mediterranean and European pigs.

Although wild pigs are indigenous in Europe and Asia and possibly in North and Northeast Africa, they were probably introduced by man and are feral in North, Central and South America, the Caribbean, Australasia and the Pacific and Indian Ocean islands.

The original domestic pigs of Central and South America were introduced by the Spanish in the fifteenth century, first into the Caribbean islands and later to the mainland. They were presumably Mediterranean-type pigs, many of them hairless.

Throughout Southeast Asia domestic breeds similar to the Chinese and Siamese type are still found, although they are rapidly disappearing as they are being upgraded by the use of exotic breeds.

Domestic pigs are scarce in the African countries inhabited by Hamitic and Semitic peoples, and in the Congo. There are, however, domestic pigs in the Cameroun Republic and in other countries on the West African coast. These pigs are small, usually black in colour and possess erect ears. It is probable that they are related to the Mediterranean-type pig.

In Australasia domestic pigs were imported mainly from Britain.

Today, everywhere in the tropics, indigenous breeds are being up-graded or replaced by imported, exotic breeds, particularly of British, American and Scandinavian origin, as it has been found that these latter breeds will generally thrive in the tropics if they are properly fed and managed, and they are invariably more productive than the indigenous pigs. Thus pigs with more or less the same ancestry are now found everywhere in the tropical world.

Major breeds used in the tropics

Pig breeds may be classified into three types: pork, bacon and lard pro-ducers. In this section details of the major British and American breeds are given first as they have been used so widely in the tropics for upgrad-ing and crossbreeding purposes. Some details are also given of other recognized breeds, although it will be appreciated that there is little information available concerning some of them.

Unless otherwise stated, a major part of the information on the breeds has been derived from the publications of Mason (1969) and Davidson (1948).

British breeds

Berkshire. This is the British breed that was first brought to a high standard of perfection. In 1790 Berkshires were described as very large, black in colour, long and crooked snouted, with a long, thick but not deep body and short legs. Around 1800 the original type was crossed with Chinese pigs and later with Siamese and Neapolitan pigs. Today there are two distinct types – the British pork type that is characterized by early maturity and medium fecundity, and the Canadian type that is slower maturing and is used for bacon production. The modern Berkshire is a medium-sized animal, black in colour with six white points on the feet, nose and tail, respectively. The ears are erect, the nose short and the face somewhat dished. The Berkshire is well liked and widely used in tropical countries.

Large Black.   A breed developed by crossbreeding indigenous pigs from the eastern counties of England and Neapolitan pigs. It is a long, black pig with lop ears and good hams and is considered a good grazer and mother. It can be utilized for the production of pork or bacon and has been used extensively for crossing with indigenous pigs in various regions of the tropics.

Large White or Yorkshire.   The influence of this breed has probably been more widespread than that of any other, but within the breed there is a great deal of variation in type between individuals. This may account in part for its adaptability under varying conditions. It is a large, long, white pig with a body neither as wide or as deep as the lard-type pigs (Plate 12.1). It is probably the most prolific of all British or American breeds and the sows are heavy milkers and good mothers. Although pigs of this breed are not very quick in maturing they are efficient converters of feed, being used primarily for the production of bacon in the temperate zone and pork in the tropics. They are also widely used in crossbreeding programmes. Unfortunately, pigs of this breed are very susceptible to sunburn, especially at the base of their ears.

Middle White.   This breed has been developed from the same basic stock as the Large White, but it demonstrates more influence of the Chinese pig than any other British breed. It has been extensively used in Southeast Asia to upgrade Chinese-type pigs, but it is not now popular in Britain on account of the relatively fat carcase that it produces.

Tamworth.   This is a breed developed in the West Midlands of England. Davidson (1948) stated that the foundation boar used for fixing the golden or chestnut colour was a jungle pig imported from India by Sir Francis Lawley of Middleton Hall, Tamworth, around 1800. The Tamworth is a long, narrow pig with coarse hair, is usually considered slow maturing and is used for the production of bacon pigs. In many respects it is the most undeveloped of all the British breeds. It is thrifty, very hardy and less susceptible to sunburn than many other temperate-type breeds. It has been widely used in crossbreeding programmes and it can be a very useful breed in those tropical countries where feeding and management are not of the highest standard.

Other British breeds, of which there are many, have been little used in the tropics.

American breeds

Duroc Jerseys.   These were large, red-skinned pigs of the lard type, noted for their feed capacity and fecundity. They originated in the eastern region of the United States and there is some controversy as to their ancestry. They probably developed from a mixture of Old English colonial breeds,

Plate 12.1   Large White boar (G. S. McCann).

Plate 12.2   Duroc (United Duroc Swine Registry, Peoria, Illinois).

red Guinea pigs from West Africa and red Mediterranean-type pigs from the Iberian peninsula. During recent times the Duroc (Plate 12.2) has been transformed by selective breeding from a lard- to a pork-type breed, and because of its colour and hardiness is popular both in Southeast Asia and in the American tropics.

Hampshire. These pigs are very distinctive in appearance as they are coloured black with a white belt around the forequarter of the body. They are medium in size, prolific, good nursing mothers and efficient converters of feed. The breed is quite popular in the American tropics.

Poland China. This is a very large, lard-type pig, well fitted to convert maize into fat meat. It is similar in colouring to the Berkshire except that it has a white point on its nose. It is used to some extent in the American tropics as it is an efficient feed converter.

Other American breeds have not been used very extensively in the tropics.

Other breeds from the mid-latitudes

Landrace. There are now several types of Landrace – Danish, Swedish, American, etc. The first Landrace breed to achieve prominence was the Danish. It was derived from crossbreds between Large White boars imported from Britain in 1895 and local sows. Selective breeding and progeny testing were then used to produce the very excellent, long, all-white, bacon type pig that is characteristic of the breed. The Swedish Landrace was derived from the Danish. American Landrace are derived from the Scandinavian Landrace types but are said to possess some genes from the Poland China breed.

Landrace pigs (Plate 12.3) have been widely used for crossbreeding purposes in the tropics, particularly in Southeast Asia. They thrive under close confinement feeding, but they must be well managed and fed. Certain strains exhibit weakness of the feet and all Landrace are very susceptible to sunburn.

Craon and Edelschwein. These pigs have also been exported to the tropics from Europe, but they have made no particular impact and are of no importance in tropical countries.

There are a number of other European breeds that are important in Europe, but they have not been utilized in the tropics.

Southeast Asian breeds

Cantonese – synonym: Pearl River Delta. This is the characteristic black and white sway-back type of pig indigenous to south China (Plate 12.4). It is usually called the *Chinese* in Britain and the *Macao* in Portugal

Plate 12.3   Danish Landrace boar (Sales and Export Organisation for Breeding Pigs, Axelborg, Copenhagen).

Plate 12.4   South Chinese type sow (from Epstein, 1969).

and Brazil. The head is small with a moderately dished profile; the back is hollow and the belly pendulous. It is very fecund. The average litter size is twelve and litters of up to twenty are not uncommon (Epstein, 1969). The number of teats possessed by the sows range from fourteen to sixteen. Fat pigs weigh approximately 75 kg (165 lb) at 12 months of age. Sows farrow twice a year and gilts are bred at 5 months old (Phillips *et al.*, 1945). The sows are said to be excellent mothers and piglet mortality due to 'overlaying' is low as the sow always lies down very carefully. Pigs of this breed are said to exhibit some tolerance of kidney worm and liver fluke. A variety of the Cantonese is the *White Yanghang* or *Szechwan*, which is characterized by black spectacles around the eyes.

Other breeds found in the tropical and sub-tropical areas of southern China are the *Wansham*, a dwarf breed from Hainan Island, the lop-eared pigs of *Northern Kwangtung* that are also very fecund, and the *Luchwan* of Kwangsi (Epstein, 1969).

Chinese or Malayan.   Formerly common in Malaysia but now rare due to continuous upgrading. This breed has been extensively crossed in the past with Middle White and Large Black pigs and more recently with Large White and Landrace.

Vietnamese, Laos and Thai.   These breeds are very similar to the Chinese and have also been extensively upgraded.

Balinese and Sumba.   A large, black lard-type pig of the sway-back conformation. Virtually every household in Bali owns a few that scavenge around outside the house. It is a very hardy and prolific breed and has been exported to other islands in the Indonesian archipelago.

Philippine pigs – the Ilocos, Jalajala and Koronadal.   These are three Philippine sway-back breeds that are usually black in colour. They are rather small and less prolific than the Cantonese or the Malayan. They are disappearing rapidly as they are upgraded by the use of exotic breeds. The University of Philippines College of Agriculture has recently produced a crossbred (50 per cent Large White; 25 per cent Landrace; 25 per cent Philippine indigenous pig) that is said to combine high feed efficiency, fast growth and good carcase quality.

Burmese and Chin Dwarf.   The Burmese is generally black in colour, while the Chin Dwarf is very small, weighing approximately 30 kg (66 lb) at maturity.

Iban or Kayan breed of Sarawak.   Pigs of this breed (Plate 12.5) are said to be direct descendants of the wild pig, *Sus vittatus*. They certainly possess a distinctive appearance. They are rather small and the normal coat colour appears to be black or black and white. They possess a very

Plate 12.5 Typical Iban longhouse sow in Sarawak.

long snout and a head that is narrow between the eyes, with a short neck and small, erect ears. Their back is slightly concave and there is a line of coarse bristles along it that are erected when they become angry. Their belly is somewhat convex but does not drag on the ground. They are not very productive.

African breeds

West African. There are many different types found throughout West Africa that appear to have a common origin, their ancestors possibly coming from the Mediterranean. They vary somewhat in colour, being black, white or pied. They generally have a poor conformation, are not very fecund, grow slowly and are generally unproductive. The *Bakosi* from Cameroun is probably the best-known breed. It is a small, black, long-bodied pig possessing a long, conical head. Exotic breeds are now used throughout this region.

Elsewhere, there are some very poor types of domestic pig in isolated areas of the Sudan and adjacent countries. All domestic pigs in East, Central and South Africa have originated from imported stock.

Central and South American breeds

In general, the breeds descended from pigs introduced by the Spanish and Portuguese are either scavengers or were originally raised for lard production. Many of them are hairless. The *Pelon* is a hairless Mexican lard pig; the *Cuino*, said to be descended from Chinese pigs, is a small, fine-boned, curly-coated breed often crossed with Berkshires to produce the *Cuino de Pachuca*. The *Criollo* and the *Nilo* are lard-type breeds that are found in many regions of South America. The *Zungo Costeño* and *Congo Santandereano* are the common indigenous breeds of Colombia and Venezuela. The *Canastrão* and its derivative the *Pereira*, probably produced by crossing the *Canastrão* with the *Duroc*, are Brazilian lard-type pigs as are the hairless *Tatu* and the nearly hairless *Pirapitinga*, considered to be breeds of Chinese origin. The majority of pigs in the region are now derived from exotic breeds or their crosses.

Reproductive behaviour

Pigs are polyoestrus, females coming into heat on average at 21-day intervals (19 to 24 days) throughout the year. Gilts tend to have a shorter heat period than sows. Within this cycle the heat period lasts up to 48 hours. Females in heat are characterized by grunting, restlessness and by a swelling of the vulva. The period of maximum fertility in the female occurs during mid-oestrus, around the ovulation period. As the shedding of the large number of ova produced by the sow takes place over a period of several hours maximum fertilization can only be obtained with a reasonable degree of certainty by mating twice during the oestrous period. Service should therefore take place during the first day on which heat is observed and be repeated 12 to 24 hours later. Service lasts much longer in pigs than with any other farm animals except the llamoids; as long as from 5 to 20 minutes. Some authorities advocate the use of a different boar for the second service as it is claimed that this practice tends to increase average litter size by approximately 1·0 to 1·5 pigs per litter.

Gilts should be bred for the first time on or after their third heat period. This should occur when they are 6 to 8 months of age and when they weigh approximately 102 to 113 kg (225 to 250 lb). Sows may be bred at the first heat period after weaning if early weaning is practised and they are in good condition. Otherwise they should be bred at the second heat period after weaning.

Boars may be used for the first time when they are 7 to 8 months old, as long as they are well grown. They are considered to be sexually mature at 15 months of age. A mature boar should be able to serve twenty to forty times per month if he is managed together with the females. Immature boars, under 15 months of age, should be used for service no more than twenty-five times per month. Boars must be kept in a thin, thrifty condition if they are to remain sexually active. A breeding crate should be utilized when old, heavy boars are used to breed gilts. Unless matings are seasonally concentrated, the ratio of boars to females can be 1:50.

The average gestation length of pigs is 114 days (112 to 120 days) so that it is possible for a sow to produce two or more litters a year.

Infertility

The economic importance of efficient reproductive behaviour is obvious. Infertility may be due to a multiplicity of factors including genetical abnormalities in the breeding stock, poor nutrition, disease and the effect of the climatic environment. There are a number of genetical abnormalities that cause infertility and strict culling should be practised to remove gilts or sows that do not conceive after the second breeding to fertile boars. Boars with genetical defects that affect fertility should never be selected for breeding purposes. As the nutrition of pigs is usually entirely controlled by the commercial farmer, the occurrence of infertility due to nutritional causes can only be due to poor feeding and/or managerial techniques and with good management should be minimal. The major diseases that affect fertility in pigs are brucellosis and leptospirosis, but fortunately these are not common in the tropics. Nevertheless, vigilance is required to prevent reproductive inefficiency due to disease.

Effect of climate

Male sexual libido appears to be affected by the climate. Steinbach (1972b) stated that refusal to mount and ejaculate was positively related to the effective mean monthly temperature in Nigeria and that boars need more time to ejaculate during the hottest months of the year. Climate does not appear to effect the ovulation rate of female pigs. However, it does appear to affect the oestrous cycle. According to Steinbach (1972a), with female pigs in Nigeria oestrus lasts longer during the cooler months and the incidence of missed heats increases when the ambient temperature rises above 23°C (73°F). Extreme heat may increase embryonic mortality (Edwards *et al.*, 1968) and this is confirmed by an experiment conducted by Omtvedt *et al.* (1971). These workers investigated the effect of heat stress at 37·8°C (100°F) for 17 hours and at 32·2°C (90°F) for the remaining 7 hours of the day, as against a controlled temperature of 23·3°C (74°F) on first-litter gilts. They found that heat stress during the first 8 days after oestrus reduced the pregnancy rate at 30 days after oestrus by 43 per cent, while heat stress from the eighth to the sixteenth day reduced it by 21 per cent. The number of viable embryos was significantly lower in the stressed group in both periods. Heat stress during mid-pregnancy (53 to 61 days) did not appear to affect the gilts significantly in any way. On the other hand, heat stress towards the end of pregnancy (102 to 110 days) had a very significant effect on the gilts. In the stressed group two gilts died. The number of piglets born alive and stillborn were 6·0±0·76 and 5·2±0·62 in the stressed group and 10·4±0·76 and 0·4±0·62 in the control group, respectively. Of the piglets born alive 71·7 per cent survived to 21 days in the stressed group and 88·5 per cent in the control group. The results of this experiment and other evidence suggest that in the practical management of breeding pigs it is particularly important to protect sows and gilts from extreme heat stress at the time of service and for some period afterwards, and again towards the end of the gestation period.

There is some experimental evidence that the gestation period may be slightly shortened in hotter climates.

Some reproductive and other data for a sow herd at Ibadan in Nigeria are shown in Table 12.3. Fecundity is about the same as it would be in

Table 12.3   *Data from the sow herd at Ibadan in Nigeria for the years 1967 to 1969*

Trait	Breed	
	Large White*	Landrace*
Conception rate (%)	67	61
Farrowing interval (days)	176	177
No. litters per sow per year	2·1	2·1
Litter size		
No. at birth	8·9	9·2
No. at weaning	7·0	7·2
Stillborn (%)	4·5	7·5
Piglet mortality (%), birth to weaning	21·4	22·2
No. pigs reared per sow per year	14	15
Litter weight (kg (lb))		
At birth	11 (24·3)	13 (28·7)
At weaning†	42 (92·6)	44 (97·0)
Total weaning† weight per sow per		
year (kg (lb))	86 (189·6)	91 (200·6)

* Descendants of Large White and Landrace foundation stock originally imported from the United Kingdom and Sweden, respectively.
† Age at weaning, 35 days.
Source: Steinbach (1973).

the temperate zone, but weaning weights are low and the stillbirth and piglet mortality rates are high. It is not possible to state with any certainty what part of this lower productivity is due to the effects of the climatic environment.

Selection of breeding pigs

Gilts should be selected for the breeding herd at 4 to 5 months of age, when they should weigh 68 to 91 kg (150 to 200 lb). Where it is possible they should be selected on the basis of records to ensure that they do not possess any inherited defects and that they come from families noted for large litters and early sexual maturity. They should be healthy, possess sound feet, be well grown, have at least fourteen prominent teats and a good carcase conformation and they should have exhibited a rapid rate of liveweight gain and good feed conversion efficiency up to the time of selection.

As on average only one or two boars have to be selected for every fifty gilts even more care should be taken in the selection of the boar. Individual record, pedigree, family information and, if available, progeny-testing information should all be used in the selection. Progeny testing is not a general practice in tropical countries, but it is being used in Taiwan.

Artificial insemination

In most tropical countries where the pig is an important domestic animal the majority of producers only manage a small number of sows. It is obviously costly and wasteful of resources for each producer to keep a boar, as one boar can service fifty gilts or sows per year. Even if a number of producers use one boar cooperatively there is a very real danger that he will transmit disease from one farm to another. Under these circum-stances an artificial insemination (AI) programme has considerable relevance.

Unfortunately, there are at present very real problems that prevent the widespread use of AI in pigs. Boars ejaculate approximately 200 ml of semen at one time, but this semen generally declines considerably in its capacity for fertilization after one day of storage and on average one boar's ejaculate can only be diluted to inseminate eight to ten females. Nevertheless, considerable progress is constantly being made in the techniques of storage and dilution of boar semen, and sows on heat will readily stand for insemination. This is best carried out with a disposable plastic pipette that possesses a tip with a short bend, as this aids penetration of the cervix.

If the organization of an AI service for small farmers is contemplated in a tropical country, then expert advice should be sought as to the techniques to be employed and on the training of technicians.

Crossbreeding

Crossbreeding is the breeding method of choice for commercial opera-tions in the tropics, as it is in the mid-latitude regions. The expected advantages that accrue from operating a crossbreeding programme are listed in Table 12.4. These advantages are due to crossbreds exhibiting hybrid vigour; traits in which the most hybrid vigour is expressed being those with the lowest heritabilities; heritability being defined as that part of the total variability in characteristics between animals that is due to inherited traits. The generally reciprocal relationship between hybrid vigour and heritability is shown in Fig. 12.1.

There are several methods by which continuous crossbreeding might be organized. One is to practise criss-crossing or a two-breed rotation.

Table 12.4 *Expected advantages of crossbred over purebred pigs*

	Expected advantage of crossbreds as percentage of purebreds	
	First cross *Boar: Purebred* *Sow: Purebred*	*Multiple cross* *Boar: Purebred* *Sow: Crossbred*
Litter size at farrowing	0	5
Survival	7	12
Litter size at weaning	10	20
Liveweight at 154 days	11	14
Total litter weight at 154 days	22	30

Source: North Carolina State University (1967).

In this system boars of two different breeds are used in alternate generations. Another is triple crossing or a three-breed rotation. This latter system involves the use of boars from three different breeds and is based on the idea of capitalizing on particularly strong traits possessed by individuals of each of the three breeds selected.

It would be very difficult, if not impossible, for small-scale pig producers to operate continuous crossbreeding programmes. One solution to the problem of organizing a pig industry so that the small producers can use crossbred pigs would be for the government, cooperatives or private breeders to organize the distribution of crossbred gilts to small pig farms from a central crossbreeding station. Action along these lines is now under consideration in several tropical countries.

As stated earlier, exotic breeds are now used all over the tropics and the indigenous breeds have been upgraded to such an extent that in many areas they have all but disappeared. This is an undesirable situation and an effort should be made in all countries to keep at least a limited

Production trait	*Heritability*	*Hybrid vigour*
Litter size at weaning	*	***
Litter weight	*	***
Survival ability	*	***
Rate of gain	**	**
Efficiency of food conversion	**	*
Percentage lean in carcase	***	
Backfat thickness	***	
Body length	****	

Note: The relative degree of heritability or hybrid vigour is expressed by the number of asterisks.

Fig. 12.1 The relationship between heritability and the expression of hybrid vigour in some production traits of pigs.

number of purebred indigenous pigs. There are several reasons for this suggestion. First, some indigenous breeds may exhibit desirable traits needed in boars that will be required for use in continuous crossbreeding systems. An example of such a trait would be the very high prolificacy of Cantonese pigs. Secondly, indigenous pigs may exhibit traits that are not required or perhaps not even recognized as useful at the present time. Examples could be immunity to specific parasites and diseases and ability to thrive on low-nutrient-content feeds. It would be a biological tragedy if these traits were lost for ever. Finally, there is an aesthetic and cultural argument for preserving at least a minimum number of pigs of all indigenous breeds that apparently have no economic value under present circumstances.

Disease and parasites

One of the major problems confronting pig producers in the tropics, particularly in the humid regions, is the high mortality rate experienced. For example, it has, been reported from the Philippines that the mortality rate from birth to maturity is approximately 50 per cent. Even in countries such as Fiji where there are no major epizootic diseases, mortality rates in the local pig population have been as high as 30 per cent.

Some diseases such as brucellosis, leptospirosis, metritis, mastitis and agalactia are found mainly in breeding stock. Brucellosis and lepto-spirosis may be the cause of abortion or the birth of weak piglets, etc. These two diseases, as well as metritis, also cause sterility. Mastitis and agalactia are difficult to control, result in weak piglets and increase piglet mortality.

Other diseases, such as transmittable gastroenteritis (TGE) and swine influenza, mainly affect younger pigs. The incidence of TGE is sporadic, but in infected pigs mortality can be very high. Swine influenza is very contagious, but most infected piglets recover unless they contact a secondary infection such as broncho-pneumonia.

Diseases such as hog cholera (swine fever) or African swine fever and swine plague attack pigs at all ages. Hog cholera, caused by a virus, is the most serious tropical pig disease in the Americas and Southeast Asia. It can be controlled by proper vaccination. African swine fever, caused by a very similar virus, is of equal importance in Africa and is now spreading outside that continent. Swine plague is a major disease in Southeast Asia where pigs are subject to any form of stress.

Pigs in the tropics suffer badly from the effects of two external parasites, mites and lice. Control of these parasites can be achieved by washing both pigs and pens thoroughly with a solution containing 0·06 per cent lindane or 0·025 to 0·40 per cent chlordane. The wash should be repeated 10 days later.

Internal parasites are also the cause of considerable mortality, lack of vigour and unthriftiness in young pigs. The most important internal parasites are: lungworms (*Metastrongylus* spp.); intestinal roundworms such as *Ascaris lumbricoides* var. *suis*; nodular worms (*Oesophagostomum* spp.); threadworms (*Strongyloides*); whipworms (*Trichuris* spp.); and the kidney worm (*Stephanurus dentatus*). Threadworms are particularly difficult to control as the sow can infect the unborn piglet, they can be passed to the new-born piglet through the colostrum and are able to penetrate unbroken skin. The kidney worm is undoubtedly the cause of much unthriftiness and dwarfing in improperly managed pigs. Once the worm has entered the pig's body it cannot be eliminated, so that control has to be exercised through proper management.

Details of the control of intestinal worms by the use of piperazine are given in the section concerned with management. The correct dosage of piperazine is 1 mg per 4·5 kg (10 lb) of body weight.

Even where diseases and internal and external parasites are of no major importance large numbers of piglets are lost at birth due to 'overlaying' by the sow (Table 12.5).

Table 12.5   *The cause of death of piglets in an experimental herd in Fiji during 1955*

Cause of death	Breed				All breeds	
	Tamworth	*Berkshire*	*Large White*	*Crossbred*	*Total*	*As percentage of total*
Stillbirth	8	7	9	8	32	17·4
Eaten by sow	–	1	–	–	1	0·5
Genetical defect	2	–	–	1	3	1·6
Overlaid	7	20	83	12	122	66·3
Enteritis	1	–	–	3	4	2·2
Pneumonia	–	1	–	–	1	0·5
Unknown	–	8	–	13	21	11·5
Totals	18	37	92	37	184	100·0

The most effective control measure against disease is preventative action. As stressed pigs are likely to succumb to disease and parasites, the most effective preventative action is to reduce nutritional, climatic and other environmental stresses to a minimum by good management. Some measures that can be taken are:

● The use of vaccination in those cases where vaccines are available and effective;
● The control of internal and external parasites by spraying and/or drenching when necessary (see section on management);
● Adequate feeding at all stages and the amelioration of climatic stress by the provision of suitable housing and fine water sprays;
● The segregation of individual diseased animals and premises when outbreaks of disease occur;

- The proper disposal of diseased pigs, by slaughter if necessary, and of infective material by burning or other suitable means;
- The cleaning and disinfection of all premises and equipment after an outbreak of disease and non-use of the premises for 3 or 4 weeks.

Feeding

The importance of proper feeding is very great as the cost of its food represents a very high proportion of the total cost of production of a pig – sometimes as much as 80 per cent. This is because the pig grows so rapidly and consequently its food demands are very high. A baby pig may weigh 1·4 kg (3 lb) when it is born and 163 kg (360 lb) 18 months later. Thus in 18 months it multiplies its weight by 120, or it grows twelve times as fast as a calf that weighs 41 kg (90 lb) at birth and will weigh 408 kg (900 lb) 18 months later. If fed over-generous rations pigs fatten very rapidly. This tendency is highly inheritable. It is also uneconomic.

The pig is omnivorous, i.e. it can eat all types of food, but although it likes to graze or chew forage in its pen it cannot digest too much fibre and unlike domestic ruminants it cannot live entirely on roughage. The pig has a very differently fashioned mouth and teeth from ruminants, being equipped to eat food on the surface of the soil or to root it out from the ground. Unfortunately pigs thrive best on just those foods that are suitable for humans, but fortunately they also thrive on by-product feeds and other materials which are practically useless as food for man. If, however, the latter are the only feeds used the plane of nutrition often falls below the optimum level and the rate of liveweight growth is slowed down to an uneconomic extent. Therefore, it should be the pig farmer's aim to use the cheaper, lower-grade feedingstuffs to the fullest extent and to supplement them by the more expensive nutritious feeds to the point that true economy dictates.

There are innumerable feedingstuffs that may be suitable for pig feeding and these are detailed in books on animal feeding or they are listed in local publications that the pig farmer is advised to study. The following are some that are widely used in the tropics:

Feeds containing mainly carbohydrates

1. Cereals and cereal products
Barley.   Barley is commonly used in Europe, Australia and in parts of Africa. It has approximately 90 per cent of the feeding value of maize, it should be ground before use, and can be used at a high level in rations.

Corn and cob meal.   This is a meal made from the whole maize cob. It has about two-thirds the nutritive value of maize with a higher crude fibre content and a lower soluble carbohydrate content. It can be used with advantage in sow and boar rations.

Maize or corn.   Of all cereal grains, maize is one of the richest in carbohydrate and fat. Yellow, but not white, maize is also rich in carotene or provitamin A. It should not be fed alone as its protein is deficient in certain essential amino acids. It can be used at the rate of 85 per cent of the ration for growing pigs and at a somewhat lower rate for pregnant sows. Rations high in maize are said to produce a soft fat. It should be coarsely ground or crushed before feeding. New varieties of maize with a higher lysine content – one of the amino acids deficient in present varieties – have recently become available for general use in some regions of the tropics.

Oats.   This cereal is not generally available in the tropics, but it may be grown in some montane regions. It has a lower feeding value than maize, partly on account of its relatively high fibre content. No more than 30 per cent of crushed or ground oats should be used in a ration.

Rice.   Paddy has a somewhat similar feeding value to wheat, but as the hull has a high fibre and lignin content it is not a particularly satisfactory grain feed and its use should never exceed 25 per cent of the ration although some authorities have suggested that up to 50 per cent can be used.

Rice and/or wheat shorts or middlings.   These are by-products of the milling of rice or wheat, but they do not contain hulls. Their feeding value may be 90 to 115 per cent that of maize and they may be used at the rate of 60 per cent of the total ration.

Rice bran.   This is not to be confused with the rice husk. It consists of the outer layers of the rice kernel and contains a high percentage of fat and fibre. It has a somewhat lower feeding value than has wheat bran. It should not be fed at all to piglets, or at more than the rate of 30 to 50 per cent of the total ration to fatteners on account of its high fibre content and laxative effect. In many parts of the monsoonal tropics it is often almost the sole feed available for pigs and as a consequence they grow slowly, develop a soft fat and frequently scour. If large quantities of rice bran have to be fed then the bran should preferably be purchased from old, inefficient mills as their product usually contains varying proportions of broken rice grain.

   In some tropical countries paddy is still prepared for cooking by pounding. It should be realized that the rice bran obtained by pounding often has a lower feed value than that obtained by milling as it may sometimes consist of both the rice husk and the outer layers of the rice kernel.

Rye. This cereal is not normally available in the tropics, except perhaps in a limited number of montane areas. It possesses 90 per cent of the feeding value of maize, but it is not so palatable as many other cereals and should only be used at a maximum rate of 50 per cent in rations. It is best used ground and mixed with other grains.

Sorghum and millet. These cereals possess approximately 95 per cent of the feeding value of maize. A growing–finishing ration may contain as much as 85 per cent of sorghum, but as this cereal produces a soft fat it is usual to feed it at the rate of 50 per cent of the total ration. Millet should be fed at the rate of 35 per cent of the total ration. They should both be crushed or ground before feeding.

Wheat. Wheat is commonly fed to pigs in Australia and in South America and is sometimes available in montane and/or dry tropical regions. It possesses a feeding value equal or slightly inferior to that of maize. For best results it should not be ground too fine.

Wheat bran. This feed is now often available in tropical countries as wheat-milling complexes have been built at the ports. It has a feeding value equivalent to 85 per cent of maize, but on account of its high fibre content it should only be used in the rations of fatteners and breeding sows. To these classes of pigs it can be fed at the rate of 40 per cent of the ration. Wheat bran is to be preferred to rice bran.

2. Root crops

Arrowroot (Maranta spp.). This root can be used in the same way as cassava.

Cassava – synonyms: tapioca, manioc, yuca (Manihot esculenta). Cassava and cassava peelings are both very suitable feeds and pigs fattened on them develop a good, firm fat. This root is widely used for pig feeding in Southeast Asia, Africa, Central and South America. Four parts of the cassava root replace one part of maize meal in pig rations. It is advisable to cook cassava before feeding in order to destroy the poisonous cyano-genetic glucosides found in the skin of some varieties. It can also be used as a silage. In Taiwan cassava and sweet potato silage are used to replace 40 per cent of the grain in pig rations. Dried cassava root or the flour made from it has the same feeding value as maize and is widely used in Europe. It can be used at the rate of 30 per cent of the total ration.

Potato (Solanum tuberosum). Potatoes are available in the montane and/or dry areas of the tropics. They may be mixed with grain in the ratio of three parts of potato to one of grain. The feeding value of this mixture is 30 per cent that of maize. Potatoes may also be dried and made into a flour and this can form up to 30 per cent of the ration.

Sweet-potato (*Ipomoea batatas*).   Raw sweet-potato is unsatisfactory for piglets but can be fed to older pigs. It should be used in the same way as is cassava. In regions where the kidney worm is not a problem pigs can be allowed in the fields to lift the crop themselves and they will then eat both the tops and the roots. The roots can be processed into a flour that has a feeding value equivalent to maize meal and can replace 35 to 50 per cent of the grain in a ration. Like cassava, sweet-potato roots can also be ensiled.

Taro (*Colocasia* spp.).   The peeling and the whole root are very useful pig feeds that should be used in the same way as cassava.

Yam (*Dioscorea* spp.).   This root is used in a similar way to taro and cassava. In the tropical world outside the Americas caution should be exercised when feeding the roots of wild yams as some contain toxic substances. The most poisonous species is one found in Malayasia – *D. hispida*. It contains an alkaloid known as dioscorine. A common African species, *D. dumetorum*, also contains a toxic alkaloid, as do several others. The roots of these yams can be detoxicated by thorough washing of the sliced roots in water.

3. Miscellaneous

Cane molasses.   In many tropical countries this was often – but may be no longer – the cheapest carbohydrate feed available. Some pigs will eat it readily, others do not like it. It is generally mixed with the meal and can improve the palatability of the ration. It can be used at a rate of up to 20 per cent of the fattening ration, but when more is used it may cause scouring. Young piglets should not receive more than 5 per cent of molasses in their ration. When molasses is combined with a little sugar, feed efficiency is greatly improved.

Citrus molasses.   This feed has approximately the same nutritive value as cane molasses, but as it possesses a bitter taste and is usually unpalatable it can only be used in relatively small quantities in the ration.

Sago (*Metroxylon* spp.).   Five types of feed can be obtained from the sago palm, but only two are suitable for pigs. These are the crude wet sago (representing 40 per cent of the original sago log) and sago flour. Sago flour should not be included in a ration above the 20 per cent level. It tends to produce a pig with a lean carcase and a soft fat. One difficulty in using sago flour is that it often has a rather high moisture content and is consequently difficult to store.

Sugar.   Raw sugar can be used for pig feeding when its cost is comparable to that of other carbohydrate feeds. It can be introduced into piglet rations at the rate of 10 to 20 per cent of the total ration and can probably be fed in larger amounts to older pigs. There are valid reasons

for using it – at the rate of approximately 5 per cent in baby-pig rations –
even when it is more expensive than other carbohydrate feeds. Piglets
will start eating a ration containing sugar much earlier than one that
does not contain it.

Feeds containing mainly protein

Blood meal.   Where this feed is available, as it often is in South America,
it can be used at the rate of 5 per cent of the ration.

Copra cake or meal (coconut meal).   This is the meal manufactured from
the cake that remains after oil is expressed from dried coconut, commonly known as copra. It is available in many regions of the tropics and
can be used at a maximum rate of 30 per cent of the ration. As the protein
in the meal has an unbalanced amino-acid content it should only be used
at low levels in the ration of young piglets. It apparently stimulates milk
secretion and is very suitable for the feeding of lactating sows. Copra
meal made by the expeller method is more valuable as a feed than that
made by the solvent method.

Cottonseed meal.   Some meals contain a toxic substance known as
gossypol and so care should be taken in their use. Inclusion should never
exceed 10 per cent of the ration. De-gossypolled meals are available in
some countries.

Fish meal.   Apart from the ordinary fish meals, whale and shrimp meals
are also available in some regions. In many tropical countries there are
two types of fish meal available, one sun dried and the other artificially
dried. Sun-dried fish meal usually has a lower protein content and a
higher oil content and it may be dangerously contaminated with bacteria.
The amount of fish meal used should never exceed 10 per cent of the
ration, and normally a smaller proportion is fed as high levels impart a
fishy taste to the pork. It should never be used during the final stage of
fattening.

Linseed meal.   This meal should not be used at the rate of more than
5 per cent of the ration.

Maize (corn) by-products.   Corn germ meal, corn gluten meal and dried
corn distillers' solubles have a reasonably good feed value and the latter
is a valuable source of B-complex vitamins. The protein of corn germ
meal is of a better quality than that of corn gluten meal or corn gluten
feed. These by-products are best used in combination with other feeds
and their use in a ration should not exceed 5 per cent of the total.

Meat and meat and bone meals.   The quality of meat meal varies considerably as many so-called meat meals are really meat and bone meals.

If either meal is available at an economic price it can be used at the rate of 5 to 10 per cent of the ration.

Milk and milk by-products.   Buttermilk or separated milk is sometimes available where there are milk-processing factories. A ration containing buttermilk or separated milk and cassava or maize is a very satisfactory rearing and fattening ration. It is probably only economic to use skim-milk powder in baby-pig starter rations at levels varying from 10 to 30 per cent of the total ration.

Peanut meal – synonym: groundnut cake.   Although peanut meal is a very useful protein concentrate care must be taken in its use because of the possibility that it may be contaminated with a fungi (*Aspergillus flavus*) that produces a toxic material known as aflatoxin. This meal also goes rancid if it is stored for a long period.

Safflower (Carthamus tinctorius) meal.   The utility of this meal is very limited and it should only be used in very small quantities.

Sesame – synonym: sim-sim (Sesamum indicum) meal.   This meal is used to some extent, particularly in South America, and it can be included at the rate of 2 to 5 per cent in the ration.

Soybean meal.   If it is available this is the best-quality plant protein feed available for young growing piglets and brood sows. Solvent extracted is better quality than expeller processed meal.

Yeast.   This is an excellent protein concentrate and a very rich source of the vitamin B complex. It can be fed at the rate of 2 to 5 per cent of the total ration. Live yeast must be killed by cooking before it is fed, or it may cause scouring.

Miscellaneous feeds

Avocado pear (Persea americana).   Small amounts of waste avocado pears can be fed to pigs. Three parts of avocado replace one part of maize.

Bananas and plantains (Musa spp.).   Green and overripe bananas can be fed to pigs as a source of energy. They are more palatable when they are overripe. Waste green bananas from packing stations should be cooked before feeding. Plantains are equally useful. Three parts of over-ripe banana replace one part of maize and investigators in Latin America have reported that bananas can replace 20 to 30 per cent of maize in a ration. Banana meal made from dried bananas can be used at a level of 25 to 40 per cent in growing–finishing rations and in rations for gestating sows.

Breadfruit (Artocarpus altilis).   This fruit is fed in a similar manner to cassava, yam and taro.

Brewers' and distillers' grains.   Both products can be used for feeding fattening pigs over 45 kg (100 lb) liveweight. Distillers' grains have a slightly higher feeding value. Wet grains must be ensiled unless they can be fed immediately after production.

Cocoa meal.   This meal is not suitable for pig feeding.

Citrus fruit.   Pigs will eat waste citrus fruits but they do not thrive on them, although it is safe to feed small quantities.

Fermented feeds.   Many by-product feeds such as corn cobs, rice bran and banana stems as well as seaweed can be fermented before feeding. Fermented feeds alone do not apparently exercise beneficial effects on liveweight gain and feed efficiency, but they are very palatable and when mixed with other feeds improve feed consumption.

Forage.   It has been stated in a previous section that it is difficult to manage pigs on pasture in the humid tropics on account of the internal parasite problem. Pigs do, however, benefit from receiving green forage even when fed complete concentrate rations indoors. Adult pigs may be given up to 4·5 kg (10 lb) per day unless they are fed rations containing a grass or legume meal. Guinea, para and elephant grasses are all suitable as are banana stems, cassava (not all varieties) and sweet-potato tops, browse plants such as *Sesbania grandiflora* and water plants such as *Ipomoea reptans.* A meal made from the artificially dried leaves of the legume bush known as *Leucaena leucocephala* is often added to mixed feeds. The feeding rate should not exceed 5 per cent of the total ration.

Green copra.   Although green copra is usually too expensive to feed to pigs it is sometimes used in coconut-growing areas. It produces a soft fat and should not form too large a proportion of any ration.

Papaya (Carica spp.).   Small quantities of papaya are an excellent feed for pigs. If fed at the rate of 25 per cent of the ration five parts of papaya replace one part of maize meal.

Pineapple bran.   This is the dried outer flesh and core of the pineapple. It is very fibrous and should not be fed to pigs until they weigh more than 45 kg (100 lb), and then only in small quantities.

Pumpkins.   Pumpkins are a useful feed, seven to nine parts of pumpkin replacing one part of maize.

Ramie (Boehmeria nivea).   When ramie is immature it is not fibrous and it is an excellent, succulent pig feed.

Sugar cane.   Can be fed as part of the forage component of the ration. It is only a suitable green feed when it is young.

Tomato.   Waste tomatoes should only be fed in small quantities at the rate of ten parts for one part of maize.

Additives

A number of additives to pig rations have been advocated, but only two – antibiotics and copper – are considered to be of value to the tropical pig farmer.

Antibiotics.   The addition of a small amount of antibiotics to pig rations usually results in an improvement in the rate of liveweight gain and in the efficiency of feed conversion, but has no effect on carcase quality. These improvements are most marked where the protein in the ration is derived solely from plant sources, and the feeding of a ration containing antibiotics may have a particularly beneficial effect on the growth of runt pigs. There is no benefit to be obtained from feeding antibiotics to pigs which are receiving large amounts of skim-milk or buttermilk. Recommended levels of antibiotics in rations are given in Table 12.6.

Table 12.6   *Recommended levels of antibiotic and copper in pig rations*

	Piglets (g/t (oz/ton) of complete feed)	Growers (g/t (oz/ton) of complete feed)	Finishers (g/t (oz/ton) of complete feed)
Antibiotic*	40 (1·5)	10–20 (0·4–0·8)	10 (0·4)
Copper compounds			
Cupric carbonate ($CuCO_3$)	250 (9·0)	250 (9·0)	–
Cupric oxide (CuO)	160 (6·0)	160 (6·0)	–
Cupric sulphate ($CuSO_4$ $5H_2O$)	500 (18·0)	500 (18·0)	–

* Bacitracin, chlortetracycline, hygromycin B, neomycin, oleandomycin, oxytetracycline, procaine penicillin or streptomycin may be used.
Source: Durrance (1971).

Copper.   This is of course an essential mineral nutrient, being necessary for haematopoiesis, but under certain circumstances the addition of copper over and above normal nutrient needs to pig rations improves rate of gain and feed efficiency. The feeder must always remember that copper is toxic when fed in excess and that a safe level in rations is considered to be no more than 125 parts of copper per million parts of feed. Recommended levels of copper that may be added to the ration of growers are shown in Table 12.6. The farmer should remember when feeding additional copper to his pigs that the excretion of additional quantities of this element may interfere with beneficial bacterial action in pig effluent-disposal systems.

These additives will produce the best response in pigs weighing less than 34 kg (75 lb), but there is evidence that when antibiotics are omitted from the diet of older pigs that received them at a younger age, then the rate of gain of the pigs is reduced and if antibiotics are to be used it is necessary to feed them throughout the fattening period.

Preparation of feeds

In general it is neither desirable nor necessary to process feeds for pigs, but there are some important exceptions to this rule.

The mixing of rations is a time-consuming operation, but often has to be carried out by the farmer in the tropics as there are too few feed-processing firms. The pig farmer should plan his feed store in such a way as to use the minimum of labour, and the installation of modern mixing machinery should be considered by the larger pig farmer as many types of mixer suitable for farm operations are now available.

Milling. All grains should be coarsely ground or cracked, as should grain legumes. Coarse grades of protein concentrate feeds such as coconut cake should also be ground for use in self-feeders. Grinding increases the food value of the grains by some 20 per cent, but feeds should not be ground too fine as this reduces palatability, increases the possibility of the meal becoming caked and, in addition, finely ground grain does not run so well in a self-feeder.

Soaking. This practice does not improve the food value or the palatability of feeds and it is impossible to feed soaked feed in a self-feeder or in automatic feeding systems. There may, however, be something to be said for the dampening of a dry-feed mixture that is hand fed, particularly if the mixture contains a high proportion of coconut meal. If molasses is fed it can be used to dampen the feed mixture. There is no value in feeding a sloppy feed mix unless a supply of fresh water is not available in the pen.

Cooking. This does not usually improve the food value of feeds, but it is essential to boil or pasteurize skim-milk or buttermilk from cows that may be infected with tuberculosis. All slaughterhouse offals and swill must be boiled for 30 minutes in order to kill any pathogenic organisms that they might harbour. It is general experience that all roots and root peelings are better fed cooked than raw as they are slightly more digestible when they are cooked. There is a special reason for cooking cassava or cassava peelings as this destroys the poisonous substances that are found in the skin of some varieties. Cooked tapioca packed in a pit makes good silage that keeps well for many months and is always relished by pigs.

Method of calculating rations

Pigs require different rations at different stages of life. As the pig grows older, protein, mineral and vitamin requirements decrease. Animal protein, in particular, is more essential for the young than for the older animal, and the ability of the pig to deal with roughage increases with age. The most expensive ration is required for the suckling pig.

Theoretically, pigs require the following types of ration:

- A relatively expensive ration for creep feeding suckling pigs up to 7 weeks of age that should contain 19 to 20 per cent of crude protein (CP) – a large proportion of which should be of animal origin. The mineral and vitamin content of this ration should be high, the fibre content low and the ration should be very palatable. If it is desired to early-wean piglets a ration with an even higher CP content of 20 to 22 per cent should be fed and the piglets weaned on to the creep-feeding ration or on to a starter ration.
- A starter ration for weaned pigs. This should contain 18 per cent CP, a low fibre content and be highly digestible. It may be fed until the pigs are 14 to 23 kg (30 to 50 lb) liveweight.
- A grower ration with approximately 16 per cent CP, preferably still containing some protein of animal origin, still very palatable and with some fibre. This is fed to pigs weighing 23 to 55 kg (50 to 120 lb).
- A fattening ration containing 14 per cent CP, none of which need be of animal origin for pigs weighing 45 to 91 kg (100 to 200 lb).
- A ration for gestating females that can be of relatively coarse texture. The ration for gilts should contain 16 per cent CP, while that for sows should contain 14 per cent CP during the first two-thirds of gestation and 16 per cent CP during the final months of gestation.
- A ration for lactating females that should contain 16 per cent CP.
- Rations for young boars less than 15 months of age containing 16 per cent CP and for older boars containing 14 per cent CP.

In practice it is usually possible to reduce the number of different rations used by combining two or more of the above types to substitute for one of the others.

A nutritionist can calculate the exact feeding value of different foods when mixing a ration, but it is not necessary for the farmer to do this. Instead of working out the starch equivalent (SE) or total digestible nutrients (TDN) and the digestible protein (DP) of a ration the farmer can use a simple method in which all he needs to know is the nutritive ratio of the feed, i.e. the ratio of protein to carbohydrate food constituents, and its feeding value assessed in relation to 1 kg (2·2 lb) of maize meal. The nutritive ratio of rations for different classes of pigs and the approximate average daily feed intake are shown in Table 12.7, while

Table 12.7 *Essential data required for the calculation of rations for pigs and for assessment of their performance*

Class and liveweight of pigs (kg (lb))	Nutritive ratio required in the ration	Average daily feed intake (kg (lb))	Expected average daily liveweight gain[1] (kg (lb))
Piglets (Birth to 14 (birth to 30))			
Creep feed for early weaners	1·0:4·0–4·5	0·14–0·7	0·32 (0·70)
Creep feed for normal weaners		(0·3–1·5)	
Weaners (14–23 (30–50))			
Starter rations	1·0:4·5	0·7–1·4 (1·5–3·0)	0·29 (0·65)
Growers (23–54 (50–120))	1·0:4·5–5·5		0·64 (1·40)
25 (55)		1·4 (3·0)	
32 (70)		1·8 (4·0)	
41 (90)		2·0 (4·5)	
Fatteners (45–91 (100–200))	1·0:5·5–7·0		0·84 (1·85)
45 (100)		2·3 (5·0)	
59 (130)		2·5 (5·5)	
68 (150)		2·5–2·7 (5·5–6·0)	
Pregnant gilts and sows	1·0:5·0	2·3 (5·0)	
Suckling gilts and sows	1·0:5·0	5·4 (12·0) or 0·9 (2·0) plus 0·5 (1·0) for each suckling pig	
Boars	1·0:5·0		
< 15 months of age		2·7 (6·0)	
> 15 months of age		2·3 (5·0)	

Source: (1) Durrance (1971).

the nutritive ratio and maize meal equivalent of some common tropical feeds are given in Table 12.8.

The farmer using this method of making up rations must of course use his common sense. The meal unit will not only have to contain the

Table 12.8   *The nutritive ratio and maize meal equivalent of some tropical feeds*

	Nutritive ratio	Amount equivalent to one unit of maize meal
Cereals and cereal by-products		
Barley		1·0
Millet	1·0:8·2	1·1–1·2
Rice (paddy)	1·0:10·7	1·1–1·2
Rice bran	1·0:7·0	1·2
Sorghum	1·0:8·5	1·0–1·1
Wheat	1·0:6·2	1·0
Wheat bran	1·0:4·0	1·3
Root crops		
Cassava (tapioca)	1·0:40–58	3·5–4·0
Potato	1·0:12·4	4·0–5·0
Sweet-Potato	–	3·5–4·0
Taro	1·0: 10·0	4·0
Yam	very variable	very variable
Miscellaneous carbohydrate feeds		
Molasses (cane)	–	1·3–1·4
Molasses (citrus)	–	1·3–1·4
Feeds containing mainly protein		
Coconut meal (expeller grade)	1·0–3·3	1·0
Cottonseed meal (43% CP)	1·0–1·0	1·1
Fishmeal (white)	1·0–0·2	1·1
Meat meal	1·0–0·5	1·5
Milk (separated)	1·0–1·6	9·0
Peanut meal (41% CP)	1·0–0·6	1·3
Soybean oil meal	1·0–0·9	1·0
Miscellaneous feeds		
Avocado pear	–	3·0
Banana (ripe)	–	3·0
Brewers' grain (wet)	1·0:2·3	5·0
Papaya	–	5·0
Pumpkins	1·0:6·0	8·5
Tropical pasture grass (good quality)	1·0:4·8	5·0

equivalent in TDN of 1 kg (2·2 lb) of maize, but also all the other food constituents that the pig requires.

The protein fraction of the ration must contain all the essential amino acids. There are twenty-three known amino acids in proteins and ten of these are essential at some stage in the life of the pig for optimum growth and/or performance. These essential amino acids are arginine, histidine, isoleucine, leucine, lysine, methionine, phenylalanine, threonine, tryptophan and valine. Generally, animal protein feeds contain more of the essential amino acids than plant protein feeds. The relative value of different protein concentrates (in terms of dried skim-milk being equivalent to 100), the percentage of these concentrates that are normally used in rations and some notes on their evaluation are given in Table 12.9.

Table 12.9 *Data on the relative feeding value of some common protein concentrates*

Protein concentrate	Relative value*	Percentage that may be used in the ration	Evaluation†
Coconut meal		0–30	
Cottonseed meal (41% CP)	90	0–10	Low in lysine; toxic if not processed
Fish meal (60% CP)	100–110	0–10	High quality
Linseed meal (35% CP)	70	0–5	Low in lysine
Meat meal‡		0–10	
Meat and bone meal (50% CP)‡	75–85	0–5	Low in tryptophan
Peanut meal (47% CP)	95	0–5	Low in lysine
Skim-milk powder (34% CP)	100	0–30	Excellent quality
Soybean meal (44% CP)	100	5–25	High quality

* In terms of dried skim-milk powder being equivalent to 100.
† In terms of essential amino-acid content.
‡ These feeds vary very considerably in composition.
Source: Partly from Durrance (1971).

Minerals are essential for many vital metabolic processes in the pig's body and are important constituents of the skeleton. They should be fed as a supplement to all rations. Mineral requirements for pigs, expressed as a percentage or as the amount per kg (lb) of the total ration, are given in Table 12.10.

Table 12.10 *Mineral requirements for pigs*

Mineral elements*	Liveweight of pig (kg (lb))		
	6·5–11 (10–25)	12–34 (26–75)	35–102 (76–225)
Calcium (%)	0·80	0·65	0·50
Phosphorus (%)	0·60	0·50	0·40
Salt (%)	0·50	0·50	0·50
Copper (ppm)	6	6	6
Iodine (ppm)	0·2	0·2	0·2
Iron (ppm)	80	80	80
Manganese (ppm)	20	20	20
Zinc (ppm)†	50	50	50

* Expressed as percentage of or parts per million (ppm) of total ration.
† Increase to 100–150 ppm if the ration contains excessive calcium.
Source: National Research Council (1973).

Vitamins are also required nutrients, and although many pigs will receive adequate quantities of some vitamins from their rations it is a good insurance to feed a vitamin supplement. The vitamin requirements for pigs expressed as the amount per kg (lb) of the total ration are given in Table 12.11.

Table 12.11   *Some vitamin requirements of pigs (expressed as amount per kg (lb) of total ration)*

Vitamin	Liveweight of pig (kg (lb))			
	4·5–11 (10–25)	12–23 (26–50)	24–34 (51–75)	35–102 (76–225)
Choline (mg)	500	400	n.e.*	n.e.*
Niacin (mg)	10	8	6	5
Pantothenic acid (mg)	6	5	5	5
Riboflavin (mg)	1·5	1·4	1·2	1·0
Vitamin A (IU)	1,000	800	600	600
Vitamin B_{12} (μg)	10	7	5	5
Vitamin D (IU)	100	90	90	60

* n.e. means that the requirements have not yet been established.
Source: National Research Council (1973).

Farmers cannot be expected to mix their own mineral and vitamin supplements as they do not possess the equipment or, normally, the technical competence. These supplements can be purchased as a premix from reliable feed merchants in most tropical countries. Instructions as to the quantity of premix that should be added to different types of ration should be provided by the supplier.

If vitamin and mineral premixes are not available the farmer should see that all classes of his pigs receive some fresh succulent forage daily and a simple mineral mixture may be made up on the farm by mixing 60 per cent ground sea shell with 30 per cent bone meal and 10 per cent iodinized salt. This latter mixture should be added to all rations at the rate of 1·4 kg (3 lb) per 45 kg (100 lb) of ration. A little fresh soil or grass sod may also be placed in the pens daily if it is thought that the pigs may suffer from an unknown trace-element deficiency.

Finally, the farmer must ensure that not only is the nutritive ratio, the nutrient content of the feed and the amount of feed fed approximately correct, but that his pigs are receiving adequate quantities of water and that the feeds do not contain too much fibre or any toxic materials. Some details of the approximate water requirements of different classes of pigs in the tropics are given in Table 12.12. If it is possible, automatic watering devices should be installed. The farmer should also remember that rapid growth up to 47 kg (100 lb) will encourage the formation of muscular tissue, but that beyond this liveweight too rapid a growth will

Table 12.12 *Approximate water requirements of pigs in the tropics*

Class of pig	Approximate water requirements (Litre (gal))
Growing pigs (weeks of age)	
8–12	3·5 (0·8)
13–18	6·0 (1·3)
19–24	7·5 (1·6)
25	8·0 (1·8)
Pregnant gilts and sows	
First 3 months	10–15 (2·2–3·3)
Last months	16–20 (3·5–4·4)
Lactating sows with:	
5–7 piglets	20–25 (4·4–5·5)
8–10 piglets	22–27 (4·8–5·9)
11–14 piglets	28–35 (6·2–7·7)
Boars	20–25 (4·4–5·5)

Note: If water is used for cleaning and mist spraying, requirements will be double those given in the table.

encourage the formation of fat. Restricted feeding is usually necessary to limit fatness (Lucas, 1964).

Pigs are creatures of habit and it is very essential that they should be fed regularly. It is also important that the changeover from one ration to another should be accomplished gradually.

The number of different rations that can be compounded are infinite as there are so many different types of food available in different countries. Consequently, no attempt is made here to evaluate typical rations for different classes of pigs. In order to check the efficiency of the rations that he uses, it is suggested that the pig farmer compares the growth of his pigs against the expected average daily liveweight gain data given in Table 12.13. Further details on specific feeding practices for different classes of pigs are given in the management section.

Table 12.13 *Expected liveweight for age under good average feeding and managerial conditions*

Age (week)	Liveweight (kg (lb))
3	5 (11)
8	14 (31)
10	19 (42)
12	24 (53)
15	37 (82)
20	54 (119)
24	72 (159)
28	90 (198)

Management

Successful management of pigs in any part of the world depends primarily on intelligent planning that is based on a knowledge of the biology of the pig.

In most tropical countries in the past, the indigenous producers did not attempt to obtain maximum productivity from their pigs but managed them primarily as scavengers. Although pigs are still used as scavengers, in most countries there is also an ever-expanding commercial pig industry. Methods of management in this new commercial section should not necessarily be based on those now practised in the temperate zone.

Adaptive physiology

The pig is essentially a non-sweating species and is very sensitive to changes in the climatic environment. While discussing the origin of our present major breeds it was suggested that the majority of the pigs managed in the tropical world today are derived from the wild species of Southeast Asia and/or Europe. Thus, modern pig breeds are derived, at least in part, from a wild species that was adapted to a warm, shaded, humid environment. These facts probably explain why temperate-type breeds of pigs, unlike temperate-type breeds of cattle, thrive in the humid tropics under suitable managerial and feeding conditions.

The following facts have been established with regard to the effect of ambient temperature on pigs.

The baby piglet at birth does not appear to possess a very efficient temperature-regulating mechanism. It is incapable of protecting itself against either excessive heat or cold. Newland *et al.* (1952) have shown that the body temperature of the baby pig of typical American breeding falls 1·7° to 7·2°C (3° to 13°F) during the first 30 minutes of life and then slowly returns to normal during the next 48 hours. The body temperature falls most rapidly in small piglets that weigh under 0·9 kg (2 lb) and takes a longer time to recover to normal if the air temperature is low. These workers suggested that cold air temperatures contribute to an increase in the mortality of piglets during the first 2 or 3 days of life, particularly as chilled piglets stand and shiver, become sluggish in their movements and are likely to be more easily 'laid-on' by their mother. Later work has confirmed these suggestions, and in practice during the first 2 days of life the ambient temperature for piglets should exceed 32·2°C (90°F) and be gradually lowered as the piglets age. It is now normal practice in temperate-zone countries to use infra-red lamps to warm the piglets immediately after birth, so that they do not get chilled. This managerial practice unquestionably reduces piglet mortality. In the tropics where mean annual air temperatures vary around 26·7°C (80°F) the problem is not so acute as it is in the temperate climatic zone. However, it has been found that even in a tropical climate piglet mortality due to overlaying may be reduced by the use of an additional heat source for the baby piglets during the first few days of life.

As pigs age and grow the optimal ambient temperature for maximum liveweight gain and efficiency of food conversion changes. Heitman and Hughes (1949) raised pigs in a controlled climatic chamber for periods averaging 7 days in air temperatures ranging from 4·4° to 46°C (40° to 115°F) at a comparatively constant relative humidity and airflow. They found (Fig. 12.2) that liveweight gain and efficiency of food conversion

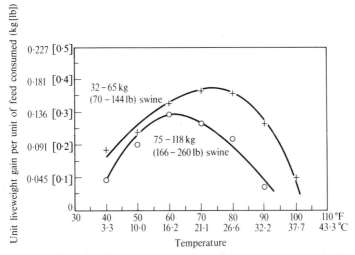

Fig. 12.2 The effect of ambient temperature on the efficiency of food conversion in pigs.

was at a maximum at approximately 24°C (75°F) for pigs weighing 32 to 65 kg (70 to 144 lb) and at approximately 15·6°C (60°F) for pigs weighing 75 to 118 kg (166 to 260 lb). They also noted that if the air temperature rose the respiration rate of pigs also rose very rapidly. Other American workers have shown that at temperatures of 32·2°C (90°F) and above, respiration rates of 150 to 200 per minute are common in pigs. Under these circumstances the pigs stop eating and lose weight, and if forced to exercise may even die of heat exhaustion. The general observations of Heitman and Hughes (1949) have been confirmed by other investigators. Recently, however, Verstegen *et al.* (1973) have stated that although energy retention in the pig depends upon ambient temperature and feeding level, nitrogen retention is not influenced by ambient temperature.

Mean annual temperature in most regions of the tropics are only 2·8° to 4·4°C (5° to 8°F) above 24°C (75°F), so that tropical pigs weighing 32 to 65 kg (70 to 144 lb) are probably being reared under almost optimal environmental conditions, but as pigs grow older and heavier normal tropical temperatures would be too high for maximum productivity. Thus, in the tropics the aim should be to raise a porker weighing approximately 54 to 64 kg (120 to 140 lb) and not bacon or lard pigs weighing 91 to 109 kg (200 to 240 lb).

During the daytime, particularly during the hottest months, tropical ambient temperatures are usually well above 24°C (75°F) and the larger fatteners, as well as the gilts, sows and boars, may require some amelioration of the climatic stress if they are to produce at a maximum. Under such conditions relief from the adverse climatic conditions can be obtained by the provision of adequate shade and fine water sprays or wallows. For adequate shade the roof of the pig pen should not be too low and should preferably be constructed of thatch (unless vermin are a major nuisance) or asbestos sheet or tile; if it is necessary to use corrugated iron then the roof should be painted black on the underside with aluminium paint on the top surface. The most suitable site for water sprays is in the dunging passage, if the buildings are provided with such a facility. Wallows should be approximately 25 cm (10 in) deep with a surface area of approximately $1 \cdot 5 \, m^2$ ($16 \, ft^2$) per sow and should preferably be covered with a roof. Wallows should be constructed so that the water in them can easily be changed as they rapidly become very dirty. If energy is relatively cheap and engineering skill available an alternate cooling device that has been advocated is a forced cool-air draught. This can be particularly useful for cooling the sow in a farrowing pen when the young piglets require a relatively high ambient temperature, whereas the sow, if she is to milk adequately, requires a lower ambient temperature. Under the restricted conditions of a farrowing pen a forced cool-air draught can be directed on to the head of the sow and some relief can be provided for her without radically reducing the overall ambient temperature within the pen.

There is limited information on the effect of high temperature on carcase characteristics. In two experiments Holmes (1971) compared the carcase characteristics of a group of Large White and Landrace pigs raised at 31° to 32°C (87·8° to 89·6°F) and 32° to 33°C (89·6° to 91·4°F) with a group raised at 21° to 24°C (69·8° to 75·2°F) and 22° to 26°C (71·6° to 78·5°F). Carcase length (one experiment) and back fat thickness (both experiments) were significantly greater in the heat-stressed group and the weight of the liver was significantly less (one experiment). If future investigations confirm that heat stress increases back-fat thickness this will be an additional reason for adopting practical methods of ameliorating heat stress in fattening pigs.

It may be thought that pigs in the tropics can be properly managed either in or out of doors and that it might be less expensive to provide adequate shade and wallows out of doors. Unfortunately, there is one major difficulty experienced in managing pigs outdoors and that is the very high incidence of certain internal parasites. This is particularly so in the humid tropics which provide an almost perfect environment for many parasites. The most dangerous of these is the kidney worm (*Stephanurus dentatus*), and in many regions the population of this parasite is so high that pigs can only be managed properly on floors that can be cleaned daily. Even a very strict rotation of pigs around a series of outdoor paddocks is an inadequate precaution. Pig breeds do vary in their tolerance of a high incidence of kidney-worm infection and some indigenous Southeast Asia breeds appear to be considerably more tolerant than do breeds originating from the temperate zone.

Systems of management

These may be conveniently classified into those suitable for the peasant or village producer and those that can only be practised by large-scale commercial producers.

The peasant or village producer

In most villages, in regions where pigs are kept as domestic livestock, there are pigs that are free to roam where they will. They are useful as scavengers, sometimes cleaning up human and domestic animal faeces and always picking up offals where they can.

Quite simple arrangements could be made to improve the productivity of these scavenging village pigs. Some of these are as follows:

1. The feeding of supplementary feeds, either once or twice a day. In an area adjacent to the house the pigs could be fed waste feed, such as rice bran and the peelings of root crops. If the householder is willing to cook the waste feeds so much the better. This is a system that is widely practised by the Dayak people of Sarawak, who boil roots and green leaves and pour the hot mixture over rice bran spread on the bottom of wooden troughs. The greatest difficulty encountered is that of keeping neighbouring pigs away from the feed.
2. Where land is plentiful the pigs can be managed in simply fenced paddocks adjacent to the household in which some root crops are grown and into which all household offals are thrown and where the cooked feeds can be fed secure from neighbouring pigs. The fences might be made of netting wire, if this is available at an economic price, or they can be made of platted bamboo, paling wood or a closely planted live-fence species. The paddock should be sub-divided into four to six smaller areas so that the pigs can be moved from one enclosure to another at 10-day to 2-week intervals, thus reducing the incidence of parasitic infection. Water and shade would have to be available within the paddock. Pigs raised in this manner might not, in the first place, be very much more productive than scavenger pigs, but females could be bred to selected sires so that the stock could be slowly improved.

3. A further improvement would be to construct simple pens in which pigs could be confined. Productivity would, of course, only be improved if there was sufficient food available from village resources to feed the confined pigs and if they were regularly fed and watered. Several types of simple pen can be constructed and the authors have inspected many different types used in different regions of the tropics. Some suitable types are as follows:
   (a) A simple type of deep litter pen. This could be constructed of rough timber with a thatch roof and an earth floor. Coarse hay, straw, rice hulls, reed, etc., can be thrown continuously into the pen in order to create a suitable type of litter. It would be necessary to construct such a pen on a well-drained site.
   (b) A conventional pen with a concrete floor that can be washed or cleaned in some other manner. The pen could be constructed of rough timber with a thatch roof. If it was built close to a stream that was not otherwise used by humans, water could be diverted to run through it. This running water could be used both for drinking purposes and for cleaning the pens.
   (c) A timber pen with a thatch roof could be built with a slatted bamboo floor, either over a fish pond or over a drainage channel. This is a type of simple and practical pig pen that is often used in Southeast Asia.
4. Still further improvements could be affected by the distribution of improved sires for upgrading purposes and by the provision of high-protein and mineral feed supplements. In any upgrading programme great care must be taken not to upgrade too quickly or too far. The feeds available to the average villager are not usually suitable for the proper feeding of high-grade exotic pigs, although increases in productivity may be achieved by the use of first-cross exotic sires. The possible use of high-protein and mineral supplements depends upon whether the farmer has a sufficiently high cash income to afford to purchase supplements and/or the availability of such supplements.
5. There is of course no reason, circumstances permitting, why the village pig-keeper should not be encouraged to use some of the more advanced managerial practices described below. The suggested managerial improvements described above are only considered as useful first steps in the raising of the general level of management of pigs in the village.

The large-scale producer

The managerial methods used will depend upon what labour and feed supplies are available and at what cost, and on the incidence of disease and parasites.

The total number of large-scale pig farms in the tropics has been increasing rapidly during the last decade, particularly in such Southeast Asia countries as the Philippines, Singapore, Malaysia and Thailand. Despite these developments it is likely that the majority of pigs in the tropics are still managed under village conditions, although the proportion of the total pig population managed by large-scale producers is likely to continue to increase.

Accompanying this increase in large-scale operations, there has been increasing specialization and development of the use of ever-increasing quantities of commercially prepared feeds. Nevertheless, the pig industry still depends mainly upon continuous and large supplies of by-product feeds, the difference being that a considerable proportion of these by-product feeds are now incorporated into commercial feed mixes. This is a highly desirable development as available by-product feeds will, in general, be used more economically.

Large-scale pig production is therefore likely to develop in those regions of the tropics where ample supplies of by-product feeds are available and where there is a large consumer demand for pork. Southeast Asia is one such region. Not only are there very large quantities of rice-milling by-products available, but wheat by-products are also now available from new mills at the ports and maize by-products from new processing plants. In addition a variety of high-protein meals are produced, such as coconut, sesame, peanut, cottonseed and oil palm, and there are expanding fishmeal and abattoir by-product industries.

Despite increasing specialization within the industry, the large-scale breeding of purebred lines and/or hybrid pigs for use by the commercial sector has not yet developed in most tropical countries, and the government is often the only source of supply of breeding stock and crossbred pigs. It is therefore usually necessary for the large-scale pig farmer to raise the majority of his own breeding stock. In order to do this he will need accommodation for farrowing, creep feeding and fattening and for in-pig gilts and sows, boars and young breeding stock. He will also probably require feed-milling and mixing equipment, storage for straight and mixed feeds, weighing facilities, loading places, a piped water supply and facilities for the removal of manure.

1. Intensive systems

All pigs should be raised on concrete floors or on some other form of flooring, such as one made of slats, that can be cleaned daily. This should ensure that internal parasites can be adequately controlled and that labour costs are reduced to a minimum. Concrete floors should not be too smooth or the pigs may skid on them, nor should they be too rough. Litter may or may not be used according to circumstances. If a slatted floor is favoured the slats may extend over the dunging passage or cover the entire area of the pen. The latter is more expensive but preferable. The slats may be made of wood, concrete, steel and/or aluminium and should be spaced sufficiently close so that the pigs do not get heir feet trapped. The slat width should be 10 to 13 cm (4 to 5 in) and the space between slats should be 2·5 cm (1 in). If the slats extend over the whole pen there is no need to provide a dunging passage. The space below the slats should slope towards a drainage outlet so that dung can be flushed off the slats with water that will drain away. Slats should not normally be used for the floor of farrowing pens. If they are used the slats should be covered with a grating before the sow farrows.

One of the most suitable and cheapest pens is one that is half-covered by a roof so that the pigs can shelter if necessary. The roof should be 2·4 to 3 m (8 to 10 ft) at the highest point and 1·8 to 2·1 m (6 to 7 ft) in height at the eaves. It can be made of thatch (coconut frond, nipa, reed, grass, etc.) or of a conventional material such as galvanized iron. A layer of thatch (5 cm (2 in)) attached by netting wire beneath a galvanized iron roof will improve the micro-climate of the pen. Alternatively, as stated earlier, the galvanized iron can be painted black on the underside with aluminium paint on the top side, or aluminium roofing material can be used that is painted black on the underside. The pen can be constructed of any suitable material, but perforated are superior to solid internal walls. Due consideration must be given to both the free circulation of air and the provision of shelter from cold, driving rain.

A simple and very flexible system for the smaller farm is a series of pens that can be adapted for farrowing, fattening or breeding stock, according to the dictates of farm policy. Some difference in the size of pens is desirable as this increases the flexibility of the system. Farrowing pens should be equipped with farrowing rails or a farrowing crate and with creep-feeding facilities. A 2·4 × 4 m (8 × 13 ft) pen will accommodate a sow and her litter, up to twelve porker pigs, eight bacon pigs or three breeding sows.

The larger pig farmer will want to build more specialized housing and some general details on housing requirements are given in Table 12.14.

Table 12.14   *Housing requirements: the area required per pig*

Liveweight (kg (lb))	Area required* (m² (ft²))
11–18 (25–40)	0·4 (4·0)
18–45 (40–100)	0·5 (5·4)
45–68 (100–150)	0·7 (7·5)
68–95 (150–210)	0·8 (8·6)
Sow	1·5 (16·0)
Sow with piglets	10·0 (108·0)

*This area excludes feeding and dunging passages.

Feeding troughs should be designed so that the minimum of labour is used for feeding and so as to prevent feed from being wasted. They can be fixed or movable and should be made of materials such as sealed concrete, glazed pipe or galvanized iron so that they can easily be cleaned and are not pitted. Feeding troughs finished only in raw concrete will soon be pitted by food acids, particularly if skim-milk is fed. Concrete troughs should therefore be finished inside with a substance that gives a smooth, glazed and permanent finish. There are several such proprietary compounds on the market. Details of the length of feeding troughs required by different classes of pig are given in Table 12.15. If self-feeders

Table 12.15   *Housing requirements: length of feeding trough per pig*

Liveweight of pig (kg (lb))	Length of trough required (cm (in))
14 (31)	15 (6)
20 (44)	17 (7)
40 (88)	21 (8)
60 (132)	25 (10)
90 (198)	30 (12)
120 (265)	35 (14)
Sows	50 (20)

are provided, one self-feeder hole will provide feeding space for four pigs under – and three pigs over – 15 weeks of age.

Water should be available in all pens for drinking purposes and in all feed alleys for cleaning purposes. The feeding troughs can also be used as water troughs, but pigs tend to lie in them and automatic water cups are preferable if they are available at a reasonable price. One automatic water cup is required in each pen of 20 to 25 pigs. Water should also be available for sprinklers and/or wallows. Drinking water should be as cool as it is possible to provide and water pipes should not be exposed to the hot sun if other arrangements are practicable.

Bedding may be provided on concrete floors, but is not essential in most tropical environments.

Tree shade over the piggery building is usually desirable if it can be provided – with the exception of buildings in the hurricane zones.

In specialized piggeries all kinds of labour-saving devices can be introduced, including automatic feeders. When planning a piggery it should be ensured that all feedingstuffs and manure are carried only downhill. This can be arranged by siting the feed mixing and/or storage shed at the highest level and the midden or manure-collecting area at the lowest. It should be possible to site the piggery so that manure can be removed with minimum effort. The approximate quantities of manure that may be produced by different classes of pigs are shown in Table 12.16.

Pig manure may be sun-dried and sold as a fertilizer. In some Southeast Asia countries sun-dried manure is a very profitable by-product of the industry. It can also be used for the production of methane gas or for the culture of chlorella. Details of these processes should be obtained from a local agricultural extension officer.

In some areas of Southeast Asia pig farming is associated with fish-

Table 12.16 *Approximate daily manure production of pigs*

Age (weeks)	Liveweight (kg (lb))	Volume of solid and liquid manure (litre (gal))
8–12	14–24 (31–52)	1·5–2·0 (0·3–0·4)
13–15	24–37 (53–82)	2·0–3·0 (0·4–0·7)
16–20	37–54 (82–119)	3·0–4·5 (0·7–1·0)
21–24	54–72 (119–159)	4·5–7·0 (1·0–1·5)
25–28	72–90 (159–198)	7·0–8·0 (1·5–1·7)
Sow with litter		14·0 (3·0)

pond culture. Effluent from the piggeries is run into fish ponds as it is believed that it improves the growth of micro-organisms and plants on which the fish feed. This practice is controversial as often only phosphatic fertilizers are needed in the ponds, nitrogen being fixed very effectively by blue-green algae and potassium being very rarely in short supply. Effluent nitrogen can in fact be counter-productive as it may inhibit the production of blue-green algae. Also, the organic materials in the effluent may produce deoxygenation in the pond water as they contain carbohydrates that have to be broken down by bacteria which use oxygen dissolved in the water. Nevertheless, large quantities of fish are produced in ponds into which pig effluents flow – particularly in Southeast Asia.

Pig effluent may also be channelled into irrigation canals in order to fertilize fruit or other crops or it may be collected in a sump, filtered and the liquid fraction pumped into an overhead spray irrigation system.

In most temperate-zone countries the disposal of effluents from large-scale piggeries has become a major problem because of stringent environmental regulations with regard to disposal methods, but in most tropical countries no such regulations have yet been enacted. Farmers should consult their local extension office for information on regulations concerned with the disposal of effluents.

2. Semi-intensive systems

There are many variations of the semi-intensive system. Unfortunately, this system can only be practised in those regions of the tropics where the kidney worm and other internal parasites can be adequately controlled. As the kidney-worm parasite takes at least one year to grow to maturity within the pig and produces eggs that are voided in the pig's urine, some authorities advocate the management of breeding stock on pasture in regions where there is a low intensity of kidney-worm infestation by only retaining gilts to produce three or four litters. The authors do not subscribe to this managerial practice.

Usually breeding pigs are raised outside on grass and fattening pigs are raised intensively in buildings. The most common system is to allow the gilts and the in-pig sows to graze with or without the boars. They must be rotationally grazed around a series of paddocks. These should be located on well-drained soils, low-lying marshy areas being fenced off, provided with adequate shade and a water supply and be well fenced, preferably with pig netting. Mud wallows inevitably become centres of parasite infection and if they are used they should be frequently cleaned and dried out in the sun. Sows that root should be nose-ringed.

Sows with litters, housed in portable sheds, can also be rotated across grazings. The portable shed can be fenced with portable mesh or an electric fence, or alternatively the sow can be tethered. This system is labour intensive as feed and water have to be carried to the pigs, but in regions free of the kidney worm the young pigs are usually very healthy.

Breeding pigs or fatteners can be run in semi-covered yards, fresh litter being thrown into the yard daily. This is a form of deep litter management.

3. Extensive systems

All pigs can be put out on grazings or in semi-covered yards. Rotation is essential on grazings and labour costs are high. It is doubtful whether this is a very suitable managerial method in the tropics. One reason is that it needs more supervision and skilled labour than intensive methods, and both are in short supply in most tropical countries. Another reason is the possible presence of kidney worm.

Methods of management

Suitable methods of management for the different classes of pigs will be considered in sequence: breeding stock, pregnant gilts and sows, suckling pigs, weaners and fatteners.

1. Breeding stock

Young breeding stock should be separated from the remainder of the litter at about 3 months of age. More pigs should be selected for breeding than will be eventually required as it is difficult to finalize which animals will be required for breeding at an early age. If breeding stock are purchased, only those with a known history should be accepted and they should be tested for brucellosis and leptospirosis before they are imported on to the farm and allowed to mix with other pigs.

All breeding boars and gilts should possess twelve to fourteen teats. They should exhibit no obvious inherited defects such as a misshapen jaw and they should be selected from lines that have no history of inherited defects. They should also exhibit the characteristics of rapid growth with maximum economy of gain.

Boars and gilts can be reared together until they are approximately 4 months old. They should then be segregated and are best reared out of doors. As this managerial practice is not usually feasible for the reasons discussed in previous sections, they should be fed green feeds daily indoors, together with their normal rations. Boars of different age and size should not be put together.

Gilts should be first served when they are 7 to 8 months of age and weigh 102 to 113 kg (225 to 250 lb). It they are well grown and heavier than 113 kg (250 lb) they can be served at a slightly earlier age. They should not be mated with too large a boar as he may injure them during service. Gilts and sows in oestrus exhibit a swollen, red vulva and are inclined to stand very still when pressure is exerted on their hindquarters. The gilt or sow should be served twice, as explained in the section on reproductive behaviour. Pregnant gilts should not be put together with pregnant sows.

Boars in the tropics are usually quiet and easily handled. However, they should not be shut up alone or they may develop vicious habits. They are best managed by running them with other boars or with in-pig sows.

The use of boars for service has already been discussed in the section on reproductive behaviour.

As a boar ages, his tusks should be cut off as they can become dangerous.

2. Pregnant gilts and sows

Whatever the system of management the gilt or sow should be separated from the other pigs before farrowing. The approximate date of farrowing should be known as breeding females should be individually mated and accurate records maintained. Gilts will show some signs of udder development after 2 months of pregnancy. Sows normally show signs of new udder development some 2 or 3 weeks before farrowing.

(a) *Farrowing*

It is good practice to bring the pregnant female into the farrowing pen at least one week before she farrows, so that she feels comfortable and at home before parturition occurs. It is also good practice to deworm the pregnant female, using a mild vermifuge such as piperazine, one week before she is brought into the farrowing pen. Pregnant females should also be washed down with soap and a mild antiseptic before they are moved into the farrowing pen. Some days before farrowing the pregnant female should be provided with some clean litter with which she can build a nest. Long is preferable to chopped straw as the pigs like to chew the litter into small pieces. Although pregnant females should be generously fed during the last 6 weeks of pregnancy, they should not be fed for 24 hours before farrowing.

The farrowing pen should include an area that can be kept dry and within which the pregnant pig can farrow. The farrowing pen should always be kept very clean and free of faeces. There should be no loose troughs in the pen, particularly water troughs, as the pig may upset them immediately before farrowing and wet the litter. The pen should be

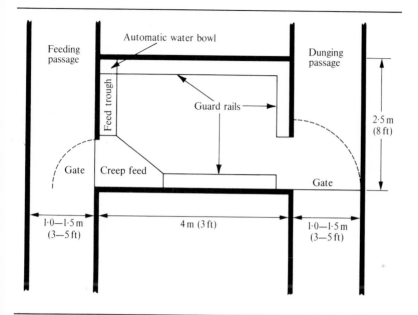

Fig. 12.3 A simple type of farrowing pen.

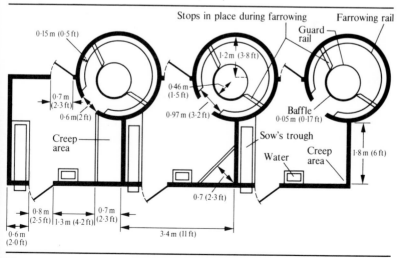

Fig. 12.4 Ground plan of Ruakura round farrowing house.

equipped with farrowing rails (Fig. 12.3). These should be spaced at least
20 cm (8 in) from the wall and 25 cm (10 in) from the ground. They can be
made from 5 cm (2 in) water pipe or from 7·6 cm² (3 in²) hardwood timber.
These farrowing rails provide an area within which the young piglet can
be protected against its mother inadvertently lying upon it. Gilts are the
least danger to their piglets, but as sows become older and heavier the
possibility increases of them lying on and crushing their piglets.

Plate 12.6   Tropical type round farrowing house (Fiji Public Relations Office).

Some farmers use a farrowing crate instead of rails. This is a crate in
which the sow is confined at farrowing, the piglets being able to creep
out of it. Farrowing crates should measure 2·2 to 2·4 m (7·2 to 7·9 ft) × 0·6
to 0·7 m (2·0 to 2·3 ft) with at least a 20 cm (18 in) floor clearance in order
to allow the piglets to run around freely. The disadvantage of the farrowing crate is that the pig is very cramped. She is usually removed from

the crate a few days after farrowing. If this is the practice then a pen with farrowing rails is still required.

A modification of the New Zealand type of farrowing pen known as the Ruakura round farrowing house (Fig. 12.4), suitable for use in the tropics, was devised by the author (Plate 12.6). Practice in both Fiji and East Africa demonstrated that this is a very successful farrowing pen. In a trial using thirty-six litters piglet mortality in an orthodox farrowing pen was 29 per cent while it was 1·2 per cent in the tropical-type round house.

Mature sows of good breeding that are well fed and managed usually farrow eight to fourteen piglets. Gilts normally farrow less.

Some 36 hours before gestation the vulva swells and the teats harden. Sows do not usually have any trouble in delivery. The new-born pig is small and may be delivered head or tail first. Piglets are usually born over a period lasting 1 to 12 hours. They are covered by a membrane that is ruptured at birth and thrown off by the piglet. Occasionally this membrane gets entangled over the snout and the piglet is suffocated. The first piglet will suckle before the last piglet is born. When all piglets are born the afterbirth is expelled and the gestating pig usually eats it. This is quite natural.

Generally farrowing should not be assisted, but it is wise to return from time to time to watch the farrowing in order to be satisfied that all is proceeding smoothly. For example, the occasional piglet that does become entangled and is suffering in the foetal membrane may be saved. The navel cord of the new-born piglet should not normally be severed as it will shrivel up quite naturally. If it is severed it should be dipped in or dabbed with an iodine solution to prevent infection. This solution should consist of 2 per cent iodine in 70 per cent ethyl alcohol. The teeth of the piglet should not be cut unless the mother's teats become very sore.

(b) *Farrowing troubles*

The major troubles at farrowing are mastitis or inflammation of the udder caused by one or more of a variety of micro-organisms and agalactia or failure to secrete milk.

Specific 'lines' of pigs are more readily susceptible to mastitis than others and it may be found advisable to stop selecting breeding pigs from these lines. Mastitis can be treated using a variety of antibiotics, and veterinary advice should be sought as to the most effective mastitis-control programme.

The causes of agalactia are not always the same. Failure to secrete colostrum during the first 24 hours may simply be due to an insufficient internal secretion of the hormone known as oxytocin. This may be remedied by the intravenous injection of 5 to 10 IU of oxytocin. Later failure of milk secretion may be due to constipation which may be cured by the administration of a suitable laxative (e.g. castor oil), or to an inflammation of the vulva and/or udder that causes a fever and may be due to a variety of causes including the retention of a foetus in the uterus. Under these circumstances professional veterinary advice should be sought.

The most serious effect of either mastitis or agalactia is that the piglets may have to be removed from the sow. They can then be either hand-reared or placed on a foster mother. The foster mother should farrow after the pigs are born so that they obtain some colostrum, and it is usually considered that there should be no more than 3 days' difference in age between the foster mother's own piglets and the orphan piglets that are given to her. Piglets can, with some difficulty, be successfully raised on diluted cow's milk together with a little antibiotic. They should be fed with a teat attached to a bottle until they learn to drink out of a shallow pan. This should be within 24 to 48 hours from the time that they are taken from their mother. Great advances have been made during the last decade in techniques for the artificial rearing of piglets and further information should be sought by the interested reader in relevant publications.

(c) *Piglet mortality*

Experimental evidence suggests that piglet mortality in the tropics is of the same order as piglet mortality in similarly managed herds in the temperate zone (Davidson, 1948). Details of the cause of piglet mortality in an experimental herd in Fiji are shown in Table 12.5. The major mortality was caused by sows overlaying piglets. This is a loss that can be drastically reduced, as mentioned above, by the use of suitable farrowing equipment. As mortality due to overlaying is usually lower in first and second litters some farmers advocate the culling of sows after two litters. This is probably an uneconomic practice and it is more rational to spend capital on the provision of properly designed farrowing houses.

3. Suckling piglets

(a) *Suckling and creep feeding*

Piglets start suckling immediately after birth. The strongest piglets find the best teats and usually after a few hours of interchange each piglet keeps to its own teat. No attempt should be made to raise more piglets than the sow has teats, however many piglets are born. Surplus piglets may be raised by hand or on a foster mother. As stated in previous sections, breeding pigs should preferably always possess at least twelve to fourteen teats.

As of one week of age solid 'creep' feeds should be introduced. Creep feeding is the practice of feeding piglets separate from their mother. It is a desirable and economic practice as the nutritional needs of the young piglet are very different from those of the sow. Feeds suitable for the sow are too coarse and unpalatable for the piglets, and feeds suitable for the piglets are too expensive to feed to the sow. Creep feeds should be fed dry and piglets prefer them to be pelleted or crumbled. Water should always be available. Creep feeds can be fed in self-feeders or ordinary troughs. What is important is that the mother should not be able to eat the piglets' feed. A simple creep-feeding area can be made quite easily by barricading off the corner of a pen. After 3 weeks the piglets will be eating a considerable quantity of the creep feed.

The total quantity of the sow's ration should be raised gradually after farrowing and should be calculated according to the number of piglets that she is suckling. Details of feeding practices have been given in a previous section. The peak of milk production occurs about 3 weeks after farrowing, after which milk production slowly declines. The natural lactation length is approximately 12 weeks, but the normal practice is to wean at 8 weeks or earlier. Under good management pigs weaned at 8 weeks should weigh 14 to 18 kg (30 to 40 lb).

If the farmer wishes to wean at an earlier age then he should feed a creep feed with a higher nutritive value than the one normally used for piglets that are to be weaned at 8 weeks of age. Early weaning does appear to offer many advantages. These include the possibility of allowing the sow to farrow three times instead of twice a year or at least five times in 2 years. Also the possibility that piglets will grow faster, achieving a liveweight of 23 kg (50 lb) at 8 weeks. The sow should not lose too much weight. Feed costs should be less as there does not have to be such a long period during which there is a double conversion of food – first by the sow into milk and then by the piglet from milk into liveweight. It should be emphasized, however, that attempts at early weaning in the tropics have not often been very successful. In order to succeed both management and feeding have to be of the highest standard. To summarize, early weaning is not advised as a managerial practice for the average farmer in the tropics.

(b) *Piglet anaemia*

Piglets are born with a relatively small reserve of iron in their body and their mother's milk does not normally provide sufficient iron for their requirements. Consequently, piglet anaemia caused by an iron deficiency often occurs in piglets raised in the temperate zone although symptoms of this deficiency are not so frequently seen in piglets raised in the tropics. Anaemic piglets are pale in the regions of the ears and belly, are listless, breathe rapidly and often exhibit diarrhoea.

Piglet anaemia can be checked by

(i) placing fresh, clean earth in the piglet's pen each day;
(ii) using soil drenched with a solution made from 500 g ferrosulphate, 75 g copper sulphate and 3 litres of water;
(iii) the daily administration of 4 ml of a 1·8 per cent ferrosulphate solution;

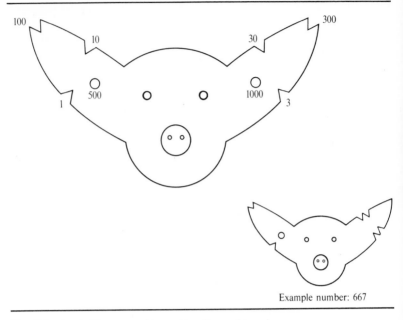

Example number: 667

Fig. 12.5   A suitable ear-punching pattern for marking pigs.

(iv) the daily painting of the mother's udder with ferrosulphate solution and sugar.

All these methods are labour intensive and the safest and easiest method of combating piglet anaemia is to inject the piglet with a minimum of 100 mg of iron in the form of iron dextran 3 days after birth. If necessary, a second and slightly smaller injection can be made some 3 weeks later.

(c) *Marking and castration*

Piglets should be ear-tattooed immediately after birth and the same animals ear-punched at 6 weeks of age (see Appendix II for further details). It is useless to ear-punch at too early an age as the punched ear of the very young pig grows together again. A suitable ear-punching

(a) The correct method of holding
(b) Holding the testicle before making the incision
(c) The incision
(d) The testicle being squeezed out
(e) Withdrawing the testicle
(f) Removing the testicle
(g) The attachment of the cord is scraped free, not cut, so as to reduce bleeding
(h) The operation is complete; both testicles being removed

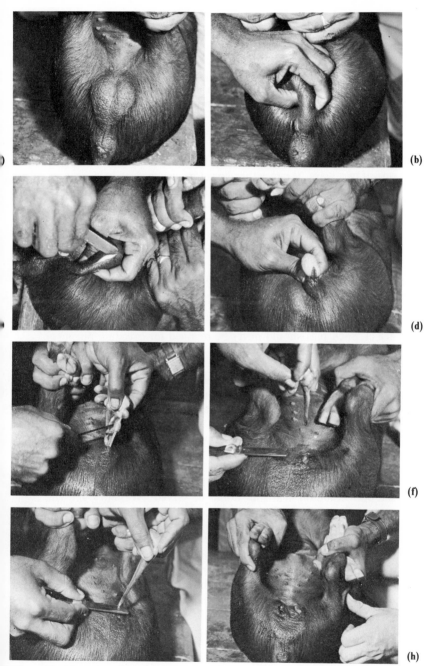

(b)

(d)

(f)

(h)

Plate 12.7 Normal method of castrating a pig.

pattern is shown in Fig. 12.5. Ear tags are not usually successful when used on pigs although there is a type of press-stud ear tag that apparently works.

Male piglets not required for breeding are generally castrated as this operation facilitates ease of management and prevents indiscriminate mating. It does, however, slightly reduce the efficiency of food conversion in the animal. The earlier castration is carried out, the easier the operation is to perform, and it is usually performed a week or 10 days before weaning. This allows the piglet to recover from the castration check before it receives a weaning check.

Castration is best performed with a knife. The piglet can be held in one of two ways. It can either be set on a board or held up by its hind legs with its forelegs on the floor. Two people are needed, one to hold the pig and one to carry out the operation. First an antiseptic should be smeared over the scrotum. A testicle should be squeezed up in one hand while a cut is made with the knife held in the other. The cut should be made as far forward as possible in order to facilitate drainage. When the testicle is exposed it should be pulled out and the cord divided by scraping. The operation is then repeated on the other testicle. Details of the operation are shown in Plate 12.7.

If one testicle has not descended from the abdominal cavity, as sometimes occurs, the pig is known as a 'rig'. This is usually an inherited defect. Such pigs should never be retained for breeding purposes.

4. Weaning and weaners

At weaning the sow should be taken away from the piglets and not the piglets from the sow. Weaning should be a gradual and not an abrupt process. At first the sow should be taken away for a few hours, then for a whole day and finally for all time. The sow's ration should be reduced gradually during the weaning period.

Piglets should be drenched with a vermifuge such as piperazine immediately after weaning in order to control internal parasites. Occasionally a sow comes on heat while she is suckling, but this is unusual. If she does come on heat she should be served. Normally, she will come on heat 2 to 5 days after she has ceased lactating. If she is not served at this time she may be difficult to get in-pig. If the piglets are weaned early the sow should be served as soon as she comes on heat, which should be within a few days of weaning.

The average number of piglets born is probably a breed characteristic, but the average number weaned and the weight at weaning is mainly determined by the standard of management and feeding.

5. Fatteners

Few pigs are raised for bacon or for lard purposes in the tropics. Most are raised for pork and they are generally slaughtered at 45 to 63 kg (100 to 140 lb) liveweight.

Pigs are usually fattened in groups of the same age. If litter mates can be fattened together, so much the better.

Details of fattening rations have been given in the section on feeding. The efficiency of management and the suitability of the rations utilized can be checked by weighing the pigs regularly and comparing their live-weights with those shown in Table 12.13. In most regions in the tropics a porker weighing 54 kg (120 lb) should be produced in 5 months. Fattening rate does, however, depend upon inherited abilities as well as on feeding and managerial practices. In general, crossbred pigs should fatten more rapidly than purebred pigs. Hogs usually fatten faster than gilts of the same breed.

Meal for fatteners can be fed wet or dry. It is normally more practical to feed it dry. It is essential to feed it dry if self-feeders or automatic feeders are used. Pigs should be fed at regular intervals as they become restless if feeding times are irregular. They should also be fed to appetite but not to repletion, and a certain finesse has to be shown in management in order to accomplish this.

Pigs should be drenched with a vermifuge such as piperazine at 15 to 16 weeks of age in order to ensure control of internal parasites.

6. Records

Breeding and liveweight records are essential for the commercial farmer. Other publications or extension officers should be consulted as to the most suitable form of records.

References

Davidson, H. R. (1948) *The Production and Marketing of pigs.* Longman: London.

Durrance, K. L. (1971) *Basic Information for Swine Production.* University of Florida: Gainsville.

Edwards, R. L., Omtvedt, I. T., Tuman, E. J., Stephens, D. F. and Mahoney, G. W. A. (1968) Reproductive performance of gilts following heat stress prior to breeding and in early gestation. *J. Anim. Sci.,* **27,** 1634–7.

Epstein, H. (1969) Domestic animals of China. *Tech Comm. Comw. Bur. Anim. Breed. Genet.,* No. 18. Comw. Agric. Bur.: Farnham Royal, UK.

Epstein, H. (1971) *The origin of the domestic animals of Africa,* Vol. 2. Edition Leipzig: Leipzig.

FAO (1973) *Production Yearbook: 1972,* Vol. 26. FAO: Rome.

Heitman, H. (Jr.) and Hughes, E. H. (1949) The effects of air temperature and relative humidity on the physiological wellbeing of swine. *J. Anim. Sci.,* **8,** 171–81.

Holmes, C. W. (1971) Growth and backfat depth of pigs kept at a high temperature. *Anim. Prod.,* **13,** 521–7.

Lucas, I. A. M. (1964) Modern methods of pig nutrition. The impact of recent research. *Vet. Rec.,* **76,** 101–9.

Mason, I. L. (1969) A world dictionary of livestock breeds, types and varieties (2nd edn). *Tech. Comm. Comw. Bur. Anim. Breed. Genet.*, No. 8. Comw. Agric. Bur.: Farnham Royal, UK.

National Research Council (1973) *Nutrient Requirements of Swine* (7th rev. edn). National Academy of Sciences: Washington.

Newland, H. W., McMillen, W. N. and Reincke, E. P. (1952) Temperature adaptation in the baby pig. *J. Anim. Sci.*, **11**, 118–33.

North Carolina State Univ. (1967), Exp. Stn Bull. No. 432 (May).

Omtvedt, I. T., Nelson, R. E., Edwards, R. L., Stephens, D. F. and Turman, E. J. (1971) Influence of heat stress during early, mid and late pregnancy of gilts. *J. Anim. Sci.*, **32**, 312–17.

Phillips, R. W., Johnson, R. G. and Moyer, R. T. (1945) *The Livestock of China.* Pub. 2249 (Far East Series 9). Dept. State: Washington.

Steinbach, J. (1972a) The oestral cycle of gilts in a tropical environment. *Proc. 7th Int. Cong. Anim. Reprod. and AI, Munich.* Summaries, pp. 425–6.

Steinbach, J. (1972b) Bioclimatic influences on sexual activity in boars. *Proc. 7th Int. Cong. Anim. Reprod. and AI, Munich.* Summaries, p. 427.

Steinbach, J. (1973) Bioclimatic influences on the reproductive processes in swine in a humid tropical environment. *Int. J. Biometeor.*, **17**, 141–5.

Verstegen, M. W. A., Close, W. H., Start, I. B. and Mount, L. F. (1973) The effect of environmental temperature and plane of nutrition on heat loss, energy, retention and deposition of protein and fat in groups of growing pigs. *Brit. J. Nutr.*, **30**, 21–35.

Zeuner, F. E. (1963) *A History of Domesticated Animals.* Hutchinson: London.

Chapter 13

Poultry

The outstanding feature of poultry production in tropical countries is the speed and extent of the changes that have taken place during the last two decades. When the first edition of this book was published in 1959 the authors could state quite categorically, 'that in few places is it [the poultry industry] a specialized industry and rarely does it form the sole means of livelihood or even a major source of income'. This is no longer true. Industrialized production methods, new breeds and improved health measures have been introduced from the temperate zone into almost all tropical countries with revolutionary effect. For example, in Malaysia in a publication entitled 'The Development of the Poultry Industry in West Malaysia' it is stated: 'Between 1956 and 1964 the Malayan poultry industry has apparently reaped the benefits of the application of a huge back-log of technological developments. Advances in the poultry industry, which it took pioneering countries centuries to complete, were achieved in eight years in Malaysia merely by the application here of practices which had become established in other countries' (Thuraisingham and Wah, 1971). In fact, Malaysian poultry production progressed between 1956 and 1964 by approximately the same degree as the Danish industry did between 1750 and 1950. Local egg production increased from 77 million eggs per year in 1956 to over 1,100 million eggs per year in 1970, and per capita consumption of eggs increased from 30 to 120 over the same period. More important still, the retail price index of eggs declined from 100 in 1950 to 57 in 1964.

It is extremely fortunate that this revolution in poultry production occurred, as during the last two decades millions of people migrated from the countryside to the cities and the per capita production of meat from ruminant animals either remained more or less static or fell in Latin America, Asia and Africa (Jasiorowski, 1973). The increased production of both eggs and poultry meat has certainly assisted in reducing the 'gap' in the supplies of animal protein for the human population in the tropics.

It must be emphasized, however, that the revolution in poultry production methods has hardly affected the subsistence and small-scale poultry producers in the myriads of villages throughout the tropics, and

595

that countless millions of people still depend upon backyard or small-scale poultry production for their supplies of eggs and poultry meat. The new poultry industry is essentially an urban phenomenon, financed by urban capital, mainly benefiting urban-orientated producers and urban consumers and generally sited adjacent to the cities and larger towns.

The increasing worldwide cost of energy and purchased feed supplies may delay or even halt the complete industrialization and urbanization of poultry production in tropical countries, and subsistence and small-scale production methods may once more become relatively attractive to some sections of the population, particularly if minor but additive improvements in production methods can be introduced at the village level. This chapter has therefore been written to provide information primarily for extension officers and farmers concerned with subsistence and small-scale poultry production.

Of the four common species of domestic poultry, namely fowls, ducks, geese and turkeys, the first named are by far the most important in the tropics – as indeed they are elsewhere. Attention will therefore be mainly centred on the problems of fowl production.

Fowls

Origin

It is believed that the modern fowl probably originated from four wild species, the Red Jungle fowl (*Gallus gallus*), the Ceylon Jungle fowl (*G. lafayetti*), the Grey Jungle or Sonnerat fowl (*G. sonnerattii*) and the Java Jungle fowl (*G. varius*), although it is likely that of the four wild species *G. gallus* is the main ancestor. The four species are closely related and are probably no more than somewhat divergent geographical races (Zeuner, 1963). They are known to interbreed.

The centre of domestication is unknown. Zeuner (1963) suggested that it was in India, but others, including Peters (1913), have concluded that it was in Southeast Asia. In view of the very wide distribution of the wild species, in the Indian sub-continent and throughout mainland Southeast Asia to the offshore islands of Indonesia, it is possible that there were several centres of domestication. Today in Southeast Asia the distribution of the Red Jungle fowl is closely associated with the occurrence of shifting agriculture (Callias and Saichuae, 1967). These authors suggest that under such circumstances domestication could easily have been initiated and they cite examples of the present-day domestication of wild birds. Certainly wild birds will interbreed with domestic fowls. An interesting example is found in the island of Madura in Indonesia, where wild cocks are captured, tamed and mated with village hens to produce *begisar* or 'song cockerels'. Zeuner (1963) has stated that domesticated fowls could certainly be found in the Indus valley by 2000 BC, that they were reared in what is now Iran by 800 BC and that the Persians probably spread them throughout western Asia and to the shores of the Mediterranean by 600 BC. They were common in Italy by 400 BC and were introduced into northern Europe by 100 BC. They were used for different purposes in different cultures. Their use in cock-fighting has an early origin and their first economic impact was probably as egg producers. They were also used both in Greece and in Rome for sacrificial and soothsaying purposes. Details of the spread of fowls east-wards and northwards into Asia from their centre of origin in South or Southeast Asia are unknown at present. They were imported into the Americas and Australia by the early European explorers and immigrants.

Breeds

The majority of breeds used today by commercial poultry-keepers are hybrids that have been bred by the large-scale international poultry-breeding corporations, and fertile eggs, day-old chicks or parental breed-ing stock are usually imported into tropical countries. The number of available breeds is large and the most suitable type to use in any specific environment is continuously changing. Under these circumstances those interested in purchasing hybrid breeding stock should consult their exten-sion organization or representatives of the international corporations who are established in many tropical countries.

If for some reason hybrid breeding stock are not available then the improved pure breeds most commonly used are of three types: those developed for high egg production, those bred specifically for meat pro-duction, and dual-purpose breeds.

The high-egg-producing breeds are mainly of Mediterranean origin and the most popular are the *Leghorn, Ancona* and *Minorcan.* The *White Leghorn* is probably the most widely used light breed. Mature cockerels and hens weigh approximately 2·7 kg (6 lb) and 1·8 kg (4 lb), respec-tively. The hens do not go broody very easily so that it is necessary to set the eggs under a hen of another breed or to incubate them artificially. Hens are very good layers with a high efficiency of feed con-version, but birds of this breed do not produce good carcases. They appear to be more heat tolerant than other commercial breeds, although in other ways they are not particularly hardy.

Meat-producing types are typified by the *Orpington, Cornish Dark* and *Jersey Black Giant.* These are heavy breeds, mature cockerels of the three breeds weighing 3·9 kg (8·5 lb), 3·9 kg (8·5 lb) and 5·0 kg (11 lb), respec-tively. These breeds are not normally economical egg producers or particularly heat tolerant. Apart from the White Leghorn, dual-purpose breeds such as the *Rhode Island Red* (RIR), *Light Sussex, New Hampshire Red* and *Australorp* are the most popular breeds used in tropical countries. Mature **RIR** and Light Sussex cockerels and hens weigh approximately 3·6 kg (8 lb) and 2·7 kg (6 lb), respectively. The **RIR** hens are good layers and meat producers, but they possess a yellow-skinned carcase. They go broody very easily, but thrive well in the humid tropics. Light Sussex birds are also hardy, but the hens produce smaller eggs. The New Hampshire Red is a rapidly maturing breed. Mature cockerels and hens weigh 4 kg (9 lb) and 2·6 kg (6 lb), respectively. Black Australorps have been extensively used in Southeast Asia, although hens of this breed do not lay as well as some of the other breeds mentioned and quickly go broody. The breed crosses well with the White Leghorn. Mature cockerels and hens weigh 3·6 kg (8 lb) and 2·7 kg (6 lb), respectively.

In some countries the government imports selected pure lines of poultry and breeds from them large numbers of exotic purebreds or crossbreds for use in village upgrading programmes or by commercial producers. The Government Poultry Breeding Programme in India is an example of such a scheme.

Where fowls have to hatch their own brood, scavenge for the major part of their food and are unprotected against predators and endemic disease, then indigenous breeds should be used. There are innumerable types.

In those countries where the main functions of domestic fowl in the past were to supply meat and provide fighting cocks, body-size and vigour have been the traits for which they have been selected. There are many breeds, the Indian *Aseel* being a typical example. These fowl grow very slowly. Even under the best of managerial conditions they only achieve a liveweight of approximately 1·8 kg (4 lb) in 6 months, but cockerels and hens grow on to achieve mature liveweights of 4·5 kg (10 lb) and 3·2 to 3·6 (7 to 8 lb), respectively. The breast and thighs of the cockerels are particularly well developed and the pullets are also valuable meat producers. The average egg production of this breed is thirty-five per annum.

There are some indigenous breeds that produce relatively large numbers of eggs in a year, but the eggs are invariably small compared with those of exotic breeds. The *White Chittagong* of India is an example of one of these breeds. The hens lay on average 130 small eggs per annum. The *Canton* of Malaysia is a similar breed. Under good managerial conditions hens of this breed will produce 120 eggs per annum with an average weight of 42 g (1·5 oz), although under village conditions the average egg production is probably no more than 80 per annum.

In general, the average indigenous fowl in the tropics probably weighs 0·9 to 1·8 kg (2 to 4 lb) and possesses a well-fleshed, compact body and a somewhat light covering of wiry feathers that are free from down. A naked neck is a feature of some breeds, while others possess naked or nearly naked thighs. The feather colouring is very varied, but most often it is a lighter or darker shade of brown intermingled with red or gold. A black colour is fairly common, as is 'barring', although a white colour is unusual. In cockerels male characteristics are marked. Females usually possess small heads and usually lay up to three clutches of twelve to eighteen eggs each year. The weight of an average egg is about 28 g (1 oz). Broodiness is pronounced. All these fowls are normally active and vigorous foragers, well adapted to tropical environments.

Often exotic purebred fowls have been used to upgrade indigenous village flocks. Experience has shown that such upgrading is not likely to be very successful unless there is at the same time a parallel improvement in management and feeding. It has also been shown to be a mistake to introduce a small number of exotic cockerels into a village flock. They are invariably intimidated and/or killed by the more vigorous indigenous cockerels. If upgrading of village flocks is to be practised all the indigenous cockerels should be replaced by exotic cockerels at one time. In India the use of exotic White Leghorn × Australorp or White Leghorn × RIR hybrid cocks for village flock upgrading has had some success, advantage being taken of the hybrid vigour of the crossbred cockerels and their superior viability in the village environment to purebred exotic cockerels.

Effect of climate

Fowls, like other domestic livestock, are homeotherms. The zone of thermoneutrality for adult egg-laying birds appears to be within the range 5° to 25°C (41° to 77°F). With increasing environmental temperature there appears to be a decrease in feed intake and alterations in behaviour, reflected by a continuous decrease in heat production. For example, Waring and Brown (1967) showed that when the ambient temperature increased from 21° to 29·5°C (70° to 85°F) the fasting metabolic rate (FMR) decreased from 106 to 96 kcal/kg$^{0.75}$ per day. Payne (1967) stated that within the temperature range −5° to 30°C (23° to 86°F) there was a reduction of about 1·6 per cent in feed intake for every 10°C (18°F) increase in ambient temperature. When ambient temperatures are above 30°C (86°F) both egg production and egg size are depressed. The relative humidity appears to have no effect on performance at ambient temperatures below 26·7°C (80°F), although it may affect performance at higher ambient temperatures.

In the case of broilers experimental data suggest that those reared at ambient temperatures within the range 1·7° to 18·3°C (29° to 65°F) are somewhat heavier than similar stock reared within the ambient temperature range of 18·3° to 35°C (65° to 95°F), but that their efficiency of food conversion is less.

Thus in the tropics, where mean annual ambient temperatures are of the order of 26·7°C (80°F), it would appear that the rearing of broilers could be more economic than in the temperate zone if equally cheap feedstuffs and good management are available. Present data also suggest that the dry tropics may be a superior environment for broiler production to the humid tropics.

In the case of egg production it is probably necessary for producers to take some ameliorative measures to protect their egg-laying poultry against the high daily temperatures experienced during some months in both the wet and the dry tropics. However, these measures should be no more costly in economic terms than those taken by poultry producers in the temperate zone to protect their birds against cold and damp. We may therefore conclude that egg production should be at least as economic in the tropics as in the temperate zone if other factors apart from climate are equal.

It is interesting to note that as small egg size is a characteristic of indigenous tropical breeds and high environmental temperatures induce small egg size in exotic breeds then this trait in the indigenous breeds may be simply an adaptation to the climatic environment. Exotic breeds imported into the tropics demonstrate a considerable degree of adaptation, as was shown by experimental work conducted 30 years ago by Lee *et al.* (1945). These workers used unacclimatized White Leghorns, Brown Leghorns, Australorps, RIRs and Minorcas and subjected them to considerable heat stress. They found that the respiration rate of the birds increased rapidly with increasing ambient temperature and that it was more or less correlated with body temperature. At an ambient temperature of 42·2°C (108°F) the birds panted with open mouths and at 45°C (113°F) they were gasping and were on the point of collapse. The loss of water from the body was very high when ambient temperatures were 37·8°C (100°F) or above. In this context it should be noted that birds do not possess sweat glands and that the only way in which they can utilize evaporative cooling is through the lungs by panting. High humidities combined with high ambient temperatures affected the Australorps more than the other breeds. Air movement did improve performance slightly, particularly when humidity was high.

The first effects of high ambient temperatures were to initiate a partial moult and radically to reduce egg laying, but with continuous exposure egg laying improved, thus demonstrating a considerable degree of acclimatization. The eggs that were laid during exposure to very high temperatures were often soft-shelled and misshapen. The actual act of laying raised body temperatures – normally 41·1°C (106°F) by 1·1°C (2°F). There was a smaller rise in body temperature on exposure to high temperatures if the birds were allowed water *ad lib.*

There were differences in the reactions of the different breeds. At low relative humidity White Leghorns were least affected by high ambient temperature while at high relative humidity the Brown Leghorns were least affected and the Australorps most affected.

The problems of acclimatization have been fully discussed by

Hutchinson (1954) and it would appear that the purebred exotic breeds that are used in the tropics will, in general, acclimatize quite well, but that they are affected by very high ambient temperatures. These conclusions agree with practical experience, as it has been found that given proper management and feeding and adequate disease control the majority of exotic breeds, whether purebred or hybrid, can become economic producers in the tropics.

Nevertheless, a tropical climate does produce problems for the poultry producer and every effort should be made to select a suitable breed and to ameliorate conditions for the birds. Suitable feeding methods, as discussed in the next section, can assist in amelioration, as can suitable buildings, discussed in a later section, and proper management.

Feeding

Very considerable advances have been made in poultry nutrition since the first edition of this book was published. For example, it is estimated that in 1966 a male broiler required 5·1 kg (11·2 lb) of feed and 74 days to achieve a liveweight of 2 kg (4·4 lb), whereas in 1975 Blair (1975) stated that 4 kg (8·8 lb) of feed and a period of 50 days are now required. In addition, a poultry-feed industry has developed in most tropical countries and commercial poultry rations are now freely available that have been formulated using least-cost methods based on linear programming. These rations are available not only to the commercial producer but also, in many tropical countries, to the small farmer and backyard poultry-keeper.

We therefore only intend to indicate briefly some recent advances in poultry nutrition, to discuss the special requirements of poultry in a tropical climate, to advise in which publications details of poultry nutritive requirements can be readily found, and to provide some general information for those small and backyard poultry-keepers who cannot afford, or do not have access to, commercial poultry rations.

In a general way poultry nutritionists are now concerned to formulate rations that do not necessarily ensure maximum production but the most economic performance. It is obvious, therefore, that information is required on the range of energy levels that can be tolerated in rations for different classes of poultry. Also very complete information is required on the amino-acid, mineral and vitamin contents of available feeds. When energy levels alter a constant energy/protein ratio is required, and as the protein level changes it is also important that the relative amounts of amino acids should remain the same. Overall, one of the major aims of poultry nutritionists is to provide specific inputs of required nutrients per unit of liveweight for the different classes of poultry. For example, it is now suggested that in broiler production males and females should be fed separately as female broilers grow at a slower rate and possibly require more feed than males.

Considerable attention has been paid to the effect of processing on the nutritive value and palatability of feeds, and major improvements in processing methods have been made. The possibility of restricting energy intake to levels below those normal where there is a free choice of feed are also under investigation. If energy intake is restricted it is of course necessary to increase the amino-acid, vitamin and mineral contents of the feed. The use of individual synthetic amino acids to fortify feeds deficient in a specific amino acid is now generally practised and the uses of new sources of protein, in particular single-cell yeast, algae and bacterial protein, are being actively investigated. There is recent information on the mineral requirements of poultry that suggests that nickel, tin, vanadium, silicon and fluorine are all essential mineral nutrients, that selenium may be an essential mineral nutrient independent of its interactions with vitamin E and that the requirements of poultry for zinc and iron are rather higher than had been recommended in the past (Taylor, 1975).

Feed requirements

Recent estimates of the nutrient requirements of poultry in the temperate zone have been published in the United States by the National Academy of Sciences (1971) and in the United Kingdom by the Agricultural Research Council (1963). A useful summary of feeding standards for poultry based on the above and other sources of information has been published by McDonald *et al.* (1973) and these are shown in Table 13.1. Some normal rates of inclusion of feeds available in the temperate zone have been published by Bolton and Blair (1974).

A major difficulty experienced in the tropics, both by the commercial formulators and small farmers who wish – or are forced by circumstances – to mix their own rations, is that data on the average nutrient content of many local feeds are not available, or if available are based on data acquired in other countries or in another region of the same country. This situation can only change as analytical facilities become more widely dispersed and available. In the interim period a wide margin of safety must be accepted in order to ensure that the feed used in the ration does contain the required level of nutrients, despite regional differences in the nutrient content of the same feed, storage losses, etc.

Special feed requirements in a tropical climate

Recent experimental work has suggested that the level of energy consumption may be a major factor affecting egg production in tropical countries.

Hens with a mature weight of 1·8 kg (4 lb) in the temperate zone receiving *ad lib* rations containing 2.750 to 2.860 kcal of metabolizable

Table 13.1   *Feeding standards for fowls*

(a) Energy (k cal ME/day)*

	Liveweight of birds (kg (lb))			
	1·4 (3)	1·8 (4)	2·3 (5)	2·7 (6)
Maintenance	165	230	285	335
Maintenance and egg production†				
20%	190	255	310	360
40%	220	280	335	385
60%	245	305	360	410
80%	270	330	385	435

(b) Amino acids (percentage of air-dry ration)

	Chicks (0–4 weeks)	Layers
Arginine	0·80	–
Glycine	1·00	–
Histidine	0·35	–
Isoleucine	0·50	0·50
Leucine	1·50	0·70
Lysine	1·00	0·50
Methionine + cystine‡	0·70	0·55
Phenylalanine + tyrosine‡	1·20	0·70
Threonine	0·55	0·40
Tryptophan	0·15	0·13
Valine	0·80	0·55

(c) Vitamins (concentration in air-dry ration)

	Chicks (0–8 weeks)	Layers
		As IU/kg (lb)
A	1,500 (700)	4,400 (2,000)
D_3	310 (140)	600 (270)
		As ppm
K	0·53–0·99	–
B_1 (thiamin)	1·00–1·80	–
B_2 (riboflavin)	3·60–4·00	2·20–2·50
Nicotinic acid	28	10
Pantothenic acid	10	2
B_6	3·00–3·50	2·00
Biotin	0·04–0·09	–
Folic acid	1·50	0·30
B_{12}	0·02	–
Choline	1,300	–

Table 13.1—*continued*

(d) Minerals (concentration in air-dry ration)

	Chicks (0–8 weeks)	Layers
		As percentage
Calcium	1·0	2·8§
Chlorine	0·06	–
Phosphorus	0·4–0·8	0·6
Potassium	0·2	–
Sodium	0·11–0·15	0·15
		As ppm
Copper	3–4	–
Iodine	0·4	0·3
Iron	40–80	–
Magnesium	250–500	–
Manganese	35–55	
Zinc	15–50	

* These values are for the temperate zone and they will be lower in the tropics.
† Percentage egg production is obtained by dividing the number of eggs laid by the number of days involved and multiplying by 100.
‡ Methionine can be partly replaced by cystine and phenylalanine partly by tyrosine.
§ Calcium requirement varies with egg productivity. This is an average figure.
Sources: McDonald *et al.* (1973). Reproduced with permission National Academy of Sciences (1971).

energy (ME) per kg of feed will consume approximately 310 to 330 kcal of ME daily when producing the maximum number of eggs. As stated in a previous section, feed consumption falls with rising ambient temperature and a decrease in feed consumption of 10 to 15 per cent is not uncommon in the tropics. This means that the daily intake of ME may be only 265 to 280 kcal and this level of intake is insufficient for maximum egg-laying performance. Thus, every managerial method of increasing feed consumption should be used. These could include encouraging feed intake in the early morning and in the evening when ambient temperatures are lower than they are during the remainder of the day; feeding high-energy diets; stirring the feed frequently; using pelleted feed; and providing ample supplies of cool, fresh water.

Laying hens normally exhibit two peak feed consumption periods – one at the time of lay and the other late in the afternoon. As hens begin to lay about one hour after first light, and light encourages feeding, the provision of additional light in the morning and again in the evening should encourage hens to eat during the cooler periods. High-energy-content diets (2,860 to 2,960 kcal of ME per kg) can also be formulated and should be used. Stirring the feed once or twice daily also increases consumption but is a labour-intensive practice. Pelleting the feed also increases consumption, but this practice does have the disadvantage that it often encourages cannibalism. It may also increase water consumption. This of course is desirable. In any case ample fresh, clean water must be available as hens in the tropics will consume on average 500 ml (0·11 gal) of water per day compared with 200 to 250 ml (0·04 to 0·05 gal) in the temperate zone. Deprivation of water for only a few hours may affect egg production for several days. High-fibre-content rations will also decrease feed intake and hence egg production.

If feed consumption decreases during hot weather then as most poultry rations are formulated with a constant ME:CP ratio the crude protein (CP) content of the ration must be increased to ensure maximum egg production. In a ration containing 2,750 kcal ME per kg with a 15·6 per cent CP content, the concentration of the latter should be raised to 17·3 to 18·3 per cent. On the other hand, if despite efforts to increase ME consumption egg production falls below 65 per cent, i.e. an egg is laid on 65 per cent of the possible days, then there is no necessity to increase the CP of the ration.

More calcium must also be fed during hot weather to prevent an increase in the number of broken and cracked eggs produced. Additional calcium added to the ration will probably make it less palatable and tend to decrease total intake so that the calcium should be supplied partly in the ration and partly in the form of oyster-shell or limestone chips.

If feed intake decreases it will also be necessary to increase the concentration of all the other minerals and vitamins in the ration.

Feeding methods for the small poultry-keeper

There is ample evidence that if the feeding of indigenous poultry is improved then they will become more productive. Improved feeding is even more important, indeed essential, if indigenous breeds are upgraded using exotic and more productive breeds.

Feeding may be improved in two ways. The birds may still be allowed to scavenge around the house compound but in addition be fed a daily basic ration, or they may be enclosed and fed complete rations. Upgraded birds may lose their scavenging abilities and it may be essential to feed them complete rations in an enclosure.

It is reasonable to suppose that scavenging poultry are usually able to secure adequate quantities of minerals and vitamins and some of their protein requirements but that they are not normally able to obtain an adequate supply of energy feeds. Thus, a ration for scavenging poultry should be energy-rich and contain moderate quantities of protein. Cereal grains are obviously suitable if they are available.

As it is unlikely that the small poultry-keeper or his extension advisers will have access to the type of data given in Table 13.1, it is necessary to provide a less sophisticated method of formulating poultry rations. Information on the CP content and perhaps part of the mineral content of local feeds may be available from proximate analyses, and so

Table 13.2   *Suggested crude protein, calcium and phosphorus nutritive levels in rations for poultry*

	Chick starter	Chick grower	Meat cockerel finishing ration*	Layers and breeders
Age (weeks)	0–8	9–20	9–12	> 20
Nutrient level				
Crude protein (%)	18	15	18	16
Calcium (%)	1·0–1·2	1·0–1·2	1·0–1·2	2·8–3·0
Phosphorus (%)†	0·8	0·8	0·6	0·6

* The age could vary as the cockerels would be finished to market weight.
† This is total and not available phosphorus.
   Source: Smetana (1966).

suggested levels of CP, calcium and phosphorus in rations for different classes of poultry are shown in Table 13.2. It is suggested that as many feeds as are locally available should be used in making up the rations. This is particularly important as far as the protein-rich feeds are concerned, as a mixture should ensure that there is a reasonable chance of the ration providing all the essential amino acids required by the birds. In addition, a mineral mixture, green feed and an adequate supply of fresh, clean water should always be available in the pen. Examples of suitable rations that have been formulated by Smetana (1966) in Burma, where the animal-feed industry is not very sophisticated, are given in Table 13.3.

Feeding methods.

Poultry that are not on range or scavenging should always be fed some hard grit as this is essential for the proper working of their digestive system. Hard metal screenings (3 mm (0·13 in)), quartz and/or granite chips or coarse sand are all satisfactory. Grit should be fed in separate containers from at least 3 weeks of age.

When household scraps are fed care must be taken to see that they contain no toxic materials. Very salty feeds can be toxic.

Water must always be available and is best provided from automatic fountains. The daily provision of some fresh green feed is desirable.

The feeds used in the formulation of a ration must of course be palatable. Mashes that are too light and dusty or too wet and sticky clog the nostrils and/or the beak and sooner or later cause aversion. Similarly, foods which distend the crop by swelling or which clog the gizzard because of their fibrous nature become unacceptable.

The main ways in which feeds are prepared and offered to poultry are as follows:

1. *Dry mash.* Only grit and green feed are fed additionally. There is often some wastage at the troughs.

Table 13.3 *Examples of poultry rations formulated in Burma*

Feed	Chick starter ration* (%)	Chick grower ration† (%)	Meat cockerel finishing ration‡ (%)	Layer rations	
				1 (%)	2 (%)
Maize	25	15	30	25	–
Broken rice	25	30	25	25	46
Rice bran	10	20	–	10	12
Groundnut meal	15	15	18	14	16
Sesame meal	10	10	10	10	10
Prawn meal§	15	7	14	10	10
Bone-meal (sterilized)	–	2	2	3	3
Oyster flour	–	–	–	3	3
Vitamin mix	+	1	1	–	–
Green feed	+‖	–	–	–	–
Coccidiostat	+	–	–	–	–
Calculated analysis					
Crude protein (%)	18·0	16·3	18·5	16·7	16·6
Calcium (%)	1·45	1·29	1·21	2·58	2·59
Phosphorus (%)	0·42	0·61	0·55	0·61	0·62

* Fed from day-old to 8 weeks of age.
† Fed from 8 weeks until maturity at 20 weeks.
‡ Fed to cockerels after they have been separated from the females at approximately 8 weeks of age.
§ 33 per cent crude protein content.
‖ It would be desirable to provide green feed to all stock and not just to the chicks.
Source: Smetana (1966).

2. *Dry mash and grain.* The dry mash should always be available and the grain fed in separate troughs once a day. As grains possess a relatively low CP content the CP, mineral and vitamin contents of dry mash feed with grain should be superior to that of dry mash fed alone.
3. *Wet mash.* There are no particular advantages in feeding wet mash and labour costs are increased.
4. *Pellets or crumbles.* The feeding of these is to some extent advantageous. There is less wastage compared with the feeding of dry mash, and birds cannot select out specific feeds and are therefore likely to obtain all the nutrients included in the ration. However, the feeding of pellets does tend to increase the incidence of cannibalism.

Feeding space

Adequate feed space is very important. The feed trough should be accessible from all sides. As a general guide to the provision of feeding space, approximately half the total number of birds should be able to eat

Table 13.4 *Feed trough requirements for different classes of poultry*

Type	Age (weeks)	Length of feed trough per 100 birds* (m (ft))	No. required and weight of feed in hanging feeders per 100 birds† (kg (lb))
Fowls			
Chicks raised for egg production	1–3	2·4 (8)	
	4–6	3·7 (12)	2 × 11·3 (25)
	7–12	4·8 (15)	
	13–18	5·2 (17)	4 × 11·3 (25)
	Layers	7·6–10·7 (25–35)	6 × 11·3 (25)
Broiler chicks	1–3	2·7 (9)	
	4–6	5·2 (17)	
	7–12	7·6 (25)	6 × 11·3 (25)
Ducks	1–3	7·3 (24)	
	Mature	12·2 (40)	
Turkeys	1–4	5·2–7·6 (17–25)	
	5–8	9·1–12·2 (30–40)	
	8–16	12·2–15·2 (40–50)	
	Breeders	12·2–15·2 (40–50)	

*These requirements are based on the assumption that the feed troughs are accessible from both sides. If this is not the case the length should be doubled.
† For mature birds the hanging troughs should be 0·3 m (1 ft) above the ground.

at any one time. Details of feed and water-trough requirements are given in Tables 13.4 and 13.5.

Feed consumption

It is important to be able to estimate average feed consumption in order to be able to budget for and purchase feeds. Monitoring of feed consumption by the poultry-keeper can also indicate changes in the health and productivity of the flock. Some information on the average consumption of food by different classes of birds is given in Table 13.6. This information should only be used as a very approximate guide as feed consumption obviously depends upon many and varying factors.

Health and disease

Poultry that have been well fed and managed and vaccinated against known local diseases usually remain healthy. The greatest emphasis should be on disease prevention, but if there is a disease outbreak, sick should be separated from healthy birds, strict sanitary measures should

Table 13.5 *Water trough requirements for different classes of poultry in the tropics*

Type	Age (weeks)	Length of water trough per 100 birds (m (ft))	No. water fountains and capacity (litre (gal))
Fowls	1–4	1·0 (3·3)	
	5–8	1·8–2·0 (6·0–6·7)	4 × 2·3 (0·5)
	9–18	2·5 (8·3)	
	Laying	2·5 (8·3)	
Turkeys	1–4	1·0–1·3 (3·3–4·0)	
	5–8	2·5 (8·3)	
	9–16	3·0 (10·0)	
	Breeders	3·0–3·8 (10·0–12·5)	

Note: The allowances are generous by temperate-zone standards, as under normal tropical conditions birds drink more frequently than they would in the temperate zone.

Table 13.6 *Approximate food consumption of fowls*

Age of bird (weeks)	Approximate food consumption	
	Per week	Progressive total
	(kg (lb))	(kg (lb))
1–8	0·14–0·50 (0·3–1·1)	2·4 (5·2)
9–20	0·54–0·90 (1·2–2·0)	10·5 (23·2)
Mature (laying bird)	0·90 (2·0)	

Notes: The estimates are for medium-size breeds. Lighter and heavier breeds will have correspondingly smaller and larger consumptions.

be applied in all housing and a veterinarian or extension worker should be immediately notified.

Major diseases and other causes of ill-health are briefly discussed.

Coccidiosis

Symptoms. The droppings of chicks become watery and spots of blood may be detected. Chicks droop, reduce their feed intake and may huddle. They are most vulnerable between the second and third and the fourth and fifth weeks of life.

Treatment. Use sulphamethezine or sulphquinozaline in the drinking water for 3 days; cease using the drug for 2 days and then use it again for a further 3 days.

Prevention. Thoroughly clean brooders between batches of chicks. Do not overcrowd chicks. Take precautions to see that chicks do not contaminate their drinking water. Use a coccidiostat, such as nitrofurazone, in the feed until the chicks are 10 to 12 weeks old.

Bacillary white diarrhoea (BWD) or pullorum disease

This is an egg-borne disease that spreads during incubation or just after hatching.

Symptoms.   White diarrhoea droppings at any time from 3 days to several weeks of age. The chicks refuse to eat, stand with their heads tucked in and their wings hanging down, huddle and make a peeping sound. The diarrhoea symptoms may easily be confused with those of other diseases.

Treatment.   There is no absolute control, but quite good results have been obtained using the drug furazolidone. Dead chicks should be burned and housing and appliances thoroughly disinfected.

Prevention.   The disease is not easily transmitted when eggs are naturally incubated. Parent stock of infected chicks should be blood-tested and day-old chicks should only be purchased from breeders who submit their birds to regular blood testing.

Fowl typhoid

This disease is caused by the organism *Salmonella gallinarum* and it is often more widespread in tropical countries than is BWD. There is an acute form of it in East Africa, known as Kikuyu fowl disease.

Symptoms.   Very similar to those of BWD.

Treatment.   With furazolidone as for BWD.

Prevention.   There is an effective vaccine and this should be used. Vaccination may be carried out when growers are moved to permanent laying quarters, i.e. when they are about 16 to 18 weeks of age. An injection of 1 ml of vaccine is made into the breast muscle of the bird. Carriers can be detected by an agglutination test and should be destroyed.

Respiratory diseases

These are most prevalent on large holdings and in the montane areas of the tropics. They can be caused by overcrowding, bad ventilation, dust, lack of protection against cold draughts and possibly by a lack of vitamin A in the diet.

Symptoms.   Birds usually emit a discharge from the nostrils and develop cheesy material in the mouth and throat.

Treatment. Antibiotics in the feed or water are quite effective. The use of potassium permanganate in the drinking water helps to prevent the spread of infection.

Prevention. Affected birds should be culled, isolated and treated. In the tropics birds in open housing can be protected from the occasional cold blast of wind and cold rain by the provision of screens made of plastic, jute bags, split bamboo or rattan, that can be rolled up or let down in accordance with prevailing weather conditions. Rations should contain adequate quantities of vitamin A or carotene.

Fowl cholera

Symptoms. Very laboured breathing, dark-coloured droppings, high temperatures and very red combs that may turn almost black.

Treatment. Sulphonamides may be used.

Prevention. The surest methods are good management, feeding and sanitation.

Fowl pox

Symptoms. Somewhat the same as in the case of cholera, but the birds will exhibit blackish warts on combs and wattles.

Treatment. Complete control can be obtained by vaccination. This may be carried out as early as 5 weeks of age. Two hypodermic needles are fitted into a cork, about 3 mm apart. One operator dips the sharp end of the needles in the vaccine, the other holds the chick in one hand while the wing is spread out using the other hand, so that the first operator handling the needle can pierce the web or the small area of skin between the first and second joints of the wing. Within a few days the bird should show a small pustule where the wing was pierced, but after a further 14 days this disappears.

Newcastle disease

This is a virus disease that is very infectious and that probably causes more losses than any other poultry disease in the tropics.

Symptoms. Rapid breathing accompanied by a gurgling noise in the throat with or without a discharge of mucus from mouth and nostrils. There may be some paralysis, with dragging of the wing or leg. Mortality is high and the spread of the disease is very rapid.

Treatment. No treatment is effective. All birds should be slaughtered after an outbreak. The meat of slaughtered birds that have shown no symptoms can be consumed, but on no account should survivors be moved into contact with other birds. Premises and equipment must always be thoroughly disinfected and restocking should not take place for at least 3 months.

Prevention.   In epizootic areas all birds should be vaccinated at 6-month intervals. The first vaccination may take place at 8 weeks of age when chicks leave the brooder. The vaccine is injected under the skin of the neck at the dosage rate of 1 ml per bird.

Other diseases

Two other diseases that may be of importance are *paratyphoid* or *salmonellosis* and *fowl paralysis*. The first disease affects all domestic poultry and is transmitted to and from human beings. It is therefore of considerable public health interest and stringent precautions must be taken if an outbreak is diagnosed. Fowl paralysis is an insidious disease that is contagious so that any 'wasting' symptoms in birds should be immediately reported to a veterinary authority.

Intestinal parasites

Infestation usually occurs when birds are kept for too long a period on the same ground or when wet patches are allowed to develop in deep-litter houses.

Symptoms.   The birds lose condition, the feathers, combs and wattles may become dull and growth or egg production decreases. There is often diarrhoea and worms may be seen in the droppings. Heavy infestation may lead to the death of birds.

Treatment.   Birds should be dewormed with the appropriate drug. It is always advisable to seek the advice of a veterinarian and to have the worm(s) typed so that the most suitable and economic vermifuge can be utilized.

Prevention.   Good hygiene and feeding and the separate rearing of various age groups will go far to reduce intestinal parasitism.

External parasites

Lice.   These are probably the most common poultry pest and they are often the cause of low egg production. They are easy to detect. If the birds are handled the lice will be seen moving about the base of the fluffy feathers found around the vent. An approved and effective insecticide should be used immediately and again 10 days later when the eggs of the lice, already attached to the birds, hatch. A light application of nicotine sulphate on the bird's hocks, just before roosting time, is a simple method of control. Perches and other wooden structures must also be dealt with and may be painted with crude oil, but this material should not be applied to nesting boxes as it may cause some contamination of the eggs.

Red mites.   These are more difficult to recognize as they do not live on the birds, but only feed on them at night. Mild infestations can be dealt with in the same manner as lice infestations, but if the infestation is very severe the house – as long as it is of simple design and cheaply con-structed – may have to be burnt.

Scaly leg mites.   These are also difficult to eradicate. The legs of all infected birds should be repeatedly dipped in kerosene, the house thoroughly cleaned and any litter removed and burnt.

Other causes of ill-health

Vitamin and mineral deficiencies in the rations can cause a variety of deficiency diseases in poultry (see Ch. 3, Pt I). Proper formulated com-mercial rations should contain adequate amounts of all the essential vitamins and minerals, but farm mixed rations may sometimes be deficient in one or another. One insurance is to provide adequate quanti-ties of green feed in the pens daily.

Poultry often exhibit vices such as cannibalism and egg-eating that cause mortality or decrease productivity.

Cannibalism.   This may commence as toe-pecking in chicks, feather-pecking in growing birds or vent-pecking in egg-layers. Once blood is drawn the trouble begins and the victim is often killed. Toe-pecking may start among very young chicks; feather-pecking can happen at any age but often occurs when new feathers are forming either during growth or after a moult; vent-pecking often begins if a hen has a prolapse. All the causes of cannibalism are obscure, but it may be due to a deficiency in the diet or to sheer boredom. The feeding of pelleted rations may also encourage it. If cannibalism occurs the nutrient content of the rations should be checked, as should the feeding management. The scattering of pelleted feed on the floor may help as this causes the fowls to scratch and to some extent relieves their boredom. Hanging bunches of green feed will also give them an additional occupation. In order to check this vice fully it may be necessary to debeak the birds. The top mandible is cut back to the quick using a sharp instrument.

Egg-eating.   This often occurs when shell-less eggs are laid or eggs are broken in the nest. Preventive measures include a check on the nutrient content of the rations to ensure that eggs with good-quality shells are laid, darkening the nest boxes and taking adequate managerial measures that reduce any likelihood of egg breakage.

Management

Breeding stock

Few poultry farmers breed their own replacements. Those who do must keep very adequate records and selection should be for performance and health. The major traits to consider are age at coming into lay, annual egg production, weight of egg, hatchability, viability of chicks, a daily live-weight gain, mature weight, efficiency of food conversion and adult viability.

The fold system of management is suitable for individual mating and the semi-intensive system for flock mating. Trap-nesting of the hens may be practised. That is, each nest box is constructed so that the hen shuts herself in as she enters and has to be released. In this way the productivity of each hen can be recorded. Group recording may be more desirable where mass selection is practised. It is certainly cheaper.

Eggs for hatching

If hatchability percentages of above 65 per cent of all eggs set are to be obtained – and this is generally considered to be a satisfactory percentage – then care must be taken in the selection of suitable fertile eggs, in their handling before incubation and in their incubation.

Infertility attributable to the cockerel may be due to a variety of causes. The bird may not be sexually mature or may be too old. Maximum sexual vigour is not usually attained until cockerels are 7 or 8 months old, although they may start to mate at a much earlier age, and sexual vigour usually declines after they are 2 years of age. The ratio of cockerels to hens may be incorrect. The normal ratio is one cockerel to twelve to fifteen hens with the higher ratio used in flock mating. Cockerels also exhibit preferences, and in a breeding pen where there is only one, he may neglect certain hens. Finally, the cockerel may be infertile for a variety of genetical, nutritional and health reasons. Some hens may also be infertile for similar reasons. Of particular importance is the effect of vitamin and mineral deficiencies in the rations on fertility. Breeding birds must receive nutritionally adequate diets if they are to remain fertile. Even if the eggs of nutritionally deficient hens are fertile the deficiency may be the cause of high embryonic mortality or the hatching of weak chicks.

Fertility depends very largely on the number and viability of the sperm produced by the cockerel and on the time relationship between mating and ovulation. Fertile eggs can be laid within 30 hours of mating, but maximum fertility, which obviously depends upon the activity of the cockerel and the viability of his sperm, is not usually attained until the fifth day (2 to 6 days) from initial mating. Sperm may retain their viability in the female tract for as long as 32 days, but the usual range is 11 to 14 days, so that when the cockerel is removed from the hens a decrease in fertility is evident by the sixth day and the decrease is very large by the tenth day. Newly laid eggs should remain fit for hatching for up to 7 days provided that they are kept at a temperature of 12·8°C (55°F) and at a relative humidity of 60 to 70 per cent. If eggs are kept at a higher temperature their fertility and hatchability rapidly decrease. This fact is obviously of very great importance in the tropics where the mean annual ambient temperature is approximately 26·7°C (80°F). If eggs are not to be incubated immediately then some provision must be made for their storage at lower than the normal ambient temperatures and preferably within the range of 10° to 21·1°C (50° to 70°F). However, eggs must not be stored in a refrigerator as this practice also reduces fertility.

Considerable agitation during transit before incubation lowers hatchability, but the effect is considerably reduced if the eggs are allowed to stand at rest for 24 hours before transit takes place. Air transport at heights up to 11,600 m (38,000 ft) does not affect hatchability, though any vibration, sudden chilling or a sudden reduction of air pressure does have an effect.

Care must be exercised in the selection of eggs for incubation. Too small ($<$50 g (1·75 oz)) or too large ($>$71 g (2·5 oz)) eggs should not be used, neither should poor-shelled, misshapen, dirty or cracked eggs. Dirty eggs may be washed with warm, clean water. Eggs which are visibly porous are particularly unsuitable for incubating in hot, dry climates.

Hereditary defects are perhaps not as common as might be supposed. A number of deformities and monstrosities which were formerly considered hereditary in origin are now known to be due to other causes. Nevertheless at least twenty lethal mutations have been recorded and probably much of the malpositioning of the chick in the shell, which is such a potent cause of unhatchability, may be directly due to hereditary factors.

Several diseases are passed through the egg, but only a few affect either fertility or hatchability. The commonest disease, or at least the best-known one, is BWD which causes the death of a certain number of infected chicks in the shell and of a great number not long after hatching. As stated in a previous section, infected hens are detected by blood tests, as are those carrying other diseases, and it is therefore advisable to obtain eggs for hatching purposes from tested adult stock.

Incubation

Eggs may be naturally or artificially incubated. The incubation period for fowls is 21 days. The method used does not affect the quality of the chicks hatched.

Natural incubation

It is by natural incubation that most chicks of indigenous breeds are produced in the villages. The village hen, sitting on the usual clutch of some eight to ten eggs, needs little food and even less attention. However, the results are usually rather poor, and if the incubating hen was only given a fraction of the care normally bestowed on an artificial incubator, major benefits would accrue. The principal requirements for a 'sitting hen' are a plentiful supply of clean drinking water, a subsistence feed supply, protection against insect pests and vermin, and, on hatching, protection of the chicks from predators. The nest should be placed in some quiet, cool corner at ground level and should be enclosed so that the hen can leave it only when permitted. This should be each morning, for about 10 minutes as soon after dawn as is convenient, and again in the evening. During these times the hen should be fed grain and provided with fresh water to drink and a sand-bath in which to dust herself. She should be left undisturbed after the eggs have started to chip and be allowed to move off the nest into her breeding quarters at will. Chaff, sawdust or sand make the best bedding. In very dry climates the nest should be dampened daily. Before the hen sits on the nest, both she and it should be liberally dusted or sprayed with an insecticide.

Artificial incubation

Large-scale commercial hatcheries equipped with various types of automated or semi-automated artificial incubators are now operating or being organized in almost all tropical countries, either by the government or by private enterprise. At the same time the age-old artificial hatching systems are still employed, particularly in Southeast Asia, and small artificial incubators are increasingly used by nascent specialist poultry-keepers, despite their relative inefficiency.

The old artificial hatching system used by the Chinese in Malaysia is well described by Thuraisingham and Wah (1971). The results obtained by this system compare quite well with those recorded from modern incubators, hatching rates of 75 to 85 per cent being normal. Eggs no more than 2 days old, of uniform size and shape, are first warmed for 20 minutes to 2 hours in the sun or on a tray over a charcoal fire. The temperature of the egg is checked by the skilled operator by placing it against his cheek, nostril or upper eyelid. The eggs are then packed in sacking in batches of approximately 100, the sacks being placed in layers in cyclindrical bamboo baskets, approximately 0·8 m (2·5 ft) deep and 0·6 m (2 ft) in diameter, that stand in wooden boxes and are insulated on the outside with rice husk and on the inside with paper. Twice a day the eggs are removed and turned, eggs with dead embryos, recognizable by a change in shell colour, being discarded. Hen eggs are candled on the third and eleventh days and duck eggs on the second and fifth days. Hen eggs are removed from the baskets on the eleventh to twelfth day and duck eggs on the fifteenth to sixteenth day. The eggs are then placed in hatching beds, consisting of wooden shelves covered with rice husk. The eggs are covered with layers of matting and the operator removes or adds to the layers of matting in order to keep the temperature around the eggs constant. Temperature testing is by the 'cheek, nostril or eyelid' method. Turning is carried out four times a day, the middle eggs being moved to the outside to help maintain a constant temperature. On hatching the chicks are placed in shallow bamboo baskets to dry. Each incubator basket will hold up to 1,000 duck eggs and proportionally more hens' eggs, the operation being large-scale in concept.

Artificial incubators can now be purchased to suit almost any circumstance and, if obtained from reputable firms and operated strictly in accordance with the maker's instructions, they should perform admirably. Very small incubators are particularly sensitive to adverse surroundings and the instructions concerning initial heating and the maintenance of correct humidity and temperature need to be intelligently interpreted and meticulously observed. The large incubators, and especially the mammoth types, carry such valuable loads that common prudence demands that they should be in the charge of trained operators.

During incubation the essential air conditions are that there should be sufficient oxygen in circulation to supply the needs of the growing embryo; that the carbon dioxide resulting from embryonic metabolism should not be allowed to accumulate; that relative humidity should be such as to allow not more than 10 per cent of the water content of the eggs to be lost; and that the temperature should be such that life within the egg is maintained at an optimal level.

In the tropics the maintenance of optimal humidity is usually more difficult than the maintenance of optimal temperature. In small incubators with a good air circulation a relative humidity of approximately 58 per cent is required at $38.9°C$ ($102°F$) up to the eighteenth day, but thereafter and until the chicks are hatched a relative humidity of 70 per cent is required. In larger, forced-draught incubators the temperature should be $37.8°C$ ($100°F$). The variation in temperature should be no more than $0.6°C$ ($1°F$). In large incubators with unassisted air circulation the usual temperatures recommended are $38.3°C$ ($101°F$) during the first week of incubation, $38.9°C$ ($102°F$) during the second week and a maximum of $39.4°C$ ($103°F$) during the final week. The incubator's thermostat should readily make the minor adjustments necessitated by moderate changes in ambient temperature, but when diurnal variations are large the thermostat may not respond with sufficient speed to give optimal results. It is therefore advisable to site the incubator in a well-insulated room or, if possible, in an air-conditioned room. Such action does not necessarily assist in regulating humidity as there are tropical climates in which relative humidity will vary by as much as 55 per cent during the 24 hours. Under these circumstances the incubators must be fitted with an egg-moistening mechanism or the incubation room be provided with humidity controls.

If the correct oxygen/carbon dioxide level is to be effectively maintained there must be a passage of fresh air not only over the eggs but also around the eggs, and therefore all air pockets must be eliminated. This is facilitated by positioning the incubator away from the walls and corners of the room so that there is space for proper ventilation.

Incubating eggs should preferably be turned at least five times daily up to the eighteenth day. All modern incubators provide some method by which this can be easily accomplished. If turning has to be done by hand it may be impractical to turn the eggs five times a day, but it must be done not less than twice.

During the fourth to the seventh day and on the sixteenth day of incubation it is customary to check and remove all infertile eggs and those with dead embryos. This is done by 'candling', which is accomplished by passing a beam of light through the egg in such a manner that surrounding light is excluded. Infertile eggs show up as 'clears', dead 'germs' are seen as a dark spot of varying size and degree of density, live ones cast a shrimp-like shadow from which radiate blood vessels. Hatchable eggs are uniformly dark with a distinct air-space at the broad end of the egg, while dead embryos appear to have an air-space at both ends of the egg.

Eggs are transferred from the setting trays in the incubator to the special hatching trays on the eighteenth day.

Hatched chicks should be transferred from the incubator to whatever type of special tray or basket can be provided.

Strict hygiene must be practised during all phases of incubation. After every hatch all the equipment should be scrubbed with a disinfectant.

Brooding

Under backyard conditions the hatched chicks are reared and protected by the broody hen. Incubated chicks must be artificially brooded. At this stage in their life chicks are very vulnerable and losses during brooding are often excessive. If the brooding methods are satisfactory mortality in chicks should not exceed 5 per cent during the first 8 weeks of life.

During the last stage of incubation the chick absorbs sufficient nutrients to last it for at least the first 48 hours of life. This is why day-old chicks can be transported in boxes for long distances. Nevertheless, it is a good managerial practice to make some food available soon after hatching.

In the tropics, if newly hatched chicks are left in the hatching tray of the incubator for 24 hours the relative humidity should not be allowed to rise above 55 per cent, as high humidity combined with high ambient temperature has a most debilitating effect on chicks. The most suitable practice is to transfer the chicks from the incubator to the brooder as soon as they have dried out. If chicks hatched under hens are to be artificially brooded they should not be transferred to the brooder until they are 48 hours old.

It is normal to identify the sex of most chicks before they are transferred to the brooder as the information is of some economic importance. There always existed the possibility that sex-linked traits could be used to identify the sex of day-old chicks (see Ch. 4, Pt I), but such traits are not necessarily correlated with production traits. Most chicks are now sexed by manipulation and examination of the cloaca, with or without instrumentation.

There are many designs of brooder. The basic requirements are that sufficient heat should be applied in a specific part of the brooder known as the *hover* to keep the chickens warm without their crowding together, that the brooder should be well lighted and ventilated, and that sufficient total space should be available to allow for growth in the chickens. The initial temperature below the hover should be 35°C (95°F) at 5 cm (2 in) from the floor, and in the tropics the hover temperature should be reduced by 2·8°C (5°F) each week until it equals the mean daily ambient temperature. This should be by the third or fourth week as the mean tropical ambient temperature is usually 26·7°C (80°F). This ambient temperature is likely to be somewhat above the optimum for the chicks at the end of the brooding period. Good light is desirable as it encourages the chicks to start feeding. In the rainy season in the tropics it may be necessary to provide some artificial light in the brooder during daylight hours. Good ventilation is also desirable, but it is often overlooked when efforts are made to conserve heat. In the tropics it is desirable to provide a brooder with a fine wire-netting floor as this not only allows droppings to be evacuated from the floor area, thus minimizing internal parasitism and disease, but also improves ventilation and reduces the internal temperature of the brooder during the hottest periods of the day. If the brooder utilized has been designed for use in the temperate zone, as is so often the case, then the number of chicks housed should be reduced by at least one-third below the manufacturer's recommendation. The minimum total floor space allowed should be 7 m² (75 ft²) per 100 chicks for an 8-week period and preferably more, but broiler chicks should have more space – 100 such chicks requiring 10 m² (107 ft²) for a period of 10 weeks. Within the hover area chicks require approximately 45 to 60 cm² (7 to 9·3 in²) of floor space so that under a circular canopy 1·2 m (4 ft) in diameter 250 to 300 chicks can be accommodated.

Types of brooder

The type that should be used depends upon the location of the farm, the cost and availability of fuel, the size of the unit and the type of housing available.

Floor brooders heated by electric elements are obtainable. They are clean, easily operated, labour saving and maintain a fairly constant temperature. Infra-red lamps are efficient and allow maximum ventilation.

A single 250 W bulb raised 38 cm (15 in) above the floor level is sufficient to brood 100 chicks. For a smaller number of chicks normal electric light bulbs placed under a canopy will suffice. However, electricity is not often available in rural tropical environments.

Kerosene brooders can be used as an alternative, but they do not maintain such a constant temperature, there is the risk of fire and the fumes can irritate the chicks.

Charcoal brooders are also cheap to operate and charcoal is usually readily available in tropical countries.

Wood-burning brooders have also been designed.

Large hot-water brooding units utilizing hot water from a central installation can also be constructed. The initial capital costs are high, but such brooders are cheap and simple to operate.

Battery brooders operating on electricity or kerosene are also available, but they are usually expensive to install and to operate.

A cold brooder should be the brooder of choice for the small poultry-keeper in all except the montane regions of the tropics. In order to breed batches of up to sixty chicks a wooden box measuring approximately $60 \times 60 \times 45$ cm ($24 \times 24 \times 18$ in) is required. One half of the top of the box should be hinged so that the chicks can be handled and the box cleaned. At the bottom of one of the walls a 15 cm (6 in) shutter should be provided so that the chicks can be moved out of the box during the daytime and be closed in it at night. Two methods of insulation may be used. For the first type rice straw is soaked in water, allowed to dry partially and is then beaten with a wooden block. The whole of the inner surface of the box is lined with this processed straw which is covered by a gunny-sack lining that is nailed to the box to keep the layer of insulating straw in position. Short lengths of internode bamboo, or some other form of pipe, approximately $1\cdot3$ cm ($0\cdot5$ in) in diameter, are then fixed in the sides and the top of the box in order to pass through the straw insulation and the sacking material, thus providing ventilation. The pipes in the sides should be fixed approximately 15 cm (6 in) above the floor level. Approximately twelve of these ventilators are required and strips of gunny sack should be suspended from the top of the box in front of them so that there is no direct draught on the chicks. Rice husks are placed on the floor of the brooder.

The second type is even more simple to construct. Strips of fabric are nailed to the roof of the box so that they dangle just above the floor. They should be closely spaced. Ventilation holes are then bored in the wooden sides and the top of the box, no pipes being needed, and the floor of the box is covered with rice husks. If the brooder is indoors the floor of the box can be made of a fine wire mesh. The box is then placed in a larger wire-meshed floor pen or can be constructed as part of it (Fig. 13.1). The latter arrangement is preferable. The efficiency of this type of cold brooder can be vouched for by the authors who have had occasion to use one.

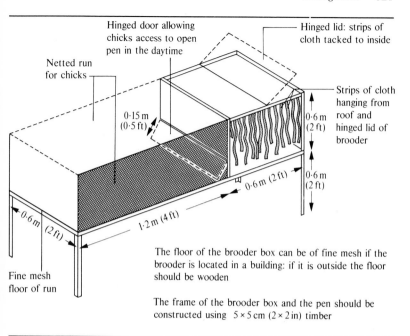

Hinged door allowing chicks access to open pen in the daytime

Hinged lid: strips of cloth tacked to inside

Netted run for chicks

0·15 m (0·5 ft)

Strips of cloth hanging from roof and hinged lid of brooder

0·6 m (2 ft)

0·6 m (2 ft)

0·6 m (2 ft)

0·6 m (2 ft)

1·2 m (4 ft)

0·6 m (2 ft)

Fine mesh floor of run

The floor of the brooder box can be of fine mesh if the brooder is located in a building: if it is outside the floor should be wooden

The frame of the brooder box and the pen should be constructed using 5 × 5 cm (2 × 2 in) timber

Fig. 13.1   A schematic design of an inexpensive cold brooder suitable for use in the tropics.

Operation of brooders

The desired temperature should be maintained in the brooder for at least 24 hours before the chicks are transferred. Chicks should be counted and examined before they are placed in the brooder, obviously unhealthy individuals being culled. During the first few days a ring of fine wire mesh will keep the chicks close to the heat source. The ring should be widened daily and removed entirely after 7 days. The distribution of the chicks under the brooder heat source should be continuously checked. If they huddle and chirp the temperature is too low, while if they pant and draw away from the brooder the temperature is too high.

Perches should be available in the brooder house at least by the time that the chicks are 3 weeks old. Details of suitable perches are given in Table 13.7.

Feed and water should be available when the chicks are first placed in the brooder. Feed should at first be fed on sheets of cardboard until the chicks become accustomed to the usual feeders. The trough length requirements are shown in Table 13.4. During the first 4 weeks 100 chicks require at least four water troughs each of 2 litre (0.45 gal) capacity. Later they will require four water troughs of 5 litre (1·1 gal) or two of 10 litre (2·2 gal) capacity. Details of the length of trough required are given in Table 13.5. At first the feed and water troughs should be placed near the heat source. Later they should be placed so that the chicks learn to use all the space that is available in the brooder. In order to reduce feed wastage feeders should never be filled to more than half their total capacity and their design should be such that the chicks cannot get inside them. Chicks should be allowed to empty the feeders completely every 2 or 3 days. At other times, feeders should always contain feed. Sand and/or grit should be fed in separate feeders and green feed can be introduced after the first week. Watering troughs should be placed on wire platforms to prevent spillage and should be designed so that contamination with faeces is reduced to a minimum.

Table 13.7 *Perch requirements for different classes of poultry*

Class	Length of perch per 100 birds (m (ft))	Cross-section of perch (cm (in))	Height above floor (cm (in))	Spacing in house (cm (in))
Fowls				
Brooders	10 (33)	3.5×3.5 (1.4×1.4)	25 (10)	–
Rearing house	10–15 (33–49)	–	61 (24)	38 (25)
Semi-intensive house				
Light breed	20 (67)	5×5 (2×2)	76 (36)	–
Heavy breed	23–30 (75–100)	5×5 (2×2)	76 (36)	–
Turkeys				
Light breed	30 (100)	–	–	–
Heavy breed	38 (125)	–	–	–

Good sanitation is of major importance in brooders. Buildings and all equipment should be cleaned and disinfected before use. Feed and water troughs should be kept as free as possible of all contamination at all times. The brooder should be separate from other poultry buildings and activities. When chicks are brooded on litter it must be maintained in a dry, friable state and not allowed to become damp.

Chicks of different age and/or breeds should not be housed in the same brooder. This is because older individuals or those of the stronger breed develop at the expense of the younger and/or weaker breed.

Rearing

At 6 to 8 weeks of age the growing birds should be transferred from the brooder to a rearing unit. Cockerels are separated from pullets if both have been reared together and the ration is changed from the starter to the grower type.

The rearing unit may be on range or it may be intensive. On small poultry farms the brooder pen may be used as an intensive-rearing pen.

If this is the case then additional space will be required as the birds continue to grow.

Range rearing

The major advantages are that the birds acquire part of their diet by scavenging for herbage, seeds and insects and that they usually remain very healthy. It is only practical if there are no daylight predators in the district. An area with shade cover is preferable to open land and the space requirement is 5 to 8 m^2 (54 to 86 ft^2) per bird (Table 13.8). A simple building in which the birds can be enclosed at night is required. The night accommodation, even if simply constructed, should possess adequate space, good ventilation, perches for roosting and proper protection against predators and inclement weather. Most housing on small poultry farms does not attain minimum standards of adequacy. Aitkens (1956) described a type of night accommodation for small numbers of range poultry, used in Sri Lanka, that would appear to be admirable. The house is about the size and shape of a small bullock cart. The walls are made of woven leaf stalks or reeds, the roof is rainproof and made of woven large leaves and the floor is constructed of slatted bamboo or other suitable materials. This house is hung between two trees and access is provided through a small door placed in one wall by a bamboo pole. After the birds have gone to roost each evening the door is closed, using the pole which is then removed to the owner's house. Baffles are placed on the rope slings that suspend the house in order to deny entry to vermin and insects. Feed and water containers should be available both on the range and in the house.

The birds should be moved at regular intervals to a different area in order to avoid a major build-up of internal parasites and disease organisms. Feeders can be closed for part of the day in order to encourage the birds to forage.

An alternative method of rearing on range is the *fold system*. This is a semi-intensive system of utilizing range. Groups of twenty-five to fifty birds, depending on their size, are confined in a movable, wired-in run with attached housing that is sufficiently large to accommodate them at night. The unit is moved to fresh ground at frequent intervals, preferably each day. The system allows the orderly use of land, decreases the possibilities of worm infestation and ensures the even distribution of poultry droppings. The stocking rate can also be high (no more than 400 birds per 0·4 ha (1 acre)). It is, however, labour intensive and a considerable amount of equipment is required. The system cannot be used either in the equatorial tropics where the land is often flooded or in the very arid tropics where shade cannot be provided. Details of the construction of a suitable fold unit are given in the section on housing.

Intensive

This is normally a well-ventilated deep-litter house. In most regions of the tropics the house does not require conventional walls, but there must be some device by which cold, driving rain can be prevented from entry during the rainy season. The space requirements in this system are shown in Table 13.8 and perching requirements in Table 13.7. Feeding-trough requirements are shown in Table 13.4. If hanging feeders are used, every 100 birds require four 11 kg (25 lb) capacity feeders.

Management during rearing

In general, birds that are brooded together should be reared together, but some re-sorting of the birds should take place when they are transferred to the rearing units – birds of the same size and weight being kept together and cockerels being separated from pullets. Transfer of birds to rearing units should be accomplished with the least disturbance and should not take place during the heat of the day. Required vaccinations should be accomplished as should deworming at 10 and 18 weeks of age. If coccidiosis is a problem then a coccidiat should continue to be used until the birds are 12 to 16 weeks old. Total mortality from hatching to maturity at approximately 20 weeks of age should be no more than 12 per cent.

Layers

Pullets should be transferred from the rearing to the laying house at 17 to 18 weeks of age. At the time of transfer they should be grouped according to size and stage of maturity. The age at first laying should be between 20 and 24 weeks. If pullets are not laying when they are 24 weeks old then they have probably been mismanaged during the brooding and/or rearing stages.

Major factors that determine the age of pullets at first laying are breed, with light breeds laying at an earlier age than heavy breeds; their nutrition during brooding and rearing, as fast growth is correlated with the rapid attainment of sexual maturity; managerial practice during rearing, as intensively reared birds usually lay at an earlier age than range-reared birds; and on the light regime to which they have been subjected, as decreasing hours of daylight discourage laying while increasing hours hasten it.

There are four major systems used for the housing of laying pullets: semi-intensive, deep litter, slatted or wire floor and battery. Some details of their construction are provided in the section concerned with housing.

Semi-intensive. This is the most common system used by small producers and it is also often used by breeders. The poultry have access to outside runs where they live during the day and to houses where they sleep at night. It is preferable that each house should possess two or more outside runs, so that one or more can be rested while the other is being used. It is also a good practice to spread lime over the land in the pen that has just been vacated, and if there is grass the pen can be grazed by other species such as calves, sheep or goats. It is usual for the birds to be fed and watered in the outside run. Space requirements for feeding and watering are shown in Tables 13.4 and 13.5. The feed and water troughs should be moved at regular intervals. Within the houses sufficient perch space must be allowed and details of requirements are shown in Table 13.7. In addition individual or communal nesting boxes and a broody coop is required. The semi-intensive system requires more land and labour than most of the other systems and the capital cost is quite high, but pullets usually thrive.

Deep litter. The housing for this system is the simplest to build and operate. The floor can be constructed of rammed earth or concrete, but in the wet tropics it is preferable to use concrete. A variety of different types of litter can be used. Nesting boxes and a broody coop are required in the house as are water and feeding troughs. Troughs are best suspended above the litter. If runs are provided it can be used as a semi-intensive house.

Slatted or wire floors. Houses constructed with slatted or wire floors are said to be cooler than other types of house. However, building costs are high and management is more complicated. Rats are often a major problem.

Batteries. This is probably the most efficient system as egg production and feed conversion efficiency are high in birds housed in battery cages. Little land is required, recording is simple and batteries can be very labour saving if they are equipped with automatic feeding, watering and cleaning devices. They are particularly useful where light breeds are utilized, land is expensive and labour is relatively expensive, as is the case in many countries in Southeast Asia. Batteries do, however, have disadvantages. They are relatively costly to install, the number of cracked eggs may be relatively high and vermin and insects can be a nuisance. Costs of construction can be substantially reduced if the cages are constructed from bamboo and/or rattan as is often the case in many Southeast Asian countries (Plate 13.1).

Whatever the type of housing used, nesting boxes should be installed before the first eggs are laid. Otherwise eggs may be laid on the floor of the house or elsewhere and this increases the possibilities of them being broken and becoming dirty. Cracked or broken eggs are an economic loss and encourage the vice of egg-eating, while dirty eggs increase production costs as they have to be cleaned.

Nesting boxes can be individual or communal. One individual box is required for every six pullets in the pen. These boxes should be located in the coolest and darkest area of the house, they should be raised 0·6 m (2 ft) from the floor, the top should be constructed with a sharp slope

Plate 13.1   The use of bamboo in a locally constructed battery unit. Located near Palembang, southeast Sumatra, Indonesia.

otherwise birds will perch on and foul them, and their floors should be covered with 5 to 8 cm (2 to 3 in) of a litter such as rice hulls or sawdust. It is also advisable to construct a small alighting perch just outside the entrance to the nest, and nests should be fitted with some device such as a bar so that they can be closed. The minimum space allowance for nesting birds should be 0.09 m² (1·00 ft²). Nesting boxes should be constructed in such a manner that egg collection is facilitated. Usually they possess a hinged top. In battery systems where the living space is also the nesting space the minimum cage sizes recommended in the temperate zone are as follows:

Size	Width (cm (in))	Depth (cm (in))	Height (cm (in))
Single bird	30 (12)	43 (17)	46 (18)
Two birds	41 (16)	43 (17)	46 (18)
Three birds	51 (20)	43 (17)	46 (18)

With gangways 1·1 m (3·7 ft) wide more than one row of cages is used. The cages are normally constructed of stout galvanized wire. The floor slopes 10 cm (4 in) from the back of the cage to the egg cradle which extends some 15 cm (6 in) in front of the cage. Underneath is a tray for droppings, and the food and water receptacles are located outside the cage.

We recommend that in the tropics only cages for single birds should be used and that the cages should be somewhat larger. At least 0·14 m² (1·5 ft²) of floor space should be allowed per bird.

Details of requirements for feed and water trough space are given in Tables 13.4 and 13.5. Where hanging feeders are used – and these are recommended in deep-litter houses – they should be suspended at a height that is approximately level with the backs of the birds.

When pullets are transferred to the laying house the ration is changed to the laying type (Table 13.3). Grit must always be available and the feeding of 4·5 kg (10 lb) of green food per 100 birds per day is desirable.

Broodiness. This is the instinct to incubate eggs and is an inherited trait. Heavy breeds go broody more often and for longer periods than light breeds of birds. In some of the new breeds the trait has been reduced by genetic selection. As broody hens cease to lay but take up nesting space they should be removed and placed in a special broody coop. This should be raised off the floor and be well ventilated. A slatted floor, together with wire and/or slatted sides, is desirable. Special feed and water containers are required in the coop. There is usually an interval after broodiness before egg laying is resumed.

Artificial light. Under natural conditions egg laying is correlated with length of daylight and artificial light is used in the temperate zone to even out egg production and to prevent pullets moulting in their first year. In the tropics where daylight length does not alter appreciably throughout the year the problem of seasonal egg production is not so acute. It is recommended that under these circumstances the most suitable management practice is to provide additional hours of light before dawn and after dusk in order to encourage the hens to eat during the cooler periods of the 24 hours. This may be achieved by fixing 40 W electric light bulbs in position 2·1 m (7 ft) above the floor. One bulb should be sufficient to illuminate 18·6 m^2 (200 ft^2) of floor space.

Moulting. This condition occasionally occurs in birds during the first year of lay. It is due to stress. The symptoms are cessation of egg laying, shedding of feathers and drying up, paleness and reduction in size of the comb. The condition may last for a few weeks or even for months. Moulting can usually be avoided by careful handling of the birds and by the avoidance of undue stress.

During their second year it is natural for most pullets to moult and cease egg production. This is one reason why it is normal for commercial egg producers to only keep their pullets for one year of egg laying. In most tropical countries, where the price of poultry meat is higher than it is in most temperate countries, it is usually even more economic to sell all pullets after one year's egg production.

Egg collection. Eggs should be collected at least twice a day and records of the number of eggs collected should be kept. The eggs should be stored in a cool place before they are marketed.

Broiler and other meat birds

In a majority of tropical countries the broiler industry has developed very rapidly during the last two decades, but there are still countries or regions within countries where meat is produced from culls or from the surplus cockerels originating out of the egg-laying flocks.

The major advantages of producing meat from poultry are that they require limited areas of land and that they are very efficient converters of feed into meat. The disadvantage is that poultry often compete with humans for feed supplies.

Where feed supplies are adequate the development of a broiler industry is indicated. Broilers are meat-type chickens that have been specially bred for marketing at an early age. They are usually sold when they weigh approximately 1·4 kg (3 lb), which occurs at 7 to 12 weeks of age, depending upon the efficiency of the operation. In many Southeast Asian countries broilers are marketed at a somewhat smaller size and younger age. The production of broilers is therefore a specialized industry which is conducted separately from egg production.

For a successful broiler enterprise a breed must be used in which both sexes exhibit fast growth and early feathering, which possesses a high efficiency of feed conversion, hopefully less than 2·5:1 and whose flesh colour must conform to local prejudices. In addition the adult pullets must be reasonably good layers so that the chicks can be produced and purchased at an economic price.

The only breeds that possess all these characteristics are the new hybrid broiler breeds produced by the international large-scale breeders. Nevertheless, in countries where the new hybrid breeds are not yet available first-cross birds that are not quite so efficient may be used for broiler production. For example, the first cross White Leghorn × New Hampshire will produce a 1·4 kg (3 lb) broiler at 11 weeks of age with an efficiency of conversion of 3:1.

For broiler production it is usual to accommodate the birds in large deep-litter houses. The more broilers that are housed together the more economic the operation becomes, so that broiler production is essentially a large-scale industry. The minimum size of an economic unit is probably 1,000 chicks, but there are many smaller broiler production units in tropical countries at the present time.

Some details of the construction of suitable deep-litter houses are given in another section. It is normal to breed the chicks in a section of the house that will accommodate the broilers so that they do not have to be moved. They will require a minimum of 9 m² (100 ft²) floor space per 100 birds (Table 13.8), and the broiler house should be sited where maximum advantage can be taken of prevailing winds for ventilation purposes unless environmentally controlled accommodation is to be used. The type of construction and the materials used in construction should be suitable for the climatic environment. It should be possible to have a throughput of four to seven batches of broiler chicks per year in any one house, depending upon the efficiency of the operation. The litter, which should be approximately 8 cm (3 in) deep, should be cleaned out between batches and the building and all equipment sterilized. If suitable chemicals are not available for the sterilization of equipment then thorough washing followed by exposure to bright sunlight should suffice.

The nutrient content of the ration is critical in broiler production. It must provide all the essential food required for rapid growth and it is normal to add antibiotics and possibly other additives. It is best fed in the pelleted form or as a crumble. A coccidiostat should also be included in the ration.

It is very necessary to reduce stress to a minimum so that the chicks should be quietly handled at all times. In the tropics environmentally controlled accommodation is the most suitable, but in its likely absence efforts should be made to reduce heat stress. One desirable managerial practice is an arrangement that allows the chicks to feed when ambient temperatures are lowest, i.e. at 03.00 to 05.00 hours in the morning and in the evenings after dusk. In order to achieve this the broiler house must be artificially illuminated from 03.00 hours in the morning and for 2 hours after sunset, and darkened during the hours when daily ambient temperatures are highest, i.e. between 12.00 and 16.00 hours. This managerial practice is only possible, of course, where houses can be darkened during daylight hours without reducing ventilation.

Caponizing

Caponization has been used for a very long time and is a technique that makes the flesh of old birds more succulent and tender. Until recent years the caponization of cockerels was carried out by surgical operation. In this operation an incision is made on either side of the body and the testicles are removed. Chemical caponization, using a hormone implanted in the back of the neck, is now the normal method (see Ch. 3, Pt I). With the advent of the broiler industry caponization is now less commonly performed than it was in the past. One disadvantage of caponized cockerels in tropical countries is that they are more susceptible to heat stress than uncaponized birds.

Housing

Poultry housing should provide adequate shelter, a healthy and comfortable environment and reduce labour requirements to a minimum.

General considerations

Requirements for housing differ from one region of the tropics to another. In the wet tropics protection is required against rain, high humidity and moderately high ambient temperatures, whereas in the dry tropics protection is required against very high and quite low ambient temperatures and possibly dust storms.

1. *Location.* If there is a choice of location all buildings should be sited on the highest ground, not subject to flooding, and where advantage can be taken of any prevailing breezes. All buildings should if possible face in the same direction and preferably be east–west orientated. There should be a distance of at least 12 m (40 ft) between individual buildings in order to reduce the possibilities of disease and parasite transference from house to house. If possible the brooder house should be completely separate from other buildings. The feed room should be centrally sited and the egg-storage room located adjacent to egg-laying units.

2. *Floors.* The most suitable material is concrete, but wooden or rammed earth floors can be used.

3. *Walls.* The walls of all except environmentally controlled houses should be open in the wet tropics. Heavy-gauge netting wire or expanded metal grilles are the most suitable material with which to screen buildings. Screening is essential as it keeps out the larger vermin and wild birds. The screened walls should be provided with some form of protective cover that should normally be rolled up or pulled to one side, but which can be used during the rainy season to protect the birds and, in the case of deep-litter houses, the litter from driving rain. Split bamboo or reed curtains or blinds are very suitable or heavy-duty plastic sheeting can be used. In dry climates the walls should be solid, at least to above the door level. Brick or clay and straw are very suitable materials. In such houses it is necessary to make adequate provision for ventilation. Although external temperatures may rise rapidly during the daytime, internal temperatures will rise more slowly in such houses.

4. *Roofs.* In the wet tropics high-pitch roofs are required that will shed heavy rain. They should overhang the eaves by at least 0·9 m (3 ft). The height of the roof should be at least 3·7 m (12 ft) at the eaves. In the dry tropics the roofs can be flat or have a low pitch, but they should be as high as is practicable and at least 3·7 m (12 ft). The main roofing materials available are corrugated iron, asbestos and thatch, although in a few tropical countries such as Mauritius and Indonesia clay tiles are cheap and can be used for roofing. Asbestos is probably the most suitable roofing material, but it is usually expensive. Corrugated iron is the least suitable, and if it is used it should be painted with aluminium paint on the upper side and with black paint on the lower side. Thatch is very suitable, but it has to be replaced quite frequently therefore maintenance costs are high. It also has the disadvantage that it harbours vermin. A wide variety of thatching materials are available in the tropics, including all types of grasses and reeds and many types of palm thatch, including doum palm (*Hyphaene*

thebaica) in the dry areas of East and Northeast Africa, coconut palm, and nipa palm (*Nypa fruticans*) in Southeast Asia and oil palm (*Elaeis guineensis*) in Africa, etc. A corrugated-iron roof can be combined with thatch which acts as an insulating material under the corrugated iron. There should be a gap of approximately 10 cm (4 in) between the corrugated iron and the thatch.
5. *General.* The dimensions of houses will obviously vary in accordance with the needs of the poultry farmer. In general, houses approximately 10 m (30 ft) wide and with 1·2 m (4 ft) internal passages have been found to be practical and useful. They can, of course, be any length that is required.

Methods of reducing heat stress

Where environmentally controlled houses cannot be utilized for economic reasons or because adequate services are not available, the poultry farmer should still attempt to reduce the possibility of heat stress in housed birds. The first consideration is adequate ventilation. In the wet tropics houses without walls should provide adequate ventilation and some degree of alleviation of heat stress on birds from improved air circulation. In the dry tropics, where the birds are enclosed, proper ventilation of the house is essential. As hot air rises, ridge ventilation is a necessity. If economic and service circumstances allow it, forced-air fans should be used.

The planting of large shade trees adjacent to and overhanging the houses will help to keep the birds cool in hot weather, although this practice is not recommended in hurricane zones. The planting of grass lawns or other vegetation around the houses can also be of considerable assistance, particularly in the dry tropics, where the vegetation will have to be irrigated.

Sprinklers can be sited on corrugated-iron roofs and this can be a very effective method of cooling the houses. The water that drips off the roofs should be used to irrigate grass or other vegetation around the houses and this can be cut and used as a green feed.

Misters or foggers are particularly useful in batteries. A water pipe with fine nozzles fixed at appropriate intervals is slung above the cages and used when ambient temperatures rise – in particular during the early afternoon.

Fold houses and pens

The runs are made of 1·3 cm (0·5 in) gauge wire netting set on a framework of light but tough wood. The frame should have a floor space of 9 m² (97 ft²). The house can be of the slatted ark type that is widely used in the temperate zone, modified for use in the tropics. It should stand 30 cm (12 in) above the ground. The floor is made of slats approximately 2·5 cm (1 in) wide and spaced 2·5 cm (1 in) apart. A movable wire-netting floor is fitted 10 cm (4 in) below the slats to prevent the entry of vermin. The walls, which also form the roof, converge steeply to the ridge about 1·2 m (4 ft) above the slats. The one wall can be enclosed, but the other should consist of a door made from a frame covered with 1·3 cm (0·5 in) gauge netting in order to permit free circulation of the air. A bamboo or plastic roll-up flap or curtain should be attached to the open wall so that protection can be provided during heavy rain.

The wall–roof can of course also be made of thatch.

Semi-intensive houses

It is advisable under tropical conditions to utilize houses that accommodate approximately fifty adult birds (Fig. 13.2).

The wire out-runs should be at least 1·8 m (6 ft) in height and should be made of 1·3 cm (0·5 in) heavy-gauge galvanized wire netting. The topmost 13 cm (6 in) should be left slack so that it does not provide birds

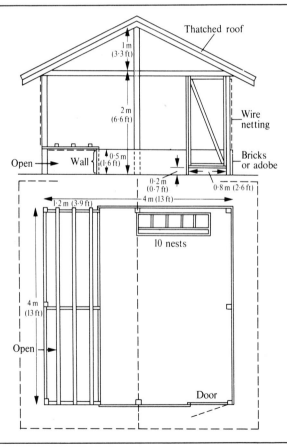

Fig. 13.2   A prototype poultry house for fifty laying hens.

with a steady foothold, and the wire should be buried 30 cm (12 in) into the ground to stop vermin burrowing under. This precaution is particularly necessary where the mongoose is a local predator.

The floor-space requirements in such a house are shown in Table 13.8. Fifty birds require 9·3 m² (100 ft²) of floor space. Details of the type of floors, walls and roofs required have been given in a previous section.

Deep-litter houses

For the small poultry-keeper who cannot afford a controlled-environment deep-litter house the main considerations are that the house should be cheap to construct, that birds are not overcrowded in the house

Table 13.8 *Approximate floor space requirements for different classes of poultry in the tropics*

Class	Floor space requirement (m² (ft²))
Fowls	
Chicks	
0–6 weeks of age	0·05 (0·5) minimum
> 6 weeks of age	
Conventional housing	0·14 (1·5)
Controlled environment	0·09 (1·0)
Broilers	0·09 (1·0) minimum
Rearing stock	
Range	
House	0·14 (1·5)
Range	5·0–8·0 (54–86)
Intensive	
Light breeds	0·19 (2·0)
Heavy breeds	0·23 (2·5)
Layers	
Semi-intensive house	0·19 (2·0)
Intensive	0·28 (3·0)
Deep litter	0·37 (4·0)
Ducks	
Ducklings up to 7 weeks	
Semi-intensive house	0·14 (1·5)
Adult birds	
Semi-intensive house	0·28 (3·0)
Turkeys	
Poults	
Intensive rearing	0·37–0·56 (4·0–6·0)
Breeders	
Small to large types	
Semi-intensive	
House	0·37–0·46 (4·0–5·0)
Yard	0·37–0·46 (4·0–5·0)
Intensive	0·56–0·74 (6·0–8·0)

and that the litter is not allowed to become damp. Space requirements are given in Table 13.8 and general information on the type of building required in a previous section.

The maximum depth of the litter should be no more than 30 cm (12 in). The normal requirements of mature birds are litter with a depth of 10 to 13 cm (4 to 5 in) accumulating to 20 to 23 cm (8 to 9 in). For chicks the initial depth of the litter should be no more than 5 to 8 cm (2 to 3 in), but it can gradually be built up as the chicks grow.

As stated previously the floor of the deep-litter house can be rammed earth, wood or concrete, but concrete is preferable. There must be a retained wall of concrete or brick around the floor at least 30 cm (12 in) high. If division walls are required inside the house the most suitable material to use is expanded metal grilles, as these allow for ventilation but are also quite rigid.

Many materials can be used as a litter including peat moss, wood shavings, sawdust, rice husks, chopped maize, sorghum or millet stalks, chopped rice straw, dried leaves, groundnut shells, or even dried cow manure. If damp patches occur in the litter it should be turned and treated with burnt lime at the rate of 0·5 kg (1 lb) for every 0·7 m^2 (8 ft^2) of litter, or with superphosphate. The advantage of using superphosphate is that unlike lime it does not release ammonia from the litter. If careful attention is given to the litter it will develop dry, crumbly characteristics after a few weeks, when new material can be added. When litter is properly managed it should last for a long period, but as a precaution against the transmission of disease it is normal procedure to clean out the litter and to renew it when a new batch of birds are brought into the house.

The litter makes a manure that is an excellent fertilizer. In one year thirty birds will produce approximately 1 t (0·98 ton) with nitrogen, phosphoric acid and potassium contents of 3, 2 and 2 per cent, respectively. The production of this manure improves the economics of deep-litter poultry production and this factor must be taken into account when deciding which poultry managerial system to use in areas where organic fertilizers have a considerable market value.

Details of feeding, watering and perch requirements are given in Tables 13.4, 13.5 and 13.7.

Battery houses

Data on the cages have already been provided. Requirements are that the house should be well ventilated, lighted and vermin-proof. On small farms a house with a concrete floor, a roof and wire-mesh or expanded metal sides would meet these requirements, but the birds will not perform quite as efficiently as they will in an insulated, controlled-environment house. In such a house the batteries of cages can be serviced by automatic watering, feeding and cleaning devices that – if powered from a reliable source and properly serviced – are very labour saving and efficient.

Controlled-environment houses

These are houses in which the optimal environment is provided for whatever form of production is planned. Ambient temperature, humidity, air movement and light must all be controlled. The building must therefore afford effective insulation from the external environment. As this is likely to be expensive in terms of capital, the cost must be distributed over a large bird population in order to make it an economic proposition. Therefore, all other factors being equal, a large unit is more economical to operate than a small one. However, the larger the unit the lower the level of husbandry inevitably becomes and the chances of introducing disease, as well as the consequences of doing so, increase. The size of the plant must therefore be closely related to the competence of the management, the skill of the stockman and the reliability of available services. It is generally agreed that broiler units housing approximately 15,000 chicks and layer units accommodating 5,000 laying hens are suitable and economic. Minimum temperatures in broiler units should be of the order of 21°C (70°F), while in layer units they can be of the order of 10° to 13°C (50° to 55°F). Relative humidity should be in the range of 35 to 70 per cent. Light should be of even intensity throughout the building.

Equipment

Designs of some simple and suitable feeding and watering devices are shown in Fig. 13.3.

Ducks

Domestic ducks, like fowls, are raised throughout the tropics, but they are most numerous in regions of high rainfall, in riverine areas, in deltas and in coastal districts. They are of particular importance in the rice-growing areas of Southeast Asia.

The total number of domestic ducks in the world is small compared with the total number of fowls and it could be assumed that it is the exacting nature of their climatic requirements which restricts their suitability for domestic use, together with the fact that they eat more feed than fowls and that some people do not find either their eggs or their meat quite as palatable as those of fowls. On the other hand, ducks lay more and larger eggs than indigenous fowls, they grow to a greater size, they require little in the way of housing, they are not so susceptible to disease and parasites, they are better able to protect themselves from marauders and they are excellent foragers.

In all suitable regions, and in many that on account of the dryness of the climate would appear unsuitable, domestic ducks are kept by householders. In Southeast Asia, however, they are the sole source of livelihood

(a) For chicks

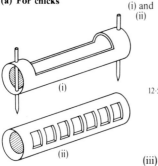

(i)

(ii)

(i) and (ii)   Chick feeders of any length may be made by cutting a 5 to 8 cm (2 to 3 in) diameter bamboo at two of the nodes. A strip approximately $3.5\,cm^2$ ($1.5\,in^2$) wide along almost the whole length of the bamboo, or a series of holes $3.5\,cm^2$ ($1.5\,in^2$), may be cut out of one side. Feeders can be anchored by providing pegs at either end or by attaching them to stands

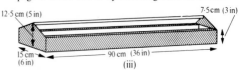

12·5 cm (5 in)   7·5 cm (3 in)

15 cm (6 in)   90 cm (36 in)

(iii)

(iii) A wooden open trough chick feeder

(b) For adult birds

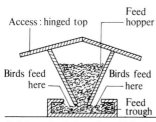

Access : hinged top   Feed hopper

Birds feed here   Birds feed here

Feed trough

(i) Schematic design of a self-feeder

(ii)   Metal waste-preventing hanging feeder. The cylinder is set on three adjustable legs so that it can be raised or lowered. A pitched lid prevents birds roosting. When used outside this lid should project 20 cm (8 in) from the barrel in order to protect the feed against rain

Hanging feeder

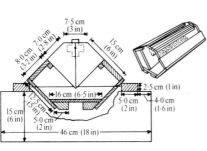

7·5 cm (3 in)
8·0 cm (3·2 in) 7·0 cm (2·8 in)
15 cm (6 in)
16 cm (6·5 in)
12·5 cm (5 in)
2·5 cm (1 in)
5·0 cm (2 in)
4·0 cm (1·6 in)
15 cm (6 in)
5·0 cm (2 in)
46 cm (18 in)

Wooden waste-preventing feeder developed at the National Institute of Poultry Husbandry, Newport, Shropshire, U.K. The distance apart of the rails governs the height of the feed trough from the floor

Lid

Bar

Cylinder   Height adjustment
45 cm (17·7 in)   3·5 to 5 cm (1·4 to 2 in)

Adjustable legs

15 cm (6 in)

A   A

A   A

5 cm (2 in)

30 cm (11·8 in)

40 cm (15·7 in)

(c) A watering device for chicks, and/or adult birds

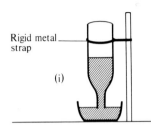

Rigid metal
strap

(i)

(i) A bottle filled with water is turned upside down in a shallow bowl, dish or tin. The bottle may be held in an inverted upright position by a rigid metal strip, wire loops or pieces of wood and can be attached to a special stand, post or tree.

Water flows from the bottle into the drinking container until the level of water in the container seals its mouth. As water is drunk from the container and the level falls it is replenished from the bottle. Thus the level in the container remains constant until all the water in the bottle is utilised.

Small containers and bowls, for chicks and larger ones for adult birds may be used.

Fig. 13.3   Simple types of feeding and watering equipment.

of a considerable number of people who may own very large flocks. Commercial, large-scale duck-keeping is now expanding outside the Southeast Asian tropics in such countries as Colombia in South America (Warren, 1972).

Origin

With the exception of the *Muscovy* or South American Criollo most breeds of ducks appear to have been derived from the wild mallard (*Anan platyrhyncha*). It is likely that the centre of domestication was somewhere in Southeast Asia, although Zeuner (1963) has suggested that western Asia might also have been a centre. The Muscovy has been derived from the American tree duck (*Cairina moschata*).

Breeds and their productivity

Most tropical breeds are raised primarily as egg producers and are seldom kept specifically as meat producers. The Muscovy is an exception. This breed is distinguished by large, fleshy carbuncles on the head and by the fact that the male is about twice as large as the female.

Under subsistence conditions, ducks of such breeds as the *Indian Runner* and the *Nageswari* of India, the *Chinese* of Indo-China and the *Java* of Malaysia and Indonesia achieve mature body weights of approximately 1·8 kg (4 lb) and lay on the average sixty to eighty eggs per annum, each egg weighing approximately 57 g (2 oz). Under slightly improved farm conditions they may possibly average 150 eggs per annum. On the other hand, under intensive, improved husbandry conditions Indian Runner drakes will weigh 2·0 kg (4·5 lb) and average annual egg production of the ducks will be 200, with individual ducks laying as many as

300. Warren (1972) stated that under managerial conditions where the ducklings are fed until they are 3 months of age and are then expected to scavenge for part of their feed, ducks of the *Khaki Campbell* breed are capable of producing on average 300 eggs per year. The Khaki Campbell breed originated in the United Kingdom from a cross between Indian Runner and *Rouen* ducks, but it is a very suitable breed for the tropics. The females are light tan in colour with a blue bar on the wing; the males are very similar but possess green-coloured feathering on the head. Ducks of this breed commence laying at $4\frac{1}{2}$ months of age and continue for at least 12 months. The average egg weight is 60 g (2·1 oz), the shells being almost white in colour. The Muscovy lays only a sufficient number of eggs to hatch two broods a year.

Muscovy and *White Pekin* ducks raised under subsistence conditions can produce table birds weighing up to 2·7 kg (6 lb). Under improved management Muscovy drakes may average 4·5 kg (10 lb) and the ducks 3·2 kg (7 lb). Well-managed White Pekin will produce 3·5 kg (7·7 lb) ducklings in 7 to 9 weeks, with mature drakes and ducks weighing on average 4·1 kg (9 lb) and 3·6 kg (8 lb), respectively. White Pekin ducks cross very successfully with a temperate-type breed such as the *Aylesbury*.

Breeding and incubation

The usual number of ducks allowed to one drake is six, but if fertile eggs are the main consideration the number should be no more than four. Drakes should be placed with the ducks at least one month before fertile eggs are required. The belief that effective copulation can only take place in water is mistaken, although it is desirable that ducks should have access to water on which to swim. With water available they are able to keep themselves clean and nesting ducks are better able to keep their eggs at the correct humidity.

The Muscovy will interbreed with other types of duck, but the offspring are sterile. Other breeds of ducks are interfertile and will produce fertile crossbreds when mated with wild species such as the *Pintail* and the *Shoveller*.

Ducks normally begin to lay at about 6 months of age, although, as stated above, Khaki Campbell come into lay 6 weeks earlier. Ducks of the improved laying breeds are for all practical purposes non-broody, as are the Java ducks common in Southeast Asia. Even ducks of the White Pekin type cannot be relied on to incubate their eggs.

The incubation period is 4 weeks for all breeds except the Muscovy, for which it is 5 weeks. Muscovy ducks incubate their own eggs satisfactorily and are capable of hatching up to 30, but it is usual for other breeds to hatch 15 to 20. Hens will incubate duck eggs satisfactorily if the eggs are dampened at least once a day, and they can hatch a maximum of 12.

If duck eggs are artificially incubated the temperature should be 0·6°C (1°F) lower than is needed for hens' eggs and the relative humidity should never be allowed to fall below 60 per cent. During the first 24 hours of incubation it is advantageous that the relative humidity should be 70 per cent, and from the second to the fourteenth day the eggs should be turned twice daily and sprinkled with tepid water at least once a day. After the fourteenth day the eggs should be turned at least thrice daily and sprinkled with water.

After hatching it is simpler to sex ducklings than it is chickens.

Management after hatching

Rearing

Ducklings hatched in the incubator should be transferred to a brooder as soon as they have dried. The 'cold' type of brooder is perfectly satisfactory in a tropical climate, but if for some reason it is necessary to use artificial heat, temperatures of 29·4°C (85°F) during the first few nights gradually declining to 18·3°C (65°F) within 14 days are satisfactory. Ducklings are generally remarkably active and should be allowed ample open space during the daytime. If ducklings have been incubated naturally they will thrive best if they are left with the mother for 2 or 3 weeks. Muscovy ducks are particularly good mothers.

Choice of system

Any method of management applicable to fowls can be used for ducks, but intensive husbandry is possibly not as profitable. Managerial methods used in Southeast Asia are of particular interest and could be used elsewhere to some extent.

In marsh, seasonally flooded and rice-growing areas thousands of ducklings are hatched by the ancient Asian artificial incubation system described in a previous section. The ducklings are sexed and the young stock are divided at an early age into flocks of males and females. When sufficiently grown they are herded over the marshes or freshly cultivated paddy fields and live on forage, small fish and crustaceans, etc., gleaned from the fields. When the birds are fully grown, all except breeding stock are sold to traders who herd them towards the large towns and cities, selling eggs and stock *en route*. Smaller flocks are also kept by local farmers under similar conditions, and in almost all the rice-growing regions of Southeast Asia herders may be seen directing their duck flocks using characteristic long wands.

Another managerial method of interest is the association of duck production with fish farming. Laying houses are built over the fish pond so that the duck droppings assist in its fertilization. Fish offals and green forage from the ponds are fed to the ducks.

Where management of breeding stock on free range is not possible a semi-intensive system is the most desirable. Simple houses suffice for accommodation provided they are dry and cool. A suitable house should be situated on a dry foundation and may consist of upright poles supporting a thatch roof over a raised (15 cm (6 in)) rammed earth floor enclosed by wire netting. Adult ducks require 0·28 m² (3 ft²) of floor space; those up to 7 weeks of age about half this area (Table 13.8). An outside run is desirable, and can with advantage include an area of swimming water, but this is not essential. Wire-netting or slatted floors can be provided and these assist in keeping the house clean and dry, but they are also not essential. Straw, hay or reed can be liberally strewn on the floor as an alternative. Nest boxes should be provided at ground level at the rate of one for every five ducks. Each should be approximately 30 to 41 cm (12 to 16 in) in size and any front retaining-board that may be used should be no higher than 15 cm (6 in). Ducks prefer to nest as close to the floor as possible.

All breeds of ducks lay either at night or early in the morning, usually before 09.00 hours, and those kept on open range are usually confined to their night quarters until the sun is well up and laying has been completed. If the open range is pasture the stocking rate should be no more than 432 ducks per ha (175 per acre).

Battery managerial methods can be modified for ducks and under special and specific circumstances may be profitable.

Disease

Ducks appear to excel all other domestic poultry in their resistance to stress and they apparently exhibit a tolerance to most poultry diseases, so that in general they do not require routine vaccination. They do suffer from cholera and a form of hepatitis, and are particularly susceptible to, and intolerant of, contaminated and mouldy feed, and of a deficiency of manganese in their diet. In some environments the liver fluke, an internal parasite, can also be a problem.

Feeding

Ducklings should be fed at least four times a day until they are 2 weeks old, and three times a day for a further 2 weeks. After this the number of feeds can be gradually reduced if they are extensively managed, and as the birds' foraging power develops. Three feeds a day are essential for ducks raised in confinement until they are 8 weeks old, but thereafter two feeds a day are sufficient. Pelleted feed is very suitable for ducks.

Feeds recommended for chicks are suitable for ducklings. Day-old ducklings should be given coarse milled cereals moistened with milk or water as a first feed and then a proprietary mash or one with a composition approximating to the following:

Milled cereal	30 parts
Fine cereal bran	30 parts
Fish or meat meal	20 parts
Extracted oil-cake meal	10 parts
Fine grit and minerals	5 parts

The mash should be dampened just sufficiently to make it 'crumble'. If it is too wet much of it is lost through the sieving process to which it is subjected in the duck's bill. Feeding should always take place in flat-bottomed, shallow troughs. The feeding space required by 100 ducklings is 7·3 m (24 ft) and 12 m (40 ft) for birds up to 3 weeks old and older birds, respectively (Table 13.4). Small discarded rubber tyres cut through the centre of the tread are very suitable for use as feeding troughs. No more feed than can be eaten in about 10 minutes should be fed at any one time. Grit or sand should be available *ad lib.*

Adult ducks normally consume 170 to 227 g (6 to 8 oz) of feed per day, but some adult ducks in full lay can consume as much as 283 g (10 oz). Feeds recommended for fowls are generally suitable for ducks, but proprietary duck mashes are recommended for feeding intensively managed birds. In regions where ample supplies of fresh fish and fish or shrimp meal are available the College of Agriculture of the University of the Philippines recommends the following ration:

Rice bran	60 parts
Maize meal	20 parts
Fish or shrimp meal or the equivalent in fresh trash fish	20 parts

To this is added 2 per cent cod-liver oil and 2 per cent oyster-shell with additional green feed if the birds are continuously housed.

Under semi-intensive managerial conditions more use may be made of local feeds. One-third of the meal ration may be replaced by cheaper vegetable feeds, household scraps and fodders such as sweet-potato tops and water plants such as *kangkong* (*Ipomoea Aquatica*).

Ducks on free range obtain their protein needs by foraging for small fish, crustaceans and insects so that their evening feed should consist of cereals, cereal brans and carbohydrate feeds such as cassava, sago, sweet-potato, yam or taro.

A plentiful supply of clean drinking water should always be available adjacent to feeding troughs. Ducks constantly wash their bills in water, spilling the water all around them, so that under intensive conditions the water supply should be placed on a wire-covered platform to minimize the undesirable effects of this constant spillage.

Geese

Geese are raised primarily as meat producers. In some countries their fat and liver are particularly prized. They also produce excellent feathers. Their reproductive life is longer than that of any other domestic poultry. They are grazers, feeding on grasses, legumes and weeds, and are therefore efficient controllers of weeds in cultivated crops such as coffee, cocoa, bananas and pineapple. They can be reared most economically in an environment where a supply of young, succulent fodder is always available, such as regions of high and continuous rainfall or marsh lands.

Although certain wild species migrate to the tropics during the cool seasons of the year, no domestic breeds have been developed in the arid tropics and those evolved elsewhere do not easily adapt themselves either to arid conditions or to very high temperatures.

Origin

The goose appears to have been a more important domestic bird in the ancient western Asian and Mediterranean civilizations than it is in the world today. Not only were geese a source of meat, fat, eggs and feathers, but they were also kept for a variety of ritualistic purposes. Zeuner (1963) suggested that there could have been at least three separate centres of domestication and that geese were domesticated in Neolithic times. One centre was possibly in southeast Europe where the Greeks may have domesticated the Greylag goose (*Anser anser*), now found wild north of latitude 45° in Europe and in Asia as far east as the Amur. The Romans considered the White-fronted goose (*A. albifrons*) superior to the Greylag goose and treated goose liver as a delicacy. The Greylag and White-fronted geese appear to have been known in Egypt before the Nile goose (*Alopochen aegyptiaca*) was domesticated. It is not known at what time, or where, the Chinese goose (*Cygnopis cygnoides*) was domesticated in Southeast Asia.

Geese are easily domesticated, so that centres of domestication could have been more numerous than Zeuner (1963) has suggested. Wild geese readily cross with all domestic breeds.

Breeds and their productivity

Two breeds of European origin are the *Toulouse* and *Emden*, the former being grey and the latter white in colour. In the temperate zone birds of both breeds are large, grow rapidly and possess a propensity to fatten. The average mature weight of ganders and geese of these breeds being

12 and 9 kg (26·5 and 17·5 lb) and 9 and 8 kg (20 and 17·5 lb), respectively. Both breeds have been introduced in small numbers into various countries in the tropics.

Geese of the *African* breed closely resemble the European breeds in performance. They are grey in colour but are distinguished by a knob over the base of the bill and by a pronounced pouching of the throat.

The *Chinese* breed, of which there are two types, the brown and the white, is found throughout the humid areas of Southeast Asia. Geese of this breed are distinguished by possessing a knob over the bill, a slight pouching of the throat and blue eyes. The average weight of a well-bred and fed Chinese gander is 5·4 kg (12 lb) and that of the goose 4·5 kg (10 lb), but nondescript birds raised under village conditions will average little more than half these weights.

Geese of the *Egyptian* breed are lighter than the Chinese, but they are hardy and active foragers and quite well suited for humid tropical environments.

Breeding

Geese may begin to lay at one year of age, but they should not be used for breeding purposes until they are 3 years old. Ganders may be used when they are 2 years of age.

In the case of the larger breeds three geese are provided for each gander. Mated geese do not like changes, mating being usually for life, and difficulties may be encountered if geese are added to the established flock or if the gander is changed.

Geese of good egg-laying strains of the Chinese breed may lay up to 60 eggs per annum, but nondescript village geese in Southeast Asia only lay approximately 20 eggs per annum. Birds of the heavier European breeds lay from 30 to 40 eggs during a season. Egg laying reaches a peak during the third and fourth years of life, but geese continue to lay satisfactorily up to 10 years of age. Eggs of the Chinese breed weigh 110 to 140 g (4 to 5 oz).

A goose will sit on and hatch ten to fifteen of her own eggs, but as hens are more amenable to management than geese they are often used for hatching the eggs of high-laying strains of geese, when maximum egg production is of importance and artificial incubators are not used. Large hens should be selected and these can usually only cover a maximum of four eggs. The eggs must be turned each day and liberally sprinkled with water after the middle of the incubation period. The eggs of the lighter breeds hatch after 28 to 30 days, while those of some of the heavier breeds may require up to 34 days before hatching takes place.

In forced-air-draught incubators a temperature of 37·2°C (99°F) should be maintained, while without forced-air-draught a temperature of 38·6° to 39·2°C (101.5° to 102·5°F) is required immediately above the eggs.

Humidity requirements are approximately the same as those for duck eggs, and goose eggs must be turned, aired and sprayed twice daily up to the twenty-eighth day.

Management after hatching

Rearing

Goslings that are artificially hatched should be treated in the manner recommended for ducklings, although they are hardier, grow faster and require proportionately more food. Dry, clean accommodation is essential, but they rarely require additional heat immediately after hatching.

Adult birds

Geese are not normally managed on a commercial scale in the tropics, being maintained in small domestic flocks and invariably allowed free range, entailing little trouble or expense. They require a dry, well-ventilated house that can be simple and of inexpensive design, in which they can shelter from intense sunlight during the day and be enclosed at night.

In the temperate zone intensely managed force-fed geese will gain up to 4·5 kg (10 lb) in one month, but this practice is virtually unknown in the tropics.

Geese, like ducks, produce feathers that are difficult to pluck. Under commercial conditions it is usual for the goose to be killed and the body then dipped in hot melted wax and allowed to cool; the feathers are then peeled off with the wax.

Feeding

Day-old goslings should be fed coarsely milled cereals moistened with milk or water. After 2 days finely chopped, tender green forage can replace one-third of the cereals. For the first few days the goslings should be fed four or five times daily, but after one week three feeds per day will be sufficient. The amount of food provided should be as much as can be eaten by the bird in about 10 minutes. If succulent young pasture is available this will provide all the feed required once the birds are 3 or 4 weeks of age. If only inferior pasture is available a supplemental mash of chopped, green, succulent forage and cereal bran will be required.

Fresh drinking water should always be available. As with ducks, water in which to swim is desirable but not essential for good health and fertility.

If it is desired to fatten geese they should be confined in a cool, dry but rather dark house so that there is neither opportunity nor encouragement for them to exercise. They should be fed to appetite on inexpensive carbohydrate feeds, such as sweet-potato, yam, taro, rice or maize for about one month.

Turkeys

Comparatively few turkeys are reared in tropical countries in Africa and Asia, although they are common in some countries in Central America, from where they originated. The lighter breeds do, however, thrive very well in the dry tropics when they are allowed to range and there is adequate shade and feed. Indeed, properly managed they can be reared quite successfully in all except the very wet regions of the tropics and there is an increasing interest in rearing them in all tropical countries.

Origin

The domestic turkey is derived from the American wild turkey. The bird was apparently domesticated by the Indians in pre-Columbian times. They are mentioned by Cortes and other Conquistadores, who called them peacocks, and they were noticed by Columbus and other explorers in the Caribbean. According to Zeuner (1963) turkeys were first introduced into Europe in 1523 or 1524 and they appeared on the English menu for the first time in 1585.

There are two wild species in North and Central America. The Common turkey (*Meleagris gallopavo*), that is distributed from Canada along the eastern seaboard of the United States into Mexico, and the Ocellated turkey (*Agriocharis ocellato*), a truly tropical bird, that is found in the north of Central America and Mexico. The ancestor of the domestic turkey is *M. gallopavo* and it is assumed that the centre of original domestication was Mexico. Wild turkeys live in small groups in the forests, feeding on insects, seeds and fallen fruit. Some types are of considerable size: cockerels and hens of the Wild Bronze type weigh 18 kg (40 lb) and 10 kg (22 lb), respectively.

It is of some interest that the present domestic breeds in North America have not been derived primarily from the indigenous birds as their ancestors were introduced by English settlers from England. Improved breeds having been derived from turkeys imported into England from America. However, there has since been some use of indigenous types in crossbreeding programmes.

Breeds

Common breeds are the *Broad Breasted Bronze*, the *White Holland* and the *Beltsville Small White*. A *Large White* has been bred by crossing the

Bronze with the White Holland and selecting for size and white feathers. Other breeds used to a limited extent in the United States are the *Narragansett*, the *Black*, the *Slate* and the *Bonbon Red*. Disparities in the size of different breeds are typified by the Broad Breasted Bronze and the Beltsville Small White, as mature cocks and hens of these breeds weigh 19 kg (41 lb) and 11 kg (25 lb), and 9 kg (20 lb) and 6 kg (13 lb), respectively.

Breeding

Turkeys may commence to breed when they are one year old, but they are not fully mature until they are 2 to 3 years of age.

Hens of the improved breeds in temperate climates lay on the average up to ninety eggs per year, but there is very considerable variation in individual egg-laying capabilities. The average weight of an egg is 85 g (3 oz). Hens of the nondescript type of turkey usually reared in tropical countries may only lay twenty eggs per year with an average weight of 57 g (2 oz).

It is usual to allow one 'stagg' or cock turkey to mate with up to ten hens. Staggs tend to be selective in their mating, but one effective copulation suffices to fertilize a whole clutch of eggs and this is required only every 3 weeks or so. The size of the male can be so disproportionate that hens may be damaged by him, especially if his spurs are long and sharp.

Turkeys prefer to make their own nest, but they can be induced to lay where it is most convenient by the provision of roomy, well-protected nests. A suitable mating shelter for birds on range is a wigwam type, consisting of three poles covered on two sides by thatch, matting or sacks.

The incubation period is 25 to 28 days. Although turkey hens in the tropics are often quite good brooders it is generally more satisfactory to set turkey eggs under fowls if natural incubation is required. When artificial incubation of eggs is employed the general managerial methods advised for fowls can be adopted, but special attention has to be given to the humidity of the incubator. The relative humidity should be 63 per cent at dry-bulb temperatures of 37·2°C (99°F) and after the twenty-fourth day it should be 70 to 79 per cent at a dry-bulb temperature of 36·1°C (97°F). In forced-draught incubators the temperature should be kept at 37·5°C (99·5°F) until the twenty-fourth day and then lowered to 36·1°C (97°F). In incubators with no assisted ventilation a temperature of 38·9°C (102°F) should be maintained 4·8 cm (1·9 in) above the eggs. There should be no turning of eggs during the first day of incubation or after the twenty-fourth day.

Management after hatching

Brooding

Methods suitable for chicks are suitable for turkey poults, but the latter, when very young, are more susceptible to climatic stress. They are particularly stressed by cold, humid conditions. Ambient temperature on the first day of brooding should be 35°C (95°F) and at the end of the first week 37·8°C (100°F). Thereafter the temperature should be lowered by 0·6°C (1°F) each day until the normal ambient temperature is reached.

Within the warmed space in the brooder each poult requires a 77 cm^2 (12 in^2) area during the first week.

Rearing

Turkeys can be reared in the same way as fowls. At approximately 16 weeks of age turkeys destined for breeding should be separated and fed on a different, higher fibre ration than turkeys destined for meat production.

Breeding turkeys can be reared on open range, in semi-confinement or intensively. Under range conditions the stocking rate can be 150 birds per 0·4 ha (1 acre). The methods used are approximately the same as those used for fowls, but more feeding and watering space must be provided (Tables 13·4 and 13·5).

Feeding

Turkeys have a strong aversion to any change in their feeding routine or in the nature of their food. When poults are transferred to the brooder it may be necessary to dip their beaks into both the feed and the water as they sometimes appear to have no desire to eat and they will either die or be very slow in their initial growth. At one day old they should be offered small quantities of fine mash, dampened by milk when it is available, or they should be given finely broken grain. Well-chopped, tender green feed should also be offered to them.

Rations for fowls can be used for turkeys if the CP content is raised by the addition of a protein-rich concentrate such as fish meal. Poults up to 10 weeks of age require a ration containing approximately 23 per cent CP. The CP content of the ration should be gradually reduced to about 15 per cent for mature birds. As stated in a previous paragraph, at 16 weeks of age turkeys destined for breeding are fed a ration containing a higher CP content.

The average feed intakes of light and heavy breeds are 113 g (4 oz) and 284 g (10 oz) per day, respectively. Supplies of fresh, clean water, green feed and flint grit should always be available for all except range-fed stock. Green feed need not be fed to the latter.

In the tropics approximately 23 kg (50 lb) of feed are required to produce a 6·4 kg (14 lb) turkey at 24 weeks of age, provided the birds are well managed.

Disease

Young turkeys are very susceptible to parasitic infection as well as to most of the diseases suffered by other poultry. Two diseases particularly prevalent in turkeys are blackhead and erysipelas.

Blackhead.   This is a devastating disease of 8- to 16-week-old poults caused by the protozoa *Histomonas meleagridis*. The disease is transmitted by droppings and for this reason poults can best be managed on a wire or slatted floor. The common symptoms are droopiness, sulphur-coloured droppings and a dark head. Treatment is by administration of a suitable drug in the water or the feed. A veterinarian should be consulted for details and the dosage of suitable drugs.

Erysipelas.   The disease is caused by the bacterium *Erysipelothrix insidiosa* and infection is usually from contaminated soil. It also affects sheep and pigs. The symptoms are a sudden loss of poults that are discoloured in the face. The disease can be treated by the use of antibiotics, and if it is very prevalent veterinary advice should be sought as to whether a preventative vaccination programme should be initiated. Turkeys should not be allowed on range grazed by sheep and pigs.

Guinea fowl

Guinea fowl are indigenous to Africa, where there are still several wild species. Two species were domesticated in Greek and Roman times, one with blue and the other with red wattles. Zeuner (1963) stated that these birds were known in Greece by 500 BC and he quotes Pliny to the effect that they were the last type of poultry to be added to the Roman menu. With the fall of the Roman empire guinea fowl disappeared from Europe to be rediscovered by the Portuguese in West Africa at the end of the sixteenth century. The domesticated guinea fowl discovered by the Portuguese was *Numida meleagris*, the wild ancestor being indigenous to West Africa and the Cape Verde Islands. It is not known which West African people domesticated the guinea fowl, but the subject is of considerable interest as the guinea fowl is probably the only species of livestock that has been domesticated in Africa.

Outside West Africa only small numbers of domestic guinea fowl are raised. There are three well-known varieties: the *Pearl*, the *White* and the *Lavender*. The Pearl is the most numerous. It possesses a purplish-grey plumage dotted or 'pearled' with white. Wild guinea fowl are, however, still numerous in some regions of Africa, particularly in the drier areas of East Africa where the birds range in large groups.

The domestic bird is normally kept as a scavenger around the house. In northern Ghana, after brooding, the guinea-fowl chicks are left to fend for themselves. This is probably the norm in guinea-fowl management in West Africa. During the first weeks of brooding the chicks are fed termites supplemented with sorghum and/or millet grain. In order to trap termites Ghanaian farmers mix straw, cow dung and water in a pot, dig a small hole in the termite mound and then place the upturned pot over the hole. Once brooding is completed the guinea-fowl chicks may be fed a little grain at night in order to attract them back to the homestead.

The guinea fowl is distinguished from other poultry by its harsh cry. The birds have a tendency to mate in pairs, but one cock can be placed with up to four hens. The latter lay up to eighty eggs per year in a ground nest. The eggs are small, yellowish to brown in colour with varied mottling, weigh on average 50 g (1·75 oz) and are very palatable. The meat of the guinea fowl tastes like pheasant meat and it is relished by most African peoples.

The possibilities of improving the productivity of the guinea fowl, both as an egg and as a meat producer, are very great and are being actively pursued in Ghana at the present time.

Ostrich

It is well known that the ostrich *Struthio camelus* was 'farmed' in South Africa in the past for its feathers. Less well known is the fact that the ostrich has been used as a domesticated or semi-domesticated species in other African countries.

According to Wilson (1976) some 200 years ago ostrich feathers were one of the principal exports of Darfur (western Sudan) and ostriches were kept by many families in this region until well into the twentieth century. Whether these ostriches were captured or bred in captivity is not known. The domestication or semi-domestication of this bird may have been a very widespread practice in the past as the Burun, a pagan tribe inhabiting an area in the northeast of the Southern Region of Sudan, almost 2000 km (1243 miles) from Darfur, also kept ostriches for feathers, eggs and meat until the end of the first two decades of the twentieth century.

Marketing

The storage and transport problems associated with the marketing of poultry meat are the same as those associated with other types of meat. In most tropical countries culls and specially fed meat birds produced on small farms are marketed while still alive (Plate 13.2). Broilers are

Plate 13.2   The use of a bicycle for transporting live poultry to market. Southeast Sumatra, Indonesia.

marketed in the same way as they are in temperate countries, i.e. as frozen carcases.

Egg marketing does, however, present some special difficulties for the small producer. One of the major causes of egg spoilage is the development of the embryo in the fertile egg during the hottest periods of the year. Although some tropical peoples do not object to consuming eggs that contain an embryo in an advanced stage of development, this is not the normal attitude. Most consumers consider that an egg that has been stored under hot conditions for 48 hours is inedible.

The easiest method of dealing with this problem is to exclude cockerels from the laying flocks. If this is not practicable then the development of the embryo can be stopped by immersing freshly collected eggs in water kept at 57·2°C (135°F) for a 15-minute period. They can also be treated by freezing, by soaking in lime water for approximately 18 hours or by painting with a white mineral oil of high viscosity. If a cool room is available the palatability of untreated eggs can be prolonged by keeping them at an ambient temperature of 18·3°C (65°F).

In Southeast Asia eggs are preserved in many ways before marketing.

Two common methods are salting and preservation in wood ashes, lime, salt and tea leaves for 100 days to produce the so-called 'ancient egg'. In some areas of the Philippines the embryo in a fertile duck egg is allowed to develop until the eighteenth day or later. The embryo is then killed by plunging the egg into sufficiently hot water for a specific period. The result is a local delicacy known as *balut*.

Under normal conditions eggs do not lose much weight during storage at moderate ambient temperatures. In the dry tropics, however, at ambient temperatures above 32·2°C (90°F) and when humidity is low, the loss in weight during a short storage period may be as high as, or more than, 10 per cent.

References

Agricultural Research Council (1963) Nutrient Requirements of Farm Livestock. (1) Poultry. *Summary of Recommendations.* ARC: London.

Aitkens, J. D. (1956) *Tropical Poultry Keeping for Beginners.* Times of Ceylon: Colombo.

Blair, R. (1975) Concepts on practical diet formulation. *Proc. Nutrit. Soc.,* **34**, 43–9.

Bolton, W. and Blair, R. (1974) Poultry nutrition. *Min. Agric. Fish Food Bull.,* No. 174. HMSO: London.

Callias, N. E. and Saichuae, P. (1967) Ecology of the Red Jungle Fowl in Thailand and Malaya, with reference to the origin of domestication. *Siam Soc. Nat. Hist. Bull.,* **22**, 189–209.

Hutchinson, J. C. D. (1954) 'Heat Regulation in Birds', in Hammond, J. (ed.), *Progress in the Physiology of Farm Animals,* Vol. 1, pp. 299–362. Butterworths: London.

Jasiorowski, H. A. (1973) Twenty years with no progress. *World Anim. Rev.* (5), 1–6.

Lee, D. K. H., Robinson, K. W., Yeates, N. T. M. and Scott, M. I. R. (1945) Poultry husbandry in hot climates – experimental enquiries. *Poultry Sci.,* **24**, 195–207.

McDonald, P., Edwards, R. A. and Greenhalgh, J. F. D. (1973) *Animal Nutrition* (2nd edn). Longman: London.

National Academy of Sciences (1971) *Nutrient Requirements of Poultry* (6th rev. edn). NAS: Washington.

Payne, C. G. (1967) 'The Influence of Environmental Temperature on Egg Production', Carter, T. C. (ed.), *Environmental Control in Poultry Production,* Part I, No. 3, pp. 40–54. Oliver and Boyd: London.

Peters, J. P. (1913) The cock. *J. Amer. Oriental Soc.,* **33**, 363–401.

Smetana, P. (1966) *Poultry Production in Burma.* FAO/FFHC Poultry Training Course: Vet. College, Insien, Burma.

Taylor, T. G. (1975). Perspectives in mineral nutrition. *Proc. Nutrit. Soc.,* **34**, 35–41.

Thuraisingham, S. and Wah, L. C. (1971) *The Development of the Poultry Industry in West Malaysia.* Min. Agric. Lands: Kuala Lumpur.

Waring, J. J. and Brown, W. O. (1967) Calorimetric studies on the utilisation of dietary energy by the laying White Leghorn hen in relation to plane of nutrition and environmental temperature. *J. agric. Sci. (Camb.),* **68**, 149–55.

Warren, A. G. (1972) Ducks and geese in the tropics. *World Anim. Rev.* (3), 35–6.

Wilson, R. T. (1976) The ostrich *Struthio camelus* in Darfur, Republic of Sudan. *Bull. B.O.C.,* **96**, (4), 123–5.

Zeuner, F. E. (1963) *A History of Domesticated Animals.* Hutchinson: London.

Further Reading

Cockburn, H. *Poultry Keeping in East Africa.* E. Afric. Lit. Bur.: Nairobi, 1962.

Farkas, T. Interesting facts about the crowned guinea fowl (*Numida meleagris*). *Fauna, Flora* (*Pretoria*), No. 16, pp. 23–28 (1965).

Hurd, L. M. *Modern Poultry Farming.* Macmillan: New York, 1966.

Jull, M. A. *Raising Turkeys, Ducks, Geese and Game Birds.* McGraw-Hill: New York, 1947.

McAndle, A. A. *Poultry Management and Production* (2nd edn). Angus and Robertson: Sydney, 1965.

McAndle, A. A. *A Handbook for Poultry Officers in India.* Min. Food. Agric.: New Delhi, 1965.

Thomann, W. *Poultry Keeping in Tropical Areas.* FAO: Rome, 1968.

United States Department of Agriculture. *Raising Guinea Fowl.* Leaflet No. 519. US Govt. Print. Office: Washington, 1963.

Part III Animal Products

Chapter 14

Milk and Milk Products

by **(the late) James N. Warner**
Formerly Professor, Department of Dairy Technology, Allahabad Agricultural Institute, Allahabad, UP, India

The dairy situation

The three principal domesticated bovine species are all used as dairy animals in the tropics. Temperate-type cows produce most of the milk in the Caribbean region, tropical America, tropical Australia and in parts of Africa and they and their Zebu crosses are being used increasingly in India. Zebu and buffalo cows are important milk animals in parts of tropical Africa and Asia, respectively. In the major pastoral areas of the tropics goats and sheep are also important milk animals, while in the most arid portions of Africa and Asia the camel and to a very limited extent the mare supply milk for human use.

For decades milk has been produced in tropical areas primarily by farmers who operated a 'household', not a farm business. One or more cows may be kept to provide milk for the home rather than for sale. In a limited number of countries there have been a few specialized dairy farms, often government owned, and intended to supply milk for specific groups of consumers.

Southeast Asia, indeed much of southern Asia, except India, traditionally has not generally accepted animal milk as a human food. Wagan (1970) says, for example, that in the Philippines milk is not considered as an indispensable food. In some tropical areas of Africa, the Americas and the West Indies, there have not usually been strong cultural inhibitions to the use of animal milk and its products. Milk and milk products have always been used in the human diet in India, where they are considered very important even though the supply has been inadequate.

Dried skim-milk powder has been consumed in recent years by many people in tropical areas where milk was previously largely unavailable. This milk powder has been provided mainly through the agency of international aid and other programmes. Also, many people have moved from tropical areas to other parts of the world where milk is a widely used food. A physiological intolerance to milk has been reported with increasing frequency among both these groups of people. The condition is often characterized by such symptoms as vomiting, diarrhoea and/or cramp.

This problem has been investigated by several workers. Rosensweig

654

(1969) stated that it is a result of a deficiency of lactase in the digestive system of an individual as a consequence of long years of very low post-weaning milk intake, specifically the consumption of little or no lactose which is found only in milk and milk products. It has been also suggested that this deficiency of lactase may be an inherited characteristic (Huang and Bayless, 1968; Flatz *et al* 1969).

The intolerance appears at all ages, but is 'correlated directly with age', according to Elliott *et al*. (1967). There seems to be greater incidence of appearance of the symptoms after an intake of more than two or three cups of milk at one time, than when less is drunk. Whether the milk is reconstituted or whole seems to make little if any difference. There are some indications that the clinical symptoms appear to be more common when skim-milk rather than whole milk is consumed. It has been suggested that in those regions where lactose intolerance is a problem, lactase might be added to milk.

The intensity of milk production throughout the tropical world is, with a few exceptions, very low compared with the highly developed dairy areas of the temperate zones. Production is lower per animal, per man employed and per unit area of land. Roads are usually few and often almost impassable during seasons of adverse weather, thus inhibiting rapid and economic collection of milk. Refrigeration facilities are generally unavailable in tropical rural areas. Atmospheric and ground-water temperatures are relatively high in most areas so that milk may not be cooled promptly, if at all, without mechanical aids.

These and other factors, such as traditional standards of sanitation, result in relatively expensive milk, much of it of poor quality. These characteristics of milk have important implications in the processing and marketing of milk products in much of the tropical world.

Anker-Ladefoged (1953) estimated that the hours of human labour used in producing 4·5 litres (1 gal) of milk in certain areas were: Sri Lanka 10, South Africa 2·3, United Kingdom 0·7 and the United States 0·5. More recently Khurody (1970) stated that in order to purchase 1 litre (0·2 gal) of milk, a truck driver must work 7 minutes in the United States, Western Europe, Australia and New Zealand; 15 minutes in Italy; 35 minutes in Egypt, Syria and Jordan; 45 minutes in India and Pakistan; and 75 minutes in the Philippines. Apart from the differences in the quality of the milk, there may have been a slight decrease over a period of nearly 20 years in the work time required to earn a unit of milk, but the time required continues to be very much greater in the tropical than in the temperate dairy areas.

During recent years the average per capita supply of whole-milk equivalent has not increased significantly in the tropics. Increasing rural populations demand more milk for use in producing areas. Considerable effort has been given to organizing milk-procurement schemes for town and city supplies, and because of this effort increasingly larger quantities of milk and milk products appear to be available to tropical urban populations in many places. However, the growth during the past two or three decades of town and city populations has been such that the urban milk supply per capita has shown little genuine improvement, except perhaps in a few specific instances. Throughout the tropics plans continue to be made and implemented in an effort to provide all people, especially urban residents, with more milk and milk products (Graff, 1966).

Organizing the supply of milk

Some producers continue to supply their milk directly to private consumers, an ancient practice in the marketing of milk in some underdeveloped tropical areas. Others sell by contract to milk vendors who own one or two cans and a bicycle, take delivery of the milk at the producer's house and sell it to private consumers at their homes or to tea and coffee stalls. Alternatively, producers may deliver their milk to a point within their own or a near-by village where milk is bulked. As larger processing operations come into existence – and this is happening rapidly in many tropical markets – the bulked milk may be chilled at this point in the collection channel. In seeking to obtain greater volumes of milk, city plants reach out further into the countryside and cover larger areas to collect their supplies. As a consequence, collecting centres with chilling facilities, supplemented with insulated road transport, are becoming more common. Alternatively, ice may be used as a refrigerant during transport. In some places the processor handling small quantities of milk – perhaps in a single room in a crowded part of a town or city – is disappearing and large plants which heat-treat and package milk are becoming more common. Many of these plants produce and sell several milk products in addition to liquid or beverage milk.

The government of Maharashtra State in India has greatly expanded its procurement, processing and distribution of milk during the past 15 years. This development includes a new plant, the Worli Dairy, in Bombay. The Aarey Milk Colony now joins with the Worli Dairy in seeking to fulfil the objectives that were originally those of Aarey, which included provision of a greater supply of milk and milk products to Bombay city, together with quality and price controls. These two plants together constitute the Greater Bombay Milk Scheme, one of the largest dairy operations in the tropical world. During 1969 this scheme sold an average of about 420,000 litres (92,400 gal) of milk each day, including whole buffalo, whole cow, toned and double-toned milk. Milk is received by this scheme both from Maharashtra and from Gujarat, the bordering state to the north. Milk from Gujarat is transported about 420 km (260 miles) by insulated rail tanker and comes from the Kaira District Cooperative Milk Producers Union, Ltd, at Anand – another of the largest tropical dairy operations.

By 1971, India had eighteen plants operating, most of them less than 20 years old, each with an installed capacity of at least 50,000 litres (11,000 gal) of milk a day. Of these, six are cooperative plants, including the plant at Anand; the others are public sector plants.

Importation of milk solids from surplus countries and local preparation of reconstituted, toned and, by the addition of local vegetable fats or oils instead of butterfat, filled milk (Medora, 1971) are increasing in several places. Recombined milk is prepared in some cases (Guttfeld and Rosenfeld, 1966) by use of imported components. A programme of education is expected to be helpful in increasing both the domestic production and consumption of milk in the Philippines (Wagan, 1970). Uganda expects a more viable dairy industry within 15 years as a result of plans already made in that country (Mauger, 1965). India has at least forty-four milk plants planned that are not yet in operation, five of these each having a licensed capacity of over 50,000 litres (11,000 gal) a day. These are in addition to over seventy plants of various size now operating. A private sector plant in Jamaica has engaged in dairy development for several years, giving producers advice, making them loans, giving price incentives and providing assistance in other ways to increase production so that the volume of this plant's operation might expand.

Milk quality and its conservation

As milk is drawn from the udder it is liable immediately to absorb odours from the atmosphere and the utensils in which it is handled. Cooled milk absorbs such odours much more slowly.

The environment, the health of the producing animal and the manner in which she and her milk are cared for are the principal factors that determine the quality of market milk. Quality involves the flavour and odour of the milk, its bacterial content and its physical and chemical properties.

A healthy cow with a healthy udder produces milk containing comparatively few bacteria. The first two or three streams of milk from a teat contain more bacteria than later ones during milking (Mahanta, 1962) and for this reason these first streams are often discarded. Ill-health of the cow or of her udder may result in her milk containing larger numbers of micro-organisms, including those associated with the pathological condition of the cow. Most often pathogenic bacteria entering the milk before it is drawn from the udder are, or are closely related to, the causative organisms of tuberculosis (*Myco-bacterium tuberculosis*), brucellosis (*Brucella abortus*) and mastitis (*Streptococcus agalactiae*; *Staphlococcus aureus*). Some of these may be pathogenic to man. Many kinds of micro-organisms enter milk from external sources, i.e. from outside the udder. These may also include species which are pathogenic.

Precautions must be taken, therefore, which assure milk being safe as a human food.

The milking area should be clean, free of dust and well ventilated. A clean milking animal is essential to the production of milk that is not contaminated with odours, dirt and bacteria.

The water buffalo is especially prone to wallow in wet muddy areas, ponds, lakes and streams. At milking time buffalo cows, more often than Zebu or temperate-type cows, may be covered with the filth and stench of a stagnant mudhole. Buffaloes must be thoroughly washed and allowed to dry off before each milking; this may also be necessary, and it is certainly advisable, for temperate-type and Zebu cows.

The flavour of some plants and other materials a cow may feed upon will pass to her milk and butter fat (Major, 1967). The contamination caused by onion and some of its close relatives found in many pastures illustrates this very well. Forage plants and weeds causing flavour defects in milk and cream are numerous and species differ from place to place as well as seasonally in any one place.

Such physiologically abnormal taints (Davis, 1955) result from volatile materials which may be largely removed from milk or cream by vaporization. Commercial equipment for this purpose is used in several dairies in tropical countries. Such equipment usually consists of a specially designed pasteurizer or sterilizer, in which vapours from the heated product are removed by condensation. Direct steam injection may be employed for heating; this introduces some water into the milk which is removed by slightly more evaporation. Not only does the additional evaporation return the product to its original water content, but it also increases the degree of taint removal. Heating in a vacuum is common in such equipment for it increases the possible effectiveness of the treatment and makes possible the use of lower temperatures.

The vacreator, originally designed in New Zealand, is an example of a commercial unit which effectively employs direct steam injection in a vacuum, to pasteurize and deodorize milk or cream (Davis, 1955; Lambert, 1970). This unit processes the product in three stages. In the first, milk or cream is heated in a low vacuum of approximately 630 mm mercury pressure, to 90° to 96°C (194° to 205°F) by direct steam injection. The product then passes to the second stage which is operated at a vacuum of between 380 and 250 mm mercury pressure. Because of the heat content of the product on entering this stage, it boils vigorously and atomizes to a large extent, both processes increasing the vaporization of water and of the taint component present; the product also cools suddenly to about 71° to 81·5°C (160° to 180°F). Finally, it passes on to the third stage which is operated at a vacuum of between 75 and 50 mm mercury pressure. Again the product boils vigorously and atomizes, further vaporization takes place and the product cools to between 32° and 43°C (90° and 100°F). The vapours created in the second and third stages, containing water and most, if not all, of the taint component, are removed by condensation.

In countries where dairying has long been of considerable commercial importance, utensils are known to be the source of a major part of the bacterial contamination of raw milk. In tropical areas milk utensils may often heavily contaminate their contents. Proper utensil sanitation is comparatively difficult and expensive in tropical homes and villages. The easiest and cheapest – but not the most dependable – procedures for washing these utensils involve using whatever materials are immediately available at little, preferable at no, currency cost and with a minimum expenditure of time and effort in planning and programming. Organized dairies take considerable care and incur a great deal of expense in the proper sanitation of their utensils and equipment – competition, public health regulations, business reputation, the demands of urban society generally and other factors require this. However, tradition and limited facilities still largely determine how utensils are washed and cared for in tropical homes and villages. The rural economy of many tropical areas is such that it is practically impossible for the people to purchase any materials for sanitation purposes. Water from a well or stream is used. The palm of the bare hand or a bunch of grass or other plant fibre may serve as a brush. Often mud, or the ashes of either wood or dried cow dung, are used as an abrasive. These ashes, because they contain certain chemicals, also serve as a mild detergent, whereas ashes from other sources do not possess these same qualities. After washing and scouring with these materials and methods, the utensils are usually rinsed in the clear water available and allowed to drain, in the sunlight if convenient. In the rural homes and villages of the tropics utensils are rarely sterilized by hot water, steam or chemicals.

Unfortunately, utensils are frequently made by hand, with seams, overlaps and rivet heads that inhibit proper cleaning, particularly of their interior or milk-contact surfaces. Joints may be soldered or otherwise closed, but the utensils soon get dented and bent during use, opening these joints to the entry of milk solids that provide constant and prolonged refuge for growing bacteria. The putrefaction and decomposition products and the great numbers of bacteria in these cracks, crevices and corners may seriously, and very quickly indeed, adversely affect the quality of milk. At times, however, utensils which are made of seamless construction from suitable materials, scoured well with wood ashes, rinsed and placed to drain for several hours in a dry protected place in the hot sun, might be practically clean bacteriologically.

In some areas during parts of the year the atmospheric humidity is so high that a utensil may not really dry out from one day to the next. A thin film of moisture on the surface of the utensil provides an environment in which bacteria may survive for many hours if the temperature is suitable. If the film contains bacterial food such as milk constituents, then the micro-organisms might grow and reproduce extremely rapidly.

Under these conditions, if utensils are not sterilized immediately before they are used, they may be sources of a considerable degree of bacterial contamination of milk. Not only is it necessary to wash and clean the utensils properly, i.e. to remove from them all milk and other organic solids, it is also imperative that they be sterilized to destroy any living micro-organisms which may be present on their surfaces; it is also advisable to dry them out thoroughly so that any organisms entering after washing may not find conditions suitable to their growth and reproduction or to their survival.

Properly constructed, cleaned and sterilized utensils do not constitute important sources of contamination of milk with undesirable odours, dirt or bacteria. Small numbers of bacteria do not immediately affect the flavour and odour of milk or its physical and chemical properties. Where conditions are favourable, most bacteria common to milk reproduce very rapidly; often within an hour or two, such bacterial activity may adversely affect the milk quality. High atmospheric temperature encourages rapid growth of most bacteria which may be present in milk. In the absence of adequate refrigeration which can prevent bacterial growth, or of heat sterilization of the milk which destroys any bacteria present, quality may deteriorate very rapidly. The production of good-quality milk obviously involves special difficulties in areas of high atmospheric temperature and high humidity so common in the humid tropics.

Cooling freshly drawn milk reduces its tendency to absorb flavours or odours from the atmosphere or the utensils. Cooling also suppresses the growth of any bacteria which may be present. It is advisable, therefore, to cool fresh milk as soon as possible to 4·5°C (40°F) or less, and to hold it at this temperature.

Most tropical countries do not manufacture mechanical refrigerators in large numbers; many manufacture none. These units must often be imported when needed. Exchange and import regulations, as well as the expenses of freight and duty, contribute greatly to the very limited use of refrigeration for preserving milk and milk products in such countries. Costs of operating refrigeration compressors are increased by the high air and water temperatures in many tropical areas. Such temperatures reduce the efficiency of the condenser; high air temperatures also increase refrigeration losses. A given compressor must operate relatively longer under tropical conditions to produce a ton of ice, or its equivalent in the form of cold storage or refrigeration. The standard of living of many people in these countries is also an important limiting factor in the use of refrigeration. Ice, where available, tends to be relatively expensive. Proper refrigeration helps in preserving and making available to the consuming public good-quality milk and milk products. This is particularly true wherever atmospheric conditions are conducive to rapid bacterial activity, as they are in a large part of the tropics. Mechanical refrigeration is used to some extent for processing and preserving milk throughout tropical countries, but its proper and adequate use is primarily confined to the largest processing plants. This means of protecting the quality of milk is substantially non-existent in the homes and villages of producers, in the channels of distribution and in the homes of consumers in many of these areas.

At times milk is preserved in such areas by heating. While heat treatment, especially boiling, may slightly reduce the nutritive value of milk, it is a means of preserving milk or cream for a somewhat longer time than might otherwise be possible without refrigeration. At times the milk is transported while hot; best results seem to be obtained when the milk temperature is about 71°C (160°F) or higher. However, trouble may still result from thermophilic bacteria, i.e. bacteria which grow well at about 60°C (140°F). Milk which is heated to 70°C (158°F) or more is likely to cool slightly during holding or during transit even in hot tropical weather. The temperature then is ideal for thermophilic contaminants. In dry weather the keeping quality of milk may be increased slightly by the cooling effects of the evaporation of water from wet cloth covers on the individual milk cans. If these covers are moistened sufficiently often they may help noticeably in a hot, dry atmosphere, but not in a humid atmosphere. This principle can be used for a cloth cover over a cart or lorry carrying milk in cans. Other types of covers are used on motor vans to shade cans or bottles of milk from the sun and to protect them from rain, and perhaps also from dust during transit. In some areas these van bodies are insulated.

Insulated road tankers are frequently employed where a rural collecting centre is equipped with chilling facilities. The use of insulated rail tankers in India is mentioned elsewhere. Brazil is reported to have had one or more such rail tankers in use since 1955 (Assis and Frensel, 1966).

There are available special insulated cans having an ice chamber which may be filled with ice and inserted into the milk to keep it cool during transit or holding. Such cans are not generally used because they are quite expensive, although they are effective; furthermore, ice is unavailable or expensive in most tropical areas.

The bactericidal property of freshly drawn milk has been recognized. The suggestion made in earlier editions of this book, that this characteristic is comparatively strong in the milk of indigenous cows in some tropical areas, has not been widely accepted. However, there are at least three factors which assist in the preservation of freshly drawn milk for a few hours, even without cooling. While not necessarily in order of importance, these are:

1. The bactericidal property of freshly drawn milk;
2. The fact that bacteria entering such milk from external sources pass through a lag phase in their activity before growing rapidly; and
3. The very high atmospheric temperatures often prevailing in tropical areas tend to raise the milk temperature above that which is most suitable to rapid growth of the micro-organisms present in the milk.

It is not unknown, for example, for such milk to keep slightly longer in a particular area when the atmospheric temperature is around 45°C (113°F) than when it is between 30° and 40°C (86° and 104°F).

It is common practice to fix the time of milking of the cows according to the time interval required to move the milk, by whatever means available, to the consumer, and the time of day at which the consumer desires to use the milk. Most consumers are unable to keep a quantity of milk in the home more than a very short while – in some circumstances as little as an hour or two – consequently, they often buy small quantities of milk at frequent intervals. Lack of refrigeration, in addition to other factors, thus forces the delivery of milk to the customer, whether at the home, at shops or at sales depots, as often as twice each day or fourteen times each week in some instances. This may indeed be expensive. In many markets in industrialized societies delivery only two or three times each week is now standard practice. Producing milk in the home by maintaining one or more cows, or buying milk from a man who drives his cow along and partially milks her at the door of each of his customers, are both means by which to reduce the time interval between the production and consumption of milk. These methods of procuring milk may also offer some protection against adulteration, although the latter method is not conducive to high production.

The composition of milk

The natural variation in the physical and chemical properties of milk is significant. The control of market quality of milk and milk products is made difficult by such variation. This is especially so where milk from two or more species is commonly used. In such a situation, the preparation and enforcement of public health legislation are particularly complicated.

The presence of two or more kinds of milk in tropical areas makes necessary dairy legislation and control measures having special implications in managing the procurement, processing and distribution of milk and milk products.

India's legal definition of milk reads: 'Milk is the secretion derived from the complete milking of healthy milch animals. It shall be free from colostrum. Milk of different classes are: buffalo milk, cow's milk, goat or sheep milk....' The definition suggested in the United States for local ordinances says: 'Milk is... the lacteal secretion, practically free from colostrum, obtained by the complete milking of one or more cows.... The word "milk" shall be interpreted to include goat milk.' India provides for three classes of whole genuine milk, the United States for only one.

The gross chemical composition of certain kinds or classes of milk is shown in Table 14.1.

Table 14.1 *Gross composition of the milk of several species*

Species	Percentage composition						
	Fat	Protein	Lactose	Ash	Solids-not-fat	Total solids	Moisture
Temperate-type cow[1]	3·7	3·2	4·8	0·72	8·7	12·4	87·6
Zebu cow[2]	5·4	3·2	4·6	0·74	8·5	13·9	86·1
Buffalo cow[2]	7·4	3·8	4·9	0·78	9·5	16·9	83·1
Goat[1]	4·0	3·4	3·6	0·78	7·8	11·8	88·2
Ewe[1]	8·5	6·7	4·3	0·96	12·0	20·5	79·5
Camel[1]	2·9	3·9	5·4	0·77	10·1	13·0	87·0
Mare[1]	1·2	2·0	6·3	0·30	8·6	9·8	90·2
Human[3]	3·3	1·3	6·8	0·20	8·3	11·6	88·4

Sources: (1) Davies (1939a). (2) Schneider, *et al.* (1948). (3) Davies (1939b).

Apart from differences in the gross composition, there are also specific physical differences between the milk of the temperate-type cow, the Zebu and the buffalo. Species and breeds of dairy animals differ in their ability to remove carotene from their feed and put it into their body and milk fats (Lambert, 1970). Buffalo milk fat is almost pure white, with little or no visible natural yellow colour; the carotene content of buffalo milk is only a fraction of that of Zebu milk (Singh *et al.*, 1963). Consequently, the milk from the water buffalo is grey-white in colour, having a distinct opaque appearance most easily noticed when this milk is spread in a thin film across a clean glass surface. This colour and opaqueness helps one distinguish buffalo milk from that of either the temperate-type cow or of the Zebu cow. Zebu milk does not contain as much yellow colour as is found in milk of temperate-type cows, although enough is present to give Zebu milk a slight yellowish-white colour. Zebu cream, therefore, has a very slight yellow colour, while that of the buffalo is definitely white. The fat globules in buffalo milk are slightly larger than those of Zebu milk, and its curd is often slightly harder.

The smaller fat globules, the lower fat content and the slightly softer curd may give Zebu milk certain, but distinctly limited, advantages over buffalo milk as a food for the human infant and those who are senescent or who suffer from certain serious digestive ailments; for these same reasons goat milk may be slightly better than Zebu milk, but only for these reasons and only for these special groups of persons. For most normal people, however, because of its higher content of most solid constituents, especially fat, buffalo milk is a distinctly better food than other milks.

Preparation of milk for the market

Retail sale of bulk milk, often but not always boiled (Assis and Frensel, 1966; Prakash, 1966), is no longer so common as it was in the past. Consumers are rapidly coming to require that their milk be pasteurized and packaged (Graff, 1966; Vijai and Saraswat, 1970). Glass bottles are probably the most common container for retail packaged milk in tropical markets, but plastic and paper packages are being used.

Milk is heat sterilized in glass bottles in certain tropical dairies. The treatment involves heating the sealed bottles of homogenized milk to 104·5° to 110°C (220° to 230°F) for 20 to 30 minutes, sufficient to assure that it keeps for 7 days or more (Davis, 1955). Other methods of sterilizing milk are in use. Ultra-high-temperature (UHT) treatment of milk is a relatively new process by which milk is heat treated to increase both its safety as a food and its keeping quality; aseptic packaging usually follows this treatment. The milk is heated to between 130° and 135°C (256° and 275°F) for a few seconds. Several methods of using steam for this purpose are possible (Burton, 1965). The Tetra-Pak is a satisfactory package for this milk (Burton, 1965).

Sterilization as soon as possible after production, and as nearly as possible at the site of production, might obviate some of the need for large investment in refrigeration facilities which would otherwise be required, but are not yet available in many tropical regions. However, the expense of the sterilization process and the costly technical control which it requires are deterrents to the widespread use of this treatment of market milk, as the subsistence level of the economy makes expense a limiting factor.

During the last 25 years large quantities of skimmed-milk powder or non-fat dried milk solids have been imported into developing areas. This powder is reconstituted and used to increase the local supply of fluid milk. To make the reconstituted skim-milk more palatable and more nutritious, yet to make a product less costly than whole milk, reconstituted skim-milk is increasingly being mixed with whole milk, especially buffalo milk. Standardizing or toning milk by such methods is now a legalized and common practice in some countries. For example, India now permits the sale of the classes of milk shown in Table 14.2.

Table 14.2   *The legal minimum composition of various classes of milk sold in India*

Class of milk	Minimum composition (%)	
	Milk fat	Milk solids not fat
Buffalo*	5·0–6·0[†]	9·0
Cow*	3·0–4·0[†]	8·5
Goat or sheep*	3·0–3·5[†]	9·0
Standardized[‡]	4·5	8·5
Recombined[‡]	3·0	8·5
Toned[‡]	3·0	8·5
Double toned[‡]	1·5	9·0
Skimmed*	0·5[§]	8·7

* May be sold raw, pasteurized, boiled, flavoured or sterilized.
[†] The range reflects different standards between the States within India.
[‡] Pasteurization essential.
[§] Maximum permissible level.

The popularity of toned and double-toned milk in Bombay, India, may be indicated by the fact that in 1969 the Greater Bombay Milk Scheme distributed an average of close to 120,000 litres (26,000 gal) of toned milk and 12,000 litres (2,640 gal) of double-toned milk each day. The daily volume of milk processed in this scheme that year was nearly 420,000 litres (92,400 gal) of all types of milk, as mentioned earlier.

Filled milk has become popular in the Philippines (Medora, 1971; Wagan, 1970). Israel used this product until 1959 when vegetable fats were no longer permitted, so butterfat was again used (Guttfeld and Rosenfeld, 1966); thereafter recombined milk and whole milk were distributed.

Organizing dairy operations

Tropical people are gaining greater understanding of the special values of milk and milk products for meeting their nutritional needs. Procurement, processing and distribution of milk in their markets are developing as more, larger and better organized milk plants are established in the cities and towns to meet the growing demand. Most countries have given some attention to planning and control measures intended to assure the development of both production and processing in the local dairy industry, the control of product quality and often some degree of price regulation. Public health regulation of the dairy industry and its products is also commencing in many countries.

Private dairy companies or corporations have played an important part in the expansion of the dairy industry in several countries. The extension education programme of a private dairy in Jamaica was referred to previously. In India there are now fifteen dairy operations in the private sector; six of these each has a licensed capacity of 1,000 t (984 tons) or more a year and have commenced operations since about 1965. Three privately owned processing plants were operating in Jordan by 1965, handling fluid milk. The Philippines has several private plants which pasteurize or sterilize and bottle milk, and make some cottage cheese and ice-cream. Some of these plants produce filled milk products using imported dried skim-milk and locally produced coconut oil. Private dairies in Taiwan make milk powder and condensed milk; bottled pasteurized milk and 'lactic acid beverage' are also sold by these dairies in Taipei.

In some of the countries, cooperative societies have been encouraged to play a greater part in dairy development and many operations in this sector are working successfully. Milk-processing plants in Israel receive good-quality farm cooled milk by insulated tankers mainly from villages and *kibbutzim* or large communal farms. The dairies at the *kibbutzim* and also a majority of the transport organizations are owned and managed cooperatively (Gal, 1972). Cow and sheep milk are kept separate throughout. Milk is pasteurized or sterilized and is sold mainly in glass bottles. It is also used for making cheese and cultured milks that include yogurt, which may be flavoured.

The largest dairy in Kenya is owned by a cooperative society; its main plant is in Nairobi. Over half of the milk handled by this organization is pasteurized and much of it packed in sealed cartons. The largest company in Uganda is a cooperative, selling milk throughout that country, mostly in sealed cartons. It also manufactures a small amount of ghee.

This society markets butter, cheese, dried milk, cream and condensed milk, nearly all these products being imported from Kenya.

The Kaira District Cooperative Milk Producers' Union, Ltd, in India has been referred to; it is probably the largest milk products plant in the tropical world. Its licensed capacity is stated to be nearly 24,800 t (24,408 tons) of milk products each year. Fluid milk is not packaged by this Union. Another cooperative dairy, very similar to the Kaira Union in its organization and management, started production in 1965 at Mehsana (Desai, 1971).

Significant developments in dairying in many tropical countries have come in the public sector. These include increases in the number and size of government-owned and operated plants and in the regulation of many dairy operations through planning, licensing, import and market controls, provision of financial aid and other means. Several public sector plants in India, including Worli, have been mentioned. A government dairy at Mariakani, Kenya, assisted by the United Nations Development Programme, produces powder, ghee and cheese, and by 1966 was developing rapidly, according to the Kenya National Dairy Committee.

Some other examples of public sector participation in the dairy development include the following: production and consumption of milk in Puerto Rico increased threefold following a Milk Regulations Act passed about 15 years ago; dairy products and milk boards are functioning in Zambia and Uganda; and India established a new National Dairy Development Board in September 1965. In several other countries of Southeast Asia dairy development is being given some attention and assistance by local government.

Milk products

Tropical peoples developed many milk products peculiar to a local situation and climate. Several of these products have been made for generations and a few are important today in the dairy processing industry of particular areas. Milk products now common in world markets are also made in tropical dairy plants, primarily for domestic use. Attention is mainly directed in this section to the more important indigenous milk products.

In warm climates coagulation of milk might occur relatively soon because acid quickly develops in milk by bacterial action if the milk is not cooled. Early man observed that coagulated milk kept a little longer, was not usually harmful when used as a food, and had a flavour which he thought pleasant or which he could soon learn to enjoy. The nature of the spontaneous fermentations of milk varies from time to time and from place to place. Curd forms so universally if raw milk is held unprotected for a few hours at temperatures characteristic of warm climates or hot seasons that it was surely one of the first products of milk known to man, perhaps even the first.

Coagulation of milk by action of acid may be said to take place in three stages. In the first stage small concentrations of acid develop, but they produce no appreciable visual affect. The milk remains liquid, but acquires an acid flavour and odour and a lower heat stability which may be indicated by coagulation on heating. In the second stage, as the concentration of acid increases, the stability of the milk is so adversely affected that at ordinary temperatures a distinct visual change may be observed as the milk coagulates. This is indicated by the milk changing to a gel-like or semi-solid condition, sometimes very suddenly. The third stage will follow, either on heating the coagulated milk or on the further development of the concentration of acid. A distinct shrinking and solidifying of the curd takes place as it separates from the whey – a nearly clear, watery liquid. Certain enzymes, produced by bacteria or obtained from other sources, will also coagulate milk to form a curd.

Man gradually learned to influence the natural fermentations of milk by changing and controlling the conditions under which milk was handled until it coagulated. This contributed ultimately to the wide use of fermented milk and its products as human food, possibly even before the Phoenician era (Kosikowski, 1966). Great numbers of these products are now known and relished in the tropics (Bhattacharya and Srinivasan, 1967; Davies, 1939a; Mahanta, 1964b). They include the full unbroken curd; the mixed curd, usually broken finely enough to give a thick liquid product like cultured or artificial buttermilk; the drained or semi-dried curd; the whey; and many forms and modifications of each.

Curd

Curd may be made from whole milk or skim-milk. In a tropical home or village the milk is usually boiled, and allowed to cool to atmospheric, i.e. to incubation, temperature. It is then inoculated and incubated until the desired fermentations are complete (Davies, 1939a). Curd made one day is usually used as an inoculum or starter for making curd the next day. In addition to acid fermentation that gives a clean, sharp, acid flavour, other fermentations are often encouraged to assure other flavour characteristics according to local conditions and preferences. A fine texture and firm body which does not whey-off easily are also desired in the curd.

The unbroken or solid curd is greatly enjoyed plain, or it may be flavoured, usually with sugar, salt, fruit juices or jam. It may also be coloured. A refreshing drink or beverage is made from the mixed or broken curd (Warner, 1951). It is mixed with an approximately equal volume of water and flavoured to taste, or coloured. Essences and sometimes spices are used for flavouring solid curd in addition to the items mentioned above. Curd is a common ingredient of numerous fine dishes or preparations included in the diet in many tropical homes (Bhanu-murthi and Trehan, 1970; Rangappa, 1965; Warner, 1951).

The practice of mixing fruit products with curd has spread in recent years to temperate countries. The dairy industry in several of these countries has begun to manufacture and distribute large quantities of fruit-flavoured yogurt (Gillies, 1971).

In western Asia and in Africa, nomadic people who move their animals over large areas to provide them with adequate grazing, and people who regularly travel with caravans across large expanses of desert, continue by tradition to depend upon milk from their animals as one of their main foods. Some of this milk is used fresh, but sour milk, fermented milks, curd and cheese are commonly made from the remainder. Some curds are dried and saved for lean seasons when they are reconstituted and eaten. Ghee is also made and used – small amounts of this may be sold in the local markets near a route being followed. Cow, sheep, goat and camel milks are generally used; mare milk is utilized in some regions of Asia.

Cheese

Products of the third stage of acid and/or enzyme coagulation are usually called cheese. Several hundred kinds and varieties of cheese are known. Most cheese does not ordinarily keep for long periods of time in areas or seasons of high atmospheric temperatures without special facilities. For this reason cheese is not so common an article of diet in the tropics as in the temperate parts of the world. There are, however, several kinds of cheese made and enjoyed in hot countries. Domiati and Kariesh cheese are well known in Egypt (Hamdy, 1970; Imail and Elnahta, 1964; Kosikowski, 1966). In the Indian sub-continent several soft, high-moisture cheeses such as Surati, Dacca and Bandal are made. The latter two may be smoked (Davies, 1939a; Warner, 1951). Indigenous cheeses named Requeijao and Minas (Assis and Frensel, 1966) are made in Brazil.

Surati cheese is made by standardizing milk to 6 per cent fat and heating it to 77·5°C (172°F) for about 20 seconds; the milk is then cooled to 35°C (95°F) and approximately 14 g (0·5 oz) of an active acid starter, preferably *Streptococcus lactis*, is added for each 45 kg (100 lb) of milk, followed by sufficient rennet solution to give a firm coagulum in about one hour. By use of a spoon, thin spoon-sized pieces of the curd are dipped into a small basket. During dipping each piece is placed flat, one over another, to form layers. Salt is added to the curd throughout the dipping, at a rate equal to about 2 per cent of the weight of the milk. During draining the cheese is turned several times by first inverting an empty basket over that containing the curd and turning the two together. The whey is collected. After the prints are well formed and firm they are immersed in the whey where they are allowed to ripen at room temperature for up to a day and a half, according to the flavour and body desired. This process gives about a 40 per cent yield of cheese from standardized milk (Warner, 1951).

Butter and ghee

Acid-coagulated whole milk, particularly buffalo milk with its high fat content, may be churned to produce types of butter and buttermilk (Davies, 1939a; Mahanta, 1964a). An Indian name for this butter, i.e. '*deshi*, country or cooking butter', indicates that it is usually made by a village method and is intended for cooking purposes. The buttermilk obtained by this churning is generally used in the home as a food beverage. It contains much of the lactose, protein and ash, and some of the fat of the whole milk from which it was made (Warner, 1951). *Deshi* buttermilk is an excellent food. Throughout its preparation, therefore, it should be protected from undesirable bacterial contamination to assure its safety for food use.

Deshi butter is commonly used in homes in tropical Africa and Asia for making *ghee*. The butter is heated in an open pan to evaporate its moisture. The non-fat milk solids then settle to the bottom and the butterfat or ghee can be decanted off practically free of any of the other constituents. The heating should continue initially only until active boiling ceases, indicating that the free moisture has been separated from the fat by evaporation. This boiling will take place at approximately 100°C (212°F). Heating should continue thereafter with considerable caution. During the second part of the heating process only very slow boiling should be permitted and no more than slight foaming should occur if the control is adequate. The temperature of the butterfat during this time should not exceed 118° to 123°C (244° to 253°F). This higher range of temperature, compared to that during earlier heating, results from the absence of free moisture. Great quantities of heat are needed to change water into steam. This consumes much of the heat during the first stage of heating. Therefore, during the second stage of the heating the temperature is free to rise still higher, for the butterfat is itself then receiving almost all the heat. Skilled ghee-makers exercise the greatest possible care at this time to prevent excessive heating. Sufficient heating of the product is indicated by the non-fat solids drying out to a light amber colour. Even slight overheating at this stage will give a burnt flavour and a dark colour to the ghee, both undesirable in fine-quality market ghee.

Ghee may also be made from unsalted and uncoloured factory butter, or directly from cream (De and Srinivasan, 1958). These two methods are more common in organized dairy operations. Culturing the cream for making the butter or for heating directly is said to improve ghee flavour.

During the churning of the butter, a certain type of 'separation' of fat and the non-fat solids takes place. The physical forces that hold the fat in globule form, and dispersed throughout the serum of the curd or the cream, break down during churning to give a separation of the fat as it gathers in the form of butter granules. The serum no longer holds the fat as it did and the two fractions become more distinct or separate. This change in the product reduces the heat required for making ghee from butter as compared to that from cream. Churning cream to produce factory butter gives a greater degree of this change than does churning curd to produce *deshi* butter. Fuel requirements and the duration of heating of cream in making ghee, therefore, may be significantly greater than those for deshi butter, and those in turn somewhat greater than for factory butter.

For ghee-making, butter made by churning cream has not only the advantage of this 'separation' of the fat and non-fat solids, but also has a high fat content and comparatively low non-fat solids and moisture contents. Such butter, if not for sale as such, may contain over 80 per cent of fat, 1 to $1\frac{1}{2}$ per cent of milk solids-not-fat, and 16 to 20 per cent of moisture. Cream may contain only up to 50 to 60 per cent of butterfat, often somewhat less, but 5 to 7 per cent of non-fat solids and as much as 60 per cent or more of moisture.

The first stage of heating of cream is prolonged by the relatively large amounts of moisture and non-fat solids present. Furthermore, the undisturbed physical condition of the fat and other solids of cream complicate this part of the *ghee*-making process. Cream may boil up and froth and sputter during heating, making special care essential to prevent these troubles and the fat losses they may cause. Cream requires longer heating at this time because of its high moisture content.

The second stage of heating of cream may also require more time and fuel, and more caution, than that of factory butter, because of the higher content of non-fat solids. Not only is longer heating required in order adequately to dry out these extra solids, but they are often present in larger and thicker particles, from which it is more difficult for the moisture to escape than it is from smaller or thinner curd particles.

Experimentally, cream has been washed as a means of reducing the foaming and sputtering during earlier heating and the danger of overheating during later heating. It was hoped that this practice might reduce fuel requirements. Washing involves adding sufficient water to the cream to restore the fat content to approximately that of whole milk, then reseparating this mixture. The added water dilutes the solids in the non-fat fraction of the cream and most of these are then removed on reseparation. The addition of water and reseparation may be repeated a second time. Washed cream is not so likely to froth and foam during heating and contains very little non-fat solids. Fat losses during heating may be noticeably reduced, and the final heating more easily controlled.

An advantage of heating cream directly for ghee-making is that it avoids the extra processing and possible fat losses of churning. Washing cream, however, involves extra processing and fat losses during reseparation.

Induced stratification (De and Srinivasan, 1958; Ray, 1955) may conserve fuel during the first stage of heating when making ghee. This procedure is most effective with factory butter. The butter or cream is heated in a pan or kettle having a drain cock or valve in its bottom. This product is held at about 80°C (176°F) until it separates into two layers, the fat above and the water and most of the non-fat solids below. This may take 30 to 45 minutes, depending on the size of the batch. As much as possible of the water and non-fat solids layer is then drained off from beneath the fat. Heating then proceeds in the usual way.

Ghee made for use in the village home and not for sale might contain 2 or 3 per cent moisture, possibly more; *deshi* butter in such cases may have 20 to 30 per cent moisture (Davies, 1939a). Regulations in India require that for market purposes ghee shall contain not more than 0·3 per cent moisture; *deshi* butter, if for sale as such, at least 76 per cent of butterfat.

Products comparable to ghee and recently developed in temperate countries such as anhydrous or dry butterfat (Gunnis, 1967) and butter oil (Jenness and Patton, 1969) are not often made as yet in most tropical countries.

Butterfat deteriorates like any other organic material. However, it usually does so more slowly than other solid constituents of milk, except possibly some parts of the ash fraction. Butterfat changes chemically and physically if exposed to air, sunlight and/or certain metals from which dairy utensils and equipment are sometimes made, especially copper and iron. Some of these changes cannot be arrested or reversed after they have once started; most of them occur slowly. If ghee is made and packed so as to protect the butterfat throughout from such contacts, and also from bacterial contamination, it can be expected to keep several weeks without refrigeration. Because of its comparatively longer keeping quality, ghee is normally moved from a home or village to a market only once each week or so. Both its keeping quality and its high value per unit of weight permit its economic transport over comparatively long distances.

Factory butter for market is made in tropical countries wherever the cream supply is well organized in an intensive milk-producing area. The method used in manufacturing this product is familiar throughout the butter industry elsewhere, i.e. by batch-churning mechanically separated cream. Continuous butter-making procedures have not yet been adopted widely by the dairy industry in the tropics.

Butter is packaged for sale in 'prints' which are generally rectangular and which may be wrapped with parchment paper or in a parchment and foil laminated wrap with the foil outside. Wrapped prints may sometimes be placed in a waxed or plastic-coated cardboard carton. In many tropical areas butter is tinned. Butter requires refrigeration so as to preserve it and prevent it from melting. If it is not tinned it may flow out of the package if it melts. Refrigerated transport vehicles and retail sales cabinets are becoming more common in many cities in tropical areas and so fine-quality packet butter is consequently more widely available than it was a few years ago. In the shops of small towns and villages and at times in larger cities, packet butter may be held immersed in water on the sales counter until it is sold. This practice usually keeps the butter within the package, but contributes to rapid bacterial growth both within the butter and on its surface, as well as to very considerable further bacterial contamination of the surface of the product.

If made and packaged under conditions which are highly aseptic, tinned butter made from pasteurized cream may keep several weeks without chemical or bacterial deterioration. A physical defect, however, frequently appears in tinned butter as a result of the high temperatures to which it may be exposed in storage, in transit, in the market or in the home. Butter is likely to melt at 38°C (100°F). Should butter melt, it separates into fat and water fractions or layers inside the tin. Butter which has physically broken down in this way will not return automatically to its original physical condition, nor can the water readily be remixed into the fat as it was in the original butter. This reduces the market quality of tinned butter.

Chhena and khoa

Two products of milk made mainly in Asia, i.e. *chhena* and *khoa*, are primarily for use in sweets (Rastogi *et al.*, 1966). The first of these is closely related to cheese and sometimes called 'edible casein'.

Chhena, or *chhana*, is made by bringing a small quantity of cow milk quickly to a boil – up to 1·8 kg (4 lb) seems most suitable (Davies, 1939a). Buffalo milk is usually not used for making *chhena*. As the milk boils, or immediately after lifting it off the fire or stove while boiling, sufficient sour whey or lime juice and occasionally a strong citric-acid solution is mixed in to coagulate the milk. Complete coagulation is desired, but an excessive acid flavour will result from even a slight surplus of the coagulant. The *chhena* or curd is then recovered by draining off the whey through a cloth. Often the curd is pressed several hours to reduce its moisture content still further before it is used. Persons of Bengal origin particularly enjoy sweets made from *chhena*, such as the *rasgulla*, also called *rasogolla*.

Khoa is a form of condensed or dried milk. It is made by rapidly boiling milk in an open pan until the volume of milk is reduced 75 or 80 per cent. The milk must be stirred vigorously and constantly scraped from the bottom of the pan during boiling. There must be no scorching or charring of the milk solids whatsoever, neither burning of the protein nor caramelizing of the lactose, as these greatly damage the *khoa* flavour and detract from its appearance. Both are defects in market *khoa*. On cooling, this product is often as hard as Cheddar cheese and has a crystalline texture. Quick cooling gives a comparatively fine texture by producing smaller lactose crystals throughout the body of the *khoa*; slow cooling gives a coarse texture. A fine texture is preferred. If made from buffalo milk, *khoa* has a greyish-white colour; if made from Zebu milk, its colour may be slightly yellowish.

Standard methods of the manufacture of several products indigenous to tropical areas are not widely adopted either because they are not required under public health regulations or because competition makes them uneconomic. Indigenous tropical dairy products may not be of such uniform composition as are dairy products in the world's markets. Davies (1939a) indicated that the composition of milk curd is similar to that of the milk from which it is made. He stated that *deshi* buttermilk may contain 0·1 to 1·0 per cent fat, 3·3 to 3·5 per cent protein, 4·7 to 5·3 per cent lactose, and 0·70 to 0·75 per cent ash. Some of this variation results from the use of Zebu, buffalo or mixed milk. He also indicated that in *chhena* the fat may vary from 25 to 35 per cent, protein from 15 to 20 per cent, lactose from 2·0 to 2·5 per cent, and ash from 0·3 to 0·4 per cent. Standard *chhena*, however, should contain not less than 15 per cent of fat and not more than 70 per cent of moisture. *Khoa* may have 25 to 30 per cent protein and up to 50 per cent moisture (Rastogi *et al.*, 1966). As it is made by evaporating water from whole milk, the ratio of one solid to another will be similar in *khoa* to that between the same two solids in the original milk.

Condensed milk

Condensed milk is made by concentrating milk by removing much of its water by evaporation. Whole milk or skim-milk is used, whole milk being usually standardized before evaporation to assure compliance with legal requirements. Sugar may or may not be added before condensing. Condensed milk was first made by Appert in France; its commercial production was started in 1856 by Borden in the United States (Hunziker, 1949). Brazil began the manufacture of this milk product in 1913. One of the oldest condenseries continuing to operate at present in the tropics was started in Jamaica in 1944. A small condensery was also operating at about this time in Lahore, Pakistan.

India now has four plants each licensed to produce from 750 to 6,000 t (736 to 5,905 tons) of sweetened condensed milk a year. That country requires sweetened condensed milk to contain not less than 9 per cent milk fat, 31 per cent total milk solids, and 40 per cent cane sugar; composition limits are also prescribed for condensed milk unsweetened or evaporated milk, condensed skimmed milk unsweetened or evaporated skimmed milk and condensed skimmed milk sweetened.

Sweetened condensed milk is usually retailed in tins containing 350 to 400 g (12 to 14 oz) of product. Unsweetened condensed milk may be tinned and then heat sterilized to assure its keeping quality. The high sugar content contributes to the keeping quality of sweetened condensed milk; the added sugar would caramelize, producing a serious defect in this product if it were heat sterilized.

Dried milk

Dried or powdered milk has become increasingly familiar in many tropical countries. In many of these areas it is now made, usually by one of two processes – roller or spray drying.

When made by the roll or roller process, milk is first partially concentrated, then dried in a thin film on the surface of a metal roller that is heated from the inside by steam. Several methods are used to ensure that the thickness of the milk film on the roller surface is as uniform as possible; this is important. Commonly two rollers are used, arranged so that between them they form a trough into which the milk flows and from which it is picked up by the roller surfaces as they move upwards and outwards while turning. The temperature at which the roller operates evaporates the water from the milk film, leaving on each roller a sheet of dried milk solids that is scraped off by means of a special knife.

Irregularities in the thickness of the milk film and other factors may give rise to improper heating of some portions of this milk film. Some browning often results from overheating, given irregularly coloured powder. The intense heating denatures some of the milk protein, reducing the solubility of this type of powder.

Spray-dried milk powder is also made from partially condensed milk. This milk is sprayed or atomized directly into a blast of hot dry air which forcibly carries the milk droplets across a drying chamber or cyclone while removing water by evaporation. This reduces each tiny droplet of milk to a particle of powder. Heat application in this method of drying is comparatively uniform. It is less variable in its intensity, and consequently somewhat less denaturing of the milk protein takes place. Overheating is not so liable to occur. These factors contribute to the relatively higher solubility of spray powder which is without the colour defects of roller-dried powder resulting from browning or charring of some of the milk solids. Spray-dried milk powder is more often used for human food purposes than is roller-dried powder.

Imports of non-fat dried milk solids, or skim-milk powder, have been increasing in many developing areas throughout the past 20 years or so. In the last decade the local production of this product has become important in several tropical areas. India now has thirteen plants licensed to produce up to a total of 30,480 t (29,970 tons) a year of milk powder. In 1970 eight of these plants were in production and others were under construction. Among these, the plant with the largest licensed capacity, 7,200 t (7,080 tons) a year, is the cooperative plant at Anand, mentioned earlier. Brazil has had national inspection of powdered milk production since 1961. The growing popularity of toned, double-toned, standardized, filled and recombined milks in several countries increases the demand for the domestic production of skim-milk powder. The cost of importing milk powder often makes its use too expensive, utilizing foreign exchange that is not always readily available to a developing economy.

Ice-cream

Ice-cream is greatly increasing in popularity in hot countries. A few manufacturers are equipped – generally with a batch freezer – to produce large volumes of this fine milk product. The hand-operated freezer, using ice and salt for cooling and freezing the ice-cream, is still common where small quantities are made. In several areas the sale of soft ice-cream is increasing particularly rapidly. The special shapes and sizes of hard ice-cream on sticks are very common, as are ice-cream cones. Ice-cream is also frequently sold in waxed paper or plastic cups. In certain areas local laws and ordinances effectively define the composition of ice-cream.

A frozen product resembling ice-cream is made in the homes and villages of India and Pakistan (Davies, 1939a; Warner, 1951). *Kulafi* mix contains milk, sugar and flour of either wheat, pulses or both; it is always flavoured and usually coloured. It is frozen in small covered containers, holding about 60 g (2 oz) in a cold ice-salt brine. Dry ice might be used for this. Traditionally the containers were made of tinned or galvanized iron, but waxed paper or plastic may now be used. The freezing is without agitation, giving a coarse texture that varies with the composition, particularly with the solids content. *Kulafi* is not made commercially on a large scale, but it is commonly served in the home as a dessert at a tea or dinner for small groups.

References

Anker-Ladefoged, A. V. (1953) Dairy economy in Ceylon under present conditions of production. *Trop. Agriculturist,* **109**, 257–66.

Assis, R. J. and Frensel, O. (1966) Dairy production and industry in Brazil. *Proc. 17th Int. Dairy Congr.,* **E F**, pp. 53–66.

Bhanumurthi, J. L. and Trehan, K. S. (1970) Preservation and bottling of buttermilk. *Ind. Dairyman,* **22**, 275–8.

Bhattacharya, D. C. and Srinivasan, M. R. (1967) New varieties of *dahi* (fermented whole milk). *Ind. Dairyman,* **19**, 35–8.

Burton, H. (1965) Utra-high-temperature processing and aseptic packaging in the dairy industry. Its basic principles and development. *J. Soc. Dairy Tech.,* **18**, 58–65.

Davies, W. L. (1939a) *Indian Indigenous Milk Products.* Thacker Spink: Calcutta.

Davies, W. L. (1939b). *The Chemistry of Milk* (2nd edn). Chapman and Hall: London.

Davis, J. G. (1955) *A Dictionary of Dairying* (2nd edn). Leonard Hill: London.

De, S. and Srinivasan, M. R. (1958) Production and Marketing of Ghee. Part 1. Production. Part 2. Marketing. *Ind. Dairyman,* **10**, 156–60, 165, 216–17, 220.

Desai, M. N. (1971) Co-operative dairying in Mehsana area of Gujarat. *Ind. Dairyman*, **23**, 34–9.

Elliott, R. B., Maxwell, G. M. and Vawser, N. (1967) Lactose maldigestion in Australian Aboriginal children. *Med. J. Austral.*, **i**, 46–9.

Flatz, G., Saengudom, C. and Sanguanbhokhai, T. (1969) Lactose intolerance in Thailand. *Nature (Lond.)*, **221**, 758–9.

Gal, S. (1972) Large dairy farms in Israel. *Ind. Dairyman*, **24**, 41–6.

Gillies, A. J. (1971) Flavoured yoghurt for the home. *Queensland Agric. J.*, **97**, 139–42.

Graff, J. (1966) Improvements in the production, collection and transport of raw milk in countries in the course of development. *Proc. 17th Int. Dairy Congr.*, **EF**, pp. 35–40.

Gunnis, L. F. (1967) Techniques for the production of anhydrous milk fat. Report Commission IV (Dairy Technique), *Int. Dairy Fed. Bull.* (6), 54 pp.

Guttfeld, M. and Rosenfeld, P. (1966) Recombined milk and dairy products from milk powder and vegetable fat in Israel and its significance for other developing countries. *Proc. 17th Int. Dairy Cong.*, **EF**, pp. 27–9.

Hamdy, A. (1970) The manufacture of Domiati cheese using a microbial rennet. *Proc. 18th Int. Dairy Congr.*, **I E**, 350.

Huang, S. S. and Bayless, T. M. (1968) Milk and lactose intolerance in healthy orientals. *Science*, **160**, 83–4.

Hunziker, O. F. (1949) *Condensed Milk and Milk Powder* (7th edn). Hunziker: La Grange, Illinois.

Imail, A. A. and Elnahta, A. (1964) The variation between buffalo's and cow's milk in 'Kariesh' cheese making. *Alex. J. agric. Res.*, **12**, 195–203.

Jenness, R. and Patton, S. (1969) *Principles of Dairy Chemistry.* Wiley Eastern: New Delhi.

Khurody, D. N. (1970) Role of world dairying in filling the protein gap. *Ind. Dairyman*, **22**, 234–41.

Kosikowski, F. (1966) *Cheese and Fermented Milk Foods.* Kosikowski: Ithaca, NY.

Lambert, L. M. (1970) *Modern Dairy Products.* Chemical Pub.: New York.

Mahanta, K. C. (1962) *Dairy Microbiology.* Kitabistan: Allahabad.

Mahanta, K. C. (1964a) *Handbook of Dairy Science.* Kitabistan: Allahabad.

Mahanta, K. C. (1964b) Some technological aspects of kumiss production. *Ind. J. Dairy Sci.*, **17**, 51–4.

Major, W. C. T. (1967) Butter freed from weed taints. *Queensland Agric. J.*, **93**, 754–6.

Mauger, J. C. (1965) *Report on the Development of the Dairy Industry in Uganda*, 31 pp. Milk Marketing Board: Thames Ditton, England.

Medora, P. S. (1971) Role of filled milk in the dairy development of the Philippines. *Ind. Dairyman*, **23**, 82–5.

Prakash, S. (1966) Quality control of fluid milk in tropical climates. *Ind. Dairyman*, **18**, 347–8.

Rangappa, K. S. (1965) '*Dahi Kusum*' or Indian ice-cream. *Ind. Dairyman*, **17**, 13–15.

Rastogi, M. K., Verma, I. S. and Paul, J. (1966) Nutritive appraisal of some Indian indigenous milk sweets. *Proc. 17th Int. Dairy Congr.*, **EF**, pp. 273–8.

Ray, S. C. (1955) *Pre-stratification Method of Ghee Making.* ICAR Res. Series No. 8. Ind. Coun. Agric. Res.: New Delhi.

Rosensweig, N. S. (1969) Adult human milk intolerance and intestinal lactose deficiency. A review. *J. Dairy Sci.*, **52**, 585–7.

Schneider, B. H., Warner, J. N., Dharni, I. D. Agarwal, B. F., Sukhatmi, P. V., Pandharkar, V. G. and Samarkan, A. N. (1948) The composition of milk. *Misc. Bull.*, No. 1. Indian Counc. Agric. Res.: New Delhi.

Singh, B. S., Yadav, P. C. and Pathak, R. C. (1963) A simple method for differentiation of buffalo milk from cow milk by carotene estimation. *Ind. J. Dairy Sci.*, **16**, 121–5.

Vijai, R. G. and Saraswat, D. S. (1970) Studies on bacteriological quality of market milk in Udaipur city. 1. Enumeration of standard plate and coliform counts in raw and pasteurised milk. *Ind. J. Dairy Sci.*, **21**, 233–7.

Wagan, R. A. (1970) The Philippine dairy industry, its history and status. *Ind. Dairyman,* **22,** 288–90.
Warner, J. N. (1951) *Dairying in India.* Macmillan: Calcutta.

Further Reading

Burton, H., Pien, J. and Thieulin, G. *Milk Sterilisation.* FAO Agric. Studies, No. 65. FAO: Rome, 1968.
Hall, H. S., Rosein, Y. and Blombergsson, H. *Milk Plant Layout.* FAO Agric. Studies, No. 59. FAO: Rome, 1968.
Kay, H. D., Cattell, J. R., Hall, H. S., Mattick, A. T. R. and Rowlands, A. *Milk Pasteurisation: Planning, Plant Operation and Control.* FAO Agric. Studies, No. 23. FAO: Rome, 1953.
Srinivasan, M. R. and Anatakrishnan, C. P. *Milk Products of India.* ICAR: New Delhi, 1964.

Chapter 15

Meat and Carcase By-products

by **I. Mann**
Formerly Project Manager, Animal Health and Industry Training Institute, Kabete, Kenya

Meat

In the past, in many tropical countries, livestock were owned not only for their economic value but also for the social prestige they bestowed on their owners. Yield as meat, milk or uncured hides and skins was meagre. With the improvement of animal health and the growth of trading in imported goods, a desire to sell livestock, the pastoralist 'cash crop', has appeared.

In many tropical countries the human population tends to be concentrated in the more humid agricultural districts where cash is available and there is a demand for meat, but where the number of animals is totally insufficient to meet the needs of the people. Nevertheless, large local livestock markets are infrequent in the arid or semi-arid pastoral areas where there is a surplus livestock population. The problems resulting from this situation are intensified in those areas where industrial development has commenced.

In the tropics the considerable distances that often separate producing areas from consumers makes it impossible for the individual stockowner to sell direct. In the past the problem has been solved by a chain of middlemen each requiring a profit. As a result, the producer has received a miserable fraction of the real value of his animal, for he has also had to bear the cost of the heavy losses and shrinkage of the animals during the long trek to the consuming areas. This has had two effects: one an unwillingness to part with animals at the rate of their natural increase, leading to progressive overstocking; and the other a lack of incentive to embark upon the simplest forms of improved husbandry.

Avoidance of preventable waste

Extensive publicity has been given, and meetings and seminars held, on the magnitude of post-harvest losses in cereals, legumes, tubers, oil seeds and other foodstuffs. Statements have been made and an awareness created that these post-harvest losses caused by faulty handling, lack of storage facilities, damage by insects, fungi, bacteria, chemical changes or rodents, amount to not less than one-quarter of the total crop in developing countries. Attention has been drawn to the toxins dangerous to animal and human health that may occur in these foodstuffs and action has been taken to prevent avoidable wastage by dissemination of information and by providing insecticides, rodenticides and plans for building proper storage such as large silos that are fully equipped for dusting and fumigation, thus preventing infestation.

Unfortunately, tremendous losses and wastage due to faulty handling, lack of knowledge and scarcity of processing facilities also occur in the meat and livestock industries. Losses may even be higher than in vegetable crops on account of the susceptibility of livestock to mortality, shrinkage, bruising, etc., and to losses in meat which, being an animal protein, is liable to rapid decomposition and infestation. The danger to public health from meat-borne diseases is also often overlooked. Lack of adequate slaughtering facilities, resulting in poor environmental hygiene in and adjacent to the slaughtering place, attracts vermin, rodents and flies, so that the slaughtering place itself may become a menace to public health and a source of diseases such as plague, ratbite fever, trichinosis, schistosomiasis, leishmaniasis, leptospirosis, flea-borne typhus, etc. A whole range of gastro-intestinal infections endanger the health of handlers and consumers, and all too often the unbroken vicious circle of cysticercosis/taeniasis continues and increases.

Meat itself may have very low keeping qualities due to incorrect slaughtering practices and a lack of adequate hanging or chilling rooms, causing wastage. Lack of meat inspection deprives farmers of the benefit of information on disease within their herds, thus preventing the elimination of disease. Losses through wastage of blood, bones and hair, on account of faulty handling at the slaughterhouse, may be considerable when assessed on a country-wide basis.

The demand for meat is growing due to urbanization, nutritional development and a higher earning capacity. It has been shown in developed countries that demand for meat grows faster as real incomes rise and it is likely that the same pattern of demand will emerge in developing countries. The Food and Agricultural Organization of the United Nations' Indicative World Plan for Agricultural Development states emphatically that investment in the development of the livestock industry is sound, as the market will increase and improve over the years.

As a result of the use of improved breeding stock, better animal husbandry practices, intensified veterinary services, injection of capital and the use of industrial residues and wastes, it is to be expected that not only will the total number of animals increase but also that yield of meat per animal slaughtered will be higher. It would therefore be a tragedy to allow the wasteful harvest of slaughter stock by permitting present practices to continue on account of the lack of properly equipped modern factory abattoirs capable of using the materials available within each slaughtered animal.

The time is ripe to evoke an awareness of the urgent need to improve the slaughtering, handling and processing of meat and meat products in developing countries.

National livestock development plans

In developing countries the responsibility for undertaking formation and implementation of a national livestock development plan must always remain with the central government.

A detailed survey of the soil, vegetation, human and livestock populations, the availability of slaughtering facilities, present and potential supply of slaughter stock, the demand for meat and consumers' preferences and the need for the adaptation of existing marketing and slaughtering patterns, without disrupting the whole trade and increasing the price of meat beyond the reach of the needy, is a prerequisite for the formulation of a development plan for a satisfactory meat industry. Such a pre-investment survey must consider a multitude of factors on a country-wide basis and should be carried out by a team of experts conversant with all aspects of livestock production, marketing and processing.

The findings of such a detailed survey would then, after careful evaluation, be used to formulate a national livestock development plan with the objective of changing the existing inefficient and wasteful livestock and meat trade into an organized and efficient industry.

The principal objectives of a national livestock development plan may be summarized as follows:

1. To draft appropriate legislation clearly defining the composition, scope and authority, and the name of the organization (for instance the Livestock and Meat Board), responsible for all aspects of the livestock and meat industry, and the implementation of a national livestock development plan. The right of the authority to engage in commercial and industrial activity must be stressed; the responsibility for a realistic meat inspection service has to be stated. To ascertain from the government the promulgation and enforcement of such legislation and to ensure a clear statement as to which ministry the organization will be responsible.
2. To encourage the production of more and better livestock by the creation of incentives to the producer through the stabilization of markets and the provision of technical and financial assistance for all aspects of livestock production.
3. To harvest livestock in the most efficient way without waste and spoilage through faulty marketing, transportation, or lack of proper slaughtering, processing, storage or distribution facilities.
4. To provide the consumer with wholesome meat at a reasonable price throughout the year.
5. To establish efficient slaughtering and processing facilities that would

allow the fullest use to be made of the entire animal, including all edible and inedible products, so contributing to the stabilization of attractive prices to the producer and the lowest possible prices to the consumer.

6. To export meat and meat by-products surplus to local nutritional requirements in an acceptable form, thus earning foreign currency.

7. To educate the producer and consumer alike on the benefits to be derived from an efficient livestock industry through an efficient extension and promotion service, with emphasis on the importance of meat grading.

8. To adopt efficient, hygienic and functional methods of wholesale and retail meat distribution.

9. To train locally, or if necessary abroad, professional managerial and technical staff needed for the production, marketing and processing of livestock and the manufacturing of meat and meat products.

Slaughtering and processing facilities

Slaughtering facilities

While the definition of meat processing includes chilling, freezing, canning, drying, meat extract preparation, by-product manufacture, the preparation of boneless meat and so on, the act of slaughtering itself is of such importance that it is imperative that the slaughtering facilities should be considered as an integral part of processing. Livestock should be considered as a perishable crop requiring certain special harvesting and processing methods.

The provision of slaughtering facilities in developing countries whether it be a small slaughter slab or a factory abattoir should be considered as an integral part of a national livestock development plan whose target is to establish an efficient livestock and meat industry. The final objective, at least in densely populated areas, should be centralized slaughtering and processing operations in one or several abattoir factories with common ownership and management.

There are three types of slaughtering facilities: simple rural slaughter slabs, public slaughterhouses and factory abattoirs.

Rural slaughter facilities

In remote areas where slaughtering is still carried out by individual butchers in the field, bush or back yard, the first step in improving slaughtering is to erect slaughter slabs equipped with wooden or tubular steel gantry hoists (Plate 15.1). Such slabs will allow control to be exercised over the butchers and permit meat inspection and fuller use of by-products. Thus the slaughter slab is the first step towards centralized slaughtering.

Plate 15.1   Bush slaughtering: a slaughter slab with a gantry hoist is required (Kenya Information Office).

The main requirements are that the slaughter place should be suitably situated and be provided with the following: a smooth, impervious, non-slippery, self-draining floor; wooden or iron gallows, not less than 3·7 m (12 ft) above floor level, with hoisting facilities; floor rings to secure the animals; a water point or hosepipe; adequate effluent disposal; hanging rails; adequate artificial light, if slaughtering is to take place at night; a scalding vat for pigs, where these are slaughtered; and a fence to prevent access of unauthorized animals or persons.

Generally speaking, the code of conditions should protect the animal from undue cruelty, the neighbours from nuisance and the consumer from meat unhygienically slaughtered and handled or sold without inspection.

Slaughterhouses

A slaughter slab with gantry hoist can easily be converted into a small rural slaughterhouse by erecting walls and roofing. A further step towards increasing the throughput would be to erect several units adjoining each other but partitioned off by walls 1·2 m (4 ft) high.

Better sanitation and management can be achieved by using one or more bays for each purpose, i.e. two units for large animals, one unit for small animals, such as sheep and goats, one for pigs and another reserved for tripe processing. In this manner, step by step, a public slaughterhouse may be evolved.

In places where more meat is consumed, fully equipped slaughter-houses should be provided. Independent of whether they are small or large, there are certain basic methods of operation:

1. In underdeveloped territories where the individual butcher is accus-tomed to slaughtering his own stock and having full control over his staff and property, it is often advisable to adopt the so-called booth or individual hall system. In this system each butcher uses a booth which is a miniature, fully equipped, self-contained slaughterhouse. The disadvantages of such a system are that it is costly to erect, makes meat inspection difficult and the maintenance of hygienic standards a problem.
2. A better method is one large slaughter-hall where the beasts are stunned, slaughtered, flayed and dressed in successive operations. With this system, live animals enter the building at one end and emerge as dressed carcases at the other.

Central factory abattoirs

Rural slaughter slabs and small or larger slaughterhouses serve a rela-tively small community within a limited radius. Obviously they do not have a major impact on the national meat industry. Such impact can only come from an industrial enterprise such as a factory abattoir, assured of a substantial throughput and catering for both local needs and export. In such an enterprise all operations are conducted under one ownership and management.

A central factory abattoir is the final stage of industrial development and is reached when large numbers of livestock are to be slaughtered for distribution in a large consuming area and/or for export. Such a factory is operated on the principle that the purchase of livestock, slaughter operations, storage and processing of meat, utilization of by-products and the sale of dressed carcases to the butchers or direct to consumers remain the responsibility of one organization. A central factory abattoir, because of the large throughput and the fullest use of by-products, can provide uniform products and slaughter and inspection under ideal conditions.

The planning of a factory abattoir is a skilled and complicated task requiring the services of a group of architects and engineers specializing in this type of work. A firm of consultant engineers might be employed or the task might be performed by a firm manufacturing abattoir equipment.

As mentioned above, the basic principle of operation is that everything should be conducted by the authority owning and running the enterprise. An animal must, from the point of slaughtering, progress on a hanging rail from one operation to the next until it reaches the chilling room in the form of dressed, graded sides or quarters. The meat leaves the abattoir as fresh, chilled, frozen and canned meats, or inedible offal such as meat-meal, bone-meal and carcase meal, hides and skins and other products.

The provision of facilities to manufacture a whole range of diversified products is essential and care should be taken to provide proper storage facilities and packaging, so that the finished products reach the consumer in prime condition.

In order to deal with emergency increases in throughput, arrangements should be made to work additional shifts rather than build extra capacity. This, however, does not apply to the size of the refrigeration facilities. There should be sufficient capacity to store all the meat and meat products produced during flush periods.

Economic considerations. The economic viability of factory abattoirs depends largely on three factors: (1) the form of ownership, (2) the managerial ability of the operational staff and (3) the assurance of a regular and sufficient supply of slaughter stock in relation to the size of the slaughtering and processing facilities.

To protect the factory abattoir from unfair competition, i.e. the sale of uninspected meat derived from small abattoirs or from slaughter in the bush, it is essential that the administrative and executive agency should have powers to (1) administer for the whole country, (2) determine the need and standards for slaughterhouses, (3) decide the operational methods of all slaughterhouses and (4) establish standards for the grading of meat and meat products.

Plans for abattoirs must anticipate not only the demand for meat but also the demand for better meat, especially packed, boneless or choice cuts. These will at first be consumed mainly by hotels catering for the tourist trade, but it is likely that gradually the demand for such meat will grow.

The intricacies and difficulties inherent in selling meat for export must be realized. The market in developed countries is very sensitive to the appearance, palatability and presentation of meat and meat products, and comparisons will be made with other similar products derived from older and well-established processing plants using reputable brand names.

Requirements for efficient slaughtering

The basic requirements for efficient slaughtering are:

1. An economic size of plant in relation to throughput;
2. Pre-slaughter care;
3. A humane method of slaughter;
4. Complete bleeding of carcases;
5. Avoidance of contamination;
6. Provision of hanging space to allow cooling;

7. Facilities for meat inspection and identification of parts of the carcase with the carcase as a whole, and disposal of what is condemned; and
8. Proper sanitation.

1. Economic size

An unnecessarily large abattoir is expensive to build and maintain and the cost per beast slaughtered is therefore excessive. Too small an abattoir leads to cramped working conditions and unhygienic meat production. The throughput of a slaughterhouse is not limited solely by its size, but by its equipment and organization.

Any layout should be designed to permit extension without basic alterations to the original structure or suspension of the work.

2. Pre-slaughter care

The stock should be fasted, but have access to clean water in pens for 16 to 24 hours prior to slaughter. This fasting reduces the amount of undigested food and faeces in the intestinal tract and improves the keeping quality of the meat. Nervous excitement, causing poor bleeding, is also reduced by keeping the beasts in the lairage, where they become accustomed to the surroundings before being slaughtered. At slaughter the animals will no longer be fatigued and the setting quality of meat will thereby be improved. It is essential to provide not less than $2.23\,\text{m}^2$ ($24\,\text{ft}^2$) of space per large beast and $0.59\,\text{m}^2$ ($6\,\text{ft}^2$) for a small animal.

The lairs should not be an integral part of the slaughterhouse, but connected only by a long, straight, narrow race. This race should be 76 cm (2·5 ft) wide at the top, narrowing to 46 cm (1·5 ft) at ground level, so that the beast cannot turn round. Lairs require shade and an ample water supply, and they should have a hard, impervious, well-drained floor sloping towards the drains. A holding ground where the beasts can graze until 24 hours before slaughter should be available.

3. Humane slaughter

Humane slaughter can be achieved even under the most primitive conditions by the use of any of the well-tried humane killers. In many places electric stunning can be practised.

4. Complete bleeding

Proper bleeding should be assured by hoisting the beasts immediately after slaughter. Complete bleeding is essential to produce meat and hides of good keeping quality. A prone carcase with legs tied together does not expel as much blood as a hanging one. Further, collecting blood from the prone beast is difficult. Even small beasts should also be slaughtered in a hanging position. This may be achieved in the field by suspension from a tree, a tripod or the side of a gantry hoist. The provision of a sheep/goat dressing line in the slaughterhouse, fixed about 2·1 m (7 ft) from the ground, fulfils this requirement admirably.

Blood should be collected, because of its potential value as a stockfeed and because if not collected it clogs the drains and is very difficult to dispose of without a main sewer.

5. Avoidance of contamination

From a hygienic point of view the carcase is divided into clean and dirty parts. By 'clean' is meant the dressed carcase which should be separated rapidly and completely from the rest. This can be achieved by using proper equipment (e.g. hoists, skinning cradles and overhead rails) and by its removal from the vicinity of potential contamination.

Pigs should not be slaughtered with other animals as the steam from scalding vats creates unfavourable conditions for the setting of meat, and the scurf derived from scraping the pig carcases is heavily contaminated with meat-spoilage organisms.

6. Cooling rooms

The rapid removal of dressed carcases from the slaughterhouse to the cooling room (or, better, to the refrigeration chamber), with the least possible exposure to the slaughterhouse atmosphere, reduces to a minimum the development of the microflora in and on the meat.

The advent of refrigeration has dramatically changed the pattern of meat handling, storage and distribution. The benefits derived from installing a refrigerated chill room are too numerous to list, but some of the most important are:

(a) Regulating supply to demand;
(b) 'Ripening' the meat;
(c) The reduction in meat-borne disease;
(d) The possibility of utilizing the established refrigeration facilities for the preservation of other perishable goods, such as fish, milk or vegetables, provided they are not stored together with the meat; and
(e) The destruction of meat parasites, such as *trichinae* or *cysticerci*, by freezing, thus permitting the use of infected meat.

7. Meat inspection

Facilities for ante- and post-mortem examination should form an integral part of any design. The speedy removal of parts or carcases unfit for human consumption prevents the contamination of meat which has passed inspection. All rejects are considered 'dirty' and therefore move in the opposite direction to the clean carcases. In order to protect the consumer from potentially dangerous or inferior meat, all condemned material should be sterilized, incinerated or converted into valuable stockfeed.

8. Sanitation of slaughterhouses

An adequate water supply and efficient effluent disposal are of paramount importance. The problem of water supply can often be solved only by planning an improved supply for the whole community. The use of polluted water is a constant danger. If pure water is unobtainable it is better to avoid using water on the carcase altogether and employ the so-called 'dry-kill' method. With the dry-kill method water will still be needed for washing the floors, walls, etc., after the slaughtering operation. Contamination of the meat is avoided by keeping the carcase well off the floor (by means of a hoist and skinning cradle (Plate 15.2), and by proper bleeding and careful evisceration.

Plate 15.2   Mobile gantry hoist. Skinning in a cradle (I. Mann).

The disposal of effluents can be achieved successfully by primitive methods, provided:

(a) It is not mixed with blood;
(b) All solids are screened; and
(c) The grease is trapped.

A primitive but efficient use of effluent is for irrigation of market gardens adjacent to the abattoir. Some soils do not readily absorb water, and in this event evaporation beds, alternately flooded and dry, can be used. Soakage pits, not less than 6 m (20 ft) deep and 1·8 m (6 ft) in diameter, covered with a cement top, are satisfactory only for the smallest units and after careful grease trapping and screening. Sub-surface irrigation, consisting of a series of herring-bone trenches filled with stones, often gives excellent results, especially when trees capable of evaporating large volumes of water are planted alongside.

The control of rodents and insects (e.g. flies, mosquitoes and cockroaches) must be ensured. If dogs consume offal infected with hydatids they become a source of infection to man, and to break the cycle all dogs must be excluded, and care must be taken that dogs have no access to condemned material. Daily routine cleaning of the whole premises, including the lairs, is essential, and every care should be taken that the slaughterhouse is clean and dry before slaughtering operations begin.

This brief outline of the principles governing the erection and operation of slaughterhouses must be the foundation for a design developed from a careful survey of local conditions and suitable to the environment. The aim, no matter how small the slaughterhouse, should be to incorporate the essentials, allowing minor modifications to suit the circumstances. A compact all-stock slaughterhouse for a small throughput is illustrated by Fig. 15.1.

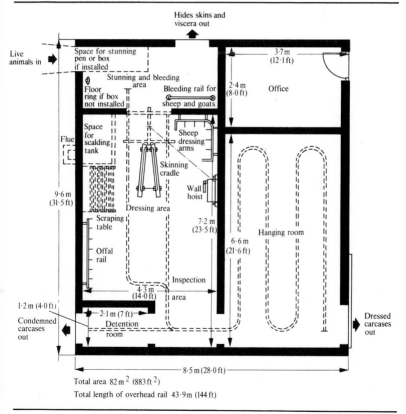

Fig. 15.1 A compact all-stock slaughterhouse for a small throughput.

Field abattoirs

In the past the standard practice was to bring the live beast from the remote rearing grounds to the consuming area, the animals moving on the hoof, by rail or by water. Because of shrinkage, mortality, thefts and predatory animals, heavy losses were suffered *en route*. Further, the beasts had to be in prime condition and excellent health to withstand the rigours of the journey, yet arrived at their destination in poor condition. Often the long treks could only be undertaken when the season permitted. With the advent of air transport the approach has been completely altered. Meat slaughtered in a field abattoir in the producing area on the previous evening can be delivered and sold in the consuming area the following day, without the use of refrigeration. Provided the meat is properly hung when loaded into the aircraft, the altitude at which the plane flies will keep it properly chilled. Hence not only can prime carcases be delivered without shrinkage but carcases of previously unsaleable stock, which have been a burden both to the owner and the land, reach the market. The use of an airlift permits the siting of factory abattoirs in the producing areas.

A simple field abattoir of prefabricated steel construction placed strategically can play a vital role in de-stocking an area and marketing the products. This is possible by enhancing the keeping quality of the meat by drying, smoking or salting. Such meats can be used where there is slow transport and simple storage, two factors of great importance. The production of this type of meat is easy. In certain parts of the world it has been made for many centuries, for example smoked meat in Nigeria, *biltong* in South Africa and *charque* in South America, and can easily be prepared in a field abattoir.

Preserved meat

Dry salting.

This is one of the traditional methods of preserving meat. Raw, fresh meat is cut into slabs averaging 1·4 to 2·2 kg (3 to 5 lb) in weight and not more than 2·5 cm (1 in) thick. These are hung in the shade to cool for about an hour. The pieces are then submerged in a saturated salt solution for approximately one hour. The meat is then drained and cured on a sloping, grooved slab under a roof. Alternate layers of salt and meat are built up to a height of about 0·9 m (3 ft). The top is covered with a few wooden planks and pressed down with heavy stones. The salt must be pure, fine and free from any reddish colour. On each of 5 consecutive days the pile is overhauled in such a way that the top pieces of meat are placed at the bottom. Fresh salt is used each time. Before the meat is exposed to final drying it may be pressed to squeeze out the surplus moisture, flatten the slices and increase their surface area. Pressing is not essential in dry climatic conditions.

Drying must be carried out very carefully and is best done in a shed or, if in the sun, only during the early morning or late afternoon when the heat is not strong enough to melt the fat. It is carried out on 2·5 cm (1 in) wire netting, bamboo slats or other local material. The meat must be turned every 2 hours during the first day and every 4 to 6 hours thereafter until drying is completed. The pieces will then resist the strongest finger pressure and when clapped together will sound dry. It is important that the product should be at all times protected from rain or dew. Dried, salted meat has good keeping qualities, is resistant to beetle infestation and to attack by moulds. It should be soaked in water before use.

The modern method of rendering meat to *dried meat powder* eliminates the disadvantages of the traditional method. Among these are the great labour involved, the small yield, the seasonal production, danger of rancidity and the higher cost of transport. The meat is first subjected to 9 kg (20 lb) pressure under live steam for about 30 minutes and then dehydrated for a further $2\frac{1}{2}$ to 3 hours in a dry-rendering melter. At the same time all the bones are 'digested' in a retort so that the fat, liquid extractives and any meat adhering to the bones are liberated from them. The liquid is drawn off and added to the drying meat. Drying is completed in some 4 hours when the residual moisture is about 5 per cent. The mass contains an appreciable amount of fat, often as much as 30 per cent. This is reduced to about 10 per cent by a centrifugal process. The mass is then milled to a fine powder and run into sterilized tin containers which are hermetically sealed. The process must be completed under the best environmental hygiene. A favourable terminal bacterial count of the product can be further ensured by the addition of 0·45 kg (1 lb) of salt to 113 kg (250 lb) of raw meat, i.e. at the rate of one per cent of the finished product. Each batch of the powdered meat should be subjected to bacteriological examination before issue.

The whole animal is used in the process with the exception of the hide, bones, hoofs, horns and intestinal tract. It is fortified by the concentrated liquor containing most of the extractives and protein of the bones.

Smoking

The simplest and oldest method consists in hanging strips of meat in a loosely woven basket above an open fire to be used as and when needed. Because it is continuously resmoked and kept in a smoky condition there is no danger of it going bad.

However, when the product has to be kept for a long period after it has been taken from the smoky atmosphere, curing as well as smoking is often necessary.

In large meat-packing plants smoking is scientifically controlled. It is done in several-storey smoke houses where the meat is hung on a shaft which rotates, pushing the meat up and down, thus achieving a uniform smoke. Heat is supplied by heat coils, and sawdust, blended from different hard woods and burned over a gas burner, is used to produce the smoke which is drawn in by suction fans.

Under primitive conditions a smoke house often has to be improvised. An air-tight brick, stone or metal building 1.8×2.4 m (6×8 ft) and 2.7 m (9 ft) in height provided with proper damping facilities is adequate for a very substantial throughput. The fire is built outside and the smoke and heat led in through a flue.

The meat should be of good quality, dry and boneless. It is cut in flat, thin slices along and not across the muscle. It is suspended from racks so that no two pieces touch. Soft or resinous woods should not be used as fuel. Hardwoods give the best results, but these should be tried out as some impart a bitter taste or a dark colour. Maize cobs make excellent fuel. More smoke and less heat should be applied during the first stages of the process so that the meat is not hard-smoked on the outside and raw on the inside. Gradually the heat is increased so that the meat is not only smoked but partially cooked. Towards the end the temperature is gradually reduced and more smoke applied. The treatment is considered finished when, on cutting, it is found that the inside is dry and of a uniform colour. During the first period of smoking the temperature should reach $60°$ C ($140°$ F) followed by a lower temperature of $49°$ C ($120°$ F) for finishing, the whole process taking up to 30 hours or more. The smoked meat should be allowed to cool slowly and then be dipped in or painted with vegetable oil. It should be stored in a dry, preferably dark room.

There are numerous variations of this process which add to the keeping qualities, palatability, nutritional value and hygiene of the product.

Curing

Drying meat originated in countries with hot climates. Curing was a method of preserving meat in cold countries. This simple fact should not be overlooked when choosing a method of preservation.

A quick cure before smoking facilitates the latter process, increases the palatability and allows larger pieces of meat to be treated. One of the following methods may be used:

1. Immersion for $\frac{1}{2}$ to 1 hour in $70°$ salometer brine (containing 13 per cent of salt);
2. Immersion for 3 to 4 hours in a saturated solution of the following ingredients:

Salt	0.9 kg (2 lb)
Sugar	0.45 kg (1 lb)
Saltpetre	28 gm (1 oz)

3. Treatment with salt or the above ingredients for at least 12 hours in the manner described under 'dry salting'.

After the meat has been treated it should be rinsed quickly in clean water to prevent the cure forming a crust during smoking.

Carcase by-products

There is a prevalent misconception that full use of animal offal can be achieved only with costly equipment and under meat-packing conditions. In many countries this obsolete approach creates the paradox that while certain raw materials, such as blood, bones or intestines, are completely wasted, costly blood meal, bone-meal or sausage casings are imported.

Even hides and skins often receive extremely careless treatment because it is not appreciated that first-class leather can be made from the local material, using simple methods and equipment, if it were only properly handled and prepared. All too often it is assumed that quality hides can only be achieved in hide cellars fitted with temperature and humidity controllers and using chemically pure salt.

It is economically unimaginative to consider an animal only as a source of meat and hide; it can yield an extensive range of by-products of benefit to the individual and the whole country and the aim should always be to make the fullest use of the whole animal. No matter how small the amount of each by-product, the aggregate on a country-wide basis will certainly add substantially towards the economy of the territory.

While it is true that large-scale utilization of slaughterhouse offal requires costly and elaborate machinery, by-products of high quality can be obtained with home-made equipment and at very low cost.

Hides and skins

Good leather can only be made from good hides and skins. With the increased cost of building and labour, the competition from plastic materials and the appearance on the market of properly flayed and cured hides and skins from countries with an established meat-packing industry or an efficient hides improvement service, there is today no chance of obtaining an attractive price for hides and skins unless they are as free from visible or invisible damage as possible.

The various processes to which hides and skins are subjected in the tannery are a combination of physical and chemical action which tends to emphasize every hole, gouge mark, pox mark or even incipient putrefaction. This is contrary to the common belief that tanning covers blemishes so that the raw material has little bearing on the finished leather.

Pre-slaughter care

It is not sufficient to start the care of the hide or skin from the moment the beast appears at the slaughterhouse, as irreparable damage can be done on live animals prior to slaughter. Indiscriminate branding, either for identification or curative purposes, applied in places which produce the best raw material, will invariably reduce the value of the whole hide. The ornamental branding carried out by certain indigenous peoples renders the hide practically worthless.

A brand should be small and placed on an inferior part of the hide or skin, such as the ear, cheek, or the foreleg below the shoulder or below the stifle of the hind leg. On humped beasts, branding on the top of the hump does not damage the hide, as during the process of tanning the hide is split in two so that the brand appears on the edge of the finished leather.

Scratches from barbed wire and thornbushes, or horn gores, yoke calluses, wounds, whip lashes and other mechanical injuries to the hide or skin during the life of the beast, will have a bearing on the quality of the leather. Parasitic diseases like ringworm, streptothricosis, mange, or other diseases such as cowpox, hyperkeratosis, sweating sickness, etc., injure the grain. Warble-fly damage, resulting in holes on the back, which is the best part of the hide, is a serious menace in countries infested with this fly. Even tick bites leave spots on the finished leather.

Avoiding damage in the slaughterhouse

Most of the damage, however, occurs either through careless handling or lack of knowledge. It may be inflicted during killing and flaying or appear in the form of bruises when the animal has been beaten prior to slaughter or cast forcibly on a hard floor. Hauling the carcase over a rough surface damages the grain, and results in so-called 'dragged' or 'rubbed' grain, especially obvious where the bones are prominent. Bad bleeding, resulting in the small cutaneous vessels being gorged with blood, may lead to putrefaction by encouraging bacterial growth and results in a raised grain ('veiny' leather).

Cuts and gouge marks caused either by the use of a pointed knife or the insecure position of the carcase, delays between slaughter and flaying, or the unnecessary use of a knife where the hide or the skin can be fisted. or pulled off, all contribute greatly towards loss of value.

Bad shape, caused through improper ripping lines, is another fault. The tanner requires a square hide, which can only be obtained by removing it according to standard cuts. To obtain the best results the following basic incisions should be made in large animals:

1. One long, straight incision, down the mid-line, from the chin to the anus (cuts reaching only to the udder or scrotum are not to be recom-

mended as the shape of the hide is affected; two unnecessary flaps are left which have to be trimmed off, thus affecting the shape and size of the hide);
2. Two circular incisions on the forelegs round the knees;
3. Two similar incisions round the hocks;
4. Two straight cuts on the inside of the forelegs from the knees to the fore-end of the breast bone; and
5. Two straight cuts on the hind legs from the back of each hock joint to a point midway between the anus and the scrotum or udder.

For sheep and goats the ripping cuts are the same, but it is much better to remove the skin in cased form. This method has been spread by the Arabs and can be highly recommended as it causes less scores and cuts than any other way. The whole skin can be drawn off like a glove once the proper initial cuts have been made.

In certain countries where whole skins were used as rafts or as containers for liquids, a method of inflation, i.e. injecting air between the skin and the carcase, was developed. When the skin is pummelled the compressed air tears the subcutaneous tissue and the skin can then be removed with the minimum use of the knife. This method should not be discouraged; on the contrary, it is strongly recommended, as skins produced in this manner are of the highest quality.

Treatment after flaying

Damage after flaying can be avoided once the basic principles of hide handling are understood. These are as follows:

1. Contamination in the form of blood, ingesta or manure may lead to rapid decomposition;
2. The delay between flaying and subsequent treatment should be reduced to a minimum to prevent bacterial action;
3. Rapid arrest of bacterial action is essential and can be achieved by depriving the micro-organisms of moisture, either by suspension drying or by salting.

These principles are achieved by the following:

1. *Washing.* After flaying, while the blood is still liquid, the hide or skin should be washed, using a scrubbing-brush, preferably under running water. Soaking in drums or troughs filled with thick, dun-coloured water, as is often seen in tropical countries, has an adverse effect, as the hide is further infected with bacteria rather than cleansed. The washed hides should be drained by hanging them over a pole or wire, and fleshed immediately.

2. *Fleshing.* This should be done so that all non-leather-forming substances, such as meat and fat, are removed, either by knife or scraper.

Over-flaying leads to loss of corium, i.e. the leather-forming substance, and is as dangerous as leaving meat or fat on the hide.

3. *Trimming.*   All irregular flaps at the edges and corners should be removed so that the hide or skin is as 'square' as possible. The switch should be cut off 15 cm (6 in) below the root.

4. *Preserving.*   When hides and skins cannot be passed absolutely fresh to the tanner, some method of preservation will generally be essential. There is a choice of three methods:

(a) *Wet salting*, where hides are built up with alternate layers of salt and cured until the salt has absorbed so much moisture that putrefaction cannot commence. This process takes approximately 3 weeks.

Salting is done by piling alternate layers of salt and hides, usually on a slatted platform, until a stack 1·2 to 1·5 m (4 to 5 ft) high has been built. After about 10 days the pile must be overhauled and a new stack built in which the top hides from the original stack form the bottom of the new. If a slatted platform is not used and the brine retained, there is a definite danger of spoilage. 'Red heat', which is a discoloration of the hide through bacterial action, can be avoided by the use of certain chemicals, such as sodium silicofluoride or 'Santobrite'.

Wet salting should be employed only where the throughput is large and a cellar with a temperature not exceeding 15·6°C (60°F) through-the year can be built. Whenever the relative humidity exceeds 90 per cent or the temperature reaches 30° to 42·2°C (86° to 108°F) deterioration of the corium, i.e. the leather-forming substance, begins.

So-called 'pickling' of hides, i.e. immersing the hides in a brine-filled drum for many days before collection, should be discontinued, as this results in loss of hide substance, hair slip and putrefaction. This method is a distorted version of the *frigorifico* method of brining, i.e. immersing the hides overnight in a saturated salt solution prior to wet salting.

(b) *Dry salting*, which is a combination of methods (a) and (c). The hides are salted for a short period to protect them from damage during the most critical time, i.e. the first few days after they have been removed from the animal, and the rest of the moisture is then removed by air drying.

(c) *Suspension drying* – drying the hides suspended in frames or from one or three wires in such a way that there is free circulation of air from all sides.

Suspension drying is the cheapest method in the tropics: it requires little control and can be carried out with simple equipment; the maximum reduction in weight is obtained; the hide will keep almost indefinitely, provided it is protected from beetle infestation; and it facilitates the assessment of weight and quality.

Suspension-drying equipment

Frames (Plates 15·3 and 15·4) can easily be constructed from any locally available timber and they should measure 2·7 × 3·1 m (9 × 10 ft) for larger beasts and 2·7 × 2·4 m (9 × 8 ft) for smaller animals. Large cattle frames can be sub-divided into four sheep or goat frames by inserting cross-pieces. The distance between the frames is customarily 23 cm (9 in).

In order to ensure the fullest air circulation care must be taken that the hides do not touch each other and that the hump, if present, is properly stretched out with a stick.

Drying in a *loop* made from green branches, a very simple and efficient method, is recommended in cases where a producer sells a beast only

Plate 15.3   Lacing skins into a frame (Kenya Information Office).

occasionally, where straight timber is costly or unavailable, and where the nomadic activities of a people precludes the carrying of heavy frames. Thick *galvanized* wire may be used in place of green branches.

Good results are obtained by drying hides and skins over galvanized wires instead of in frames, provided they are hung over one or preferably three wires in such a way that they do not touch each other at any point and that care is taken to stretch all small infolds by means of a stick or twigs.

In places where there may be depreciation from theft, vermin or rain, hide-drying sheds should be provided.

The hides or skins are laced into the frames using string, bark or preferably hide strips, from perforations around the edges. Wire should

Plate 15.4   A box frame for hides (I. Mann).

never be used, as not being elastic it tears the hole out, or rusts, leading to stains during tanning. Small pieces of wire left in the skin may cause serious damage to hundreds of skins if they are tanned in drums.

The time taken to dry naturally depends on the weather and the thickness of the hide or skin. Too slow drying, experienced in high-rainfall areas, often leads to mould growth and hairslip, while overdrying may cause cracks. It is essential to remove the hide or skin from the frame before it is completely dry, otherwise it will crack when folded. If hides and skin are orientated east–west to offset the heat of the midday sun they may be left uncovered, but in countries with excessive insolation it is preferable to protect them by providing overhead shade.

Treatment after drying

Hides and skins should be folded only once – lengthwise down the line of the backbone. During transit they must be protected from wetting, rubbing, contamination by oil, paint or grease and from binding wire.

If they are to be stored they must be kept dry by proper roofing and by being placed on a slatted platform raised not less than 15 cm (6 in) from the floor. They must also be protected from vermin. Today the hide beetle (*Dermestes maculatus*) can be completely controlled by the use of such insecticides as Gammexane or DDT powder if the floors, walls and rafters of the store are dusted as well as the hides and skins.

Good results can be obtained by applying fungicides mixed with insecticides to achieve protection both from moulds and beetles. A proved formula for such a powder is as follows:

BHC (13% gamma isomer)	6%
Boracic acid	4%
'Santobrite' (Monsanto)	2%
Kaolin, or other filler	88%

This powder will contain 0·75 per cent of BHC gamma isomer. Periodic aeration by exposure to the sun and light will help to check mould growth.

Another widely used method to control hide beetle is to dip the hides in a solution containing 0·2 per cent arsenious oxide. Alternatively, this liquid may be sprayed over both sides using a pump. The hides and skins must be very carefully dried after spraying, otherwise moulds will develop and hairslip may begin.

This method of protecting hides and skins from beetles must not be confused with the soaking of ground-dried goods for a prolonged period in a strong solution of arsenic, with subsequent stretching in frames. This fraudulent practice has only one aim – namely to make an inferior hide look better than it really is. The damage caused by this procedure is enormous, as once the resoaked hides are mixed with suspension-dried ones, the tanner accepts the consignment bona fide as all suspension-dried, and then during the process of soaking or liming, the ground-dried hide reveals serious damage to the grain or hide substance, or falls to pieces and has to be rejected. Naturally the tanner reduces the price for all goods coming from countries where this malpractice is prevalent, thus penalizing all producers for his loss. Resoaking of hides should be prohibited by legislation.

Tools and equipment

Despite their simplicity, the tools and equipment required for the proper preparation of hides and skins are of the greatest importance. Proper flaying knives with a convex edge and curved, blunt point are essential.

Their edge should always be kept keen. Separate knives should be used for butchering and flaying operations.

A hoist, which allows proper bleeding, is of the greatest importance in hide production. The use of skinning cradles to protect the hide from dirt and damage by the cement floor is another important item. The provision of ample clean water, frames of the correct size and proper transport and storage facilities all contribute towards the production of quality goods.

By-products

The by-products of hides and skins are trimmings, such as pieces of shank, lips, ears and masks, which can be dried or cured in the same way as hides and sold for gelatine or glue production. In addition tail switches, which should be cut off approximately 15 cm (6 in) from the base of the tail, can be dried and sold for local brush manufacture. For export the tail hair should be cut as near the skin as possible, washed in cold water then immersed for several hours in warm water to which 2 per cent washing soda has been added, washed again in running water and dried.

Bones

Bones amount to approximately 15 per cent of the weight of the dressed carcase, depending on the age and condition of the beast. In extremely fat beasts it may be only 12 per cent, while in emaciated cattle it can be up to 30 per cent. Fresh bones yield an appreciable amount of fat, which should always be recovered either by boiling the bones in open kettles or under pressure.

Bones are used for several purposes:

1. For the production of stockfeeds, such as meat and bone-meal when processed together with other offal.
2. As steamed bone meal, which is produced from defatted bones digested under pressure. The inorganic matter of bones consists of slightly more than 32 per cent calcium and a little more than one-half this amount of phosphorus. Both are invaluable supplements for feeding to livestock.
3. For gelatine and glue production, as ossein, the organic substance forming the bone structure, amounts to 33 to 36 per cent of the total.

A fact of immense importance is that bones, before use either as a fertilizer or as mineral supplement for stockfeed, should be properly sterilized. Otherwise they may be a source of many dangerous diseases, such as anthrax and botulism.

Bones can be sterilized merely by burning. To fire the bones they should be piled on a metal frame, for example old motor-car springs or a chassis.

Burning deprives the bones of all organic matter, leaving the mineral components in a friable form, which can easily be pulverized. This calcined bone powder is equal in feeding value to the best steamed bone-meal, although it looks like charcoal. The yield of calcined bones from freshly slaughtered beasts is approximately one-third of the green weight of bone, while from bones which have been exposed to climatic conditions for a long time (so-called 'desert' bones) the yield is approximately two-thirds.

While prolonged boiling in open kettles can be used to sterilize bones, it is safer and more economic to use retorts where pressure can be applied. When moist heat is used, 15 minutes under $1.4\,kg$ per cm^2 (20 lb per in^2) pressure is sufficient; with dry heat, the temperature must be $154°C$ ($310°F$) for not less than 3 hours.

Every precaution must be taken to prevent sterilized bones coming in contact with unsterilized material, and the strictest division observed between processed and unprocessed material.

For use as soil dressing or stockfeed the sterilized bones should be converted to a fine flour.

It can be seen, therefore, that the basic equipment of every bone plant, either stationary or mobile, should be:

1. A boiler to provide the necessary steam pressure;
2. A retort or digester, single or double jacketed, where the bones can be subjected to pressure or dry heat; and
3. A disintegrator where the sterilized bones are converted to a powder.

Bones intended for gelatine manufacture can be piled in large heaps, exposed to the elements and then crushed with a stone-crusher. The loss in weight due to exposure saves freight.

Blood

The way in which blood is often mishandled is typical of the manner in which valuable protein is continually wasted. At the same time, there are considerable difficulties in its disposal. It clogs drains, attracts vermin and may spread disease. On the other hand, the blood wasted from every $454\,kg$ (1,000 lb) beast slaughtered deprives the country of a potential $2.7\,kg$ (6 lb) of blood meal for livestock feed.

The use of fresh blood for stockfeed is limited by two factors:

1. It has a very poor keeping quality and unless fed immediately decomposes rapidly under tropical conditions; and
2. If fed unsterilized, it may transmit disease.

Methods of preparing blood for use are as follows:

1. *Absorption.*   Blood is mixed with any of the locally available cereal products, such as bran, pollards, maize or cassava flour, and then

spread out for drying on mats or on trays heated from below. In this way the low-protein vegetable matter is enriched with first-class animal protein. This process may be repeated several times, each treatment increasing the protein content of the meal.

2. *Treatment with lime.* The addition of approximately one per cent of unslaked lime to fresh blood causes it to coagulate in the form of a black, rubber-like mass. If slaked lime is used, three times as much will be needed. The advantages of this method are that the keeping quality is greatly enhanced, the coagulated blood can be carried away in baskets, boxes or bags, and there is no discharge of serum. Lime-treated blood may be fed fresh or sundried. Drying further improves its keeping quality.

As previously mentioned, the feeding of unsterilized blood is not recommended. Sterilization of blood, treated either by absorption or with lime, can be achieved easily by boiling it together with other food, such as potatoes or cassava, immediately before feeding, or by heating the dried blood on galvanized iron trays over a fire.

3. *Coagulation, pressing and drying.* Where larger quantities of blood are available, a different system is recommended. The blood should first be cooked for 15 to 20 minutes to make it coagulate; this expresses nearly half the water. Further reduction of the moisture can be achieved by putting the coagulated blood in a hessian bag and hanging it over a pole or pressing it between wooden planks weighted with stones. The mass is then sun-dried or dried over artificial heat.

Meat meal

Condemned carcases or inedible offal should be converted into meat meal rather than incinerated or dug into the ground. This applies also to dead animals, provided processing can start before decomposition sets in and provided the animal has not died from anthrax. No matter how small the production three aims should be achieved:

1. Sterilization of the material;
2. Quick reduction of moisture before putrefaction can set in; and
3. The removal of fat, which if left will cause rancidity.

Where pigs or poultry are bred near the slaughterhouse, all the parts of the carcase should be cut into small pieces and boiled under supervision. This will achieve sterilization and the meat can then be fed. Boiling is also the first step in meat-meal production, as in addition to sterilizing the material it causes shrinkage and thus reduces the moisture content. The moisture may then be further reduced sufficiently for milling by draining and pressing the boiled mass, using any available press, followed by drying on galvanized trays, heated from underneath, with occasional raking. Milling can be achieved in a simple way by using an iron drum fitted on an axle and containing a few round stones.

Commercial by-products plant

The brief description given here for the production of meat meal and blood meal is applicable only to places where offal is available in small quantities. Where the raw material, i.e. blood, bones, condemns, fleshings, trimmings, and other inedible offal, amounts to approximately one ton per day, it is economically and hygienically preferable to install a standard by-products plant. That amount of offal may be derived from one slaughterhouse or from many dispersed slaughterhouses.

A by-products plant can be operated economically, not only in the vicinity of a slaughterhouse, producing stockfeed from slaughterhouse offal, but also where, for instance, a large amount of surplus unproductive stock is available which is a burden to man and to the land. It must be borne in mind that most of the livestock with which the sellers are willing to part are animals unable to walk any great distance to an abattoir without excessive shrinkage or mortality.

Where the throughput does not warrant the establishment of a stationary plant, a mobile processing unit can be used, which by virtue of its mobility can progress either with the movement of the livestock or into unexploited areas.

The establishment of a by-products plant to utilize undersized, diseased and unproductive stock can on the one hand lead to a dramatic improvement in animal husbandry in the area, and on the other hand supply badly needed stockfeed to other areas where intensive production can then be established.

The basic equipment for a by-products plant is:

1. A boiler to provide the necessary steam;
2. A drier (called a melter or cooker) where the products are first sterilized under pressure and then dried;
3. Equipment to remove excess fat from the dried material that may be a press, an extractor, an expeller or a solvent extraction plant; and
4. A mill to reduce the dried, sterilized de-fatted material to a powder.

Hooves and horns

There is a firm market for hooves and horns provided they are properly handled. Neither hooves nor horns should be mixed with bones intended for stockfeed, but should be treated separately, if only for the reason that the price realized for hoof-and-horn meal is much higher than that for bone-meal, and its presence in bone-meal makes the mixture very unpalatable.

The horn core, or horn pith, is a bony support for the horn and contains a high percentage of gelatine. It should therefore be separated from the horn proper immediately after the horn has been cut off. This can be done by immersion in hot water and then knocking with a hammer. After this, the horns are stacked for drying in ventilated sheds, before being despatched to gelatine or glue factories.

An appreciable quantity of horns is exported for button, comb and handle manufacture. The price depends on the method of treatment, the length, hardness and colour. Exposure to the sun will cause warping and cracking and thus render horns useless: washing in warm water and drying in a shed is the only treatment they require.

Hoof-and-horn meal is a rich, nitrogenous fertilizer which is obtained by digesting the hooves and horns from cattle, sheep and goats under pressure for approximately 10 hours.

Casings

Conversion of the intestines into casing is a highly remunerative operation despite its simplicity. There is an excellent market, especially for sheep and goat casings, and the highest prices are paid for casings derived from animals which are kept exposed to the elements under ranching conditions.

The standard method is to remove the small intestines of sheep and goats immediately the animal has been slaughtered, and then to pull, i.e. to separate the intestine from the mesenterium and fat. Wherever possible, the intestines should be put into cold water to arrest fermentation and to harden the fat.

'Stripping', which follows, is a term applied to the squeezing out of the contents by pulling the guts with one hand and passing them between the first and second fingers of the other hand. Removal of the fat is called 'fatting'. This process can be performed on sheep and goat intestines by a plain wooden or bone scraper, while beef and pig casings require a pair of scissors or a knife. In order to loosen the different layers, the intestines are now subjected to fermentation. Depending on the temperature of the water and climatic conditions, this can be achieved within a few hours.

The process of 'sliming' follows until the casing is completely clean and transparent. Sliming means the removal of the mucous lining by means of a sliming knife, which is a piece of wood or bone resembling a knife. By pressing the sliming stick along the intestines the slime is gradually removed, leaving a thin transparent membrane deprived of fat, meat and dirt. This is the true casing.

During processing care must be taken to avoid damage which might result in one or several tears in the casing. The ideal is a complete, undamaged length of 24·4 to 30·5 m (80 to 100 ft) of sheep or 19·8 to 22·9 m (65 to 75 ft) of goat intestine.

The completely clean casings are now ready for curing. A choice of two methods is available:

1. Rubbing the casings with fine salt and leaving them to drain and cure for approximately 2 weeks. After this period they are shaken out and coiled in neat bundles of equal length.
2. Brining in a saturated salt solution. A wooden cask is gradually filled with casings which displace the brine. When filled, the cask is ready for shipment. If oil and petrol drums are used they should be lined with a suitable plastic film.

Cattle and pig casings are similarly prepared, but the market demand in the tropics for this type of casing is rather limited.

Hair

Pig bristles, i.e. the long stiff hairs growing on the back and tail of the pig, are a most valuable raw material. The body hair realizes a much lower price. The bristles and body hair must be deprived of any scurf or other impurities which may be adhering to them. This is done by repeated washing, first in cold and then in warm water to which soda has been added. Drying should be completed in a shed, not in the open air.

Cattle tail hair and ear hair can be treated in the same way. The body hair is more often a by-product of the tanning industry than the slaughterhouse.

Ruminal contents

The undigested food in the rumen obviously has a feeding value. By drying the contents in the sun they can be used to replace bran or pollards in poultry foods, in amounts up to 10 per cent of the total ration. Only the contents of the first three stomachs are used for this purpose, while the content of the fourth stomach, which is a liquid of low feeding value, is discarded. When dry, the protein content can be augmented by mixing the dried ruminal content with liquid blood and redrying. By repeating this process an adequately balanced ration can be produced.

Compost-making

The value of slaughterhouse offal for compost-making should not be overlooked. There is always ample material, such as vegetable waste, market waste, sweepings, cotton and maize stalks, bean, pea and sorghum straw, packing materials, wood shavings, overripe bananas and mangoes, but highly proteinous material is usually lacking. By putting alternate layers of vegetable matter and slaughterhouse offal, such as urine, blood, floor sweepings, hair, feathers, hide trimmings, and minced or chopped inedible parts or condemns, rumen and intestinal contents, a compost of the highest quality is achieved.

For a neat and clean stack it is better to use a compost bunker which can be filled, turned and loaded direct into carts. The installation of a compost bunker in the slaughterhouse compound can ensure that no matter how little or how much offal there is, it is returned to the soil again to improve gardens and pastures.

Further Reading

American Meat Institute *Science of Meat and Meat Products.* Freeman: San Francisco, 1960.

Aten, A., Innes, R. F. and Knew, E. *Flaying and curing of hides and skins as a rural industry.* FAO Agric. Dev. Paper, No. 49. FAO: Rome, 1954.

Brandly, P. J., Migaki, G. and Taylor, K. E. *Meat Hygiene.* (3rd edn). Lea and Febiger: Philadelphia, 1966.

Johnson, T. J. The elaboration and implementation of a programme for hides and skins improvement and marketing in developing countries. *UNIDO Seminar on the Development of the Leather and Leather Products Industries in Developing Countries, Regional Project for Africa.* Vienna, Austria. 22 Feb.–5 Mar. 1971.

Mann, I. *Meat Handling in Underdeveloped Countries. Slaughter and Preservation* (2nd ed). FAO Agric. Dev. Paper, No. 70. FAO: Rome, 1967.

Mann, I. *Processing and utilization of animal by-products* (2nd edn). FAO Agric. Dev. Paper, No. 75. FAO: Rome, 1967.

Mann, I. Improved slaughtering, storage, processing and distributing facilities as an integral part of a national livestock development programme. *2nd FAO African Regional Conference on Animal Production and Health. Kinshasa, Congo.* 28 Nov.–6 Dec. 1969.

Mann, I. *Rural tanning techniques.* FAO Agric. Dev. Paper, No. 68. FAO: Rome, 1974.

Nayudamma, Y. Problems and prospects for the development of the leather industry in developing countries. *UNIDO Seminar on the Development of the Leather and Leather Products Industries in Developing Countries. Regional Project for Africa.* Vienna, Austria. 22 Feb.–5 Mar. 1971.

Chapter 16

Wool Production

by (the late) G. R. Moule
Formerly Director of Production Research, Australian Wool Board,
261 George Street, Sydney 2001, NSW, Australia

General information on tropical wool sheep

Some details on typical sheep breeds indigenous to the tropics and of their husbandry are given in Chapter 7 (Part II). This chapter deals with the production, in tropical regions, of 'carpet' and 'apparel' wool.

Fleeces used for making carpets are composed of long fibres that vary greatly in fibre diameter, which is usually large. In addition, there is a proportion of medullated or true hair fibre in the fleece. Sheep growing such fleeces occur in many parts of tropical Africa, Arabia, Pakistan, India and Southeast Asia. They occur to a lesser extent in Mexico, but here, as in Peru, Chile and Brazil, apparel-wool sheep have been introduced to upgrade the wool of the indigenous breeds. Apparel-wool sheep were also introduced into tropical Australia, East Africa and Rhodesia during the latter part of the nineteenth century and in the early part of the twentieth century. Australia and East Africa remain the only countries with major aggregations of apparel-wool sheep in the tropics, although it has been found that by careful classing much of the wool produced by the so-called carpet-wool sheep of India can be processed on Noble combs to produce apparel fabrics. In East Africa wool-growing sheep occupy the highland areas at elevations of 1,524 to 2,439 m (5,000 to 8,000 ft) or more and some apparel-wool sheep are also to be found in the highlands of tropical South America.

The main aggregations of apparel-wool sheep in tropical Australia are in the States of Queensland and Western Australia. About 7 million Merinos, or one-third of Queensland's flocks, are in the tropics. Western Australia has less than one million Merino sheep in her northwest tropical areas. In each state, sheep grazing is confined to the semi-arid pastoral districts. Here the average annual rainfall varies between 254 and 508 mm (10 and 20 in) a year. Greater aridity is experienced in some parts of the sheep-raising districts of South America, in Mexico and many areas of Africa. Generally speaking, in these regions rainfall is unreliable and poorly distributed, and evaporation of free surface water may be extremely high. The highland areas where sheep are raised in the tropics have more reliable and better distributed rainfall, which makes them more amenable to pasture improvement.

Climatic conditions in the arid and semi-arid areas dictate the type of vegetation that grows. Usually it is tussocky and sparsely spaced, and in many areas prolonged periods of over-grazing have exterminated the perennials and only annuals remain. Some perennials such as *Triodia* spp., which have little value for grazing, still predominate in these over-grazed areas, while in other parts of the tropics edible trees and bushes provide a useful source of fodder for sheep. In areas where nomadism predominates, a close bond develops between the shepherd and his flock, but the animals are seldom able to enjoy adequate nutrition throughout the year. In countries where there is a firm land-tenure system the average size of sheep properties may vary between 12,000 and 16,000 ha (30,000 and 40,000 acres) or be even larger. Some tropical countries are embarking on a programme of agrarian reform and are amalgamating small farms to create large estates, which are run on a cooperative basis.

In tropical Australia, Merino sheep predominate. They usually grow long-stapled, high-yielding wool with a spinning count of 64's to 70's. In tropical Queensland, the average fleece weight decreases from about 3·6 kg (8 lb) near the tropic of Capricorn, to about 3·1 kg (6·8 lb) per head at latitude 20°S. At the same time, staple length and fibre diameter decrease. Similarly, the sheep in the more northern areas are smaller and usually weigh less than those closer to the tropic. In recent years both Corriedale and Polwarth sheep have been exported to South American and African countries as well as to the sub-continent of India. The recent relaxation of the embargo on the export of Merinos from Australia has also permitted rams of this breed to go to other tropical countries. However, as inadequate nutrition, caused by the strictly seasonal and unreliable nature of the rains, is the principal problem confronting sheep raising under grazing conditions in the tropics, and many graziers practise nomadism with its attendant problems, it is difficult to forecast that these introduced breeds will improve the indigenous animals, other than by introducing genes for a higher ratio of secondary (wool-growing) to primary follicles.

Factors influencing wool production

The size and productivity of the flocks of sheep that can be maintained depend on the amount and the continuity of the food supply. These influence both the production per head, the quality of the wool and the reproduction rate. The essential difference between carpet- and apparel-wool sheep lies in the histology of the skin, which is a closely controlled genetic factor. Two main types of wool follicles are recognizable: primary follicles, each with a sweat gland, an erector muscle and a sebaceous gland; and secondary follicles with only a sebaceous gland. The first primary follicles commence to differentiate in the foetus after about 60 days of gestation, and pairs of satellites (lateral primary follicles) then appear, the members of the pair taking positions on opposite sides of the central follicles to form 'trios'. Other follicles, called 'regional secondary follicles', are then formed from the epidermis in the vicinity of these primary groups of follicles. Later formed follicles, called 'derived secondary follicles', develop as branches from the original secondaries. At birth, all the follicles are initiated, and the primary follicles and a few of the secondary follicles are producing fibres. During the first few months of post-natal life the remainder of the secondary follicles mature to produce fibres in normal lambs. Maturation of the secondary follicles requires thyroxine and can be delayed by sub-optimal nutrition. The ratio of secondary to primary follicles (S/P) is a useful parameter that distinguishes apparel-wool sheep from carpet-wool animals (Plates 16.1 and 16.2). Differences between the population of primary follicles per unit area are not large between breeds, but there is a large variation in the S/P ratios. Average S/P ratio ranges from about 17 to 20:1 in Merinos and down to about 3 to 5:1 for the long-staple, carpet-wool sheep. Corriedale sheep have an S/P ratio in the vicinity of 8 to 10:1 and Polwarths, having a higher proportion of Merino blood, have an S/P ratio that may range from 12 to 16:1.

The density of the fleece (the number of fibres per unit area) is determined mainly by the S/P ratio, as the number of primary follicles per unit area does not differ greatly between breeds. Thus, in Merinos the selection of sheep for high density has resulted chiefly in an increase in the number of secondary follicles. Differences in density between lines selected for high and for low fleece weight have been due chiefly to the number of primary and associated secondary follicles.

The relation of staple length to mean fibre length is very variable both between breeds and strains within a breed. The ratio of mean fibre length to staple length may vary in the Merino from 0·9 to 2·1 and changes in nutritional level seem to have little effect on this ratio. Fibre length (L) has a strong positive correlation with fibre diameter (D); the ratio (L/D) differs between breeds and between strains within breeds. There is some difference of opinion on the degree to which the ratio L/D varies with season and nutritional status; recent observations using radioactive techniques to measure fibres grown over short periods of time suggest that the ratio within staples from an individual sheep is rather more stable than earlier work indicated.

The fleece-bearing skin of most breeds is smooth, but Merinos often possess folds and wrinkles. The significance of folds and wrinkles on wool weight and quality has not been fully established. In general, fibres grown by wrinkly sheep tend to be more variable in length and diameter than those on smooth-skinned sheep. In Australian Merinos wrinkly sheep, in general, have a higher greasy fleece weight than smooth-skinned

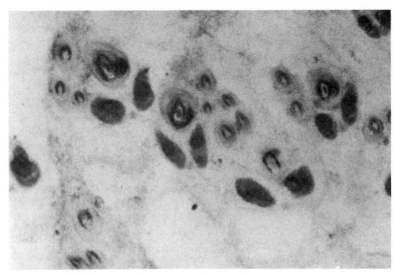

Plate 16.1   Primary and secondary wool follicles in the skin of Awassi sheep – a carpet-wool breed. The n_s/n_p ratio is 2·6 (Australian Wool Board).

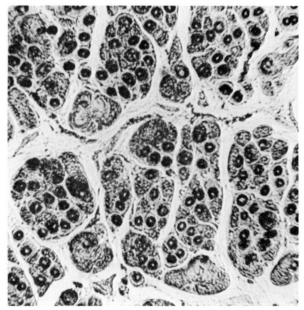

Plate 16.2   Primary and secondary wool follicles in the skin of a good average medium-woolled Merino sheep – an apparel-wool breed. The n_s/n_p ratio is approximately 23·0 (Australian Wool Board).

sheep. However, since the overall yields are less, wrinkly sheep probably only have a slightly higher production of clean wool. The development of skin folds is encouraged by a high nutritive level in early life, and there is evidence that increased levels of growth hormone in plasma are associated with skin-fold development. These effects tend to confuse the underlying relation between fold development and wool production.

Crimp frequency of wool is a character considered to be of great economic importance. However, there is still no clear understanding of the mechanism by which crimp is imposed on the fibre. Strains of Australian Merinos vary in crimp–diameter relationships. Nutritional changes have much greater effect on fibre diameter than on crimp frequency, so that crimp does not provide a reliable indication of fibre diameter. The rate of wool growth is also greatly influenced by the nutritional state of grazing sheep. Thus, marked variations in wool production per unit of time occur, and these are usually manifest by changes in fibre diameter and in staple length and are correlated with the occurrence of rain, that produces fresh green feed.

Commercial wool production is usually measured by the amount of greasy wool produced. The weight of the fleece is influenced by:

1. The weight of the wax, the suint, the dirt and vegetable matter, as well as the clean wool in each fleece;
2. Clean wool weight, which is influenced by the area of wool-bearing skin and the weight of wool per unit area of skin;
3. The wool-bearing area of skin, which is influenced by the smooth body surface and by the amount of wrinkle that occurs in the skin;
4. The weight of wool per unit area, which is influenced by the mean number of fibres per unit area of skin and the mean weight of each fibre;
5. The mean number of fibres per unit area of skin, which is influenced by the inheritance of sheep, particularly as it affects breeds and individuals within breeds, and by the level of nutrition their dams enjoyed prior to their birth and while they were young and continued to suckle;
6. The mean weight of each fibre that is influenced by the specific gravity of wool, which is fairly constant, and by the mean fibre volume;
7. The mean volume of the fibres, which is related to the mean cross-section or area of each fibre; this is usually written mathematically as πr^2 and indicates the importance of the diameter $(2r)$, which is determined by the inheritance of the animal and the level of nutrition available when growing the wool;
8. The mean fibre length, which is related to the mean staple length, but a conversion factor is employed because the fibres of each staple do not have the same length.

The apparent economic importance of these characters varies. Some are considered to be desirable for apparel-wool manufacture, and others

not so desirable for apparel manufacture but desirable for carpet manufacture. Hence the criteria for desirability changes with environments,
the use of the wool, and with markets. Increased fibre diameter means
increased wool weight, but may also mean decreased price per unit
weight, so compromises must be made between increased weight obtained
through larger fibre diameter and decreases in price received for the wool.
In Merinos, increased wrinkliness of the skin means a greater wool-
bearing surface, but also means shorter staple length, increased susceptibility to fly strike and, in some instances, decreased production rates.
Increases in fibre number must be regarded as a desirable source of increase in fleece weight and, up to a point, increase in staple length could
be desirable, but this would depend on the types of machines that were
to be used to comb the wool; French or continental combs are designed
to use shorter-stapled wool and the Noble or English comb to use
longer-stapled wool.

Smooth body surface area is influenced by body weight; both increase
together. Therefore, increased body weight could mean a larger wool-
bearing surface, but it may have disadvantages because heavy sheep may
eat more food, and therefore be more expensive to maintain. On the
other hand, increased body weight usually means increased meat production and an increased reproduction rate.

Wool characters of importance to the manufacturer of apparel wool
are as follows:

Fibre diameter.   Finer fibres are preferred for certain special fabrics.

Staple length.   Because modern manufacturing industries in many
countries are equipped with French or Continental combs there is a
current demand by the apparel manufacturers for shorter wools, but no
information is available to show that wools of shorter staple length
possess any technical or manufacturing advantages. Carding causes considerable breakage in the fibres; therefore, there does not appear to be
any valid reason for breeding for excessive uniformity in length.

Colour.   White wool without any coloured fibres in the fleece is to be
preferred.

Suint and wax content.   Breeding to develop a high content of wax in
the tip, with the resultant 'blocky tip' formation, is desirable, particularly
in the tropics where radiation is severe and can damage the sulphur
bonds in individual fibres and lead to great lack of tensile strength of
the wool grown on the sheep's back.

Character and crimp.   A well-defined crimp appears to have some
significance in processing performance and yarn preparation, and therefore influences buyers' preference.

Tensile strength. This should probably be included as another parameter because of its interaction and interrelationship with soundness–tenderness, fibre length and wastage in processing.

Characters in carpet wool of importance to the manufacturer are as follows:

Fibre diameter. Greater fibre diameter is required but uniformity of fibre diameter is not required.

Staple length. Carpet manufacture requires wools of long staple length, but some breeds of tropical sheep grow such long fibres that they have to be shorn twice a year.

Colour. Carpet wool offered for sale to carpet manufacturers needs to be unpigmented, and the frequency of unpigmented fleeces can be increased by simple selection for this character. Alternatively, the wool can be classed into white and different colours, i.e. brown and/or black, before it is sold. However, much of the wool grown by tropical animals is used in the home spinning and weaving of garments, rugs, blankets, etc. The patterns result from the use of white and naturally coloured wools, and careful thought must be given to the uses to which the wool will be put before embarking on a programme to breed all-white sheep.

Tensile strength. Tensile strength of carpet wool must be high, and some medullated fibres are permissible. These add to the resilience of the pile and hence to the good wearing qualities of the carpets.

Factors influencing the number of sheep

Wool production depends on the development and maintenance of flocks of sheep that can be exploited to man's advantage, and the size and the age and sex structure of the flock have a major influence on its productivity. Many productive characters, which are common to flocks in tropical areas, are influenced both by the system of husbandry and the inadequate and uneven plane of nutrition. Merino ewes do not exhibit the usual strict seasonal pattern of oestrus and anoestrus, and high atmospheric temperatures may render Merino rams temporarily infertile. However, studies on sheep indigenous to the tropics are too inadequate to generalize on the effects of the environment on reproductive performance as an indication of both the productivity of flocks and of the effects of the environmental influences.

In sheep husbandry, vital statistics can be used to:

1. Gather information about the ecology of flocks and breeds, with particular reference to their population dynamics including growth

rate, age and sex composition and generation length of populations, and to measure trends in either increases or decreases in numbers;
2. To manipulate the available selection pressure to change the genetic composition of the population of such productive characters as reproduction, wool growth or meat production.

There are several formulae that can be used in calculations from vital statistics that may be easily gathered. Thus, the growth rate of the flock breeding sheep will depend on the values that can be assigned to the components of the equation:

$$G = E \times \frac{M}{100} - (R + D)$$

Where G is the percentage increase in the flock in any one year, E the number of ewes mated as a percentage of the total flock, M the number of lambs as a percentage of ewes mated. R total sales and slaughterings as a percentage of the total flock and D the death rate as a percentage of the total flock. The parameters indicated by E, G, M, R and D are easily obtained and this formula has considerable field application.

Factors that determine the fertility and fecundity of sheep can be itemized as follows:

1. *Mating and gestation*
(a) The number of matings per oestrous period;
(b) The interval between first mating and conception;
(c) The percentage of females conceiving per mating;
(d) The number of females becoming pregnant as a percentage of those served per breeding season;
(e) The number of abortions per 100 pregnant females;
(f) The number of births.

2. *Offspring*
(a) The total number of lambs born;
(b) The number of stillborn lambs;
(c) The mortality between birth and sexual maturity;
(d) The number of offspring reaching sexual maturity.

These factors have been combined in a useful formula which gives convenient measures of fecundity and fertility in both rams and ewes. Ewes that do not return to oestrus within the normal period after service during the breeding season are usually considered to have conceived, and conception rate is calculated from assumed gestations from the first mating to give an index of male fertility as follows:

male fertility =

$$\frac{\text{number of pregnancies after first mating in the breeding season}}{\text{number of first matings in the breeding season}}$$

This index may be subject to error because of the inclusion of some non-pregnant ewes who do not return to service. The formula also fails to measure the fecundity of the ram because it gives no information about the number of progeny per ewe, and in this way underestimates the abilities of the ram flock.

The total number (N) of live lambs a ewe produces in her lifetime is a direct expression of her fecundity, but it also depends on the number of live lambs born per parturition, expressed by the equation N/n, where n is the total number of parturitions. The total number of lambs born per ewe, i.e. fecundity, depends upon (1) age at first breeding, (2) frequency of breeding, (3) the number of offspring produced at each breeding and (4) the length of the ewe's breeding life.

These parameters have been related in a formula using the interval between parturitions (k), age at last parturition (A), age at first parturition (a) and the total number of live lambs born (N), to provide a female fecundity index that may be represented algebraically as

$$\frac{N \times k - j}{(A+k)-a}$$

The importance of the values assigned to k should not be overlooked. In many tropical areas sheep are mated annually, but during drought periods k may have a value of 2 or 3 years, or during recovery of flock numbers in the post-drought periods it could be as short as 8 months. In addition, many infectious diseases may disrupt ovine reproduction in tropical countries, thereby increasing k.

A useful formula for estimating the number of surplus sheep in the flock is

$$S = \frac{2{,}000{,}000}{MN\,(100-D)}$$

where S is the percentage of young ewes that have to be selected to maintain flock number, M the percentage of lambs marked to ewes mustered at marking time, D the death rate of young female sheep between marking time and first mating and N the average number of times a ewe is mated in her lifetime.

By transforming the terms in the formula the values of M and/or N that would have to be maintained to allow predetermined levels of selection can be calculated, and the number of surplus sheep likely to be available with different policies for casting for age and different death rates can be found from the calculation of N. The values assigned to N are shown in Table 16.1.

Table 16.1 *Progressive totals of the number of matings that can be obtained from an initial flock of 1,000 young ewes which experience mean death rates of 5 or 10 per cent per annum, and values for N*

Age of ewes at completion of mating (year)	5% loss per annum			10% loss per annum		
	Ewes surviving for mating	Cumulative total of matings	Value of N	Ewes surviving for mating	Cumulative total of matings	Value of N
2	1,000	1,000	1·000	1,000	1,000	1·000
3	950	1,950	1·950	900	1,900	1·900
4	902	2,852	2·852	810	2,710	2·710
5	857	3,709	3·709	729	3,439	3·439
6	814	4,523	4·523	656	4,095	4·095
7	773	5,296	5·296	590	4,685	4·685

Breeding sheep for wool production

In setting up a breeding programme for wool production a clear statement is needed of the aims of the programme, i.e. is it designed to breed for apparel or carpet wool, or to upgrade carpet-wool-producing sheep into apparel-wool sheep? A statement is also needed on the extent to which the measured performance of individuals and of groups of animals can be used as an aid to selection. Knowledge is required about the structure of the breeds in relation to the existing stud sheep industry. The structure of the Australian Merino industry may serve as an example. It can be summarized as being:

1. A small number (less than 24) so-called 'parent' studs that have been closed or practically closed to introductions for a large number of years;
2. A medium number (about 300) 'daughter' studs which constantly draw rams from the same parent stud or a related daughter stud;
3. A large number (about 1,400) general studs that may buy rams from two or more unrelated studs; and
4. An exceptionally large number (120,000) of flocks which obtain their rams from one or other of the studs.

This pattern of breed structure can be of importance to developing countries that are planning to improve wool production of their flocks through breeding, as well as to those countries that are embarking on agrarian reform. It is necessary to have a small number of fairly large, superior flocks that can be used to breed improved, half-bred rams that can be distributed to other village or communal flocks. In such a system it is usually necessary to insist that the male offspring from the half-bred, improved rams are the only ones allowed to reach maturity and to serve as sires in the village or in nomadic flocks.

Generally, selection can be used to choose: (1) rams to breed rams, (2) rams to breed ewes, (3) ewes to breed rams or (4) ewes to breed ewes.

Over 75 per cent of the total genetic progress, available through selection, comes from the choice of rams; therefore, it is usually recommended that in classing the rams the work should proceed in the normal way. This is because the stud master has to meet the requirements of particular markets for the class of rams he offers for sale. Within these requirements he can, with the aid of measurement, easily make his selection for productivity. Once the young potential sires have been chosen they can be shorn and the following measurements made: (1) greasy fleece weight, (2) percentage yield, (3) clean scoured fleece weight calculated from (1) and (2), (4) staple length, (5) fibre diameter, (6) crimps per unit length and (7) a crimp fineness ratio determined from (5) and (6).

In carpet-wool production the percentage of medullated fibres can also be determined. Fortunately, the heritability for all these traits is reasonably high in the Australian Merino and progress should be made by mass selection for either or all of them. However, the matter is not quite as simple as this statement would infer – some characters are related phenotypically and some genotypically, so that selection for one character may enhance or detract from improvement in another. Thus, selection for greasy fleece weight or for clean fleece weight alone may lead to an increased number of crimps per inch, and thus to a decreased price per unit of weight for the fleece.

Thus, after the sheep breeder has determined from the formula

$$S = \frac{2,000,000}{MN(100 - D)}$$

the selection pressure he can exert on the ewe flock, he must decide on the characters, whether they be useful traits or faults, on which he will place emphasis. Similarly, in choosing the rams he must place emphasis on the characters that his aims dictate. In a programme designed to upgrade carpet-wool-growing sheep, the main emphasis will be placed on rams from breeds with a high S/P ratio. After such a programme has been pursued for four to five sheep generations (20 to 25 years), the trait for high S/P ratios will be well established and more attention can be given to other traits considered to be important.

There is evidence that in Australian Merinos, selection for high fecundity is likely to be rewarding, and the selection of rams that are themselves one of a pair of twins, and ewes that score well by the formula

$$\frac{N \times k}{(A + k) - a}$$

may be helpful.

As far as is known, the heritabilities of productive traits of breeds indigenous to the tropics as yet have hardly been explored. This could well be considered to be a research task warranting attention.

Further Reading

Moule, G. R. *Fleece Measurement for Queensland Stud Masters.* Qld. Dept. Prim. Indust. Div. Anim. Indust., Pamphlet No. 42. Queensland Dept. Primary Industry: Brisbane, 1956.

Moule, G. R. Sheep and wool production in semi-arid pastoral Australia. *Wld. Rev. Anim. Prod.,* **4** (17), 40–53; (19–20), 46–58 (1967).

Moule, G. R. The epizootiology of diseases causing infertility of sheep. *6th Meeting FAO Expert Panel Livestock Infertility.* FAO: Rome, 1968.

Moule, G. R. Vital statistics in sheep and wool production. *Anim. Breed. Abstr.*, **39,** 623–6 (1971).
Moule, G. R. Factors influencing the productivity of Australian sheep. *Ind. J. Anim. Sci.*, **41,** 751–74 (1971).
Turner, H. N. Measurements as an aid to selection in breeding sheep for wool production. *Anim. Breed. Abstr.*, **24,** 87–118 (1956).

Appendix 1

Nomadism in Africa

by **P. R. Baker**
*Dean, School of Development Studies, University of East Anglia, Norwich,
United Kingdom*

For most people the image of the African nomad is essentially a romantic
and inaccurate one: whether it be Valentino's urbane sheikh, the Riff of
the *Desert Song* or the noble savagery of the Masai. The stark misery
revealed by the calamitous drought of 1968 to 1973, which beggared
much of monsoonal Africa and Asia, stands in stark contrast to the
romantic image and has revealed finally and dramatically the rapid
breakdown of the nomadic way of life. It is all too easy to attribute the
parlous state of nomadism to the recent drought or more general
'desertification', but to do so is to ignore the mounting evidence of a
breakdown from within the system rather than through the inevitable
action of nature. It is only now, so very late in the day, that developers
and other interested parties of change have come to appreciate how much
the reality of nomadism is at variance with popular images, generalities
and 'informed opinion'. The sad fact emerges that our knowledge of the
day-to-day working of individual nomadic communities is seriously
deficient, and is in most cases inadequate for predicting the impact of
economic, technical or social change. The failure to appreciate this simple
fact in the past is, arguably, the principal factor explaining the disastrous
record of planning in areas of pastoral nomadism. If any good at all can
come out of a calamity such as the 1968–73 drought, it is that it may
shock people into rethinking old ideas while the grazing lands are given
a temporary reprieve and the shattered herds are gradually rebuilt. In
order to make serious use of this brief interval it is necessary to re-
appraise the African nomad, his way of life and the way that others
see him: particularly those who now shape policy and make decisions
affecting both him and his environment.

The first, and most fundamental, consideration in any appraisal of
nomadism in Africa should be its essential diversity and variety. Apart
from stating that these people migrate, further generalities become
dangerous and misleading. Even the nature of the movement itself,
whether it be vertical transhumance (Lozi, Turkana) or horizontal
movement (Masai, Tuareg, Jie), is varied and attributable to combinations of different factors. The most common division is into 'nomadic'
and 'semi-nomadic' by which it is usually implied that the former com-

munity has no fixed home while the latter has a home base of an identifiable nature. If this is taken to mean that the 'nomadic' community is forever wandering, then that is almost universally at variance with the truth. Even the most renowned of the *grandes nomades,* the *Bedu* of the Arabian desert, have fixed migrations and regular bases. So with the wanderers of the Sahara; the detailed moves may show an infinite variety of minor changes, but the basic pattern is regular and largely predictable. Where communities live in tents or temporary shelters, and the entire family moves, as with the Somali, then there is a temptation to see this in terms of a great wandering. This can be extremely misleading as it implies a randomness of behaviour which simply is not present when the movements are logged and studied in detail.

Very often the confusion over 'nomadic' and 'semi-nomadic' arises on account of the degree of cultivation which is practised by part or all of the mobile community. This again is part of the essential diversity of nomadic life in Africa which, for long, has been concealed under a deceptive cover of outward similarity and simplicity which so effectively belies the truth. In contrast to the Somali, the Turkana of northern Kenya and the Sakkalaven of Madagascar; the Jie of East Africa exemplify the more common type of pastoral semi-nomadic society in which livestock complement, or are complemented by, crop production. In the case of the Jie this farming activity is the particular responsibility of the women who remain on their modest plots along with the elders and the children, while the young men take the family herds westwards in search of both water and pasture. For much of the year, therefore, the two sections of the community eat very different diets and lead very different lives. To neglect this dichotomy when planning change in Jieland would be to compromise whatever development was intended. For instance, it has been a common practice to address public meetings on agricultural reform and new techniques in crop management during tours of the area by government officers. The effectiveness of the message was, however, largely lost as a result of the fact that only the men used to turn up to this 'men's business'.

It is fair to say that in nearly all cases of nomadism in Africa, movement is a matter of necessity arising from the level of technology prevailing within the community and the circumstances of the physical environment. There is little, if any, evidence of a romantic attachment to endless movement so that, for instance, "communities resist settlement as it would deprive them of a communion with nature". Nomadism is a hard and testing faith and its hold is demonstrably weak. Where, as in Saudi Arabia, it has been possible for the nomads to trade-in their camel and traditional life for a V8 truck or taxi and an urban existence they have done so, to the extent that the *Bedu* who once formed 70 per cent of the population now form less than 8 per cent. Where settlement has been resisted, the reason lies not in the nomad's soul but in defective planning which settles him on a black-cotton swamp, as in Uganda;

makes him an agent of soil destruction, as in Masailand, Kenya; or simply turns him into a highly regulated, second-class citizen bound around with petty restrictions, as in Ethiopia. In nearly all cases migration has a sound environmental basis.

Most frequently the move is due to the intense seasonality of the climatic regime in the marginal areas where pastoralists predominate. In the wetter, equatorial region and along the monsoonal coastlands of West Africa, the raising of cattle is difficult on account of the prevalence of bovine disease and the dominance of crop agriculture. The major distribution of cattle is around the central humid 'core' as is shown very dramatically by Deshler (1963) in Fig. A1.1. This outer belt extends from the Guinea savanna receiving 600 mm of rainfall through steppeland to the margins of the Namib or Sahara deserts and includes areas of quite extraordinary 'hostility' from which nomads have for centuries managed to derive an existence.

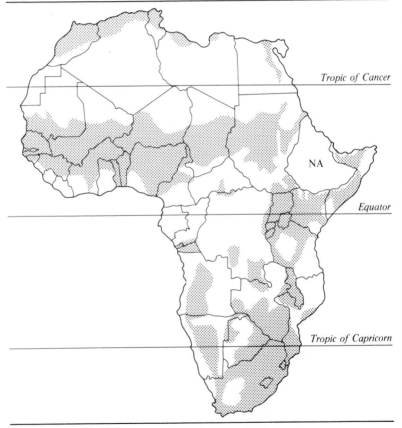

Fig. A1.1   Distribution of cattle in Africa (Deshler, 1963).

The marginal rangelands are characterized by a seasonality and variability of rainfall which becomes increasingly accentuated towards their arid extremities. This seasonality, in turn, gives rise to the 'dichotomous environment' which is characteristic of most nomadic areas so that communities may survive only by taking advantage of short periods of plenty in different locations. The factor in short supply may be water, as in parts of Karamoja (Uganda) where there is often forage which remains uneaten as there is no water sufficiently close for cattle to be able to drink while grazing. Alternatively, the shortage may be of forage where annual grasses disappear and the necessity arises to find perennials around marshes or swamps or to take animals to graze over the stubble fields of cooperative agricultural neighbours. Again, as with communities along the Upper Nile and in the western savanna of the Sudan, a contributory factor in the movement may be the incidence of biting flies and mosquitoes. In northeastern Uganda, the incidence of East Coast fever in the perennial long-grass zone of dry-season grazing, once the rains arrive, forces the Karamojong to return to the homestead area.

Some writers, such as Ruthenberg (1971), have compared nomadic pastoralism in Africa and elsewhere in the tropics to an evolutionary parallel with shifting cultivation. Both systems are based on the mobility of the community and both systems are characterized by an almost total absence of capital investment in land: the motto being 'use up and move on'. One fundamental difference may well be concealed by this comparison and that is the range of alternatives available to the two different communities. The shifting cultivator may well occupy an area of equatorial rain-forest which may be adapted to a wide variety of land-use functions. The pastoralist, utilizing range with perhaps an average of 300 mm, or less, of rainfall irregularly spread over the years, cannot always forsake nomadism for an alternative form of land use. In the driest areas there may be no alternative at all to nomadism unless modern technology is able to make available deep ground-water reserves. Yet, for at least two decades, every government in Africa which has authority over nomadic communities has committed itself to a policy of sedentarization.

The essential diversity of nomadism in tropical Africa is not confined to the nature of movement, the scale of movement or the periodicity of movement, even though within these categories there is an almost infinite variety of combinations. In addition, there is the diversity of the productive base of the various communities. Some, such as the Masai, derive their sustenance almost entirely from the recurrent products of their animals, such as blood and milk, and scorn crop agriculture. Even these, however, may have a diet which is varied, depending upon the incidence of natural death among their livestock, for although few pastoral nomads regularly slaughter their large stock for food, the depredations of nature and predators may provide fairly regular 'windfalls' of meat. The importance of small stock, the 'small change' of the cattle economy, has long been neglected as a result of a preoccupation on the part of observers with the ritual and tradition associated with cows and camels. Goats and sheep are frequent camp-followers, and in some regions they form the basis of the economy. Almost everywhere they form part of the meat supply of the nomads. Again, non-cultivating nomads such as the *Bedu* or the West African *grandes nomades*, may well have a diet which is based on cereals such as rice, wheat, sorghum or millet. This grain cannot always be obtained from their immediate environment and is provided instead by way of long-established patterns of trade between the semi-arid range and cultivated land in other regions. This trade may be an equal exchange of animals for grain between communities on the margins of the pastoral and agricultural economies, or it may be an unequal exchange, as in parts of West Africa and the Hejaz, where the cropped areas are maintained by vassals of the nomads.

In other regions, such as in the western savanna of the Sudan, the sedentary cultivators and the nomads may all belong to the same 'extended' families.

All too often the exchange of livestock for crop products was based on inequality – an inequality which derived from the traditional martial superiority of the nomads. Being mobile, and, in essence, not tied to any particular location for survival, they could impose their rule or will on the vulnerable agricultural communities who lived in fear of the burning of their crops. The prudence associated with the cultivator is a luxury that the nomad can ill afford as herds may be decimated by disease, drought or warfare. The nomad's answer to this situation was to offset losses by retaining as many livestock as possible and by raiding others. The raiding, however, far from being the sport that it is often characterized as representing, was a form of loss adjustment and part of an overall survival strategy.

The symbiosis between nomad and cultivator is perhaps best demonstrated along the Sahelian zone of West Africa. The sahel, which appropriately means boundary or shoreline, was for centuries a zone of interaction, sometimes peaceful, sometimes hostile. The cultivators and nomads made long-standing arrangements for animals to graze over the stubble fields after harvest, the dry-season liveweight losses of the livestock being reduced and the cultivated areas benefiting from the addition of manure. Understandings over the use of permanent water and cattle trails persisted for long periods as, for example, in Niger where nomads from the same community went back year after year to the same areas of cultivated land in districts where they were known. Occasionally they would herd animals owned by the farmers, running them with their own animals and returning them to their owners as and when they were needed, or they would bring some useful commodity such as salt from the interior of the range as part payment for their privileges.

On other occasions the relationship acquired more threatening or intimidating forms such as the rule of the great Fulani empire in West

Africa or the more subtle authority wielded by the Tutsi in Rwanda through the clientage or *buhake* system. In the latter case the authority of the Tutsi over the Hutu majority (*c.* 85 per cent before the massacres of 1964) was established initially by force of arms and their superiority was associated with mobility. However, in time the Hutu came to associate the superiority of the Tutsi with their possession of cattle and so the Hutu were willing to accept the confinements of bondage in order to obtain the prestigious animals from their Tutsi overlords. In this way, interestingly, the nomads brought their animals into an area where nomadism was no longer necessary and this pastoral autocracy gradually gained hegemony over an almost entirely agricultural environment. In general, however, the pastoralists, as long as they remained pastoralists and nomads, continued to inhabit the semi-arid lands on the fringes of cultivation. Some nomads gradually made the transition and became, like the Acholi and Teso peoples of Uganda, settled cultivators, but they still retained the practice of bride price and an affection for the old ways which encouraged them to breed substantial numbers of cattle and to invest spare capital in livestock.

So it is clear that the term 'pastoral nomad' conceals an enormous wealth of diversity which makes generalization on the topic of nomad development perilous and speculative. Yet generalizations have been the order of the day.

In addition to the diversity of types of pastoral nomad in Africa, there is the further question of the complexity of their life style which so rarely reveals itself to casual observation but is, nevertheless, fundamental. The basis of the pastoralist's pattern of activity is survival. This, of course, may be safely said of anyone, but for few people in the world is the problem quite so immediate or stark. For the nomad is aware that he is, perhaps, the least insulated individual on earth: if the animals succumb to drought, depredation or disease there is no alternative means of support for his family in their hostile environment. Over the centuries a body of lore has been built up, based on the bitter fruits of experience and a detailed knowledge of the minutiae of the physical environment. On account of its very rudimentary material culture necessitated by mobility, the nomadic community displays to the world an air of primitive simplicity. The real strength of the community lies in what cannot be seen: what is contained in the heads of the elders, what is sung to the children around the fire and what the outsider labels tradition.

Many have come and observed the nomad and his quaint ways and have seen in the tradition of the nomadic community a barrier to progress. Tradition is presented as an unbending set of rules mindlessly passed from generation to generation defining, without exception, what is right and wrong, good and bad. In truth, the traditions are followed not because the present generation knows nothing else but because long and cruel experience has proven, within the confines of past technology, that these are the best rules to follow. More precisely it would be correct to say that these *were* the best rules to follow for, as we shall see, the rules may remain the same but the game has changed almost out of recognition, outpacing the capacity of nomadic societies to adjust. Sadly, this wealth of local knowledge has been ignored or scorned in the past so that rarely, if ever, has anyone seriously approached a pastoral nomad and asked his reasoned appraisal of an area – and yet who better to help answer the detailed problems of soil, water and disease? When the rare detailed studies of daily life have been made among pastoral communities, the complexity and comprehensiveness of the survival strategies which emerge are very impressive and, within the confines of material technology, it is rarely possible to make any radical improvements on the old ways. However, circumstances have rendered the old ways not only inappropriate in many circumstances, but positively dangerous from the point of view of environmental conservation.

The nomad has many ways of minimizing risk and the exact stratagem selected varies from community to community and from season to season, for there is a whole armoury of strategies related to a whole variety of combinations and sequences of events. The choice of, perhaps, a particular split of animals between one area and another ultimately comes down to the fine spatial judgement of risk on the part of the herder, and that choice has repercussions on future choices. For, in the game of pastoral nomadism the alternatives for the herder are many and frequent. Do I herd all my animals myself or do I divide them among my relatives in different areas thereby reducing the loss by disease and raiding? Do I move towards the dry season grazing rapidly or slowly? Do I run 20 per cent large stock and 80 per cent small stock or a different combination in view of the pressures on grazing? Do I keep younger and more prolific cows which may die of disease or older, less prolific animals which may have acquired a high disease tolerance? Is it better for me to keep the animals through this drought and hope that they survive or sell them for rock-bottom prices to the wise Somali dealer and buy food? ... and so forth. In this way a body of responses to different combinations and values of variables resides in the lore of the community, and yet that lore is constantly being modified in the light of contemporary circumstances and experience. Tragically, the quantum jump of European technology in these areas has outstripped the ability of the lore to adjust and this, in essence, is why the measured ways of traditional pastoral nomadism are collapsing all over Africa.

It would be quite wrong to suggest that old nomadic Africa was a land at peace with itself and at one with God. The relationship that existed between man, his animals and the environment was harsh and capricious, allowing little opportunity for contemplating a future beyond the next season. Yet a relationship was always evolved that afforded the herder and his family the best prospect of survival within the confines of contemporary technology. The details of this strategy for survival vary from group to group and from area to area, but the underlying rationale is common. In an environment characterized by variability and a high degree of risk the concept of 'average' conditions is meaningless, and so the nomad organizes his herding on the basis of survival under the worst conditions. Several writers (Brown, 1971; Allan, 1965) have used the concept of the 'basic herd' in connection with pastoral societies, by which they mean the minimum number of animals which the herder considers necessary to ensure the community's survival in times of natural calamity. Over and above this number, extra animals provide additional insurance and are, therefore, intimately linked in the mind of the pastoralist with survival. This, rather than popular generalizations about pride and prestige, often explains the quantitative mentality of herders and their supposed conservatism. Where the very extensive land requirements of cattle or camels (5 to 16 ha (12 to 40 acres) per head) make it impossible for one herder to manage his animals even with the full cooperation of his 'family', livestock may be agisted to poorer relatives, thus diffusing the survival strategy through the community.

Against this reliance upon numbers, nature matched the exigencies of drought and animal disease which regularly thinned out the stock and prevented the 'insurance' concept getting out of hand and destroying the rangelands. At the same time human disease allowed only slow and episodic growth of the herding community. In this way a precarious sort of balance developed in many areas, although it was a very dynamic state of affairs based on peaks and troughs of plenty and deprivation. Certainly, on some occasions nature gained the upper hand and communities migrated *en masse* to pastures new, as seems to have happened in Ethiopia. From this land nomads spread through East Africa spawning pastoral kingdoms such as Banyoro, Kitara and Rwanda. It is true that, in the course of time, cattle and/or camels have acquired very important and distinct social and economic functions within pastoral societies, so that it has become almost impossible for a nomad to consider his herd as being too large, but these social attributes, however, must never be allowed to obscure the very basic subsistence role of the animals. The Western concept of a 'surplus' cannot easily be applied in these circumstances because the part played by animals in a pastoral society is complex and multifaceted and this, in turn, helps to explain the sometimes 'obstinate' reluctance of pastoralists to increase their offtake into the commercial market economy, for stock are wealth and the medium of economic and social change.

This then was the traditional picture, but what we see now is a hybrid of traditional activities and drastic changes brought about by colonial and post-colonial intervention which have driven pastoral societies to the edge of destruction and turned many rangelands into proto-deserts. Initially, the European presence inadvertently introduced diseases such as rinderpest and smallpox which worked havoc among tribes such as the Masai so that many of the observations made of nomadic societies, by early colonial authorities, were based on exceptional circumstances. This led the authorities in parts of East Africa to grant 'unused' land in the nomad domain to indigenous sedentary farmers or to European settlers. In this way much of the dry season grazings of the Masai became settler ranchland and the reserves of the Karamojong were given to the agricultural Suk people. At the same time casually conceived administrative boundaries balkanized Fulani or Masai country into states or spheres of influence. Movement was frowned upon by administrators as it bred hostility with neighbouring states or made the nomads very difficult to tax. From a very early date in colonial history legislation was enacted in many countries which failed to recognize the fundamental role of mobility in a nomadic system and in a dichotomous environment. In parallel with this went a continuing expansion of cultivation encouraged by the peace of the suzerain power and the discrimination in favour of settled communities. All along the West African savanna–sahel zones there was a steady encroachment of cultivators into dry-season grazing which led to a breakdown of the old symbiosis between nomad and farmer. The very humid conditions of the 1920s and 1930s encouraged the spread of cultivation into areas of Mali and Niger which are not suitable for the long-term survival of farming. The formerly superior pastoralist fast became the underdog and scapegoat of most environmental deterioration and his mobility was regarded as a rootlessness which bred irresponsibility.

The colonial era also saw the collapse of the old relationship between man, animal and environment, for many of the former checks on herd size were reduced or eliminated by an entirely new technology: water was provided from deep aquifers, vaccines were developed against diseases of livestock while the administration enforced a peace which limited raiding and warfare. The human population, too, began to grow at an accelerating rate, increasing the demand for family herds. All this was happening within the traditional framework of the 'insurance' concept and an economic and social interchange based on cattle, not money, as wealth, The net effect was to increase the size of herds dramatically while the off-take for the market remained pitifully low. Hence the frequent failure of canning factories in Somalia, Uganda, Malagasy Republic, Tanzania and other countries. Complementary advances in pasture development never occurred because the system of communal grazing rendered individual initiative an act of hostility while the prospect of cooperative action within such a loose and acephalous grouping remained largely impracticable.

So began the steady degradation of grazings seen all over monsoonal Africa whether along the sahelian margin, the Masai plains or the cattle posts of Botswana. The 'creeping desert' which first attracted the attention of the authorities in French West Africa and Nigeria in the early 1930s has now reached alarming proportions. Even though some writers speculate on changes in the world pressure system, dust in the atmosphere and retreating monsoons to explain the transformation of rangeland into desert, the evidence of man-made destruction appears incontrovertible.

The 1968–73 drought in monsoonal Africa has brought this creeping crisis into sharp focus and, although it allows a brief respite for new strategies to be evolved, it is clear that an entirely fresh approach is required to the problems of pastoral nomadism, otherwise the former process of destruction will repeat itself. In fact, what appears to have happened during the 6-year crisis period was not the visitation of some new and terrible natural calamity, for droughts are one of the facts of pastoral life. Instead, the resilience of the pastoral environment to withstand drought has been diminished decade by decade so that each drought period is more drastic in effect than the last.

Clearly, the priority must be to establish a balance once more between man, animals and the environment. Concepts such as carrying capacity are extremely difficult to apply in areas where climatic variability is so marked, but the effort will have to be made so that, eventually with controlled management, the carrying capacity will gradually improve as pastures regenerate. In some areas, such as the riverine states of the sahel or along the Nubian sandstone aquifers of southern Libya and Egypt, water is available to stabilize or settle the nomadic communities. It may well become common, as has happened in Saudi Arabia, for the 'family' to split its activities around an irrigated plot and periodic forays into the rangelands in the wet season. In Arabia, especially around the Nafud, *Bedu* now drive small water tankers and carry their stock in open trucks, thus making use of waterless range and conserving the liveweight of their animals. A similar proposal has been made for changes in the management of the livestock of the Bakhtiari nomads of western Iran.

For some states, such as Mali, the future of nomadism is critical unless some alternative form of management can be found for the cattle, which yield 75 per cent of the country's export earnings. Settlement is possible only where water is available and, even then, much of the Saharan water is fossil water which, once used, is lost for ever. Clearly, the overstocking of natural range must not be allowed to recur, but in order to prevent it alternative opportunities must be found for the excess nomad populations and that will not be easy in countries as poor as Mauritania, Mali, Niger or Chad. Somalia has opted for the radical solution of settling nomads in fishing or farming while placing its faith in a commune/cooperative approach to improving traditional pastoralism. At the time of writing (January 1976) this development is still at an embryonic stage, but, possibly because Somalia is the only African country where nomads predominate, it will be an experiment worthy of being taken seriously. If it succeeds, it will be almost the only pastoral nomad development scheme in Africa to have done so.

Over much of the drier parts of Africa it is not easy to see an alternative to the mobile system of the nomad and the fear must be that, with the passing of nomadism, vast areas of the continent will become un-productive; for there is almost nothing other than livestock which they can support. Already, the evidence from Saudi Arabia shows that the hardships of desert life are hastily put aside when alternative oppor-tunities are available. As it is so difficult to provide basic social services for the wandering communities they will soon come to appreciate their disadvantage *vis-à-vas* their settled or urban counterparts. This process, which particularly influences the young, is often exacerbated in most African countries by the urban or settled-agricultural bias of the ruling authorities who consider that nomads are often stubborn, primitive and reactionary. The decision-makers also have the problem of their own inability to perceive or cope with the breakdown of pastoral nomadism, which is essentially a complex, interrelated ecological problem involving water, marketing, social norms, agricultural, veterinary science, law and order and many other parameters. No single government authority usually has terms of reference to handle this situation effectively and, instead, various symptoms of the ecological breakdown are tackled *in vacuo*.

The 1970s should mark an era of drastic change, not only as a result of the calamitous drought but because of the lessons that should have been learned from this apocalyptic warning. It is evident that long-term strategies are needed which preserve the best of nomadism while accept-ing the inevitable changes in life style which are coming. The strategy will vary from area to area as the opportunities, land-use systems, social organization and government policies change, but, most essentially, the strategy must be based on detailed, local, integrated research. In some cases a superior alternative to nomadism may present itself, but in most cases a variant on this theme of mobility will probably be the logical choice. So far this decade we have seen the establishment of the Inter-national Livestock Centre for Africa which proposes to conduct its research activities on a system basis, ensuring the necessary integration; the Ecological Management of Arid and Semi-arid Rangelands Pro-gramme (UNEP/FAO); and a multitude of studies of nomad life arising from the drought. With the exception of recent work in the Sudan (Hunting Technical Services, 1974) there are as yet almost no data on the workings of pastoral nomadism (energy flows, basic herd requirements, census details, realistic sociological studies or nutrition surveys, etc.) and so planning still lacks a solid base. There is still, alas, a preoccupation with imported technology and tinkering about with animal health, water development and the like. All these fields of expertise will become effective only when they are successfully integrated. In terms of the tradi-tional nomadic pastoralist we are probably witnessing the last generation, but it is to be hoped that the best of this centuries-old system shattered by the pace of change may become the basis of future development where it is appropriate. However, for this to be successful major changes in subsistence patterns, commercialization and the basis of social exchange will probably be required to encourage the flow of animals to the market.

References

Allan, W. (1965) *The African Husbandman*. Oliver and Boyd: Edinburgh.
Brown, L. (1971) The biology of pastoral man. *Biol. Cons.*, **3**, 93–100.
Deshler, W. (1963) Cattle in Africa. *Geog. Rev.*, **53**, 52–8.
Hunting Technical Services (1974) *Southern Darfur Land Use Planning Survey*. Annex 3, 'Animal Resources and Range Ecology'. Hunting Technical Services: Boreham Wood, UK.
Ruthenberg, H. (1971) *Farming Systems in the Tropics*. Oxford Univ. Press: London.

Further Reading

Baker, P. R. *Pastoralism and Progress: the Development of Traditional Herding in Africa*. Univ. East Anglia: Norwich, 1975.
Irons, W. and Dyson-Hudson, N. *Perspectives on Nomadism*. Brill: Leiden, 1972.
Johnson, D. L. *The Nature of Nomadism*. Univ. Chicago: Chicago, 1969.
Monod, T. L. (ed.). *Pastoralism in Tropical Africa*. Oxford Univ. Press: London, 1975.
Stenning, D. J. *Savannah Nomads*. Oxford Univ. Press: London, 1959.
UNESCO. *Nomades et Nomadisme au Sahara*. UNESCO: Paris, 1963.

Appendix 2

Marking Livestock for Identification

It is generally desirable that farmers and/or pastoralists should be able to identify each of the animals owned by them and often essential that they should be able to prove identification to the satisfaction of others. Marking obviates disputes over lost, stolen or strayed livestock. It is of course essential for all breeders to be able to identify their animals and for all those livestock farmers who keep records.

Livestock may be marked in a temporary manner or permanently. Temporary marking is required for heat detection, disease eradication, for culling purposes, etc., and can be achieved in a variety of ways. Usually by use of a dyestuff, either dissolved in water or a fatty base, that will mark the coat of the animal for a longer or shorter period. Dyes are now marketed that will persist for several months. It is also possible to use a hair bleach solution for semi-permanent marking. Bleach marking will persist for up to one year.

The most common methods of permanent marking are by branding, tattooing, notching and tagging. Muffle prints can be used to identify cattle, but the method is cumbersome and its utility limited.

Branding

This is probably the oldest and certainly the most widely used method of identifying animals. A number, letter or design is seared on the skin or on appendage using a hot iron, caustic soda or branding irons cooled to a very low temperature. Numbers are generally used to differentiate individual animals, but a design or a combination of letters may be used to denote membership of a specific herd. The symbols may be government registered.

The suitably fashioned iron is heated to a bright red, but not white heat, and is applied to the skin with light pressure for not more than 3 seconds. The numbers, letters or design should be sufficiently large to be read at some distance from the animal and each should be at least 2·5 cm (1 in) apart from the other, in order to prevent sloughing.

The easiest and most visible place to apply the brand to cattle is on the upper aspect of the quarter, trunk or shoulder. However, in any of these positions a brand ruins a valuable part of the hide and for this reason branding should take place on the cheek, the forearm or the hind limb below the level of the stifle.

Cattle and buffaloes are often branded on the forearm, camels on the cheek and/or the neck.

The operation is unquestionably painful and other methods of branding, apart from using a hot iron, have been attempted. Branding with the use of caustic soda is cumbersome, cannot be used in the humid tropics and is probably no more humane than hot-iron branding. The new method of 'freeze' branding is now widely advocated. Freeze branding irons are usually made of solid brass and the coolant is usually liquid nitrogen or a mixture of ethyl alcohol and solid carbon dioxide. The brands are kept in the coolant and applied to the skin of the animal for between 15 and 30 seconds. Freeze branding gives very good identification, particularly on black-coated animals. The method is, however, very slow compared with the normal hot-iron branding, supplies of liquid nitrogen or carbon dioxide must be available and considerable care is needed during the operation. We do not recommend it as a method for normal marking operation in the tropics, although it could be very useful on experimental farms, etc.

Branding can also be carried out on the insensitive horn or hoof of the animals with a branding iron of appropriate size. The disadvantage of this form of branding is that numbers on the horn can only be read on close inspection and that hoof brands grow out very rapidly.

Tattooing

This operation has two drawbacks. First, the tattooed figures cannot be read without handling and close inspection of the animal, and secondly, tattoo marks are not easily legible on pigmented skin.

Special equipment is required. Tattoo imprints are most conveniently made on the inner side of the ear or they may be made on the undersurface of the root of the tail.

Tattooing is the most suitable method of marking young animals that are to be continuously handled and that can be marked for a second time, in some other manner, as adults. It is therefore widely used for marking piglets and young dairy calves.

Unsatisfactory results are most commonly caused by dirty equipment, bad ink and misapplication of the equipment.

Notching

When properly carried out notching is a very satisfactory method of marking. The notches can, however, be easily changed so that fraud is relatively simple. Ear notching is practised on cattle, buffaloes, sheep, goats and pigs, but is probably most satisfactory when applied to pigs (Fig. 12.5) and long-eared sheep and goats. A method that can be used for cattle is shown in Fig. A2.1.

Notching, slitting or punching the edge of the web of the feet of poultry

Example: number 5239

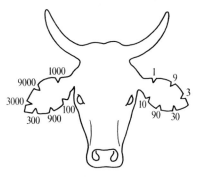

A method enabling 9999 head
of cattle to be marked

Fig. A2.1   A method of ear-notch identification for cattle.

has been used as a method of marking in the past. It is not a very
satisfactory method.

Notches in the ear are usually made with a pair of special pliers.
Round holes, in the centre of the ear, can be made with a punch. It is
of little use notching the ears of very young animals as the punched
ears grow together again. Tattooing the ear of the very young animal
and then ear-notching at weaning is a very suitable combination of
marking methods.

Tagging

Tags or labels made of metal, wood or plastic are either fixed in the ear
of the animal or on some other appendage or they may be attached to
chains or collars around the neck or the horns. There is also a type of
press-stud ear tag. The number of different types available is now very
large. In the past tags were only used by experimental stations but their

use has spread. Under intensive managerial conditions they are undoubtedly very useful, but they are not generally recommended for use under extensive conditions.

Wing tagging or banding is the most common and satisfactory method of recognizing poultry. A light metal split ring, or a plastic tag that stands out from the wing, bearing a number, is inserted through a small slit made in the fold of the skin on the front edge of the wing opposite the elbow.

Leg banding is another form of tagging used with poultry. The band is generally made of light metal and is just sufficiently large to slip over the foot. These bands are not easily read but they are easily lost.

Index

Hyphaenae coriacca, 630
Hypomagnesemia, 35

Iban pig, 550
Ibex, *see Capra ibex*
Ice-cream, 676
Identical twin cattle, 15
Identification, marking for, 732 *et seq.*
Ilocos pig, 550
Immunity, 38
Imperata spp., 116
Imperata cylindrica, 108, 319
Implements, for working cattle, 389
Inbreeding, 181 *et seq.*
Incubation: ducks, 638; fowl, 615, 616, 617, 618; geese, 643; turkeys, 646
Indian Runner duck, 637
Indigofera spp., 108, 112
Indigofera spicata, 125: toxic content, 140
Indo-Brazil cattle, 209, 249, 326
Infectious bovine rhinotacheitis, 34
Infectious kerato-conjunctivitis: in sheep, 451; in cattle, 329
Inheritance: basis of, 157; of characteristics, 162; genetic environmental interactions, 173; maternal influence, 174; Mendelian theory of, 163; mutations, 172; of sex, 169
Integration: crop production and dairying, 288; domestic and wild animals, 535; field crop and cattle, 351; tree crops and beef cattle, 351
Internal parasites: in ducks, 640; in fowl, 612; in llamoids, 514; in pigs, 557; in sheep, 452
Intestinal roundworms, *see Ascaris lumbricoides*
Iodine, 76, 82
Ipomoea batatas, 102; as pig food, 562
Ipomoea reptans: as duck food, 641; as pig food, 565
Iran thin-tailed sheep, 441
Iron, 76, 82
Ischaemum spp., 108, 112
Isoberlinia, 109
Ivory, from game animals, 532

Jaffarabadi buffalo, 398, 406
Jaffna sheep, 441
Jalajala pig, 550
Jalauni sheep, 442
Jamaica Black cattle, 209, 326
Jamaica Hope cattle, 209, 221, 247

Jamaica Red cattle (*also* Jamaica Red Poll cattle), 209, 246, 326
Jamaican Brahman cattle, 326
Jaragua grass, *see Hyparrhenia rufa*
Java duck, 637
Java Jungle fowl, *see Gallus varius*
Javanese sheep, 442
Jersey Black Giant fowl, 597
Jersey cattle, 18: body fat colour, 75; conversion of carotenoids to vitamin A, 88; crossbreeding, 258; milk production, 257; origin, 206
Julbernardia, 109
Jumnapari goat, 471, 463

Kagani sheep, 442
Kambing Katjang goats, 478
Kangaroos, 521
Kangayam cattle, 211
Kankrej cattle, 211, 222
Karakul sheep, 441
Karomojong cattle, 174, 211
Kashmiri goat, 466
Kathiawar sheep, 442
Kayan pig, 550
Kelakui sheep, wool yield, 460
Kenana cattle, *see* Sudanese cattle
Kenya Boran, *see* Boran cattle
Kenya Wild White clover, *see Trifolium semipilosum*
Keratitis, in llamoids, 514
Kerry cattle, origin, 206
Khaki Campbell duck, 638
Khoa, 673
Kidding: age at first, 473; interval, 475
Kidney worm, *see Stephanurus dentatus*
Kigezi cattle, *see* Ankole cattle
Kikuyu fowl disease, 610
Kikuyu grass, *see Pennisetum clandestinum*
Kikuyu sheep, 441
Killari cattle, 211
Kipsigis sheep, 441
Kizil sheep, 441: wool yield, 460
Kochia sedifolia, 113
Koronadal pig, 550
Kouprey, *see Novibas* spp., 211
Krishna Valley cattle, 211
Kuchi camel, 487
Kuka sheep, 442: milk yield, 459
Kumauni cattle, 211
Kundi sheep, 441
Kuri cattle, 205, 211

Lactation: length of – in buffalo, 426 – in cattle, 286 – in camels, 489 – in